There was light in a vacuum-enclosed filament of carbon, when fed an electrical current. It took a genius to find just how to do it. Thomas Edison's discovery (1879) led to the first power stations. Charles Parsons' steam turbine (1884) and the great Niagara Falls Hydroelectric station (1893) were pioneering events in the evolution of electrical engineering.

Automotive engineering really began to roll about 1885, when Gottlieb Daimler's first internal-combustion car appeared. Henry Ford's genius was to create mass-production —Model T's for the millions. Rudolph Diesel developed his famed work-horse engine in 1892. Civil engineers set out to build roads fast enough to keep up with the drivers. That race isn't over yet.

DESIGN DRAFTING

DESIGN DRAFTING

JAMES H. EARLE
Texas A&M University

ADDISON-WESLEY PUBLISHING COMPANY
Menlo Park, California
Reading, Massachusetts · London · Don Mills, Ontario

Endpaper drawings are reproduced through the courtesy of Keuffel & Esser Co.

PREFACE

The need to develop creativity and imagination has been emphasized for all levels and all areas of education. Creativity is highly essential to technology and engineering fields, for it is the basis of all new products and the industries that manufacture them. The application of creativity to the solution of technical problems is called design. Design is the theme of this book.

All the basic principles of drafting and mechanical drawing are included, but special emphasis is placed on the application of these skills to design and the utilization of the student's imagination. Mechanical drawing principles are extremely important in our present technological world; communication in many areas is not possible without an understanding of these principles. The creative person must rely heavily on this method of communication, since this is the most effective means of explaining new concepts that are completely original and therefore unfamiliar to his associates.

If the objective of creativity is recognized as important, no course can contribute more to the development of a student's creativity than can mechanical drawing. Such a course will complete the student's repertory of communication skills by adding graphical skills to his previously acquired oral and written communication skills. By using these three skills in combination, he will be able to express himself and illustrate ideas much more readily than the student who does not have a knowledge of mechanical drawing. With this background and the proper encouragement, he will not be hampered by the barriers to communication that frequently prevent a creative student from effectively developing and expressing innovative solutions to problems.

The design process is introduced to familiarize the student with the role of mechanical drawing in this method of developing new ideas. Most chapters include not only conventional problems, but also design problems for students who wish to develop original solutions while applying the principles of drafting.

This text can be used for practically any level of course, whether at the junior high, senior high, technical institute, or college level. The basic areas that are considered fundamental to mechanical drawing are presented in the earlier chapters. It is unlikely that all of the subject matter of this book could be covered during a regular one-year course. The material is organized so that it can be used in a variety of sequences, allowing the teacher flexibility in organizing a course to fit his students' needs.

Illustrations have been highlighted with a second color to clarify important constructions and details that might be overlooked if the book were printed in only one color. The more complicated problems are solved in a sequence of steps that the student can follow with the minimum of assistance from his teacher. This use of the step method is especially helpful for faster students who must work ahead of the slower students.

Career information has been included to assist the student in better understanding the opportunities available to him in engineering, technology, and architecture. The practical applications of problems and the photographs from many industries will familiarize the student with the challenges of many fields and the careers associated with them.

Two specialty areas, technical illustration and architectural drafting, are introduced in addition to the traditional fundamentals of mechanical drawing. Chapter 20 introduces the basic principles of descriptive geometry to familiarize the student with this important discipline.

Thanks are due to the hundreds of industries that have provided photographs, drawings, and examples included in this text. Special thanks are given to Mr. Howard Gibbons and the staff of the National Aeronautics and Space Administration for their review and approval of Chapter 6, as well as for many photographs. Credits would not be complete without mention of the encouragement, confidence, and assistance given to the author by the staff of Addison-Wesley Publishing Company. They have been instrumental in recognizing the need for a book of this type and in the expedition of its publication.

College Station, Texas   J.H.E.
December 1971

CONTENTS

To my wife
Theresa Gatlin Earle

Photo courtesy of the Bendix Corporation

1
INTRODUCTION
TO DRAWING

Fig. 1–1 Drawing is the language of technology and is essential to all industries. (Courtesy of U. S. Forest Service.)

1–1 INTRODUCTION

One of the most fundamental and most necessary tools used in the world of technology is drawing. Through the use of drawing and drafting whole communities are planned (Fig. 1–1) and large buildings are constructed. Instructions are given to hundreds of people, ideas are developed and refined. Drawing is truly a universal language that can be understood by people of all nations.

This book will present the basic elements of technical drawing and drafting that are common to most industries. Standard techniques of mechanical drawing will be covered, but additional emphasis will be placed on using these techniques to develop and express creative ideas as well. Each chapter will discuss two types of problems: (1) those requiring the application of basic principles and (2) those requiring the application of these principles plus a degree of imagination on the part of the student. This second type of problem will challenge the student who is interested in applying his imagination to the solution of a problem.

1–2 ENGINEERING GRAPHICS

The term "engineering graphics" describes the broad field that uses drawings as a means of solving problems and presenting their solutions. It is also used to describe college courses required for most students in engineering programs. The course offered in most high schools is called *mechanical drawing*, and is only one part of the total area of engineering graphics. The engineering graphics field consists of three rather large divisions—working drawings, descriptive geometry, and specialty areas. These major divisions are illustrated graphically in Fig. 1–2.

1–3 WORKING DRAWINGS

Working drawings are the plans that are drawn to explain the construction details for anything that is to be built. The working drawings for a go-cart have many similarities to the working drawings for a spacecraft because the same principles are used (Fig. 1–3). Since it is important that drawings be understood by a great number of people, standard practices have

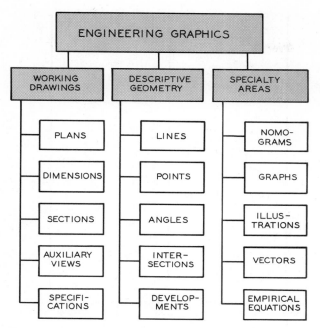

Fig. 1-2 The major divisions within the broad field of engineering graphics.

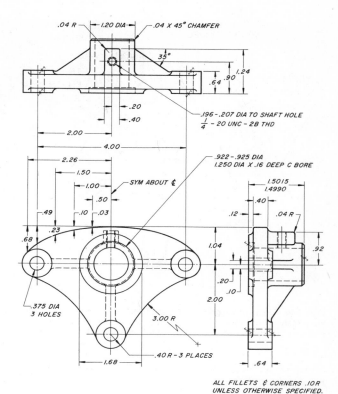

ALL FILLETS & CORNERS .10 R
UNLESS OTHERWISE SPECIFIED.

Fig. 1-3 A working drawing showing the details of a single part that will be used in an automobile. (Courtesy of General Motors Corporation.)

been developed for the preparation of working drawings. These practices reduce the possibility of a drawing's being misinterpreted.

Many principles of drawing must be understood before an accurate, effective set of working drawings can be prepared. Some of the areas that must be mastered are use of instruments, techniques of drawing, dimensioning, sections, auxiliary views, pictorials, and standard practices.

Although the draftsman has primary responsibility for the preparation of working drawings, the engineer or the designer who originated the design is responsible for the accuracy and correctness of the plans. In other words, the engineer must approve the draftsman's work and accept the blame for anything that is in error. Consequently, the engineer and designer must have a very clear understanding of working drawings and the methods used to prepare them. Without this understanding they would be unable to check the draftsman's work or even to tell the draftsman what to draw.

All areas of industry have similar requirements for working drawings. The drawings may vary in appearance, of course, because they are depicting different types of subjects. For example, the drawing for a shape made of sheet metal will look considerably different from that for one made of concrete. A working drawing of a large building will differ from the drawing for a small part that is used in an automobile. And the drawings made for an electronics system will be different from those for a piping arrangement used in a refinery. However, the *techniques* used in preparing the drawings will be very similar.

1-4 DESCRIPTIVE GEOMETRY

Descriptive geometry is a graphical method used for solving three-dimensional problems to determine specific geometric information. For example, the designer of an automobile may wish to design a clip

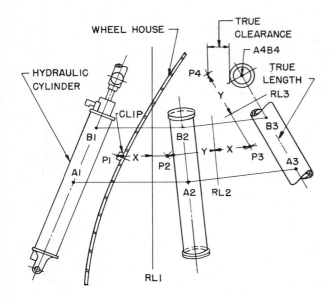

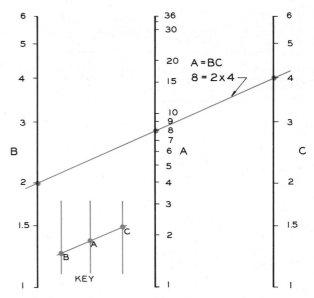

Fig. 1-4 Descriptive geometry principles are used to determine the distance from the hydraulic cylinder to the point of attachment of a clip. (Courtesy of General Motors Corporation.)

Fig. 1-5 This nomogram can be used for solving an equation by simply using a straightedge and reading the answer from the middle scale.

to attach a hydraulic cylinder to the automobile body. He can locate the cylinder and point of attachment of the clip in the working drawings. However, he cannot determine the distance in question without applying descriptive geometry. The solution to this problem is shown in Fig. 1-4. The information thus obtained is used in completing the design for the clip. Solving this problem by any other means would be more difficult.

Descriptive geometry was developed by a young French student named Gaspard Monge (1746-1818), who used this method for designing fortifications. The mathematical techniques that had previously been in use were very difficult and time-consuming. Descriptive geometry was found to be so much easier and more effective that it was kept a military secret and remained unknown to the civilian industries for a number of years. Monge became a scientific aide to Napoleon and was highly respected as a man of great knowledge.

Descriptive geometry is used by the engineer, designer, and technician to solve many types of problems involving geometric relationships. Examples are specifications for the angle between lines,

the angle between planes, lengths of structural members, and the true shapes of surface areas of planes and curved surfaces. This discipline is also important to any designer who deals with three-dimensional objects of irregular shape and size.

1-5 SPECIALTY AREAS

There are many specialty areas that use working drawings, descriptive geometry, and principles of drawing for purposes other than those listed above. These applications are so broad that only a few can be listed here as the more important areas.

Nomograms and mathematics. Graphical methods can be used to solve mathematical relationships. The problem may involve simple arithmetic or advanced calculus. A nomogram is shown in Fig. 1-5. Notice that many solutions can be found by connecting points on the scales with a straightedge. Such graphical scales can be used to solve, with a minimum of calculations, equations that are used over and over again.

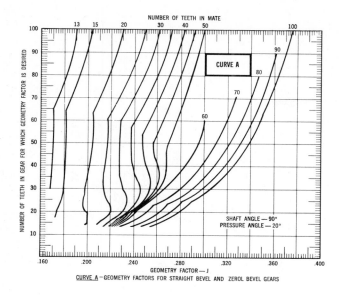

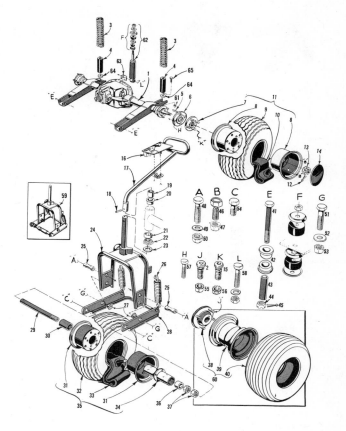

Fig. 1–6 A graph can communicate complex relationships that would be difficult to understand by other methods. This graph compares the geometries of various types of gears. (Courtesy of Philadelphia Gear Corporation.)

Fig. 1–7 This drawing was made by a technical illustrator to show the front and rear suspensions of a golf cart. (Courtesy of Versal, Incorporated.)

Graphs. Data, numbers, and lists of information may be difficult to understand unless shown in the form of a picture. The picture may be a graph, a chart, or a schematic. Almost all technical reports use graphs or diagrams to explain technical data (Fig. 1–6). Graphs are also necessary for the engineer or designer when he submits his ideas to a group in an oral presentation.

Technical illustration. The pictorial presentation of technical objects such as products made by industry is called technical illustration. Most of these drawings are prepared using mechanical drawing techniques; many, however, are drawn freehand. Usually the technical illustrator's finished drawing will be reproduced in a catalog or a publication that

explains a particular project or product. In addition to being expert in pictorial drawings, the illustrator must be able to prepare and read working drawings. Many of his illustrations must be based on working drawings which describe the object to be drawn. He must also understand descriptive geometry, since many of its principles apply to the theory of pictorial drawing. A typical illustration is shown in Fig. 1–7.

Vector analysis. Graphical methods are used to analyze structural systems to determine the loads and forces in the various members. The forces exerted by loads are represented by arrows which are known as *vectors* and are drawn to scale. Vectors can be analyzed graphically by combining principles of physics and drawing. Trusses and structural frames

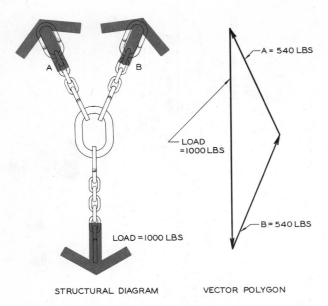

STRUCTURAL DIAGRAM   VECTOR POLYGON

Fig. 1–8 The loads in this double sling chain can be determined by a graphical procedure known as vector analysis. The vector arrows are measured to find their loads. (Courtesy of The McKay Company.)

Fig. 1–9 The designer develops many time-saving devices which improve our way of life, such as this steam iron. (Courtesy of General Electric Company.)

can be designed with the help of graphical vector analysis. The diagram shown in Fig. 1–8 illustrates how the loads in the two members can be determined when a given load is applied. The lengths of the vector lines can be measured to find these loads.

Empirical data. Data that are collected by experimentation or in a laboratory to identify mathematical relationships are called empirical data. Graphical methods can be applied to determine the mathematical equations of data that have been plotted on a graph. Once the equation has been determined, it is possible to manipulate the data mathematically and analyze them in detail.

There are other areas where graphical methods can be applied besides those mentioned here. As we stated earlier, engineering graphics is a field much broader than drafting, and the preparation of working drawings is only a small portion of the broad field.

1–6 APPLICATIONS OF DRAWINGS

The preceding paragraphs have discussed engineering graphics and mechanical drawing as they relate to technological areas and engineering in particular. Engineering has always encountered many problems requiring the application of graphical methods as a means of solution. Consequently, most applications of mechanical drawing have been directed toward this field, which has traditionally employed many draftsmen. However, this is a limited view of the applications of drawing since it can be applied to almost all fields and to all people. A few of these fields are mentioned below.

1–7 THE DESIGNER

The designer develops new products and methods that improve our way of life. He may develop a new appliance, an automobile, a coffee pot, or a time-saving device (Fig. 1–9).

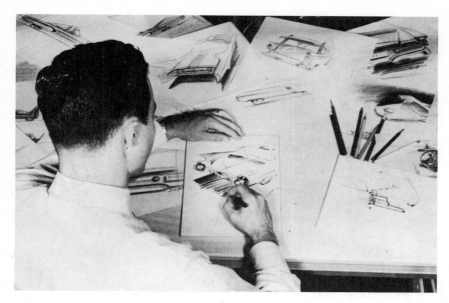

Fig. 1–10 The designer makes many freehand sketches in the process of designing. (Courtesy of Ford Motor Company.)

Often the designer is an engineer, but this is not a requirement. In general, the designer is a problem solver who is applying his imagination and creativity. He should not be thought of as a person who has flashes of inspiration in which his problems are solved instantly. Instead, the designer approaches the solution to his problem in a disciplined manner, exercising as much freedom of thought as possible while remaining within the limitations of cost, manufacturing methods, and other restrictions that may exist.

In developing a solution to a problem, the designer must use mechanical drawing techniques even though his first drawings are in the form of free-hand sketches. He makes many, many sketches in the process of thinking with his pencil. Actually in this process the designer communicates with himself. With each drawing or sketch he becomes more familiar with the problem and comes closer and closer to its final solution (Fig. 1–10). It would be almost impossible for the designer to function without the ability to use drawing methods.

1–8 THE ARCHITECT AND ENGINEER

The architect and engineer are two members of the technological team who must use drawings and supervise draftsmen who assist them. Both deal with designs that cannot be explained without the use of drawings which must be accurate and completely detailed with notes and specifications.

The architect designs and details buildings, homes, schools, shopping centers, and residential developments. He must prepare drawings that show floor plans, elevations, and construction details, and pictorials that explain the appearance of his proposed design (Fig. 1–11). He cannot communicate his ideas without drawings.

The engineer may assist the architect in specialized areas. He will probably design and specify the structural beams and columns that will support a structure to meet the necessary safety standards. He may design the air-conditioning system, assist in supplying the specifications for the foundations, or design mechanical systems in a commercial building.

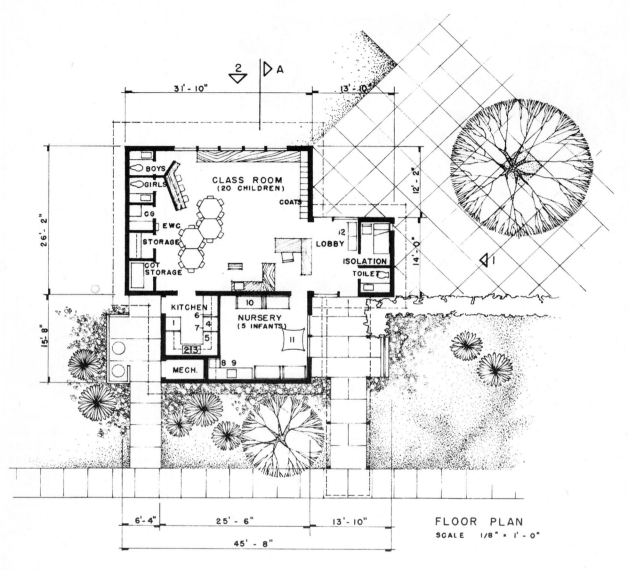

FLOOR PLAN
SCALE 1/8" = 1'-0"

Fig. 1–11 The architect must use drawings to communicate his designs. (Courtesy of Naval Facilities Engineering Command.)

He must use drawings to communicate his ideas to the contractors and construction workers who will build the structure he has designed.

The engineer works in many areas other than architecture. He has a prominent role in all industries and is responsible for the design and development of aircraft, bridges, machines, products, and utilities which serve entire cities. Before his designs can be built, he must supervise the preparation of detailed drawings and specifications (Fig. 1–12).

Fig. 1–12 The engineer must know how to make drawings and be able to supervise draftsmen working for him. (Courtesy of U. S. Air Force, Hill Air Force Base.)

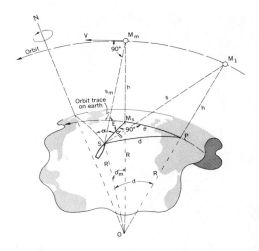

Fig. 1–13 A scientist could not have explained the geometry of an orbit without the use of a drawing. (Courtesy of the Coast and Geodetic Survey.)

1–9 THE SCIENTIST

The scientist may be a specialist in oceanography, biology, astronomy, chemistry, mathematics, or other scientific fields. Although he is more concerned with the development of fundamental principles than with their application, he must nevertheless use and refer to drawings.

Data gathered from research and experiments must be analyzed and presented in a meaningful way. Information of this type can be plotted in the form of a graph for easy interpretation. He must also use drawings to explain how his experimental apparatus is to be set up. Complicated relationships are difficult to explain without drawings such as the one shown in Fig. 1–13. The results of his experimentations are usually published in a technical report or in a scientific journal. This makes it even more important to have graphs, drawings, and schematics to explain his findings and to reduce the need for complex verbal explanations.

1–10 THE TECHNICIAN

The technician is a semiprofessional assistant to an engineer or architect who assumes responsibility for many routine tasks. He may be in charge of a drafting room, he may work under the supervision of an

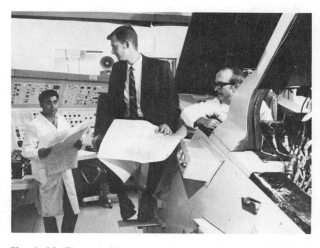

Fig. 1–14 The technician must understand drawings to effectively function as a member of the engineering team. (Courtesy of U. S. Air Force.)

architect or engineer, or he may be a laboratory assistant. Like the engineer, he must be able to prepare or supervise the preparation of working drawings. He must also be able to read and interpret drawings that will provide instructions necessary to the performance of his job (Fig. 1–14).

Fig. 1–15 The work of the skilled craftsman is directed by drawings. This extra-high-voltage aluminum conductor could not have been built if the craftsmen had not understood working drawings. (Courtesy of ALCOA.)

Fig. 1–16 This illustration is an example of a drawing which combines the skill of the artist with the technical accuracy of the technical illustrator. (Courtesy of Ryan Aeronautical Company.)

1–11 THE CRAFTSMAN

The craftsman is a skilled workman who works in the final stages of the construction of a project. He may be a carpenter, a machinist, or an electrician (Fig. 1–15). His work will always be directed by the working drawing which specifies the details of construction. It is necessary for him to be able to read drawings which describe the jobs that he is to perform.

1–12 THE ILLUSTRATOR

The illustrator may be a person skilled in preparing either artistic drawings or technical illustrations. Although artistic drawings are to a great extent prepared freehand, the illustrator must have a knowl-

edge of the mechanical drawing principles used by the technical illustrator. The illustrator's drawing of the lunar module in Fig. 1–16 is an example of the combination of freehand art and mechanical drawing principles. The technical illustrator's work usually requires a minimum of artistic expression. The primary goal is to clearly represent the part of the product being drawn. The illustrator must apply a wide range of graphical principles.

1–13 THE BUSINESSMAN AND AVERAGE CITIZEN

The man on the street may not make many drawings as a part of his job. However he must be able to sketch a map to give directions, communicate his ideas to a repairman who is modifying his home, and

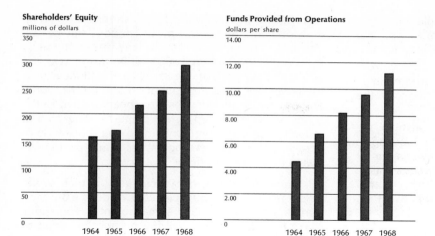

Shareholders' Equity
millions of dollars

350
300
250
200
150
100
50
0

1964 1965 1966 1967 1968

Funds Provided from Operations
dollars per share

14.00
12.00
10.00
8.00
6.00
4.00
2.00
0

1964 1965 1966 1967 1968

Fig. 1–17 A businessman or housewife can read a financial report at a glance when it is presented graphically. (Courtesy of Burroughs Corporation.)

use drawings to explain himself when all other methods fail. The average person is quick to say that he does not know how to draw, but he is much more familiar with drawings than he really knows. He can read a financial report that is illustrated by a graph (Fig. 1–17), interpret a weather report which is graphically presented, or read a complicated travel map. He also has an instinctive feeling for drawings that are incorrectly made even though he cannot explain why they appear incorrect.

Drawings illustrating an object that will be used by a nontechnical person are in most cases pictorials rather than working drawings. Examples are instructions showing how to put together a product that has been received unassembled. In this case it is important that all parts be recognized and that their relationship to other parts be clearly understood with a minimum of written instructions. Pictorials serve this purpose very well.

1–14 SUMMARY

The field of engineering graphics can be divided into three general areas—working drawings, descriptive geometry, and specialty areas. In all industries, working drawings are used to express the ideas of the designer and engineer or architect. Descriptive geometry is the method of solving complex geometric problems by use of mechanical drawing techniques. This is a course required for most freshman engineering students at the university level.

Drafting is the preparation of working drawings. The draftsman usually works from a freehand sketch or a preliminary drawing made by an engineer. The finished drawing must be approved by the engineer, who is responsible for the draftsman's accuracy and must therefore be familiar with working drawings also. Drafting is only a portion of the total field of engineering graphics.

Graphical principles and related specialty areas are used by the designer, architect, engineer, scientist, technician, craftsman, illustrator, businessman, and the average citizen. Our world is a technological world. It is impossible for a member of this world to function effectively unless he is familiar with the language of technology. Engineering graphics and its subareas are fundamental to the development and communication of technological concepts. They are the language of technology.

PROBLEMS

These problems are to be completed on 8½″ × 11″ grid sheets or plain bond paper. All answers should be typed or handwritten as neatly as possible. Place your name, the date, and the name of your school on each sheet in accordance with your teacher's instructions.

1 Write verbal instructions to explain how to get to your home from your school. Have a classmate read your instructions and evaluate the clearness of your explanation. Then make a sketch to explain the way to your home from the classroom and let a classmate evaluate the clearness of your graphical instructions.

2 Clip several drawings of technical subjects from magazines or newspapers. Paste these onto notebook sheets and write a brief description of the purpose of each drawing.

3 Many general and scientific relationships are shown in the form of graphs. Find several examples of data that are shown as graphs in newspapers or magazines. Clip and attach these to notebook sheets for inclusion in your notebook. Explain in a brief paragraph why the graph was more effective than the data in their original form.

4 In as few words as possible, try to describe one or more of the following objects without the use of drawings of any type. (This exercise points out the need for graphical methods to explain the form and shape of almost any object.) A ball point pen, a T-square, a 45° triangle, a pen staff, a hammer, a study lamp, a pair of scissors, a door knob, a drawing compass.

5 Write a brief report (not more than two pages long) that will discuss one of the following topics. You should use your school library and reference books or encyclopedias that may be available to you in addition to this textbook. The topics are: (a) descriptive geometry, (b) Gaspard Monge, (c) nomography, (d) graphs, (e) technical illustration, (f) vector analysis.

6 List some designs developed during the last fifty years that have made an important contribution to our way of life. Give a brief description of each,

identify the people who were responsible for their development, and explain the importance of the designs. (For example: The airplane was invented by the Wright brothers in 1903. This design was the fulfillment of man's dream to fly. The airplane is now the means for rapid transportation around the world, and aeronautical principles have been applied to the problems of travel to other planets. The aircraft industry is a major industry employing thousands of people and has been responsible for many improvements in our way of life.)

7 Drawings are used by scientists in their work. Select from one of your science textbooks a drawing that is used to explain some scientific principle. Make a sketch of this drawing on another sheet of notebook paper and write a brief description of what the drawing shows and why the drawing is important to the explanation of this principle.

8 Write a paragraph to explain why it is important for each of the following craftsmen to know how to read drawings: plumber, electrician, bricklayer, machinist, carpenter, equipment operator, automotive mechanic.

9 Clip examples of the work of a technical illustrator from magazines or newspapers. Paste these onto sheets that can be included in your notebook for future reference.

10 Clip examples of drawings that are used by architects and engineers. Many examples can be found in magazines, newspapers, and technical brochures. Paste these onto notebook sheets and explain each with a brief paragraph.

Photo courtesy of AT & T

2
TECHNICAL CAREERS

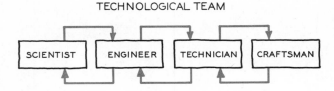

Fig. 2–1 The members of the technological team.

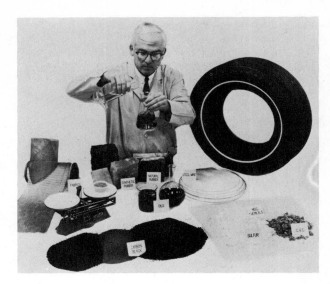

Fig. 2–2 Scientists, such as this chemist, conduct research to establish fundamental relationships. This chemist is trying to determine the best combination of ingredients to yield a better tire. (Courtesy of Uniroyal, Inc.)

2–1 INTRODUCTION

The modern world is an exciting place. Man has accomplished more technologically in the last few decades than in all the previous years of civilization. He has gone to the moon and is planning extensive exploration into outer space. In many of his endeavors he has been aided by the computer, which came into being in the 1950's and has had a great impact on our way of life. For example, our gasoline bills and bank accounts are maintained by computer. Its possibilities for future use appear to be enormous.

The student should give a great deal of thought to his role in our technological world. There are many occupations and professions to choose from that will provide challenges and opportunities. The world of technology offers an increasing number of very promising careers that are stimulating to those who pursue them. However, before a student can select a career or prepare himself adequately, he must be familiar with the various occupations and their requirements.

The following paragraphs will discuss a few of the more prominent career areas. Each of these areas will be viewed in the context of the broad technological field and a few of the related areas. All of these areas use engineering graphics, technical drawing, or drafting as their primary language and as a method of solving problems. It is hoped that this survey will help the student to grasp the enormous scope of the technological world and the variety of occupations within it.

2–2 THE MEMBERS OF THE TECHNOLOGICAL TEAM

Technology today is a combination of many professions, and it is expected that more and more professions will enter the combination as technology becomes more and more complex. It is becoming increasingly difficult to clearly separate the various professions and areas of specialization. For example, the profession of medicine has become an area of technology requiring medical staffs to be familiar with many mechanical and electronic life-saving devices.

In the broadest sense, the technological team is composed of a number of members who can be grouped generally according to their job titles. Each of these members makes his own particular contribution to the development of tomorrow's world. They will probably work together as a team more in the future than in the past, because of the complexity of tomorrow's problems. The members of the technological team are the scientist, the engineer, the technician, and the craftsman (Fig. 2–1). Although their roles and problems are somewhat different, one member of the team is no less important than any other. The continued existence of technology depends on all of them.

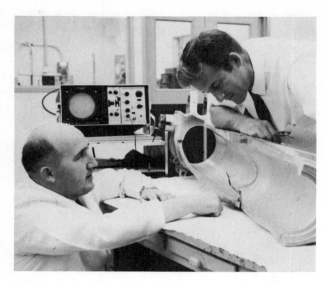

Fig. 2–3 An engineer and a technician review cracks in a B-52 landing gear before an engineering modification. (Courtesy of U. S. Air Force, Hill Air Force Base.)

2–3 THE SCIENTIST

The scientist is often misunderstood by the general public despite the fact that most people feel they have a fairly accurate idea of what he does. The scientist is primarily concerned with developing basic principles in an area such as physics, oceanography, biology, or chemistry. Many of his findings have immediate applications that can be used beneficially, but applications are not the scientist's primary concern. The scientist's main goal is the discovery and establishment of fundamental principles (Fig. 2–2).

A scientist usually spends his life in a laboratory conducting research or gathering scientific data. In developing his concepts, he uses ideas and methods from a number of areas of science and mathematics. Because of the specialized nature of his work, the career field of the scientist is not a large one. He often works as a researcher for a large corporation, a university, or a governmental agency involved in basic research.

2–4 THE ENGINEER

Whereas the scientist establishes basic principles through research, the engineer uses these principles in specific practical applications that will be beneficial to mankind. Consequently, the engineer must have a general understanding of certain scientific areas as well as a good foundation in practical engineering, manufacturing, and economics.

According to the Engineers' Council for Professional Development, "Engineering is the profession in which knowledge of the mathematical and natural sciences gained by study, experience, and practice is applied with judgment to develop ways to utilize, economically, the materials and forces of nature for the benefit of mankind." To fill the needs of his profession, the engineer must be a creative individual. He must be able to manage teams of people who are working separately but toward a common goal. He must be concerned with labor relations, economics, marketing, manufacturing, and construction. Not only must he have a strong formal education in a number of technical and nontechnical areas, but he must continue to study in order to keep abreast of a rapidly changing technological world.

An engineer in one specialty area may be quite different from an engineer in another area. Though both are engineers, they may perform widely different duties. For example, an aerospace engineer may be concerned with the design of a component for an aircraft (Fig. 2–3), while an industrial engineer may be concerned with the design of an entire manufacturing operation in a new plant. However, many of the engineer's basic tools—mathematics, physics, and engineering sciences—are the same in all specialty areas. You should keep in mind that engineering is an immensely broad field.

2–5 THE TECHNICIAN

In the past few years technology has expanded to the point where it is inefficient for the engineer to perform every duty on a project, from top to bottom. He can be more productive if some of the routine chores of his job are performed by skilled assistants. These specially trained assistants are called technicians. The technician is a semiprofessional who can communicate both with the engineer and with

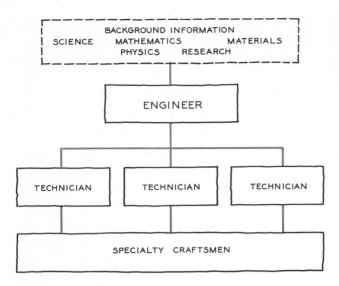

Fig. 2–4 The engineer usually supervises three to six technicians who assist him on his projects.

Fig. 2–5 Craftsmen, welders in this case, are shown cutting pipe that will transport natural gas across the country. (Courtesy of Trunkline Gas Transmission Company.)

the craftsman who will implement the engineer's plans.

The technician may work in the drafting department supervising a number of draftsmen, or he may assist the engineer in a testing laboratory. He may be charged with the supervision of the production or manufacture of a product. The average engineer has between three and six technicians working directly with him (Fig. 2–4). It is anticipated that the need for technicians will increase rapidly in the coming years.

2–6 THE CRAFTSMAN

The craftsman is the skilled worker who makes the products or constructs the projects designed by the engineer. He may be a plumber, a heavy-equipment operator, a bricklayer, or a member of an assembly line in a manufacturing plant (Fig. 2–5). He is a very important member of the technological team; his skill is necessary to ensure that the end product is acceptable. The craftsman must gain his skill through years of experience and practice.

All the members of the technological team—the scientist, the engineer, the technician, and the craftsman—are equally important, though each contributes in a different way. Each member must perform his job well if the project the team is working on is to be successfully completed.

2–7 CAREERS IN ENGINEERING

The following articles give brief reviews of the various fields of engineering to provide a basic understanding of the available careers in engineering (Fig. 2–6). These reviews are necessarily brief and do not give detailed information about all areas in these fields. A student who is interested in learning more about a specific area should write to the professional societies listed at the end of the chapter for additional information.

Related careers that are not always considered to be part of engineering are also included. Architecture, for instance, is discussed to show its relationship to engineering. The field of engineering technology, which includes the technician and the

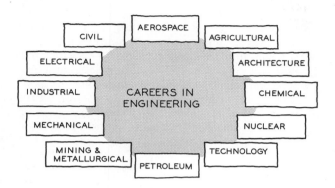

Fig. 2–6 The more prominent careers that are available in engineering and related areas.

Fig. 2–7 The BQM-34A Firebird Drone, shown being launched, was designed, developed, and tested by aerospace engineers. (USAF photograph.)

draftsman, is discussed to clarify the positions of these members of the technological world.

2–8 AEROSPACE ENGINEERING

The aerospace industry employs more people than any other in the United States. It is second only to the automobile industry in sales.

The aerospace engineer is concerned with all aspects of the design and development of aircraft, including commercial planes, helicopters, military craft, rockets, and spacecraft (Fig. 2–7) [1]*. There are two main divisions within the aerospace field: research and design [2]. The research aerospace engineer explores new ideas and concepts that might be applied to aircraft. The design engineer applies the findings of the research engineer to the production of new aircraft. Both work as a team in solving problems and facing the unknown.

Aerospace engineers work with problems of flight in all its aspects, at all speeds and altitudes.

*Numbers in brackets are keyed to the References at the end of the chapter.

Such problems range from those encountered by spacecraft traveling 350 million miles to Mars to those of hovering aircraft used for deep-sea exploration [2]. There are many specialized areas within the aerospace field. Most aerospace engineers specialize in one of the following: (1) aerodynamics, (2) structural design, (3) instrumentation, (4) propulsion systems, (5) materials, (6) reliability testing, or (7) production methods. An aerospace engineer may also specialize in a particular commercial product of aerospace engineering. Typical products include conventionally powered planes, jet-powered military aircraft, rockets, satellites, and manned space capsules.

The aerospace engineer can study a wide variety of engineering systems within this ever-expanding field of engineering. The challenges of aerospace engineering are attractive to creative engineers who are seeking the excitement of exploration in a young field.

The professional society of the aeronautical engineer is the American Institute of Aeronautics and Astronautics (AIAA). Student branches of

Fig. 2–8 This newly developed lettuce harvester was designed by an agricultural engineer. It has mechanical fingers which feel each head of lettuce as it moves along. (Courtesy of U. S. Department of Agriculture.)

this society are open to college and high school students. Interested students can join by applying to the national headquarters of the AIAA.

2–9 AGRICULTURAL ENGINEERING

The agricultural engineer is trained to serve the world's largest industry—agriculture. He is concerned with all aspects of agriculture, including production, processing, and handling of food and fiber [3]. The four major areas of specialization in agriculture are mechanical power and machinery, farm structures, electrical power and processing equipment, and soil and water control and conservation [4].

Mechanical power. The agricultural engineer has increased agricultural production and efficiency through improvements in the design of farm machinery. Machinery is used in almost all areas of

agriculture—to process and pasteurize milk, to process fruit, to cure hay electrically, and to control environments in which animals are raised (Fig. 2–8). Consequently, the agricultural engineer must be familiar with gasoline and diesel engines, pumps, irrigation machinery, and tractors.

Farm structures. The planning and design of shelters, silos, granaries, processing centers, and other agricultural buildings requires the assistance of agricultural engineers. These buildings must be properly ventilated and heated, and must be constructed so as to be as efficient and economical as possible. The agricultural engineer may conduct research to determine possible improvements in farm structures.

Electrical power. The agricultural engineer designs electrical systems and selects equipment that will be as economical and efficient as possible for agricultural needs. A great portion of the equipment used in agriculture is operated by electrical power. A knowledge of electricity and its applications enables the agricultural engineer to improve rural working and living conditions.

Soil and water control. The agricultural engineer is responsible for devising ways of improving drainage in irrigation systems, resurfacing fields, and constructing water reservoirs. These activities may be performed in association with the U. S. Department of Agriculture or the Department of the Interior, with state agricultural colleges, with consulting engineering firms, or with irrigation companies.

Most of the 12,000 agricultural engineers are employed in private industry, especially by manufacturers of heavy farm equipment and specialized equipment for home and barnyard use. Others are employed by electrical service companies and distributors of farm equipment and supplies [1]. Although the agricultural engineer should have some firsthand knowledge of agricultural problems, it is not necessary that he live on a farm.

One farmer today can supply food for 32 people, whereas 100 years ago he could supply only four persons besides himself. This increased production and efficiency is due in part to the efforts of agricultural engineers. The field of agricultural engineering is expected to grow as agricultural needs increase with the expanding population.

The professional society of the agricultural engineer is the American Society for Agricultural Engineers.

2–10 ARCHITECTURE

The architect is a designer of buildings and structures that are efficient, functional, and safe as well as attractive in appearance. The architect of a building works closely with engineers, urban planners, and landscape architects in planning neighborhoods and even whole cities (Fig. 2–9).

The architect meets with his client, who needs a design for a structure, to determine the client's wishes and the cost limitations. With these guidelines in mind, the architect studies the local and state building codes to make sure that his design meets these requirements. His most important concern is that of function. He must design structures that serve the purpose for which they are designed in the most efficient manner possible. Usually the more functional buildings are also the more attractive ones.

Many preliminary drawings must be made to develop a design that can be shown to the client for his approval. Once accepted, the plans are translated into working drawings in which every detail, including air conditioning, plumbing, heating, and electrical installations, is dimensioned and specified. Many of these drawings are coordinated with drawings made by engineers serving as consultants on the job. The architect and the engineer may jointly prepare the specifications that give the detailed instructions for construction.

The architect assists his client in selecting a contractor who will build the structure. He also makes periodic visits to the site in order to inspect the work in progress. His fee is usually a percentage of the total cost of the project.

Approximately 34,000 licensed architects are employed in the United States; of these, 40 percent are self-employed [5]. Some of the projects frequently undertaken by self-employed architects are homes, churches, hospitals, office buildings, and airports. Self-employed architects are also often involved in the planning of urban renewal projects,

Fig. 2–9 Architects design buildings such as the one shown here. They plan and design homes, schools, hospitals, and even entire communities and cities. (Courtesy of ALCOA.)

schools, and industrial parks. Architects usually specialize in a particular type of structure or project.

To gain experience, an architectural graduate may work in a large architectural office as a draftsman, designer, specification writer, or construction supervisor. A construction supervisor makes sure that the project is being constructed according to plans.

The employment outlook for architects is excellent because of the growth in the volume of nonresidential construction. Moreover, the complexity of modern buildings requires the services of an architect to ensure that they are economically feasible. Architects are expected to be needed to plan communities and solve urban planning problems. More information on architecture can be obtained from the American Institute of Architects, the professional society for architects.

2–11 CHEMICAL ENGINEERING

Chemical engineering involves the design and selection of equipment that will facilitate the processing and manufacture of chemicals in large quantities [1]. Chemistry and engineering principles are combined in the development of chemical products that are economical and profitable to manufacture.

Chemical engineers design systems that transport fluids through pipes or ducts, solid materials through conveyors, heat from one substance to another, or that expedite such chemical processes as absorption of gases, evaporation of liquids, and distillation of liquids. Chemical reactions are used in the manufacture of chemical products. A few of the common reactions are oxidation, hydrogenation, reduction, chlorination, nitration, sulfonation, pyrolysis, and polymerization [6].

Important areas of chemical engineering are process control and instrumentation; these are especially important where large quantities of chemicals are handled. Process plants must be designed to be as automatic as possible, with highly accurate instruments for the measurement and gauging of quality and quantity. The design of control systems and instrumentation is a responsibility of the chemical engineer.

The chemical engineer works with many different products. He works with drugs, medicines, cosmetics, explosives, ceramics, cements, paints, petroleum products, lubricants, synthetic fibers, rubber, and detergents. He also designs equipment for food preparation and canning in mass production plants [6].

Fig. 2–10 Chemical engineers are responsible for the planning of process plants that will provide large quantities of chemicals and chemical products. (Courtesy of Monsanto Corporation.)

The chemical engineer must be well versed in a number of areas other than chemistry. He must be familiar with the layout and construction of processing plants and he must understand the principles of their operation (Fig. 2–10). Approximately 80 percent of the more than 50,000 chemical engineers work in manufacturing industries—primarily in the chemical industry [1]. Other, newer fields are the nuclear sciences, rocket fuels, and environmental pollution. The development of new drugs, fertilizers, paints, and chemicals is expected to increase the demand for chemical engineers in the coming years.

The professional society for chemical engineers is the American Institute of Chemical Engineers (AIChE). Publications, research projects, and other activities sponsored by the society are useful to chemical engineering students and the professional chemical engineer.

2–12 CIVIL ENGINEERING

Civil engineering is the oldest branch of the field of engineering and is closely related to practically all our daily activities. The buildings we live in and work in, the transportation facilities we use, the

Fig. 2–11 The civil engineer develops complicated traffic systems to handle today's growing traffic. (Courtesy of the Houston Chamber of Commerce.)

water we drink, and the drainage and sewage systems we employ are the products of civil engineering [6]. The most prominent areas of specialization within civil engineering are construction, city planning, structural engineering, hydraulic engineering, transportation, highways, and sanitation (Fig. 2–11) [6].

Construction engineers are responsible for the management of resources, manpower, finances, and materials necessary for construction projects. These projects vary from the erection of skyscrapers to the movement of concrete and earth.

City planners develop plans for the future growth of cities and the various systems necessary for their operation. Street planning, zoning, and industrial site development are some of the problems encountered in the field of city planning.

Structural engineers are responsible for the design and supervision of the erection of structural systems, including buildings, dams, powerhouses, stadiums, and bridges. Strength and appearance are important considerations in the design of structures

of this type, which must economically serve the needs they were intended to serve.

Hydraulic engineers are concerned with the behavior of water and other fluids, and with the means of conserving and transporting them. They design wells, canals, dams, pipelines, drainage systems, and other methods of controlling and utilizing water and petroleum products.

Transportation engineers are involved in the development and improvement of railroads and airlines in all phases of their operations. Railroads are built, modified, and maintained under the supervision of civil engineers. Design and construction of airport runways, control towers, passenger and freight stations, and aircraft hangars are supervised by civil engineers who specialize in the field of transportation.

Highway engineers develop the complex networks of highways and interchanges needed for moving automobile traffic. These networks require the design of tunnels, culverts, and traffic control systems.

Sanitary engineers assist in maintaining public health by designing systems for purifying water, controling water pollution, and disposing of sewage. Such systems involve the design of pipelines, treatment plants, dams, and related systems.

Approximately 180,000 civil engineers are employed; most of them are associated with federal, state, and local governmental agencies and the construction industry [1]. Others are employed as consultants for architectural firms and as independent consultants. Civil engineers also work for public utilities, railroads, steel industries, educational institutions, and other manufacturing industries.

The need for civil engineers is expected to increase in the years immediately ahead. Problems that will need assistance from civil engineers are housing, water and air pollution, and the needs of an increasing population.

The professional society for civil engineers is the American Society of Civil Engineers, founded in 1852, the oldest engineering society in the United States.

Fig. 2–12 The electrical engineer worked in conjunction with the civil engineer to design Hoover Dam and the power generation facilities shown here. (Courtesy of the Bureau of Reclamation, Department of the Interior.)

2–13 ELECTRICAL ENGINEERING

Electrical engineering is concerned with the utilization and distribution of electrical energy for the improvement of industry and efficiency in the home. The two main divisions of electrical engineering are (1) power and (2) electronics. The power field deals with the control of large amounts of energy used by cities and large industries; electronics is concerned with small amounts of power used for communications and automated operations. Areas of specialization within these two major fields are discussed in the following paragraphs [6].

Power generation is concerned with the development of transmission equipment and the design of generators. The electrical engineer has developed methods of generation and transmission that make electricity our most economical source of industrial energy (Fig. 2–12).

Power applications such as washers, dryers, vacuum cleaners, lights, and other appliances for the home account for 25 percent of the total consumption of electrical power. About half of all electrical energy consumed is used by industry for metal refining, heating, motor drives, welding, machinery controls, chemical processes, plating, and electrolysis.

Transportation industries require electrical engineers to develop electrical systems for automobiles, aircraft, and other forms of transportation. These systems are used for starting, ignition, lighting, and instrumentation. Locomotives and ships may power their own generators, which supply electrical power to turn their driving wheels or propellers. The sophisticated signal systems necessary for all forms of transportation require the work of electrical engineers.

Illumination is required for various human activities and in various sectors of man's environment. The improvement of illumination systems and the economy of illumination energy are challenging areas of study for the electrical engineer.

Industrial electronics has made it possible for sensitive manufacturing operations to be performed by computer more accurately and with less effort than by a human operator. Computerized operations have reduced the need for the tedious human effort that often produces more errors at higher cost. The area of industrial electronics is closely related to those of instrumentation and communications.

Communications is the field devoted to the improvement of radio, telephone, telegraph, and television systems, which are the nerve centers of most industrial operations. Communication systems are vital in the dispatching of a taxicab, the control of ships and aircraft, and many other everyday personal and industrial activities.

Instrumentation is the study of systems of electronic instruments used to control industrial processes through precise measurement. Extensive use has been made of the cathode-ray tube and the electronic amplifier in industrial applications and atomic power reactors. Instrumentation has been increasingly applied to medicine for diagnosis and therapy.

Military electronics is utilized in practically all areas of military weaponry and tactical systems, from the walkie-talkie to distant radar networks for detecting enemy aircraft. Remote-controlled electronic systems are used for navigation and interception of guided missiles. Revolutionary advances in military applications of electrical engineering are expected to continue.

More electrical engineers are employed than any other type of engineer—more than 230,000. They are employed chiefly by manufacturers of electrical and electronic equipment, aircraft and parts, business machines, and professional and scientific equipment. This field is expected to continue to grow in coming years [1].

The professional society for electrical engineers is the Institute of Electrical and Electronic Engineers (IEEE). With 150,000 members, this is the world's largest technical society; it was founded in 1884.

Fig. 2–13 Industrial engineers analyze data to determine the most efficient means of solving industrial problems. (Courtesy of Standard Oil of New Jersey.)

2–14 INDUSTRIAL ENGINEERING

One of the newer branches of engineering, industrial engineering is concerned with determining the most effective methods of using the basic factors of production: machines, materials, and personnel [1]. This field is related to all areas of engineering and business. It is more closely related to people and their performance and working conditions than are most other fields of engineering.

The industrial engineer is responsible for plant layout, the development of plant processes, and the determination of efficient plant operating standards. Other closely related concerns of the industrial engineer are cost analysis and quality control, which are essential to a profitable manufacturing industry.

Several specific areas of industrial engineering are management, plant design and engineering, electronic data processing (Fig. 2–13), systems analysis and design, control of production and quality, performance standards, and research. From

this wide-ranging list of specialty areas, it is obvious that the industrial engineer must work with engineers from other branches of the profession [7].

People-oriented areas include the development of wage incentive systems, job evaluation, work measurement, and the design of environmental systems. The industrial engineer is often involved in management-labor agreements that affect the operation and productivity of an industry. He is also responsible for improving safety in industrial plants.

More than two-thirds of an estimated 120,000 industrial engineers are employed in manufacturing industries. Others work for insurance companies, construction and mining firms, public utilities, large businesses, and governmental agencies. With the increasing complexity of industrial operations and the increasing use of automated processes, the field of industrial engineering is expected to grow. Approximately 1300 industrial engineers will be needed annually to fill vacancies and to assume new positions that are created in the field.

Fig. 2–14 A mechanical engineer is responsible for designing components such as this landing gear. He must see that specifications meet the requirements stated in the engineering drawing. (Courtesy of Hill Air Force Base.)

The professional society for industrial engineers is the American Institute of Industrial Engineers (AIIE), which was organized in 1948.

2–15 MECHANICAL ENGINEERING

Mechanical engineering is a very broad branch of engineering with applications to almost all other branches. The major areas of specialization are power generation, transportation, aeronautics, marine vessels, manufacturing, power services, and atomic energy [6]

Power generation requires that energy be provided to electrical generators which produce electricity in power plants. The mechanical engineer designs and supervises the operation of steam engines, turbines, internal combustion engines, and other movers of power generators.

Transportation vehicles are designed and manufactured by mechanical engineers. Some of the various types are automobiles, trucks, buses, locomotives, marine vessels, and aircraft. The mechanical engineer also designs the power, fuel, and structural systems used in these vehicles.

Aeronautics is a specialty area in which the mechanical engineer develops systems used in aircraft, including power systems, structures, and environmental control equipment for all altitudes of flight (Fig. 2–14).

Marine vessels must be equipped with systems designed by the mechanical engineer. He is responsible for power, water, refrigeration, and ventilation systems throughout the vessel.

Manufacturing and mass production of products, as well as the design of the factories in which they are produced, is a major concern of the mechanical engineer. He works closely with the industrial engineer to maintain efficiency and economy of manufacturing.

Power services include the movement of liquids and gases through pipelines, refrigeration systems, elevators, and escalators. Problems involving services of this nature are solved by the mechanical engineer.

Atomic energy, with its many applications, requires the work of mechancial engineers for the

Fig. 2–15 The mining and metallurgical engineer is involved in the mining of raw ore and its processing. This is a gold-mining operation near Fairbanks, Alaska. (Courtesy of the U. S. Forest Service.)

development and handling of protective equipment and materials. Mechanical engineers also assist with the development of nuclear reactors which provide energy and power.

More than 180,000 mechanical engineers are employed in manufacturing industries. The outlook for this field is promising because of the increasing need for mechanical engineers [1].

The professional society for the mechanical engineer is the American Society of Mechanical Engineers (ASME). There are 60,000 members, 10,000 of whom are from student sections.

2–16 MINING AND METALLURGICAL ENGINEERING

Although the mining engineer and the metallurgical engineer are different, they belong jointly to the same branch of engineering. The mining engineer is responsible for the extraction of minerals from the earth and the preparation of them for use by manufacturers (Fig. 2–15). He works with the geologist to locate mineral deposits and then develops and supervises the underground operations necessary for economical removal of the ore. He must provide for

safety, ventilation, a water supply, and communications.

The metallurgical engineer develops methods of processing and converting metals into useful products. The two main areas of metallurgical engineering are called extractive and physical. Extractive metallurgy is concerned with the extraction of pure metals from raw ores. Physical metallurgy is the development of new products and alloys for new industrial applications.

The metallurgical engineer may work with a manufacturer of machinery, electrical equipment, or aircraft components. New metals are constantly in demand for space flight vehicles, jet aircraft, missiles, satellites, and many other new applications. Approximately 10,000 metallurgical engineers are employed in the United States [1].

An estimated 15,000 mining engineers are employed, with three-quarters of them employed by the mining and petroleum industries. Those who work at mining sites are usually employed near small communities or in out-of-the-way places, while those in research and consutling may live in cities. The employment needs for mining engineers in the future are not expected to be as great as in other branches of engineering. The depletion of high-

Fig. 2–16 This pulsing reactor is being operated by a nuclear engineer to test the effect of extremely high radiation on delicate equipment. (Courtesy of General Dynamics.)

Peaceful applications are of two main types: radiation and nuclear power reactors (Fig. 2–16). Radiation is the propagation of energy through matter or space in the form of waves. Of particular interest in atomic physics is electromagnetic radiation, in which energy is propagated in pockets called protons [8].

A major peaceful application of nuclear energy is its use to produce the mechanical or electrical power needed by industry. Nuclear energy is provided by controlled reactions of the atom's nucleus in a device called a reactor [9]. The energy provided by these reactions is used to produce steam that will drive a turbine which in turn generates electrical power.

Because of its newness, nuclear engineering is a field with many unexplored frontiers. Most training is centered around the design, construction, and operation of nuclear reactors. Other areas include the processing of nuclear fuels, thermonuclear engineering, and the application of various nuclear by-products.

The total employment in atomic energy work is approximately 135,000. About 101,000 people are employed by the Atomic Energy Commission, while the others are employed in privately owned facilities. Two-thirds of those employed by private firms are concerned with peaceful uses of atomic energy. These figures include all levels of employees, including nuclear engineers.

The professional society for this field is the American Nuclear Society.

grade ore is expected to create a need for methods of mining in locations that at present are seldom used as mining sites [1].

The professional society for this field is the American Institute of Mining, Metallurgical, and Petroleum Engineering (AIME) [1].

2–17 NUCLEAR ENGINEERING

Nuclear engineering is one of the newest branches of engineering Many exciting developments in this field are expected in the future.

Although most applications of nuclear energy have been military, many civilian applications have been developed in recent years. For example, nuclear energy has been used in medicine and in other fields as a power source.

2–18 PETROLEUM ENGINEERING

Petroleum engineering is the application of engineering to the development and recovery of petroleum resources. The petroleum engineer is primarily concerned with the recovery of petroleum and gases; however, he must also develop methods of transportation and separation of various products.

With the increased consumption of petroleum products each year, the conservation of petroleum reservoirs has become an important concern. New processes have been developed for recovering increased amounts of petroleum from dormant oil reserves that had previously been abandoned.

The petroleum engineer cooperates with engineers from other branches to develop and improve methods of production. New production methods have led to the emergence of new petroleum products and completely new industries.

The geologist assists the petroleum engineer in locating and exploring sites where petroleum might be found (Fig. 2–17). Advanced devices such as the airborne magnetometer and seismographs are used to analyze the subsurface and to estimate the possibility of finding oil or gas. The only sure way is to drill a well. A typical wildcat oil well costs between $50,000 and $80,000 [11].

Oil-well drilling is supervised by the petroleum engineer, who also develops the drilling equipment in cooperation with engineers from other branches of the field. The petroleum engineer is responsible for devising piping systems to remove oil from a well and to transport it to the point of processing. He works jointly with the chemical engineer to develop processing methods and equipment.

A great many engineers will be needed in the future to develop oil and gas production in countries with undeveloped resources. Petroleum engineers will also be required to stimulate new sources of petroleum when present fields have been depleted.

The professional society for petroleum engineers is the Society of Petroleum Engineers, which is a branch of the American Institute of Mining, Metallurgical, and Petroleum Engineering.

Fig. 2–17 The petroleum engineer is concerned primarily with the exploration and extraction of petroleum products from the earth. (Courtesy of Humble Oil and Refining Company.)

2–19 THE TECHNICIAN

The technician has gained identification as a separate member of the engineering team. He is trained as a specialist to assist the engineer at a semi-professional level. His assistance provides the engineer with increased time for work which requires the skills and knowledge of an engineer.

The technician works not only with the engineer, but also with the craftsman who will actually construct or build the structures or devices designed by the engineer. Consequently, the technician must be somewhat familiar with production skills and methods, but he must also be acquainted with some of the technological principles used by the engineer. In short, the technician serves as a liaison between engineering and production.

Many of the assignments of technicians were previously done by engineers and required much of their time. Some of these duties require the ability to analyze and solve engineering and scientific problems and to prepare formal reports on experiments, tests, or other projects (Fig. 2–18). All the duties of the technician are performed under the direction of an engineer, but with a minimum of supervision.

The specific duties of a technician are determined by the industry in which he is employed. Some of the better-established areas of technology are aerospace technology, chemical technology, civil engineering technology, and electronic technology. Technicians in these areas work with engineers who are specialists in these particular fields.

Fig. 2–18 A research technician is testing a tire with a laser beam to detect hidden flaws or cracks without destroying the tire. (Courtesy of Uniroyal, Inc.)

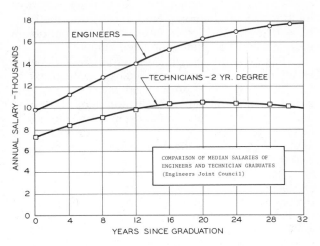

Fig. 2–19 A comparison of engineers' and technicians' salaries. (Courtesy of Engineers' Joint Council.)

Approximately 620,000 engineering and science technicians (exclusive of draftsmen) are employed in all industries. Eleven percent of these are women. Almost 450,000 technicians are employed in private industries [12]. The industries that employ most technicians are producers of electrical equipment, machinery, chemicals, aircraft, missiles, and spacecraft. Approximately 85,000 technicians are employed by federal agencies, the largest number being in the Department of Defense.

During recent decades, technicians have constituted one of the fastest growing occupational groups, and continued growth is expected with the expansion of industry. Annual salaries of graduates of two-year technical institutes are compared with those of engineers in Fig. 2–19. Information concerning technicians can be obtained from the American Society for Engineering Education.

2–20 THE DRAFTSMAN

Originally, the draftsman made ink tracings or copied drawings made by an engineer so that they could be reproduced by the rather crude equipment that was formerly available. The draftsman exercised very

little imagination and performed his job in a very routine manner.

The situation has changed. Reproduction methods have improved, making possible reproduction of pencil drawings. Consequently, the draftsman has been required to assume more responsibilities. Engineers no longer have time to devote to the routine development of drawings for the draftsman to trace.

Today's draftsman is usually called a *detailer* or *detail draftsman*. The detailer is an expert in the production of working drawings that will be used in manufacturing. He may make simple decisions, but in general he receives explicit instructions from an engineer or technician. He must be well-grounded in dimensioning practices and in the fundamentals of depicting designs [13].

Layout draftsmen are technicians who transform sketches, models, or verbal instructions into drawings that will be elaborated by the detailer. The layout draftsman is trained in a two-year technical program in which he receives instruction in tolerances, algebra, geometry, and trigonometry. It is desirable for him to have previous experience as a detailer so that he can work closely with this member of the technological team.

Fig. 2–20 The draftsman must detail an engineer's design before construction can begin. The draftsman here is preparing a drawing of a heavy-duty conveyor trolley. (Courtesy of Jervis B. Webb Company.)

Fig. 2–21 The craftsman in the shop works from the draftsman's drawings under the engineers' supervision to manufacture and assemble the trolley shown in Fig. 2–20. (Courtesy of Jervis B. Webb Company.)

The *senior draftsman* is often referred to as a designer, since he contributes to the development of the finished product instead of being concerned solely with the expression of an idea in graphic form. He requires experience in various areas of drafting, as well as a fund of technical know-how accumulated over the years.

Drafting is a semiprofessional activity that plays an important role in the engineer's conceptualization of a design (Fig. 2–20). The engineer must rely on the senior draftsman's assistance in reviewing the preliminary sketches of a design, which may be in the form of freehand sketches. The senior draftsman works with the layout draftsman in developing a general layout of the graphical details of the design, which will be reviewed and perhaps modified by the engineer. The interrelationship between engineer and draftsman continues in this manner until certain components have been sufficiently refined to require the preparation of detail drawings by the detailer. The completed drawings must be closely checked by all members of the drafting team, from detailer to senior draftsman and engineer, to ensure that the proper specifications are provided to the craftsman

who will construct the finished product (Fig. 2–21). The ultimate responsibility for the correctness of a set of drawings lies with the engineer, who must have a complete understanding of the drafting requirements of the project.

Approximately 300,000 draftsmen and designers are employed by industry, and a very critical need for these specialists is foreseen for the next decade. The need for draftsmen is expected to increase at the same rate as technology increases. A number of technological changes are expected to take place in the drafting occupation in the late 1970's [13]. Many computerized drawing systems are expected to be in operation in large industries that have heavy drafting requirements. With the draftsman working at a console, these systems will reduce the need for men on the board (Fig. 2–22). They will not lessen the need for a knowledge of drafting and graphical principles by the draftsman and engineer, but will provide a different medium of expression. The need for detailers may decrease after about 20 years, but the draftsman-designer who cooperates in the development of a product or a design will still be in demand.

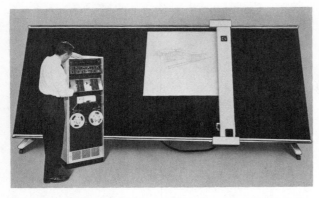

Fig. 2–22 An automatic drafting system. (Courtesy of Gerber Scientific Instrument Company.)

2–21 PREPARATION FOR YOUR CAREER

One of the most important decisions that you will make is the selection of the occupation in which you will spend the remainder of your life. A decision this important should be thoroughly analyzed and carefully made. Your decision should be based on an assessment of aptitudes, interests, and ambitions. The areas in which you are interested are the ones in which you will probably be successful. However, you must be honest with yourself in deciding whether or not you have the ability to meet the academic requirements of the field of your choice.

Many students have a natural aptitude for academic studies which gives them a decided advantage in preparing for their career. However, this talent is often wasted because students are not willing to discipline themselves in preparing for an occupation. Students with less natural ability may compensate for this shortcoming by hard work as they progress through high school and college. Aptitude alone is not enough to determine your field; you must be interested enough to be willing to apply yourself.

Once you have decided that your interests, aptitudes, and academic qualifications match the requirements of the occupation of your choice, you must then prepare yourself for the occupation. This preparation may vary from a two-year college program to a course of study extending to graduate and professional colleges. The preparation for most occupations is specifically outlined. The following articles will discuss the training and aptitudes required in the broader areas of the world of technology. Additional information to assist you in planning your career should be obtained from your counselor and from the organizations listed at the end of this chapter.

2–22 INTERESTS AND APTITUDES

The first factor to influence a person's selection of an occupation is usually his natural interest in a particular field. Consequently, it is apparent that men employed in two widely separated occupations would probably have entirely different interests. For example, the interests which influenced a person to become a machinist would be different from the interests of a person working in nuclear science.

The scientist is interested in discovery, analysis, and investigation of unknowns. His work is usually highly theoretical and abstract, while the craftsman deals with the basic realities of construction or fabrication. The craftsman builds or repairs equipment, appliances, or structures. The scientist seeks to discover fundamental principles that may not actually be applied for many years.

Often the line between related occupations is not a clear one. It may be difficult to establish clearly the difference between a scientist and an engineer or between an engineer and a technician. The reasons for this are the wide variation in the types of work done by members of the technological team and their effort to work together as a team.

The general relationship among the most common positions in technology is shown in the graph in Fig. 2–23. The two curves represent involvement in theoretical concepts and involvement in the building of a finished project. The pure scientist is concerned almost entirely with theoretical or abstract principles. The engineer or architect is more interested in manufacturing and construction, but he also has a high degree of interest in the theoretical concepts of the scientist. The technician is in the middle area; his interests are equally divided between scientific principles and practical skills. At the extreme right of the graph is the craftsman, who is almost exclusively interested in construction or repair at the level of practical applications and is minimally concerned with theoretical concepts.

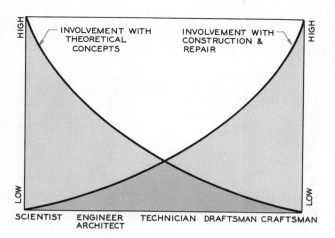

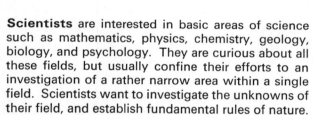

Fig. 2–23 A comparison of the involvement of the members of the technological team in various aspects of theoretical concepts, on the one hand, and construction and repair, on the other.

Fig. 2–24 Engineers must work as members of a team with other professionals. (Courtesy of Hill Air Force Base.)

Scientists are interested in basic areas of science such as mathematics, physics, chemistry, geology, biology, and psychology. They are curious about all these fields, but usually confine their efforts to an investigation of a rather narrow area within a single field. Scientists want to investigate the unknowns of their field, and establish fundamental rules of nature.

Science requires a high degree of patience and self-discipline. Much of the scientist's work is performed independently, with little help from non-scientists. His work is usually performed in a laboratory.

The student who is interested in science should be interested in his school studies in science. He must have a desire to do much more studying, because a career in science demands that he continually study the developments in his field. A scientist must have the ability to write effective papers to explain his experiments and his findings.

Do you like to test principles in your chemistry classes to be sure that they are correct? Had you rather prove a mathematical or physical relationship than memorize the resulting equation? Can you approach the solution of a problem with a minimum of supervision? If your answers to these questions are yes, you may have the aptitude and interest to become a scientist.

Engineers, like scientists, must have some understanding of why things work and how they work. The engineer needs this knowledge in order to apply the scientist's principles. A student who is interested in "tinkering" or craftsmanship may not necessarily be qualified to become an engineer. He must be strong academically as well, especially in mathematics and science. The engineer must be a creative person who likes to try new approaches to the solution of a problem. The word "engineer" is derived from the same Latin source as the word "ingenious." The engineer's interest in applying imagination and creativity to the solution of a problem is probably the single trait that most clearly identifies his function. In addition to creativity, the engineer needs a competitive attitude and persistence to motivate him toward the solution of problems.

The engineer must work as a member of a large team composed of craftsmen, technicians, and scientists (Fig. 2–24). He must have an aptitude for teamwork, supervision, and management. He must also be capable of dealing with materials, people, and money.

The ability to communicate—orally, graphically, and in writing—is essential to the engineer. He must be able to write effective reports which explain his

Fig. 2–25 Engineers must confer with design draftsmen when modifications in design are made. (Courtesy of Hill Air Force Base.)

Fig. 2–26 The architect uses drawings, pictorials, and even models to communicate his designs to his client. (Courtesy of Burlington Industries.)

ideas or projects to others, such as other engineers or members of management. A good command of language will help the engineer to give effective oral reports and communicate with his associates. Most oral and written reports are prepared and presented with the aid of graphics to explain important technical points. All of the engineer's finished designs are presented as detailed working drawings at the final step of his project; consequently, he must be well versed in engineering graphics (Fig. 2–25).

Technicians are equally interested in engineering science and the skills of craftmanship. They may select this area because of their interests or because they lack the background or motivation for a professional engineering career.

Technicians are usually interested in shop courses and building experimental projects in high school. They usually do fairly well in mathematics, physics, and science, but will probably have less interest in the theoretical side of these subjects than the engineering-oriented student. A technician is

not necessarily skilled as a craftsman, but he must be very familiar with instruments, equipment, and techniques used by craftsmen.

A design draftsman is considered to be a technician who can assist the engineer in developing the solution of a problem. The design draftsman is more skilled than the detail draftsman, who must be closely supervised and who does not assist in design development.

Architects have a high degree of interest in designing and creating solutions to problems that involve both engineering and artistic principles. The architect is interested in improving the buildings in which we live so that they are in keeping with the needs of today. Consequently, he is very observant of the problems around him—social as well as technical. He has an appreciation for beauty and can see beauty in a well-engineered project.

The architect must have the engineer's ability to communicate graphically, orally, and in writing, but he will probably have greater artistic aptitude than the

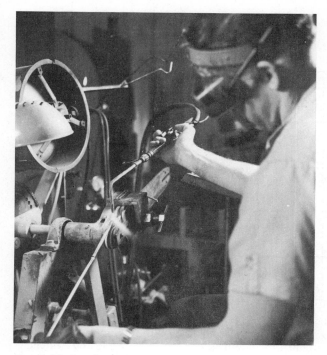

Fig. 2–27 A craftsman is shown performing a welding operation in accordance with engineering drawings. (Courtesy of Omark Industries.)

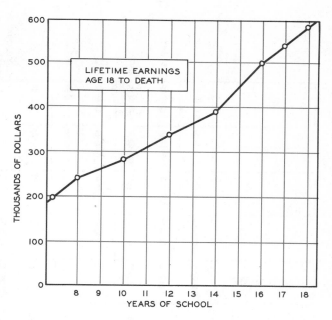

Fig. 2–28 The lifetime earnings of the average employee increase with each year of education that he receives. (Courtesy of U. S. Department of Labor.)

engineer. His profession will require that he develop many drawings and pictorials that must be clearly understood, not only by people within the industrial field, but also by the client, who may have little understanding of detailed working drawings. Therefore, the architect uses perspectives and artistic methods to transmit his ideas so that they can be understood, approved, and finally realized in buildings (Fig. 2–26).

The architect must understand the technical aspects of engineering well enough to know how to obtain help when it is needed. A typical project requires him to be a coordinator of many technical fields. It is virtually impossible for him to be proficient in all the relevant fields, such as structures, air conditioning, heating, and landscaping; consequently, he must use consultants on large projects.

He should have aptitude in mathematics, graphics, English, social topics, physics, and art. His need for chemistry is less than that of the engineer.

Craftsmen are interested in projects which require them to use their hands to build or repair a piece of equipment or a structure. They usually have manual dexterity and a feeling for the use of tools. They can follow plans and instructions with a high degree of accuracy.

Their skills are usually developed in a specific area such as carpentry, plumbing, painting, excavation, machining, repair, electricity, bricklaying, or tool or die making (Fig. 2–27). They are more interested in learning by doing than by formal training. Their skills are usually developed through apprenticeship and on-the-job training.

2–23 TECHNICAL TRAINING

Technical training as discussed here is training beyond the high school level. It is essential that every student complete four years of high school regardless of his occupational intentions. A high school diploma will greatly improve his opportunities (Fig. 2–28).

	ENGLISH	HISTORY	MATH	SCIENCE & PHYSICS	LANGUAGE	TYPING	INDUSTRIAL ARTS	ART	BUSINESS
SCIENTIST	●●●	●●●	●●●●	●●●	●●	●			
ENGINEER	●●●●	●●●	●●●●	●●●	●●	●			
ARCHITECT	●●●●	●●	●●●	●●	●●	●	●	●	
TECHNICIAN	●●●●	●●	●●●	●●		●	●●		●
CRAFTSMAN	●●●●	●●	●	●●		●	●●●		●

Fig. 2–29 Suggested high school courses for those interested in careers related to engineering and technology.

Technical training at the college level requires an appropriate background of high school courses. For the scientist, engineer, and architect, this training is very similar. The general requirements are four years of English, three years of history and social studies, two years of a foreign language, three years of mathematics, and two years of chemistry, physics, or biology. Figure 2–29 illustrates the high school courses that are recommended to prepare the technological team.

High school courses for the technician and craftsman may be similar, though the technician needs more mathematics and science than the craftsman. Both technician and craftsman may benefit from applied shop courses and industrial arts subjects. Electives such as typing, bookkeeping, and art could prove helpful to them. Figure 2–30 illustrates the amount of training usually required for most positions. This chart applies primarily to fields associated with engineering.

College training for the scientist includes four years of college courses in broad areas of science and mathematics, with special emphasis in a single major field. For example, the graduate scientist may major in chemistry, biology, astronomy, physics, geology, meteorology, mathematics, or psychology. Other subjects taken as supporting fields may be a language, English, philosophy, economics, and humanities.

It is more necessary for a scientist than for an engineer to obtain a Master's degree and perhaps a Doctor's degree. Since the scientist's primary goal is the pursuit of knowledge and facts, it is important for him to obtain as thorough a background as is possible. A Master's degree usually takes one year beyond the four-year Bachelor's degree. The Doctor's degree requires two or three years beyond the Master's degree.

College training for the engineer requires a four-year program to obtain a Bachelor's degree. The first two years cover courses that are common to most branches of engineering. The most common courses are English, analytical geometry, calculus, chemistry, physics, engineering mechanics, engineering graphics, thermodynamics, and history. The last two years are devoted to courses in the student's major field of engineering. Additional courses are taken in other fields of engineering to broaden the

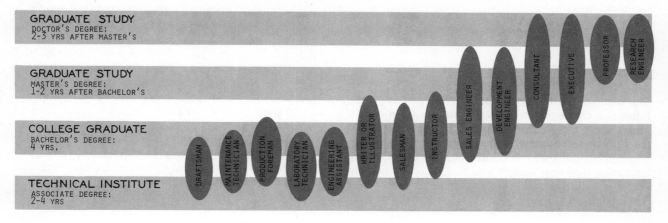

GRADUATE STUDY
DOCTOR'S DEGREE:
2-3 YRS AFTER MASTER'S

GRADUATE STUDY
MASTER'S DEGREE:
1-2 YRS AFTER BACHELOR'S

COLLEGE GRADUATE
BACHELOR'S DEGREE:
4 YRS.

TECHNICAL INSTITUTE
ASSOCIATE DEGREE:
2-4 YRS

DRAFTSMAN · MAINTENANCE TECHNICIAN · PRODUCTION FOREMAN · LABORATORY TECHNICIAN · ENGINEERING ASSISTANT · WRITER OR ILLUSTRATOR · SALESMAN · INSTRUCTOR · SALES ENGINEER · DEVELOPMENT ENGINEER · CONSULTANT · EXECUTIVE · PROFESSOR · RESEARCH ENGINEER

Fig. 2–30 A comparison of the various jobs in engineering with respect to the level of education required. (Courtesy of the Institute of Electrical and Electronics Engineers, Inc.)

student's understanding of engineering. During these years he will apply his education to actual engineering problems and design projects.

Some Bachelor's degrees in engineering require five years to complete.

Recent emphasis has been placed on the Master's degree for engineers. This helps the engineer to obtain increased depth in his education. Many engineers participate in continuing education programs after they have begun practice as a means of keeping up to date in an ever-changing field. Those interested in research are encouraged to obtain a Doctor's degree.

College training for the architect is a five-year program with design emphasized throughout the entire period. He will take basic courses in mathematics (but with less emphasis than for engineers), graphics, materials, physics, engineering mechanics, history, structures, environmental studies, city planning, mechanical and electrical equipment, and landscaping. During each year of his college training he will work on realistic design problems that will prepare him for entry into his profession.

Many architects carry double majors whereby they obtain an engineering degree or a business administration degree in addition to architecture. The Master's degree is being taken by more archi-

tects now than in the past. However, the Master's degree is less important for the architect than for the engineer.

College training for the technician is usually a two-year program offered by a technical institute or a community junior college. The training is a combination of theoretical and practical subject matter with considerable laboratory experience. Courses are specialized toward a particular branch of engineering to prepare the technician for immediate employment after graduation in such fields as radio, television, civil technology, automotive technology, electronics technology, design and drafting technology, and many others.

Some colleges provide a four-year technology degree in which the student can receive advanced preparation. The upper two years provide additional specialty courses in a selected area. Experience from on-the-job training rounds out the technician's training.

Training for the craftsman may include a background from a vocational school or a high school, with the remainder of his training obtained as an apprentice in a commercial shop. In this situation he learns by doing and by assisting a skilled craftsman. He then progresses to the status of journeyman, where he must fulfill the requirements of his trade, which are usually established by his trade union.

2-24 SUMMARY

The world of technology offers many varied opportunities and challenges to those interested in becoming a part of the technological team. You may wish to be a scientist, an engineer, a technician, or a craftsman.

Remember that the choice of a career is a very important decision. Since you will be spending the rest of your life in your chosen career, you should be as familiar as possible with the various fields you might enter. Understanding the fields is the first step toward preparing for the careers that they offer.

In selecting a career, consider your interests, aptitudes, and abilities. Consult your counselor and also people employed in the professions that interest you. Try to select an occupation that will give the rewards and opportunities that you most desire.

Study the requirements of each profession to determine the type of training and part-time work that would be beneficial to you while preparing for entry into the field. Write to colleges to determine their course offerings and entrance requirements. Do not fail to plan sufficiently in advance to be able to pursue the occupation of your choice.

PROBLEMS

1 Write to one of the societies listed at the end of the chapter to obtain brochures and information pertaining to the field of technology in which you are interested. Summarize the information that you receive in the form of a written report not longer than two pages.

2 Make a visit to an engineer, a technician, or a craftsman in your community to determine what he does on his job. Write a brief report of not more than two pages to summarize this visit.

3 Write a letter to a university, a technical institute, or a junior college in which you are interested to obtain information about its offerings in the field of your choice. Also review the requirements for entry and acceptance. Summarize your findings in a two-page report.

4 Visit your school counselor and discuss your interests, aptitudes, and record to determine your qualifications for training as an engineer, scientist, or technician. Summarize your discussion in a two-page report.

5 Select a particular area of engineering in which you are interested as a possible career. Make a comparison of the jobs performed by a technician in this field with the jobs performed by the engineer. For example, what does the civil engineer do in comparison with the civil engineering technician ?

This information can be obtained from the professional societies listed at the end of the chapter, from personal interviews with people in the field, from your counselor, or from your school library.

6 By referring to a university catalog, prepare a list of courses that you must take each semester to complete the college course in the career of your choice.

7 Write to the Department of Labor to obtain information about opportunities and rates of pay for the occupation of your choice.

8 By referring to Fig. 2-28, determine the amount per month you would earn if you quit school this year with the amount you would earn if you graduated from college. Assume that your years of employment would begin with your present age and extend through age 65. Using these figures, determine how much per hour you earn for the time you spend in college. For example, assume that college requires 40 hours per week for four years (nine-month years). Divide this number of hours into the increased income that you can expect to receive because of graduating from college.

9 Select a career in the world of technology that is of interest to you. Write a two-page report outlining the applications of drawings and drafting that would be necessary in this career. For example, what type of drawings and drafting would be necessary for the aerospace engineer to do his job properly?

10 Write a paper comparing the draftsman, the illustrator, and the design draftsman and the training required by each. Refer to your school library and local libraries. Write letters as necessary.

11 Prepare a semester-by-semester list of the courses that you have taken since entering high school. Prepare a list of courses that you plan to take during future high school semesters. Compare these lists with Fig. 2–29 to determine which area of study your background best prepares you for.

12 Write a two-page report explaining why an engineer or technician must be creative to be successful. Give examples of engineering and scientific achievements that are the result of individual and group creativity. Refer to encyclopedias to discover men in history who have been creative.

REFERENCES

1. U. S. Department of Labor, *Employment Outlook for Engineers*, Bulletin No. 1650-23. Washington: U. S. Government Printing Office, 1970.

2. R. Paul Harrington, *Your Career as an Aerospace Engineer*. New York: American Institute of Aeronautics and Astronautics.

3. *Agricultural Engineering*. St. Joseph, Mich.: American Society of Agricultural Engineers.

4. *Occupational Briefs—Agricultural Engineers*. Chicago: Science Research Associates, Inc.

5. U. S. Department of Labor, *Employment Outlook for Architects*, Bulletin No. 1550-5. Washington: U. S. Government Printing Office, 1968.

6. *Engineering—A Creative Profession*. New York: Engineers' Council for Professional Development, Inc., 1963.

7. *Industrial Engineering—The Profession with a Future*. New York: The American Institute of Industrial Engineers, Inc.

8. *Nuclear Terms—A Brief Glossary*. Oak Ridge, Tenn.: United States Atomic Energy Commission, 1964.

9. Lyerly, Ray L., and Walter Mitchell III, *Nuclear Power Plants*. Washington: U. S. Atomic Energy Commission, 1966.

10. United States Atomic Energy Commission, *The Nuclear Industry*. Washington: U. S. Government Printing Office, 1967.

11. Weaver, Elbert C., *The Story of Gas*. New York: American Gas Association, 1964.

12. U. S. Department of Labor, *Occupational Outlook Handbook—Employment Outlook of Technicians*, Bulletin No. 1650-27. Washington: U. S. Government Printing Office, 1970.

13. U. S. Department of Labor, *Technology and Manpower in Design and Drafting*, 1965–75. Washington: U. S. Government Printing Office, 1966.

SUGGESTED READING

Engineering: General

Accredited Curricula Leading to First Degrees in Engineering in the United States (published annually), Engineers' Council for Professional Development, 345 East 47th Street, New York, N. Y. 10017. (25¢)

Accredited Engineering Technology Curricula in the United States (published annually), Engineers' Council for Professional Development, 345 East 47th Street, New York, N. Y. 10017. (25¢)

Engineering—A Career of Opportunity, National Society of Professional Engineers, 2029 K Street NW, Washington, D. C. 20006.

Glennan, T. Keith, *Should you Be an Engineer?* Career Information Service, New York Life Insurance Company, Box 51, Madison Square Station, New York, N. Y. 10010.

After High School What? Engineers' Council for Professional Development, 345 East 47th Street, New York, N. Y. 10017.

Women in Engineering Careers, Society of Women Engineers, 345 East 47th Street, New York, N. Y. 10017.

Fields of Engineering

Aerospace Engineering

Your Career as an Aerospace Engineer, American Institute of Aeronautics and Astronautics, 1290 Avenue of the Americas, New York, N. Y. 10019.

Agricultural Engineering

The Profession with a Future, American Society of Agricultural Engineers, 420 Main Street, St. Joseph, Mich. 49085.

Ceramic Engineering

For Career Opportunities Explore the Wonder World of Ceramics, American Ceramic Society, 4055 North High Street, Columbus, Ohio 43214.

Chemical Engineering

Will You Be a Chemical Engineer? American Institute of Chemical Engineers, 345 East 47th Street, New York, N. Y. 10017.

Civil Engineering

Golze, Alfred R., *A Definitive Study of Your Future in Civil Engineering*, American Society of Civil Engineers, 345 East 47th Street, New York, N. Y. 10017.

Electrical and Electronics Engineering

Your Challenge in Electrical Engineering, Institute of Electrical and Electronics Engineers, Inc., 345 East 47th Street, New York, N. Y. 10017. (25¢)

Industrial Engineering

Industrial Engineering—The Profession with a Future, American Institute of Industrial Engineers, 345 East 47th Street, New York, N. Y. 10017.

Mechanical Engineering

Mechanical Engineering, American Society of Mechanical Engineers, 345 East 47th Street, New York, N. Y. 10017. (25¢)

Metallurgical Engineering

Careers in Metallurgy and Metallurgical Engineering, Metallurgical Society of AIME, 345 East 47th Street, New York, N. Y. 10017.

Mining Engineering

Opportunities Unlimited—Careers in the Mineral Industry, Society of Mining Engineers of AIME, 345 East 47th Street, New York, N. Y. 10017.

Petroleum Engineering

Careers in Petroleum Engineering, Society of Petroleum Engineers of AIME, 6300 North Central Expressway, Dallas, Texas 75206.

Engineering Technician Careers

Can I Be a Technician? Let's Find Out, Public Relations Staff, General Motors Corporation, Detroit, Mich. 48202.

The JETS Program, The Junior Engineering Technical Society, 345 East 47th Street, New York, N. Y. 10017.

Technician Career Opportunities in Engineering Technology, American Society of Engineering Education, 1346 Connecticut Ave. NW, Washington, D. C. 20036. (25¢)

Careers in Engineering

Amstead, B. H., and Wilbourn McNutt, *Engineering as a Career Today*. New York: Dodd, Mead & Co. ($3.75)

Love, Albert, and Childers, James S., eds., *Listen to Leaders in Engineering*. New York: McKay Co. ($6.95)

Whinnery, John R., ed., *The World of Engineering*. New York: McGraw-Hill. ($5.95)

ADDRESSES FOR PROFESSIONAL SOCIETIES

American Institute of Aeronautics and Astronautics
1290 Avenue of the Americas, New York, N. Y. 10019

American Institute of Architects
1735 New York Avenue NW, Washington, D. C. 20006

American Institute of Chemical Engineers
345 East 47th Street, New York, N. Y. 10017

American Institute of Industrial Engineers
345 East 47th Street, New York, N. Y. 10017

American Institute of Mining, Metallurgical, and Petroleum Engineering
345 East 47th Street, New York, N. Y. 10017

American Nuclear Society
244A East Ogden Avenue, Hinsdale, Ill. 60521

American Society of Agricultural Engineers
420 Main Street, St. Joseph, Mich. 49085

American Society of Civil Engineers
345 East 47th Street, New York, N. Y. 10017

American Society for Engineering Education, Technical Institute Division
1346 Connecticut Avenue, Washington, D. C. 20036

American Society of Mechanical Engineers
345 East 47th Street, New York, N. Y. 10017

The Institute of Electrical and Electronic Engineers
345 East 47th Street, New York, N. Y. 10017

Society of American Registered Architects
1821 Jefferson Place NW, Washington, D. C. 20036

Society of Petroleum Engineers (AIME)
6300 North Central Expressway, Dallas, Tex. 75206

ADDRESSES FOR TECHNICAL SOCIETIES

American Association of Junior Colleges
1777 Massachusetts Ave. NW, Washington, D. C.

American Federation of Technical Engineers
900 F Street, Washington, D. C. 20004

American Institute of Design and Drafting
18465 James Couzens, Detroit, Mich. 48235

American Society for Engineering Education, Technical Institute Division
1346 Connecticut Avenue, Washington, D. C. 20036

National Council of Technical Schools
1507 M Street NW, Washington, D. C. 20036

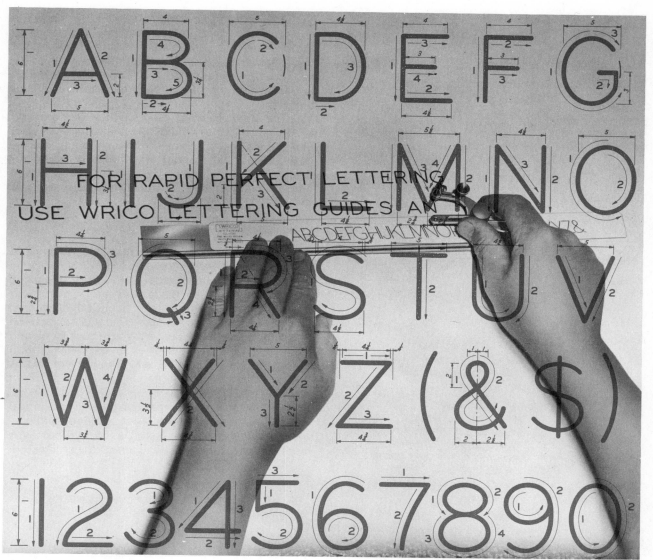

Photo courtesy of Wood-Regan Instrument Co.

3
LETTERING

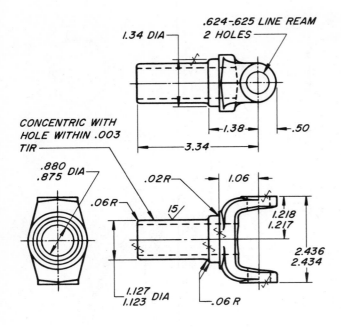

.624-.625 LINE REAM
2 HOLES

1.34 DIA

CONCENTRIC WITH
HOLE WITHIN .003
TIR

.880
.875 DIA

.06R

.02R 1.06

15

1.218
1.217

2.436
2.434

1.127
1.123 DIA

.06 R

3.34

1.38

.50

UNLESS OTHERWISE SPECIFIED:
±.XX TOLERANCE ON
MACHINING DIM.

HEAT TREATMENT:
MCQUAID-EHN GRAIN SIZE 5-8
HEAT TO 1550F AND QUENCH
IN OIL. DRAW TO BRINELL
HARDNESS 241-285. 100%
BRINELL REQUIRED.

MACHINING DRAWING

Fig. 3–1 Lettering is essential to a good working drawing. (Courtesy of General Motors Corporation.)

3–1 THE IMPORTANCE OF LETTERING

Lettering is an important part of any type of drawing. The lettering that is used to convey notes, dimensions, and specifications must, above all, be readable. The uniformity and accuracy with which notes are lettered greatly affects the readability of any drawing.

Engineering offices and other agencies that produce working drawings place great emphasis on the importance of good lettering. This is usually the criterion considered most seriously in hiring an individual for a position which requires involvement in the preparation of engineering drawings. In many instances, the lettering of the information required on an application form for a job is used to evaluate an applicant.

The drawing in Fig. 3–1 is typical of a drawing used to specify the manufacture of a part. The notes, dimensions, and specifications are uniformly lettered in a professional manner that leaves no room for misinterpretation. These particular letters were made with a lettering template that will be discussed in Article 3–11.

3–2 GOTHIC LETTERING

The standard type of lettering that is recommended for engineering drawings is *single-stroke Gothic lettering*. This form of lettering is given this name because the letters are made with single strokes and the form is derived from a variation of Gothic lettering. Gothic lettering is very simple. There is no variation in the width of the lines used to make each letter, and there are no serifs on the letters as are usually found on letters used in printed text (though not in this book). Examples of single-stroke Gothic lettering are shown in Fig. 3–2.

Gothic lettering falls into two general categories: *vertical* and *inclined*. Each type is acceptable; however, each company or industry has its own standards or policies concerning the preferred type of lettering.

3–3 GUIDELINES

The most important rule of lettering is: Use guidelines at all times. This rule cannot be stressed too much. Guidelines are essential for attractive, readable lettering.

An example of the use of guidelines is shown in Fig. 3–2. Guidelines should be constructed using a very sharp pencil, either a 4H or a 6H. These lines should be drawn lightly, so that they can be seen for the construction of the letters but will not be noticeable when the lettering has been completed.

The height of the letters, *H*, in engineering drawings is usually one-eighth of an inch, as shown in Step 1 (Fig. 3–2). This has proven to be a comfortable size for lettering and produces a very read-

FIGURE 3-2. CONSTRUCTION AND USE OF GUIDELINES

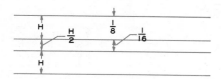

← RANDOMLY SPACED GUIDELINES

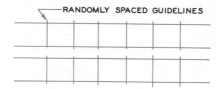

VERTICAL CAPS

Step 1. Letter heights, *H*, are laid off and thin construction lines are drawn with a 2H, 3H, or 4H pencil. The spacing between the lines should be no closer than *H*/2, or $\frac{1}{16}$″ when $\frac{1}{8}$″ letters are used.

Step 2. Vertical guidelines are drawn as very light, thin construction lines. These are randomly spaced to serve as a visual guide in lettering.

Step 3. The letters are then drawn with single strokes using a medium-weight pencil, H, F, or HB. The guidelines need not be erased since they were drawn lightly.

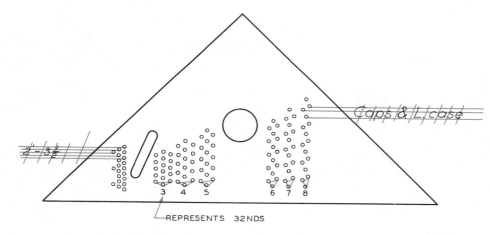

REPRESENTS 32NDS

Fig. 3–3 The Braddock-Rowe triangle serves as a lettering guide and as a triangle. The numbers under the series of holes represent thirty-seconds of an inch. For example, 8 represents $\frac{8}{32}$″ or $\frac{1}{4}$″. The holes at the left are used for guidelines for fractions. The slot is used for inclined lettering. (Courtesy of Braddock Instrument Company.)

able letter. The spacing between lines of lettering should be no closer than *H*/2, which is $\frac{1}{16}$″ in this case. Often the spacing between lines is the same as the height of the letters. In Step 2, vertical guidelines are drawn to be used as a guide in constructing vertical letters. Vertical guidelines are spaced randomly to be used as a visual guide. No attempt should be made to place these guidelines to correspond to vertical elements of individual letters. Vertical letters are shown in Step 3 along with the guidelines used in their construction.

The *Braddock-Rowe lettering triangle* is an instrument that is widely used to aid in the construction of guidelines for lettering (Fig. 3–3). Sets of holes are designated with numerals which repre-

sent thirty-seconds of an inch. For example, 8 represents $\frac{8}{32}$″ or $\frac{1}{4}$″, which is the height of the capital letters made with this set of holes. This instrument is used in conjunction with a straightedge held firmly in position, with the triangle placed snugly against the edge. A sharp 4H pencil is placed in the holes selected until the point is in contact with the paper. The pencil is guided across the drawing while keeping the triangle in contact with the straightedge as the light guidelines are drawn. The pencil is placed in the next hole and guidelines are drawn in the opposite direction while the straightedge is held in the same stationary position. This operation is repeated until a sufficient number of guidelines are drawn.

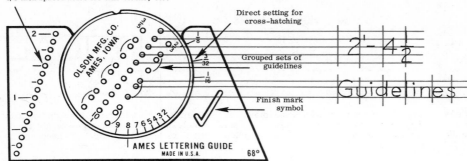

1/8 inch spaced holes for title blocks, etc.

Direct setting for cross-hatching

Grouped sets of guidelines

Finish mark symbol

AMES LETTERING GUIDE
MADE IN U.S.A.
68°

Fig. 3–4 The Ames lettering instrument can be used for the construction of guidelines in much the same manner as the Braddock-Rowe triangle. An adjustable disc can be set on the letter height desired as seen at the bottom of the disc, where the numbers represent thirty-seconds of an inch. The disc is shown set at $\frac{8}{32}''$ or $\frac{1}{4}''$. (Courtesy of Olson Manufacturing Company.)

These guidelines can be used for vertical capital letters. Those shown in Fig. 3–3 are inclined. The holes at the far left of the Braddock-Rowe triangle are equally spaced $\frac{1}{16}''$ apart for numerals and fractions, which will be discussed in Article 3–5.

The *Ames lettering instrument* is another lettering device for constructing guidelines. A movable disc can be turned to an index that indicates the height of the capital letters desired. In Fig. 3–4, the disc is set on 8, which means $\frac{8}{32}''$ or $\frac{1}{4}''$. The numbers on the index represent thirty-seconds of an inch. A pencil is inserted in the set of holes selected and the guidelines are drawn in the same manner as with the Braddock-Rowe triangle mentioned above.

A scale or bow dividers can be used for construction guidelines when an instrument of the type discussed here is not available. Horizontal lines are simply located $\frac{1}{8}''$ apart and drawn very lightly with a T-square.

Remember that guidelines should always be used in lettering, whether for a single letter or an entire paragraph.

3–4 VERTICAL CAPITALS

Capital letters (often called upper-case letters) are the most commonly used letters on most working drawings. This is a very legible type of letter that is easy to make and to read. Lower-case letters are sometimes used in engineering work, but to a lesser degree. A comparison of upper-case and lower-case letters is shown in Fig. 3–5.

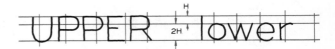

Fig. 3–5 Upper-case letters are capital letters. The bodies of lower-case letters are usually two-thirds the height of upper-case letters.

The vertical upper-case alphabet is shown in Fig. 3–6. A square box has been drawn around each letter and a horizontal guideline drawn across the middle of each box to help you to recognize the proportions of each letter. Many letters require the full square, others more or less. These proportions should be studied, because proportions are important to proper lettering.

The arrows indicate the direction of the strokes normally made by right-handed students. These strokes are intended only as a guide for you. If other strokes are more comfortable and are equally effective in producing good lettering, use them. Lettering is a personal skill that should be developed to be as effective and as functional as possible by each individual. Left-handed students should develop their own style and order of strokes.

The letters shown in Fig. 3–6 are obviously freehand letters. You should not assume that your lettering should look as if made with a lettering template; this is not an objective of lettering used on engineering drawings. Instead, freehand lettering is used as a rapid means of communicating information on a drawing. Even though each stroke of the letters is not perfectly straight or round, your lettering will

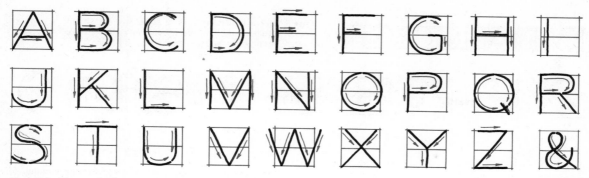

Fig. 3–6 The vertical upper-case alphabet. The form of each letter is shown in relationship to a square.

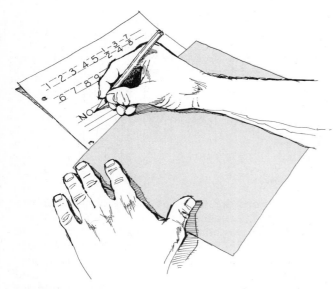

Fig. 3–7 Lettering can be improved if the drawing is placed on the table at an angle to give you a more comfortable stroke. Smudges can be reduced by placing a protective sheet of paper between your hand and the drawing surface.

be acceptable if each letter conforms to the guidelines and the correct form of each letter.

Lettering can be improved if the drawing is placed on your table at an angle aligned with your natural stroke. This is usually about 30° upward to the right, as shown in Fig. 3–7. If this is not possible, it will be helpful to change your position to obtain the most advantagous angle for lettering.

Fig. 3–8 An H, F, or HB pencil should be used for lettering. It should be sharpened to a slightly rounded, conical point. Graphite dust should be wiped from the point with a cloth or tissue before the pencil is used for lettering on the drawing.

Smearing or smudging lettering and drawn lines with your hands is a hazard. This danger can be reduced if a second protective sheet of paper is placed under your hand as shown in Fig. 3–7. This keeps your hand from coming into contact with the paper and with the lines previously drawn. Hands should be kept clean at all times. Lettering instruments should be cleaned periodically to prevent smudges.

A medium weight pencil, either an F or an HB, should be used for lettering. The weight of the pencil will vary with the paper used, since some films require a harder pencil than do softer papers. The pencil point should be sharpened to a gradually tapered point with a slightly rounded tip (Fig. 3–8). The pencil should be sharpened often to ensure that lines are uniform at all times.

The pencil should be held firmly, with your hand resting lightly on the drawing surface. If you are not comfortable, it is likely that your lettering will be poor. Position yourself to be as comfortable as possible. Bear down firmly to ensure that your lines are dark and opaque. This is necessary when your lettering will be reproduced as a blue-line print. Gray or fuzzy lines are unacceptable. Avoid going

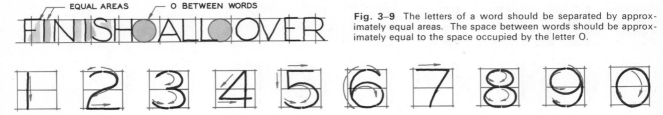

EQUAL AREAS — O BETWEEN WORDS

FINISH ALL OVER

Fig. 3–9 The letters of a word should be separated by approximately equal areas. The space between words should be approximately equal to the space occupied by the letter O.

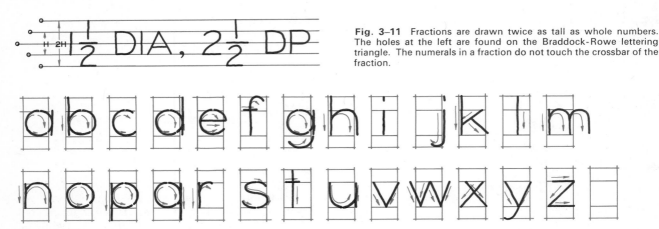

Fig. 3–10 Vertical numerals.

H 2H 1½ DIA, 2½ DP

Fig. 3–11 Fractions are drawn twice as tall as whole numbers. The holes at the left are found on the Braddock-Rowe lettering triangle. The numerals in a fraction do not touch the crossbar of the fraction.

a b c d e f g h i j k l m
n o p q r s t u v w x y z

Fig. 3–12 Vertical lower-case letters.

over a stroke that has been drawn; usually this will result in a line of variable width that is noticeable at a glance.

Spacing between the letters of a word will vary with each letter because each letter has a different shape. The spacing is best when the areas between the letters are about equal (Fig. 3–9). The spacing between words should be about equal to the area of the letter O.

3–5 VERTICAL NUMERALS

Vertical numerals are shown in Fig. 3–10. Each number is enclosed by guidelines that form a square to show the proportions of the number. You should practice making these numerals to become accustomed to their proportions. Numbers are drawn the same height as upper-case letters used on the same drawing.

Fractions are twice as tall as single numbers (Fig. 3–11). Note that the crossbar used for fractions is placed horizontally at the center of the single numeral. The holes used for constructing the guidelines can be seen on the left side of the Braddock-Rowe lettering triangle in Fig. 3–3. These are placed $\frac{1}{16}''$ apart. The numbers used in a fraction should not touch the crossbar. The numerals in a fraction are slightly less than the height of a whole number.

3–6 VERTICAL LOWER-CASE LETTERS

Lower-case letters can be compared with upper-case letters in Fig. 3–5. These are often used in engineering work such as field notes and problem solutions, and sometimes on working drawings. However, upper-case letters are used much more frequently, since they are easier to make and easier to read.

Fig. 3–13 The lower-case letters shown here extend below the base line to a line called the drop line. Other letters may extend above the waist line to the cap line. Capital letters extend from the base line to the cap line.

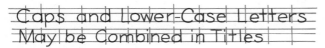

Fig. 3–14 Capital and lower-case letters may be used in combination in titles and notes.

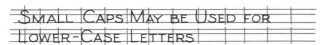

Fig. 3–15 Small capitals may be used as lower-case letters in titles and notes.

Fig. 3–16 Inclined capitals are inclined at a 68° angle. A slot in the Braddock-Rowe triangle or a beveled side of the Ames instrument may be used for constructing these inclined guidelines.

The vertical lower-case alphabet is shown in Fig. 3–12. Note that lower-case letters are drawn with a waist line that is two-thirds the height of upper-case letters. This relationship is shown in Fig. 3–13. Some styles of lower-case letters have a waist line that is three-fifths the height of capital letters. These proportions are indicated on the Ames lettering guide (Fig. 3–4). Some lower-case letters extend above the waist line to the full height of the upper-case letters, and some extend below the base line to a line called the drop line. A square box is drawn around the body of each letter in Fig. 3–12 to establish the proportions of each letter. It is essential that the student learn these forms if he is to use this type of letter effectively.

Capital (upper-case) letters are used in conjunction with lower-case letters in much the same manner as when a sentence is typed with a typewriter. The beginning word of each sentence is capitalized, as are the proper nouns. Sometimes capitals and lower-case letters are used in notes or titles (Fig. 3–14). In this case it is permissible to capitalize each major word to make the title more prominent.

It is also permissible to use small upper-case letters in place of lower-case letters (Fig. 3–15). This practice is often used in titles. The waist line is constructed as a guide for the height of the letters used as lower-case letters. These are two-thirds the height of the upper-case letters.

3–7 INCLINED UPPER-CASE LETTERS

Inclined upper-case letters have the same proportions as vertical letters and differ only in their angle of inclination of 68° (Fig. 3–16). The angle of 68° can be made by using the slot on the Braddock-Rowe lettering triangle or the side of the Ames lettering instrument. A series of inclined guidelines should be randomly spaced at intervals to serve as a visual guide in lettering.

When a lettering instrument is not available, it is easy to construct guidelines by drawing a right triangle. This method is illustrated in Fig. 3–17, where a right triangle is constructed from which the guidelines can be drawn. This guideline triangle is constructed with five vertical units and two horizontal units. The hypotenuse forms the angle for the inclined guidelines.

The alphabet of inclined upper-case letters is shown in Fig. 3–18. The parallelograms drawn around each letter are as wide as they are tall; they may serve as a reference in learning the letter forms.

Note that circular shapes are drawn as ellipses in inclined lettering. The strokes suggested for making the letters are similar to those for making vertical upper-case letters. Memorize these letter forms to aid you in improving your lettering.

Fig. 3–17 Inclined guidelines may be constructed using a 2 × 5 right triangle. A triangle and straightedge are used to construct a series of guidelines for inclined lettering.

Fig. 3–18 Inclined upper-case alphabet. The letters are drawn on a rhombus to relate the proportion of each letter to an inclined square.

Fig. 3–19 Inclined numerals.

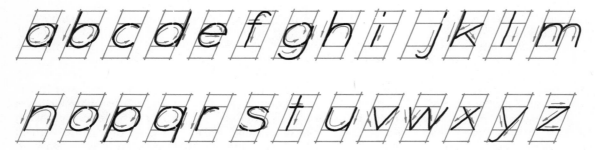

Fig. 3–20 Inclined lower-case alphabet.

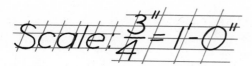

Fig. 3–21 Upper-case and lower-case letters may be used in combination. Note that fractions are twice as tall as whole numbers.

3–8 INCLINED NUMERALS

Inclined numerals are constructed to have the same height as the upper-case letters with which they are used. Their form is much the same as vertical numerals except for their inclination (Fig. 3–19). An example of numerals and fractions can be seen in Fig. 3–3, where a Braddock-Rowe lettering triangle is illustrated. Fractions are twice as tall as whole numbers.

3–9 INCLINED LOWER-CASE LETTERS

The alphabet of inclined lower-case letters is shown in Fig. 3–20. These are also inclined at 68°, as are the numerals and the upper-case letters. Inclined lower-case letters are very similar to the vertical lower-case letters previously discussed.

An example of lower-case letters used in combination with capital (upper-case) letters is shown in Fig. 3–21. Note that a fraction is twice as tall as a whole number.

Either inclined or vertical letters may be used, but at no time should these two types of letters be combined in the same notes or sentences. For the most pleasing appearance, the lettering on a single drawing should be either all vertical or all inclined.

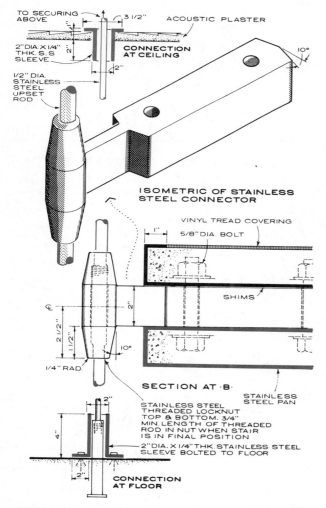

Fig. 3–22 Architectural lettering is often of a different form than engineering lettering. (Courtesy of U. S. Steel.)

3–10 ARCHITECTURAL LETTERING

The lettering used on architectural plans by architects and architectural draftsmen is usually less restricted than engineering lettering. Consequently, architectural lettering takes a variety of forms. Examples of architectural lettering can be seen in Fig. 3–22. Note that this is attractive, easy-to-read lettering, but it does not conform to the letter forms of engineering lettering previously discussed. Another style of architectural lettering is shown in Fig. 3–23.

Architectural lettering is made with single strokes and without serifs or fancy curls at the ends of the letters. The primary difference between engineering and architectural lettering is the form of the letters. Note also the placement of the horizontal elements in letters such as E and F; these elements may be placed above or below the usual position.

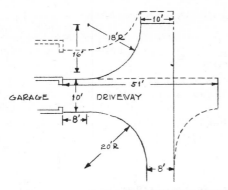

DIMENSIONS FOR A DRIVEWAY TURNING AREA
DOTTED LINES SHOW THE ADDITIONAL SPACE
NEEDED FOR A 2-CAR GARAGE AND AN
ALTERNATE ARRANGEMENT FOR BACKING
STRAIGHT OUT.

Fig. 3–23 A style of architectural lettering.

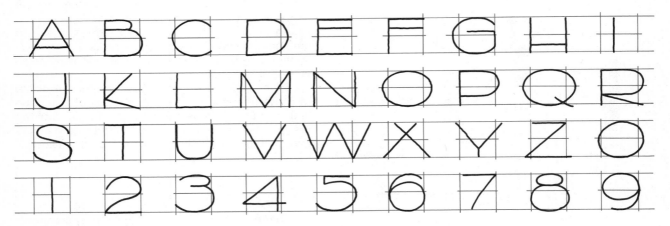

Fig. 3–24 An example of an architectural alphabet.

SLANT BAR ————————

HORIZONTAL BAR ————————

Fig. 3–25 Fractions are often drawn with a slanted crossbar in architectural lettering instead of the horizontal bar.

An alphabet of architectural letters is shown in Fig. 3–24. These letters are somewhat wider than they are tall in comparison with engineering lettering. A square has been drawn around each letter to establish its proportions. This alphabet should not be accepted as the only architectural alphabet; it is merely one example. Engineering lettering is just as acceptable on architectural drawings as on engineer-

Fig. 3–26 A Wrico lettering template can be used for mechanical lettering. (Courtesy of Wood-Regan Instrument Company.)

Fig. 3–27 A typical india ink fountain pen that can be used for mechanical lettering. (Courtesy of Koh-I-Noor, Inc.)

Fig. 3–28 A lettering template that can be used with an india ink fountain pen. (Courtesy of Koh-I-Noor, Inc.)

Fig. 3–29 Some lettering devices use a scriber in conjunction with a template which is placed below the line of lettering to be drawn. (Courtesy of J. S. Staedtler, Inc.)

ing drawings. You may wish to develop your own alphabet for architectural drawings that will be attractive and that best suits your style of lettering.

Some architectural lettering makes use of a slanted fraction bar instead of the horizontal bar used in engineering lettering. A comparison of both methods is shown in Fig. 3–25.

3–11 LETTERING INSTRUMENTS

A number of lettering templates are available for lettering mechanically, in contrast to freehand lettering. The use of a template ensures that the letters are uniform and are of the proper form. The only judgment left for the draftsman is the spacing between the letters or numbers that will give the most attractive arrangement.

Mechanical templates are more often used for ink lettering than for pencil lettering, because ink requires less pressure on the paper than does a pencil. Some templates do not have adequate space for the pencil point to properly fit the template, whereas inking pens are available that are specially designed for this purpose.

The *Wrico* lettering template (Fig. 3–26) is a template that can be placed against a fixed straightedge so that each letter is drawn in its proper position. The template is moved from position to position, the straightedge being used as a guide to ensure that the letters remain in a straight line. The portion of the template that is in the area of the

letters is designed to be raised above the surface of the paper to prevent the template from coming into contact with the wet ink of the previously drawn letter.

Wrico pens are available for each size of letter that is to be made with a Wrico template. A number of india ink fountain pens are also available for use with these guides. One of these pens is shown in Fig. 3–27. A small tubular point is designed to be in contact with the paper. The tubular point is kept clear by a small plunger that fits in the tube. It can be cleared at intervals by gently shaking the pen up and down to activate the plunger. These pens can hold a supply of ink that will be sufficient for hours of use. An alternative type of lettering template is shown in Fig. 3–28.

Fig. 3–30 This portable typewriter can be placed on the drawing surface so that notes and numerals can be typed on a drawing. (Courtesy of Grintzner, Inc.)

Fig. 3–31 Transfer lettering can be transferred from film to the drawing surface. Transfer lettering comes in many sizes and styles. (Courtesy of Artype Incorporated.)

The lettering template shown in Fig. 3–29 is not placed directly over the letters to be made, but is positioned slightly lower than the line of lettering. A stylus is guided by the template; the stylus, in turn, guides the ink point, which is in contact with the paper. A straightedge must be used to align the template. An inking stylus is available that will hold an inking fountain pen, as shown in Fig. 3–27, to reduce the need for replenishing ink when lettering is done for prolonged periods of time.

3–12 LETTERING BY TYPING

Some drafting departments type many of their notes and specifications to reduce drafting time and to improve the readability of a drawing. Large typewriters are available with long carriages that will accept extremely large drawings. The notes are simply typed in position in the same manner as a conventional typewriter would be used.

A portable typing device is shown in Fig. 3–30. This is a portable typewriter that can be placed on top of a drawing and held in position by a straightedge. Numbers and letters are then typed after the drawing has been made.

Many innovations of this type are being used extensively by industries to improve their efficiency and to save time. Shortcuts should always be considered if they are truly efficient and as effective as the more conventional methods.

3–13 TRANSFER LETTERING

A number of brands and types of transfer lettering are available from commercial sources. This lettering comes printed on transparent sheets with adhesive backings on one side. Each sheet contains a number of prints of each letter of the alphabet. A guideline is drawn on the drawing and the guideline on the sheet of letters is aligned with it, as shown in Fig. 3–31. The letter is then cut out with a stylus or a razor blade and is burnished to the drawing surface to hold permanently.

Letters of this type are available on a glossy transparent sheet or a transparent mat sheet. In the case of the mat sheet, the portion of the sheet that has been burnished to the drawing surface is hardly noticeable. The glossy sheet leaves a shiny surface that can be seen. When a tracing has been printed as a blue-line reproduction, neither type of background sheet is noticeable.

A variety of styles of letters is available, from old English to modern contemporary lettering. These are very effective for large display drawings that will be used for presentations. Architects often use these letters for major titles and headings on cover sheets and on perspective displays drawn on illustration board. You should be familiar with this type of letter, since it has applications that may save valuable time.

3–14 SUMMARY

Lettering is a very important aspect of a working drawing. Poor lettering reduces the effectiveness of an otherwise well-prepared drawing. Poor lettering may even cause a drawing to be rejected in its entirety.

Good lettering can be achieved best by the use of guidelines, horizontal and vertical. Lettering instruments are available to assist the draftsman in improving his lettering, although these are not essential to good lettering. Probably the most important prerequisite for good lettering is the desire to letter well. If you use the proper proportions to draw letters with the aid of guidelines, your lettering will probably be acceptable regardless of minor variations in each stroke. You should not feel that your freehand lettering is supposed to look like instrument lettering. Instead, your lettering should look like freehand lettering and yet it should have the same proportions as mechanical lettering.

Vertical or inclined lettering can be used at your option, unless you are directed by local standards or by your instructor. Lower-case lettering is permissible, although your time would be better spent in becoming skilled in lettering using all upper-case letters. This is the type of lettering used most often on engineering drawings.

Architectural lettering can be styled to suit the draftsman; there are fewer restraints on architectural than on engineering lettering. However, engineering lettering can be used on architectural drawings if desired.

A number of mechanical lettering aids and templates are available. There is no substitute for good freehand lettering, but you should become familiar with the various devices that are available. These are usually advertised in technical publications.

3–15 SOLUTIONS OF PROBLEMS

Problems are provided at the end of each chapter to afford the student the opportunity to test his understanding of the principles covered in the preceding text. These problems are designed to cover the major points of each chapter.

The form of problem solutions should comply with the standards used in the preparation of working drawings. Problems may be taken from printed problem manuals, or problems from the ends of chapters may be solved on blank paper. The following formats are suggested for the layout of blank sheets whether drawn on detail paper or tracing paper. Most problems will be drawn on $8\frac{1}{2}'' \times 11''$ sheets as shown in Fig. 3–32. A title strip is suggested in this figure, with a border as shown. Care should be taken in laying out each sheet, since the title strip and borders are important parts of a drawing. Guidelines should be drawn very lightly to be only faintly visible. The $8\frac{1}{2}'' \times 11''$ sheet is called Size A.

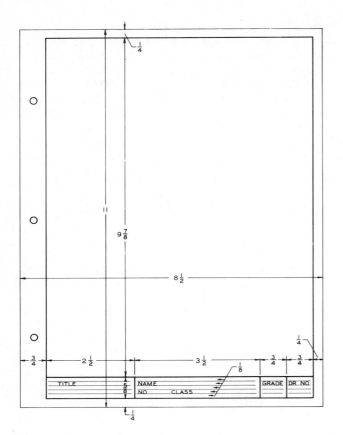

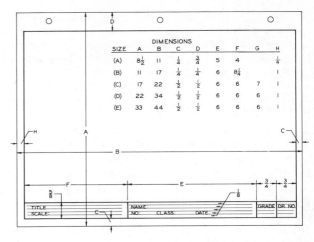

Fig. 3–33 The general format for the basic sheet sizes suggested for solving problems at the ends of chapters.

| | | DIMENSIONS | | | | | | |
SIZE	A	B	C	D	E	F	G	H
(A)	8½	11	¼	¾	5	4		¼
(B)	11	17	¼	¼	6	8¼		1
(C)	17	22	½	½	6	6	7	1
(D)	22	34	½	½	6	6	6	1
(E)	33	44	½	½	6	6	6	1

Fig. 3–32 The format and title strip for a Size A (8½″ × 11″) sheet suggested for solving problems at the end of each chapter.

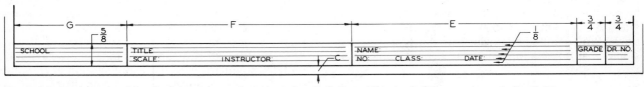

Fig. 3–34 An alternative title strip that can be used on sheet sizes B, C D, and E instead of the one shown in Fig. 3–33.

The 8½″ × 11″ sheet can be turned lengthwise, as shown in Fig. 3–33, with the holes in the sheet placed at the top of the page. The various standard sizes, A through E, are shown in the table in Fig. 3–33. The various dimensions for each size can be taken from this table. Your instructor may wish to assign other dimensions than those shown in the table. The title strip is designed for ⅛″ lettering. An alternative title strip for Sizes B, C, D, and E is shown in Fig. 3–34. Guidelines should always be used for lettering in title strips.

An alternative title block and parts list is given in Fig. 3–35. These are placed in the lower right-hand corner of the sheet against the borders. When both are used on the same drawing, the parts list is placed directly above and in contact with the title block or the title strip, as the case may be. The various parts shown on the sheet are listed in the parts list.

Many problems may be solved on paper with a printed ¼″ grid to assist in laying out the problems. The grid of the problems given at the ends of chapters represents either ¼″ or ⅛″ intervals that can

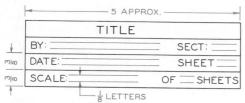

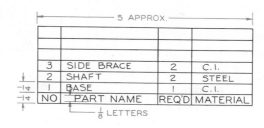

Fig. 3–35 A title block and parts list.

be counted and transferred to a similar grid paper or scaled on plain paper. Each problem sheet should be endorsed using the title strip as shown in Fig. 3–32. All points, lines, planes, and significant features should be lettered using $\frac{1}{8}$" letters with guidelines in all cases.

The answers to essay-type problems should be lettered, using single-stroke Gothic lettering as introduced in this chapter. Each page should be turned in to the instructor for grading and review. All solved problems should be maintained in the student's notebook for future reference during the course and in other courses later in his studies.

The student should refer to this article when solving problems from other chapters as he progresses through the textbook.

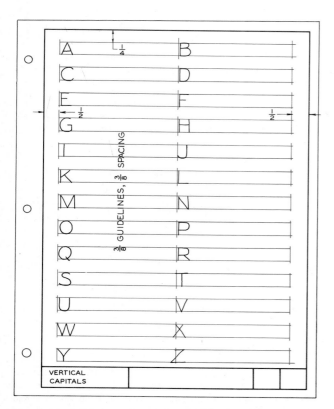

Fig. 3–36 Problem 1. Construct each vertical upper-case letter four times.

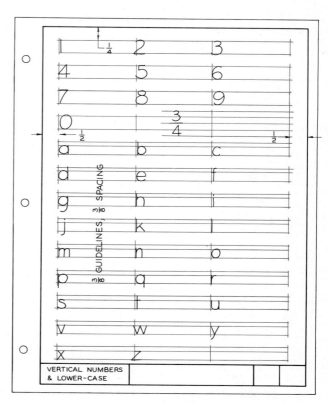

Fig. 3–37 Problem 2. Construct each vertical numeral and lower-case letter three times.

PROBLEMS

Problems should be presented on $8\frac{1}{2}'' \times 11''$ paper, plain or grid, using the format shown in Fig. 3–32.

1 Practice lettering the vertical upper-case alphabet shown in Fig. 3–36. Construct each letter four times: four A's, four B's, etc. Study the form of each letter. Use a medium weight pencil—H, F, or HB.

2 Practice lettering the vertical numerals and the lower-case alphabet as shown in Fig. 3–37. Construct each letter and number three times: three 1's, three 2's, etc. Study the form of each letter. Use a medium weight pencil—H, F, or HB. Use a hard pencil for guidelines—4H, 3H, or 2H.

3 Practice lettering the inclined upper-case alphabet shown in Fig. 3–38. Construct each letter four times: four A's, four B's, etc. Study the form of each letter. Use a medium weight pencil—H, F, or HB. Use a hard pencil for guidelines—4H, 3H, or 2H.

4 Practice lettering the vertical numerals and the lower-case alphabet shown in Fig. 3–39. Construct each letter and number three times: three 1's, three 2's, etc. Study the form of each letter. Use a medium weight pencil—H, F, or HB. Use a hard pencil for guidelines—4H, 3H, or 2H.

5 Construct guidelines for $\frac{1}{8}''$ capital letters starting $\frac{1}{4}''$ from the top border. Each line should end

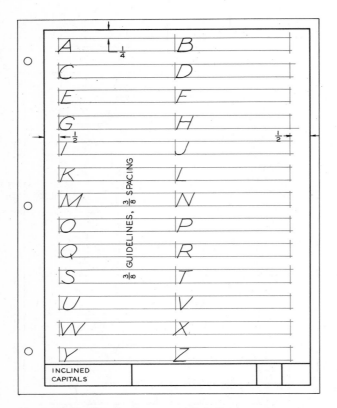

Fig. 3–38 Problem 3. Construct each inclined upper-case letter four times.

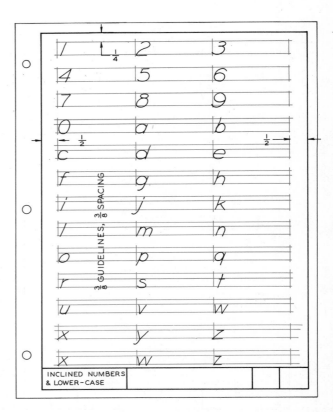

Fig. 3–39 Problem 4. Construct each inclined numeral and inclined upper-case letter three times.

$\frac{1}{2}''$ from the left and right borders. Using these guide-lines, letter the first paragraph of the text of this chapter. Use all vertical capitals (upper-case letters). Spacing between lines should be $\frac{1}{8}''$. This exercise will enable you to familiarize yourself with lettering instruments and the techniques of engineering lettering.

6 Repeat Problem 5 but use all inclined capitals (upper-case letters). Use inclined guidelines to assist you in achieving uniformity of inclination of the letters.

7 Repeat Problem 5 but use vertical capitals and lower-case letters in combination. Capitalize only those words that are capitalized in the text.

8 Repeat Problem 5 but use inclined capitals and lower-case letters in combination. Capitalize only the words that are capitalized in the text.

9 Design an architectural alphabet. Show each letter four times. Use the format and guidelines shown in Fig. 3–36.

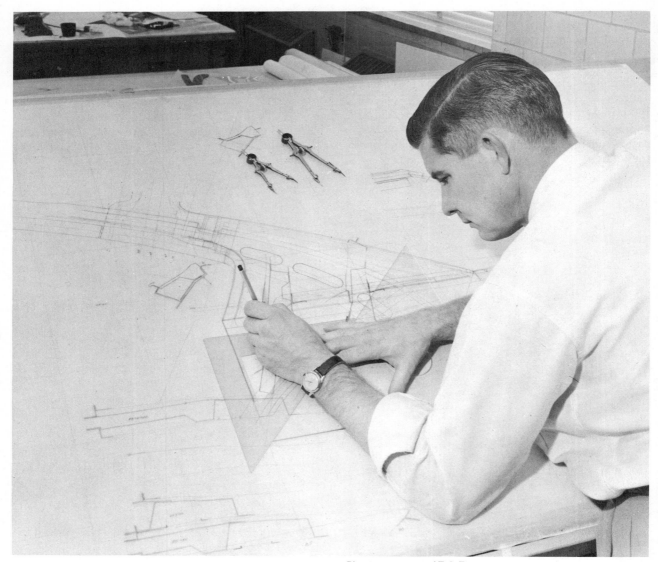

Photo courtesy of AT & T

4
THE USE OF
INSTRUMENTS

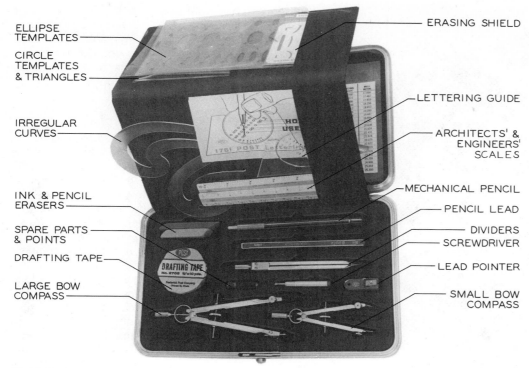

ELLIPSE TEMPLATES

CIRCLE TEMPLATES & TRIANGLES

IRREGULAR CURVES

INK & PENCIL ERASERS

SPARE PARTS & POINTS

DRAFTING TAPE

LARGE BOW COMPASS

ERASING SHIELD

LETTERING GUIDE

ARCHITECTS' & ENGINEERS' SCALES

MECHANICAL PENCIL

PENCIL LEAD

DIVIDERS

SCREWDRIVER

LEAD POINTER

SMALL BOW COMPASS

Fig. 4–1 A compact set of drafting instruments for the student. (Courtesy of Frederick Post Company.)

4–1 INTRODUCTION

The development of skill and an understanding of drafting begins with the knowledge of how to use instruments most effectively. This chapter is devoted to a discussion of the basic drafting instruments and their fundamental uses. As he gains experience, the student will discover additional shortcuts and techniques in using instruments.

Through the proper use of drafting instruments a person with only a moderate degree of artistic ability can produce drawings of a caliber that is usually associated with special artistic talents. Instruments are designed to help the draftsman produce his drawings in the minimum of time with the least amount of effort. Although anyone can draw a straight line with a straightedge, skill is required to produce a straight line that is uniform in

darkness and thickness. This skill can be developed only through practice.

The use of instruments will be discussed for both pencil and ink drawings. These two types of drawings are equally important to the draftsman. Their basic principles are very similar; the major differences between them arise from the nature of the tools used.

4–2 STUDENT EQUIPMENT

The case of instruments shown in Fig. 4–1 is a self-contained set of instruments that is adequate for most students. This set was developed to provide a compact case that could easily be carried and would require no more space than a typical textbook. The case can be closed as shown in Fig. 4–2.

Fig. 4–2 The kit of instruments closes into a package no larger than a textbook. Two sizes are shown here. (Courtesy of Frederick Post Company.)

This set contains the minimum number of instruments considered necessary for most assignments likely to be attempted by a student. Seldom used instruments and attachments have been eliminated to reduce the kit to a functional and economical package.

Some of the instruments in this kit cannot be clearly seen in their pockets. These are shown separately in Fig. 4–3. Many additional drafting aids are available besides those shown here. Drafting instruments vary greatly in cost, the higher-quality instruments costing much more than economy instruments. A student who wishes to purchase his own set of instruments should discuss the various

types with his teacher to ensure that he is spending his money wisely.

The instruments shown in Figs. 4–1 and 4–3 will be discussed individually in this chapter. Exercises are provided at the end of the chapter to familiarize the student with the use of these tools.

4–3 THE T-SQUARE AND DRAWING BOARD

The T-square is the most basic instrument used by the beginning draftsman. It may be made entirely of wood, plastic, or steel, or a combination of materials. A typical T-square is shown in Fig. 4–4. This T-square has plastic edges to allow a better view while drawing lines. The head is attached to the blade at a 90° angle. It is extremely important that the head and blade be tightly and firmly joined. Any looseness between them will cause inaccuracies in the student's drawings.

Although the T-square is a very simple tool, one should take great care of it, since a slight nick in the drawing edge of the blade will cause imperfect lines. Occasionally the underside of the blade should be wiped clean with a slightly damp cloth to prevent a drawing from being smudged by carbon on the underside.

The size of a T-square is indicated by its length. A student's T-square is seldom longer than 36", but some are available up to 72" in length for special applications. The standard sizes are 18", 24", 30", 36", and 48".

The T-square must be used in conjunction with either a drawing board or a table top. The term "drawing board" is generally understood to mean either a table top or a separate board. Most schools and industries are equipped with smooth drawing surfaces built onto the tops of drafting tables. However, separate boards are often used by students who must work at home or who do not have a proper drafting table with an adequate drawing surface. The use of a T-square in combination with a drawing board is shown in Fig. 4–5.

The typical drawing board is made of basswood, which is light yet strong. Standard sizes are 12" × 14", 15" × 20", and 21" × 26". The working edge of a drawing board is the edge where the T-square head is held in position to allow a horizontal line to be drawn. The head can be slid

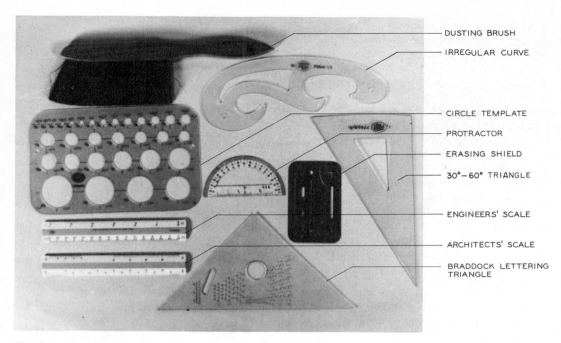

- DUSTING BRUSH
- IRREGULAR CURVE
- CIRCLE TEMPLATE
- PROTRACTOR
- ERASING SHIELD
- 30°–60° TRIANGLE
- ENGINEERS' SCALE
- ARCHITECTS' SCALE
- BRADDOCK LETTERING TRIANGLE

Fig. 4–3 Individual instruments of the compact set shown in Fig. 4–1.

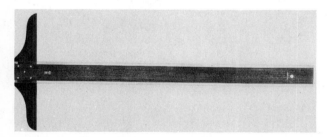

Fig. 4–4 A typical T-square with plastic edges. (Courtesy of Keuffel and Esser Co.)

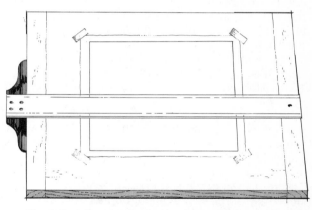

Fig. 4–5 A T-square used with a basswood drawing board.

Fig. 4–6 The drawing should be attached to a drawing board with a piece of masking tape about 1″ long.

4–3   **The T-square and drawing board**

along the working edge to give a horizontal line in any position desired. For a higher degree of accuracy, some drawing boards are constructed with a steel working edge.

The sheet of drawing paper should be attached to the board as shown in Fig. 4–5, with the sheet aligned with the blade of the T-square. Short pieces of masking tape can be used at each corner of the paper to attach it firmly to the board (Fig. 4–6). Thumbtacks, staples, and cellophane tape can also be used, but masking tape is recommended as the most practical method which causes least damage to the board. If the board is not perfectly smooth, a second sheet can be placed under the drawing paper to provide a smooth surface.

4–4 PAPERS

A number of drafting surfaces are available on which a drawing can be prepared. These vary from illustration boards to plastic films and inking cloths. A standard type of paper, used extensively in classrooms, is medium weight drawing paper that can be used for both pencil and ink. This paper is slightly colored in tints of green and cream or white. Since this paper is opaque (one cannot see through it), it cannot be used if blue-line prints are to be made from the original.

Drawing paper is available in rolls or in individual sheets. Sheet sizes are $9'' \times 12''$, $11'' \times 15''$, $12'' \times 18''$, and $18'' \times 24''$. Larger sizes are also available.

Tracing paper, film, or tracing cloth must be used if prints are to be made from the finished drawings. Some high-grade tracing papers can be used for ink drawings, but these are generally not suitable for erasing ink lines without leaving holes in the paper. Tracing cloths or films are recommended for inking, since their surfaces are much tougher and will withstand erasing. In the case of films, special erasers or solutions are used to remove lines. Films are also available for pencil drawings.

4–5 PENCILS

Since any drawing begins with the pencil, the selection of the proper pencil is a very important step. Pencils are identified by numbers and letters which

Fig. 4–7 As the pencil grades get progressively softer from 9H to 7B, the diameter of the lead becomes larger.

Fig. 4–8 A mechanical drafting pencil. (Courtesy of J. S. Staedtler Company.)

specify the hardness of the lead. The following is a list of pencils and their suggested uses:

Designation	Weight	Use
7B	Soft	
6B	Soft	
5B	Soft	Sketching and artistic
4B	Soft	applications
3B	Soft	
2B	Soft	
B	Medium	Sketching
HB	Medium	Sketching, lettering
F	Medium	Object lines, lettering
H	Medium	Object lines
2H	Medium	Centerlines
3H	Medium	Centerlines
4H	Hard	
5H	Hard	
6H	Hard	For highly technical
7H	Hard	constructions, guidelines,
8H	Hard	and accurate measurements
9H	Hard	

Cross-sectional views of three of the extreme pencil grades listed are shown in Fig. 4–7. Note that the soft pencils have larger diameters than do the hard pencils. The lead diameters vary slightly from grade to grade. Specific applications of pencils of various grades will be discussed later.

Pencils may be wooden or mechanical; an example of a mechanical pencil is shown in Fig. 4–8. Either can be used with equal effectiveness.

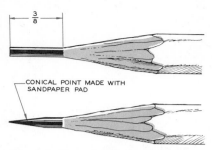

CONICAL POINT MADE WITH
SANDPAPER PAD

Fig. 4–9 The point of the drafting pencil should be sharpened to expose about $\frac{3}{8}''$ of lead. This pencil is sharpened to a slim conical point with a point sharpener.

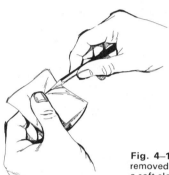

Fig. 4–10 A sandpaper pad is a commonly used sharpener for pencil points. (Courtesy of Keuffel and Esser Co.)

Fig. 4–11 A pencil point can be sharpened by holding the sandpaper pad and stroking the point while the pencil is rotated to give a uniform, conical point.

Fig. 4–12 The professional draftsman uses a mechanical lead pointer of this type. The pencil is inserted and revolved about the axis of the sharpener. (Courtesy of Keuffel and Esser Co.)

Fig. 4–13 Graphite dust should be removed from a sharpened pencil with a soft cloth before the pencil is used on a drawing.

4–6 SHARPENING THE PENCIL

The most frequent cause of imperfections in the drawing of the beginning student is failure to sharpen his pencil properly. Sharpening pencils is not difficult, nor does it require a special skill; however, a proper point is essential to a good drawing.

The pencil point suggested for most general-purpose drafting is shown in Fig. 4–9. The pencil is sharpened either with a penknife or with a draftsman's pencil sharpener, which leaves approximately $\frac{3}{8}''$ of lead exposed for sharpening with a sandpaper pad (Fig. 4–10) to give a smooth conical point as shown in Fig. 4–9. The pencil should be sharpened by stroking the sandpaper with the pencil point while the pencil is being revolved between the fingers (Fig. 4–11). The conical point should be similar to the point shown in Fig. 4–9.

While the pencil is being sharpened, the sandpaper pad should be held off the edge of the drawing board, *not over the drawing.* This will prevent the drawing from becoming messy and smudged with carbon.

A pencil pointer (Fig. 4–12) can be used with either a wood or a mechanical pencil. The pencil is inserted in the hole and revolved to sharpen the lead into a slightly conical point. A small pencil pointer is shown in the kit in Fig. 4–1; this device can be used to point the lead after the wood has been removed.

Regardless of the device or method used, it is likely that the point obtained after sharpening will be too sharp. A sheet of scratch paper should always be available to provide a surface on which the point can be rounded or refined to give the width of line desired. In addition, it is wise to wipe the pencil point after each sharpening with a soft cloth or tissue to remove loose graphite dust that might cause smudges on the drawing surface (Fig. 4–13).

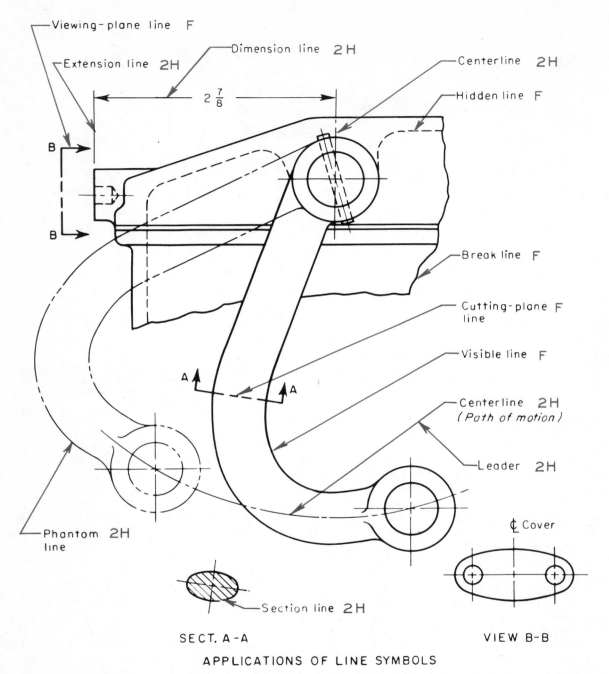

Viewing-plane line F

Extension line 2H

Dimension line 2H

$2\frac{7}{8}$

Centerline 2H

Hidden line F

B

B

Break line F

Cutting-plane F line

Visible line F

A

A

Centerline 2H
(Path of motion)

Leader 2H

Phantom 2H line

℄ Cover

Section line 2H

SECT. A-A

VIEW B-B

APPLICATIONS OF LINE SYMBOLS

Fig. 4–14 Line weights recommended for engineering drawings with the suggested pencils for each line. (Courtesy of American National Standards Institute.)

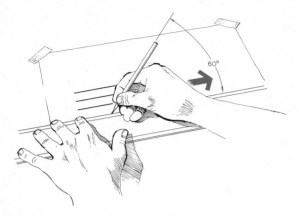

Fig. 4–15 Horizontal lines should be drawn with the pencil held in a vertical plane making a 60° angle with the drawing surface. Horizontal lines are drawn from left to right.

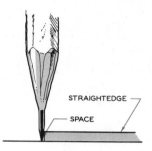

Fig. 4–16 When looking at the end of the straightedge, the vertical plane of the pencil can be seen. Note that there is a small space between the straightedge and the pencil point.

4–7 ALPHABET OF LINES

The type of line produced by a pencil depends on the hardness of the lead, the drawing surface, and the technique of the draftsman. The lines used in drafting practice are standardized to give uniform line widths for various applications. Examples of these lines and the types of pencils suggested for drawing them are shown in Fig. 4–14.

The pencil grades suggested might not give the desired results in all cases. For example, a paper with an abrasive surface will require harder grades of pencils. The various applications of the lines defined in Fig. 4–14 will be discussed in later chapters where these lines are used extensively.

Even though different pencil grades are used, all lines which are to be clearly visible in the finished drawing should have one characteristic in common: *they should be solid black lines*. The variations in lines should come from the lines' widths, not from their degrees of blackness or solidity. A thin line should be just as black and solid as a wide line such as a visible line (object line). However, lines used for laying out a drawing in the preliminary stages can be drawn very lightly with a hard pencil such as a 4H. If they are drawn lightly, these construction lines do not need to be erased later when the final lines are drawn.

4–8 HORIZONTAL LINES

Construction of horizontal lines with a T-square is a basic exercise for the beginning student. The T-square is held firmly against the working edge of the drawing board in the desired position. The pencil is held at an angle of approximately 60° with the paper and inclined in the direction in which the line is to be drawn (Fig. 4–15)—this is left to right for right-handed students. A small space should be maintained between the upper blade of the T-square and the pencil point (Fig. 4–16). With a little practice, the student will be able to hold his pencil at a constant angle as he draws the line; maintaining this constant angle is important in order to obtain a uniform line.

Only the upper edge of the T-square blade should be used. It is helpful to rotate the pencil slowly so that the point will wear evenly and there will be a minimum of variation in line width.

Left-handed students may wish to use the right edge of the drawing board, or else devise their own system that will give satisfactory results.

4–9 VERTICAL LINES

To draw vertical lines one uses a T-square in combination with a standard triangle, which is a right triangle with one 90° angle and two 45° angles.

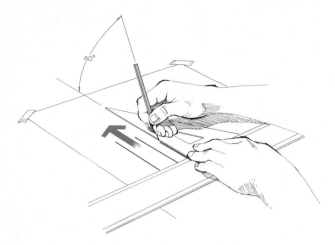

Fig. 4–17 Vertical lines should be drawn with the pencil held in a vertical plane making a 60° angle with the surface. Vertical lines are drawn in an upward direction.

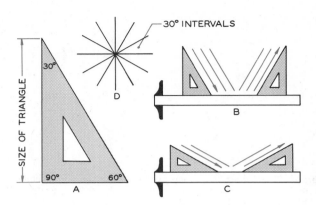

Fig. 4–19 The 30°-60° triangle and the lines that it can be used to draw.

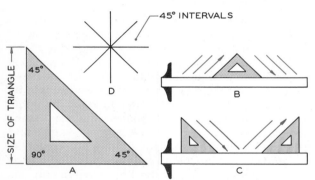

Fig. 4–18 The 45° triangle and the various lines that it can be used to draw.

While the T-square is held firmly with one hand, the triangle can be placed where needed and used as a guide for the vertical lines (Fig. 4–17).

Vertical lines should be drawn in an upward direction. This direction will be found much more comfortable than the downward direction. As when drawing horizontal lines, the pencil should be held at an angle of approximately 60° with the paper, as shown in Fig. 4–17.

4–10 THE 45° TRIANGLE

The standard triangle is often referred to as the 45° triangle (Fig. 4–18A). Note that the size of the triangle is specified in terms of the length of one of the sides adjacent to the 90° angle. Standard sizes vary in 2″ intervals from 4″ to 24″. A 6″ triangle is sufficient for most student applications.

The standard angles that can be made by the 45° triangle are shown in Fig. 4–18B, C, and D. The arrows indicate the directions in which the lines should be drawn for the best results.

4–11 THE 30°-60° TRIANGLE

The 30°-60° triangle is a versatile triangle that is required for most drafting projects. Its size is specified in terms of the length of the longer of the two sides adjacent to the 90° angle (Fig. 4–19A). Standard sizes vary in 2″ intervals from 4″ to 24″. The 8″ and 10″ sizes are adequate for most student needs.

This triangle can be used in conjunction with the T-square to draw lines making angles of 60° with the horizontal in the directions shown in Fig. 4–19B. When the triangle is turned as shown in Fig. 4–19C, lines making angles of 30° with the horizontal can be

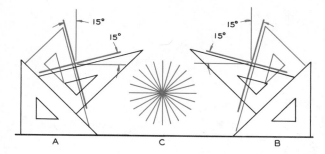

Fig. 4–20 A 45° and a 30°-60° triangle can be used in combination to draw lines at intervals of 15°.

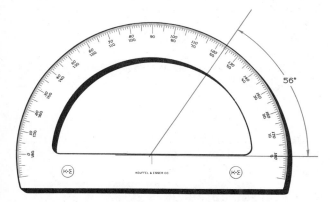

Fig. 4–21 The measurement of an angle with a protractor. (Courtesy of Keuffel and Esser Co.)

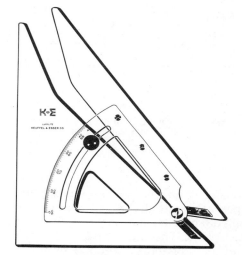

Fig. 4–22 An adjustable protractor for drawing and measuring lines. (Courtesy of Keuffel and Esser Co.)

drawn. All the possible combinations of lines that can be drawn with the 30°-60° triangle are shown in Fig. 4–19D.

4–12 ANGULAR LINES

When a 45° triangle is used in combination with a 30°-60° triangle, lines can be drawn at intervals of 15°. Lines making angles of 15° with the horizontal and vertical are shown in Fig. 4–20A. The 45° triangle is held firmly in contact with the T-square and the 30°-60° triangle is positioned along its edge as illustrated.

By changing the position of the 45° triangle as in Fig. 4–20B, lines can be drawn to make 15° angles with the horizontal and vertical in different

directions. The 30°-60° triangle can also be used as the "base" triangle instead of the 45° triangle.

The angles that can be drawn using the 45° triangle and the 30°-60° triangle separately and in combination are shown in Fig. 4–20C. The lines are spaced at intervals of 15°.

4–13 THE PROTRACTOR

When lines must be constructed or measured at angles other than 15° or multiples of 15°, an additional device is required. This is the protractor (Fig. 4–21). Protractors are available as semicircular (180°) shapes or as circular (360°) shapes.

When the angle to be measured is with the horizontal, the protractor can be used in conjunction

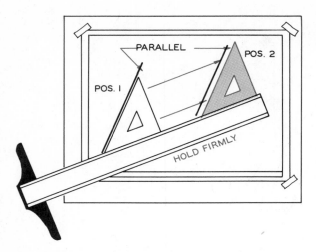

Fig. 4–23 A T-square and 45° triangle can be used for drawing lines parallel to a given line. A 30°-60° triangle could be used in this manner also.

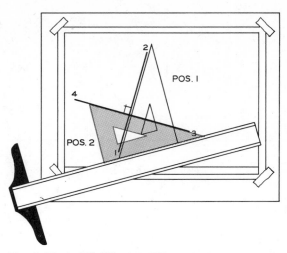

Fig. 4–24 A 30°-60° triangle is used to construct line 3–4 perpendicular to line 1–2.

with the T-square. One of the lines forming the angle must pass through the zero point of the protractor, and both lines must meet at the center of the circle or semicircle. The angle can be read from the outer arc of the protractor. An angle of 56° is measured in Fig. 4–21.

The adjustable triangle (Fig. 4–22) can be used as a combination triangle and protractor. The triangle can be adjusted at any interval within a 45° range. This device saves time when many angles must be drawn and measured.

4–14 PARALLEL LINES

A series of lines can be drawn parallel to a given line by using a triangle and a straightedge. This is illustrated in Fig. 4–23 with a 45° triangle and a T-square.

The 45° triangle is placed parallel to the given line in position 1 with the T-square turned to be in contact with one edge of the triangle. With the T-square held in place, the triangle can be moved to position 2, where the parallel line is drawn.

Another triangle can be used as the straightedge when the working space is small, as on an 8½″ × 11″ sheet. When the parallel lines required are at angles

of 30°, 60°, or 45° with the horizontal, the standard triangles and a T-square can be used as illustrated in Figs. 4–18 and 4–19.

4–15 PERPENDICULAR LINES

When preparing a drawing, it is often necessary to construct a line perpendicular to another line. This construction is possible with either of the standard triangles.

A 30°-60° triangle is used with a T-square to construct line 3–4 perpendicular to line 1–2 (Fig. 4–24). One edge of the triangle is positioned parallel to line 1–2 in position 1 with the T-square in contact with the triangle. With the T-square held in place, the triangle is turned to position 2, where the 90° angle can be drawn to establish line 3–4. This same procedure can be used with the 45° triangle as well.

4–16 ERASING

Erasers are available for all types of surfaces and media used for drawings. Surfaces may vary from soft drawing papers to plastic films on which lines are drawn in ink or pencil. The two main media are pencil and ink.

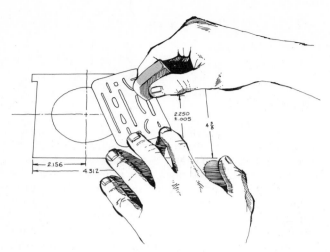

Fig. 4–25 The erasing shield is used to protect surrounding lines while small errors are being erased.

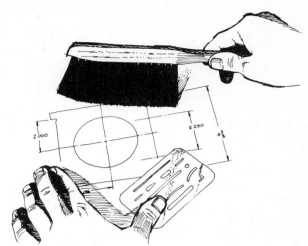

Fig. 4–27 The dusting brush should be used to brush the drawing clean after each erasure.

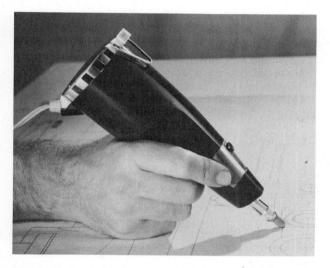

Fig. 4–26 An electric erasing machine that can be used for rapid erasing. (Courtesy of Keuffel and Esser Co.)

As a general rule, in order to cause as little damage as possible to the drawing surface, one should use the softest eraser that will serve the purpose. For example, ink erasers should not be used to erase pencil lines because ink erasers have a tendency to damage the surface of the paper. You should consult the latest drafting supply catalogs to determine the best eraser to use for your particular needs.

An erasing shield is a helpful instrument to assist with your erasing. It is used for erasing in small areas that might otherwise be difficult to erase without accidentally erasing the wrong lines. If the erasing shield (Fig. 4–25) is placed so that one of the openings is over the area to be erased, the surrounding lines will be shielded. This technique can also be used effectively for converting a solid line to a dashed line.

Several types of electric erasers are available for a draftsman who spends a great deal of his time at the drawing board. A typical electric eraser is shown in Fig. 4–26. This type of eraser allows erasing with the minimum damage to the drawing surface. Pressure can be applied gently as the eraser rotates at a high speed in contact with the drawing surface. Erasers for both ink and pencil lines are available to fit electric erasers. Erasing shields can be used effectively with electric erasers.

All erasing should be followed by brushing to remove erasures and "crumbs" from the drawing. The brush (Fig. 4–27) should be used lightly to avoid smudges. Failure to remove erasures and graphite from a drawing will cause the drawing to become soiled when triangles and T-squares are moved about the drawing surface. Since it is difficult to remove

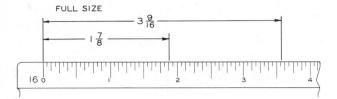

Fig. 4–28 The 16 scale is used to measure full-size dimensions. Each inch is divided into sixteenths.

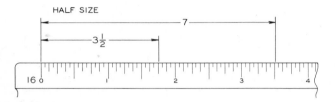

Fig. 4–29 The 16 scale is used to draw lines half size.

every trace of graphite, one should whenever possible lift the instruments when moving them from position to position, to avoid sliding them on the drawing.

4–17 SCALES

All engineering drawings require the use of scales to measure lengths, sizes, and other measurements. Consequently, it is necessary that you understand scales and their various applications to drawings.

The most common scales used in engineering drawing are the architects' scale and the civil engineers' scale. These are either 12" or 6" long.

Architects' Scale

The architects' scale is given this name because it is used to dimension features usually encountered by the architect. These include building designs, cabinet work, interior plumbing, and electrical layouts. In general, most indoor dimensions are measured in feet and inches as with an architects' scale. It is obvious that few drawings can be made full size; consequently, scales are used to draw the layouts in proportion at reduced sizes. The architects'

scale has the following graduations:

Full size		$\frac{3}{8}" = 1'-0"$
$3" = 1'-0"$		$\frac{1}{4}" = 1'-0"$
$1\frac{1}{2}" = 1'-0"$		$\frac{3}{16}" = 1'-0"$
$\frac{3}{4}" = 1'-0"$		$\frac{3}{32}" = 1'-0"$
$\frac{1}{2}" = 1'-0"$		

The architect is usually concerned with drawings of buildings that would be impossible to represent except at a reduced scale. Since he makes measurements in feet and inches, the architects' scale is graduated in inches on one end to permit measurements in these units. The 16 scale is the scale used for full-size dimensions with each inch divided into sixteenths. This scale is the same as the one found on most yardsticks, folding rules, and measuring tapes used by the workmen who will be constructing the finished components from architectural drawings. The full-size scale is used for drawing small parts or enlarging specific details for easier interpretation.

Full size. The use of the 16 scale for measuring a full-size line is shown in Fig. 4–28. One end of the scale is placed at zero and the measurement is made to the nearest $\frac{1}{16}"$.

Half size. The 16 scale is used for measuring half-size drawings. On a drawing that is to be made half-size, a 7" measurement would be drawn $3\frac{1}{2}"$ long (Fig. 4–29). When a measurement is taken from a half-size drawing, the 16 scale is used and the measurement is doubled.

General scales. On the scales labeled $\frac{1}{8}$, $\frac{1}{4}$, $\frac{1}{2}$, etc., the fractions of an inch indicated represent one foot. For example, scale $\frac{1}{4}" = 1'-0"$ means that each $\frac{1}{4}$ inch is equivalent to $1'-0"$.

All these scales are used in much the same way. A typical example is illustrated in Fig. 4–30 with the $\frac{1}{2}$ scale. Measurements are first made to the nearest whole foot which is not in excess of the actual measurement. The remainder is then measured at the end of the scale, which is calibrated in inches (Fig. 4–30). This allows one to read fractions of a foot in inches. Although the divisions at the end of the scale vary according to the size of the scale used, the same method of scaling applies to all scales.

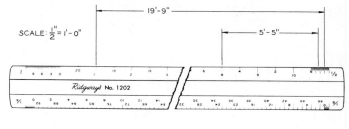

SCALE: $\frac{1}{2}'' = 1'-0''$

Fig. 4–30 Architects' scale: measurement of lines at a scale of $\frac{1}{2}'' = 1'-0''$.

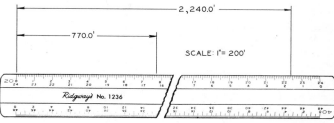

SCALE: $1'' = 200'$

Fig. 4–31 Engineers' scale: measurement of lines at a scale of $1'' = 200'$.

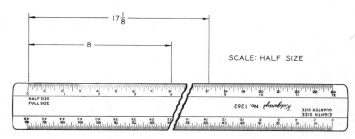

SCALE: HALF SIZE

Fig. 4–32 Mechanical engineers' scale: measurement of lines at a scale of half size.

Civil Engineers' Scale

The civil engineers' scale is a decimal scale (Fig. 4–31). This scale is used for engineering drawings of structures or projects erected outdoors, such as streets and drainage systems. Since the divisions are in decimals, it is easy to perform multiplication and division; there is no need to convert feet and inches, as there is when the architects' scale is used. Areas and volumes can be found easily with the civil engineers' scale.

Typical scales are:

10 scale:
 $1'' = 0.1''$, or $1'' = 1''$, or $1'' = 10''$, etc.
20 scale:
 $1'' = 20'$, or $1'' = 200'$, or $1'' = 2000'$, etc.
30 scale:
 $1'' = 300'$, or $1'' = 3000'$, or $1'' = 30,000'$, etc.

40 scale:
 $1'' = 40'$, or $1'' = 400'$, or $1'' = 4000'$, etc.
50 scale:
 $1'' = 50'$, or $1'' = 500'$, or $1'' = 5000'$, etc.
60 scale:
 $1'' = 600'$, or $1'' = 6000'$, or $1'' = 60,000'$, etc.

These are examples of typical scales that can be read directly from the civil engineers' scale. Many other combinations may be obtained by increasing or reducing the scales by multiples of ten. For example, the 10 scale can be used for $1'' = 0.0001''$ or $1'' = 10,000'$ by simply moving the decimal point as desired.

Mechanical Engineers' Scale

When rather small machine parts are drawn, the mechanical engineers' scale is used (Fig. 4–32).

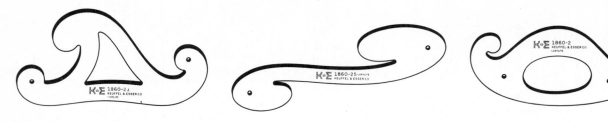

Fig. 4–33 Types of irregular curves. (Courtesy of Keuffel and Esser Co.)

FIGURE 4–34. USE OF THE IRREGULAR CURVE

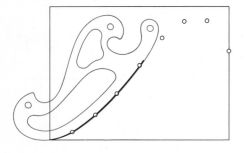

Step 1. Points on an irregular curve must be connected with a smooth curve. The irregular curve is positioned to pass through as many points as possible. This portion of the curve is drawn.

Step 2. The irregular curve is positioned for drawing another portion of the curve.

Step 3. The last portion of the curve is drawn to complete the curve. Most irregular curves must be drawn in several steps as shown here.

This scale gives reduced sizes for inches, with one end of the scale dividing the inch into fractions of an inch. This scale is normally used not for measurements in feet and inches, but for measurements entirely in inches and fractions of an inch.

4–18 IRREGULAR CURVES

Although most features on a mechanically prepared drawing are composed of either straight lines or arcs, it is often necessary to draw irregular curves. Examples of common devices for drawing irregular curves are shown in Fig. 4–33. These are made of transparent plastic for easy visibility.

The application of these instruments to the drawing of a curve through plotted points is shown in Fig. 4–34. Usually the instrument must be repositioned several times as the curve is being drawn. A properly drawn curve will be smooth with-

Fig. 4–35 A flexible spline can be used for drawing irregular curves for special applications. (Courtesy of Keuffel and Esser Co.)

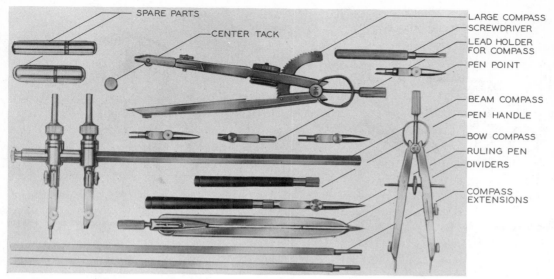

Fig. 4-36 Instruments commonly found in drafting sets. (Courtesy of Keuffel and Esser Co.)

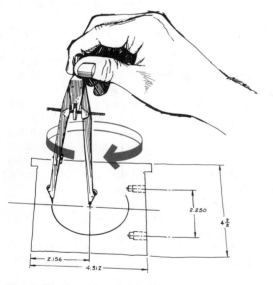

Fig. 4-37 Drawing a circle with a compass.

out noticeable gaps or irregularities if the instrument is placed to give a series of slightly overlapping segments.

A spline curve is shown in Fig. 4-35. This is a flexible device, useful in drawing large curves, that can be molded to fit the desired curve.

4-19 DRAFTING INSTRUMENTS

A basic set of drawing instruments is shown in Fig. 4-1. Another set is shown in Fig. 4-36. In these figures the various instruments have been labeled so that you can familiarize yourself with their names. Sets of instruments vary from the comprehensive set shown in Fig. 4-36 to sets consisting of only a few instruments.

The following articles will discuss briefly the uses of each instrument in the kit. Though some instruments will be used much more often than others, the draftsman will have a need for all the instruments at one time or another.

4-20 COMPASS

The compass is used to draw circles and arcs (Fig. 4-37). In order to draw a good circle with a compass, the pencil point must be properly sharpened as illustrated in Fig. 4-38. The basic angle of sharpening is shown in Fig. 4-38B and C; it is recommended that this angle of sharpening be on the outside of the lead (Fig. 4-38). The needle point for the compass should be turned so that the shoulder is used to prevent damage to the table top. If possible, the

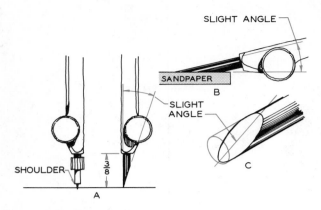

Fig. 4–38   Sharpening the compass point.

Fig. 4–39   The drop compass for drawing small circles in pencil and ink.   (Courtesy of Keuffel and Esser Co.)

Fig. 4–40   Drawing circles with a circle template.

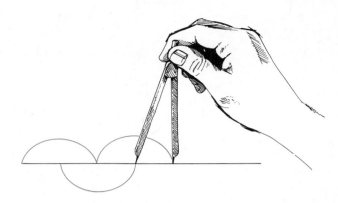

Fig. 4–41   Using dividers to step off dimensions on a line to divide it into equal parts.

point should not be inserted completely to the shoulder in the drawing board.   When a single center is used for a number of arcs, the center tack (Fig. 4–36) can be used over the center.   The compass point is placed in this center rather than in the board; in this way the drawing and the table are protected from damage through repeated use of the compass point.

Most compasses have extensions such as the one illustrated in Fig. 4–47.   These are used for large circles and arcs.   In addition, the beam compass (Fig. 4–36) can be used for large arcs.   Compasses for small circles are usually called bow compasses. For very small circles that must be drawn accurately, the drop compass is recommended (Fig. 4–39).

In many cases it is more convenient to use circle templates than the compass to draw circular features. The template permits a circle to be drawn as a continuous line of constant weight and darkness, since the same pressure can be applied throughout (Fig. 4–40).

4–21 DIVIDERS

Dividers are an instrument that looks much like a compass but is used for laying off and transferring dimensions on a drawing.   For example, equal

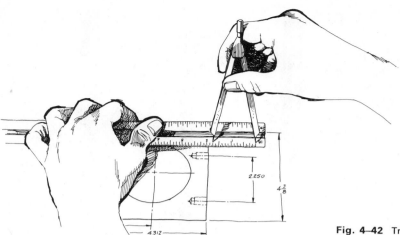

divisions can be stepped off rapidly as shown in Fig. 4–41. A slight impression is made in the drawing surface with one of the points as each measurement is made; the drawing can be completed from these impressions.

Dividers can also be used to transfer dimensions from a scale (Fig. 4–42) to a drawing. Yet another use for dividers is dividing a line into a number of equal divisions. This is a trial-and-error process that begins with estimating the spacing and stepping off the space the number of times desired. The spacing is varied until it comes out equal to the length of the line.

4–22 INKING

Although the majority of drafting and design work is done in pencil, inking is required for many applications, especially for drawings that will be used in publications and reports. Ink drawings have many advantages over pencil drawings, both in their preparation and in their final use. Pencil drawings have a tendency to lose their sharpness while they are being prepared, as instruments are moved about the drawing surface. In the case of ink drawings, the lines remain dark and distinct without any danger of losing their original quality. All pencil guidelines can be erased without damage to the inked lines.

For many projects ink is specified as the medium of presentation. This is done to ensure that the drawings can be reduced in size and reproduced by a printing press for inclusion in a set of plans. Besides lending themselves to reduction, ink drawings give better prints than do pencil drawings when reproduced by most methods—diazo, blueprints, or microfilming.

The following articles discuss instruments and techniques for preparing ink drawings. You should experiment with this medium to learn its applications, advantages, and disadvantages.

4–23 MATERIALS FOR INK DRAWING

An average good grade of tracing paper can be used for ink drawings, but only by a skilled draftsman. The attempt to erase errors may produce holes in the paper or perhaps damage the surface. The student and the less skilled draftsman should use tracing cloth or film for ink drawings. The tracing cloth is a semitransparent starched linen that has a mat surface on which to draw. The cloth body of tracing cloth gives a durable, tough surface that will withstand many erasings and corrections without serious damage. An erasing machine is most effective for erasing ink lines. When ink lines are erased by hand, care should be taken not to abuse the surface.

A variety of drafting films are available for inking purposes. Some can be used for both pencil and ink drawings, and others are recommended only for one or the other. Erasures can be made on some of these films with a damp cloth or with a special eraser made for the particular film. One side of the film—or sometimes both sides—has a matt surface that is specially prepared to take the ink lines. Erasures can be made on this material numerous times.

Some tracing cloths and other inking materials work better if their surfaces are prepared to take ink. For each of these materials there is a powder suggested by the manufacturer that can be sprinkled on the surface and rubbed with a felt pad. This powder or pounce absorbs oily spots that would not take ink properly. Another method of preparing the surface is to go over it lightly with a soft eraser to remove these spots before beginning. Care should be taken not to leave fingerprints or oily spots on the surface.

The drawing ink used for engineering drawings is called india ink and is available under numerous trade names. This is a dense black, carbon ink that is much thicker and faster-drying than regular fountain pen ink. Some draftsmen prefer to "season" their ink by leaving the top of the bottle off for several days when the bottle is new to allow the ink to thicken to the desired degree.

Ink should be removed from instruments before it dries to prevent clogging that restricts an easy flow of ink from the pen to the paper. This easy flow is essential to efficient inking. Inking instruments will not work or will work very poorly unless kept clean of dried ink.

4–24 BASIC INSTRUMENTS

The ruling pen and the compass are the two primary instruments used for inking. Three common types of inking pens are shown in Fig. 4–43. The two points (nibs) of the ruling pen are separated by a thumbscrew to vary the width of the inked lines. The wider spacing gives a wider line.

The ruling pen should be inked with the spout that is attached to most india ink bottles. This method is shown in Fig. 4–44. Care should be taken not to overload the pen with ink, since this will cause the lines to be wet and perhaps run on the drawing. The

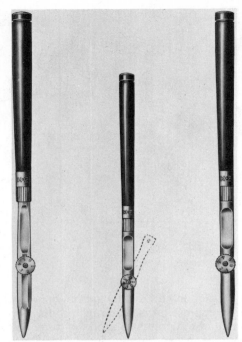

Fig. 4–43 Standard types of ruling pens for ruling ink lines. (Courtesy of Keuffel and Esser Co.)

amount of ink suitable for each pen can be determined easily by experimentation in a few minutes. Some pens have a greater capacity than others.

The ruling pen is held in the same position as the pencil for drawing vertical and horizontal lines. An important rule to remember is to maintain a space between the ruling pen and the straightedge. Note in Fig. 4–45A that there is a space between the straightedge and the line being drawn. This figure shows the correct position of the pen as viewed from the end. The ruling pen is usually held at an angle of 60° to the drawing surface.

An extra margin of safety can be obtained by placing a triangle or template under the straightedge as shown in Fig. 4–45B. This prevents the wet ink from coming into contact with the straightedge and causing the line to be smeared.

The inking compass is usually the same compass used for pencil circles with the inking attachment

Fig. 4–44 Inking a ruling pen with a bottle-top quill.

Fig. 4–46 Inking a circle with a compass.

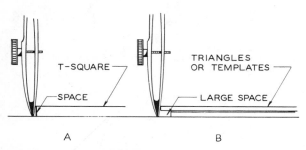

Fig. 4–45 The position of the inking pen when viewed from the end of the straightedge. Ruling pens should be held in a vertical plane at a 60° angle with the drawing surface. Added protection can be gained as shown in B, where a triangle is placed under the straightedge used for ruling the lines.

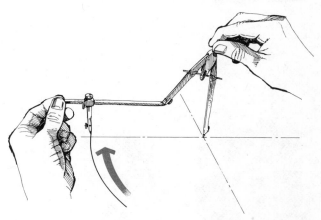

Fig. 4–47 Inking a circle with an extension beam used on a compass.

inserted in place of the pencil attachment. The inking attachment of the compass usually has an "elbow" which allows the attachment to be bent until the point is approximately perpendicular to the drawing surface. A bow compass is preferable for inking (Fig. 4–46) to prevent the radius of the compass from varying as the arcs are drawn. Extension beams can be used with most compasses for drawing large circles and arcs (Fig. 4–47). The inking attachment of the compass is inked in the same manner as the ruling pen described above.

4–25 LAYING OUT THE DRAWING

The inked drawing should be laid out with a 2H pencil using light construction lines. Circle centers should be located and the arcs drawn first as shown in Step 1 of Fig. 4–48. Straight lines that are tangent to arcs are then drawn. The points of tangency are located by constructing lines from the centers of the arcs that are perpendicular to the tangent lines.

In Step 2, the arcs are inked from tangent point to tangent point, making sure that the arcs do not extend beyond these points. In Step 3, the straight

FIGURE 4-48. INKING A DRAWING

CONSTRUCTION LAYOUT	INK ARCS	INK STRAIGHT LINES

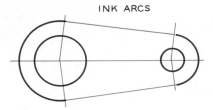

Step 1. The drawing is laid out with light pencil lines. All centers and tangent points are accurately located.

Step 2. The arcs and circles are always inked first. Arcs should stop exactly at their points of tangency.

Step 3. Straight lines are drawn to match the ends of the arcs. Centerlines are shown to complete the drawing.

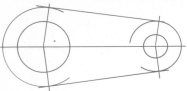

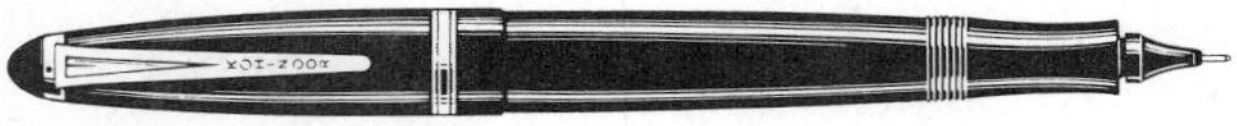

Fig. 4-49 A typical india ink fountain pen that can be used for inking a drawing. (Courtesy of Koh-I-Noor, Inc.)

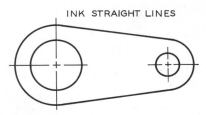

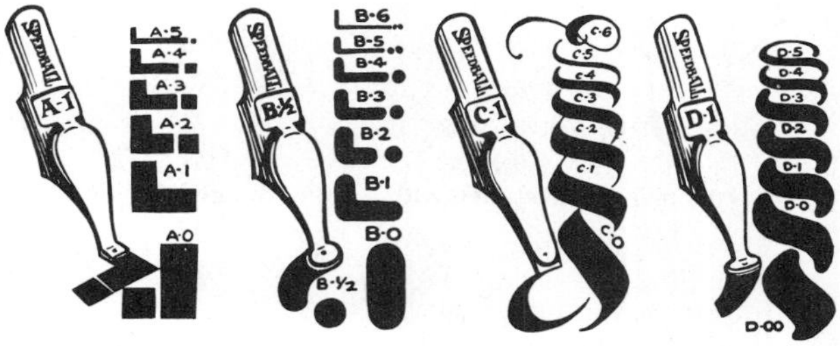

Fig. 4-51 Special inking pen points are available for different lines. These are used for freehand lettering and drawing. (Courtesy of Speedball Corp.)

TANK PEN

GILLOTT 404

GILLOTT 303

GILLOTT 170

GILLOTT 290

GILLOTT 659

Fig. 4-52 Pen points are available for freehand drawing and lettering. Pen points of this type usually have very fine points for thin lines and crosshatching. (Courtesy of Gillott Corporation.)

Fig. 4-50 Inking pens are available in complete sets with a separate pen for each line width. (Courtesy of Koh-I-Noor, Inc.)

A   B

Fig. 4-53 Special inking devices can be used for inking pens. (Courtesy of Higgins Ink Company.)

lines are drawn from tangent point to tangent point. The construction of the centerlines completes this part of the drawing.

Arcs should always be drawn first. If straight lines are drawn first, it is very likely that the circular features will not exactly match the ends of the straight lines; the result will be noticeable flaws in your drawing.

4–26 SPECIAL INKING EQUIPMENT

Specially designed india ink drawing pens have been used widely in recent years instead of the conventional ruling pens. An example is shown in Fig. 4–49. These pens are available in a number of point sizes for various line widths. Pen sets are available (Fig. 4–50) in which a complete range of pens is provided in a compact container.

Lines drawn by ink fountain pens of this type dry rapidly because the ink is not applied as heavily as when a ruling pen is used. Pens of this type are excellent to use with templates for drawing ellipses, circles, and irregular shapes.

Inking pens that are inserted in penholders are shown in Fig. 4–51. These varying types of points are used for special applications such as posters, but, except for the very small round points, usually not for engineering drawings. The more conventional points are shown in Fig. 4–52.

Several devices are available for rapidly and easily inking pen points (Fig. 4–53). The ink cartridge (Fig. 4–53A) eliminates the need for an ink bottle. When an ink bottle is used, the automatic ink dispenser allows a pen to be inked with only one hand.

4–27 MISCELLANEOUS INSTRUMENTS

A wide variety of special drafting instruments and equipment is available for special applications. This equipment varies from small, economical devices to highly expensive items. For example, drawing templates are available in many forms and sizes (Fig. 4–54). These can be used for both inking and pencil work.

Drafting machines are commonly used in industry to assist the draftsman (Fig. 4–55). These machines can be positioned at any desired angle by fingertip controls and returned to their original index position. The vertical and horizontal blades are attached to a head that can be moved over a wide

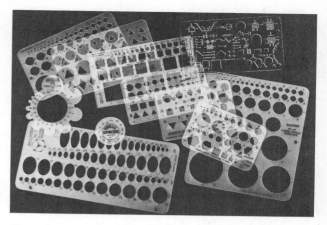

Fig. 4–54 Many types of templates are available to aid the draftsman in his work. (Courtesy of Rapidesign.)

Fig. 4–55 Most industries provide drafting machines for their draftsmen. (Courtesy of Keuffel and Esser Co.)

area of the drawing surface. Drafting machines eliminate the need for alignment of the drawing with an edge of the table, as is necessary when a T-square is used.

The parallel blade (Fig. 4–56) offers many advantages to the draftsman who must work with extremely long lines, especially to the architectural

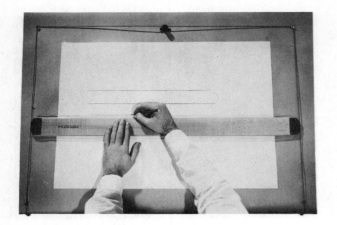

Fig. 4-56 The parallel blade is recommended for drawing long horizontal lines such as occur in architectural drawings. (Courtesy of Keuffel and Esser Co.)

draftsman who works on large plans. The blade is attached to a cable that permits it to move up and down freely while remaining parallel to its original position. The angle of the blade can be varied by readjusting the cable at the upper side of the drawing board. This device gives a very accurate straightedge for horizontal lines, since both ends are held firmly by cables. (In the case of the drafting machine and the T-square, the blades are attached at only one end; consequently, there is a certain degree of flexibility at the free end unless the blade is held with your hand.)

PROBLEMS

These problems are to be solved in accordance with Article 3–15 and the specifications of your instructor. Most problems are to be solved on standard size paper ($8\frac{1}{2}'' \times 11''$) in ink or pencil. Refer to the articles in this chapter when necessary to assist you in your solutions.

General Problems

1 Using your architects' and engineers' scales, lay out the lines in Fig. 4–57 according to the scales given. Letter the number of the problem, the length of the line, and the scale used as it appears in Fig. 4–57. Show each line as shown in the two examples.

2 Draw the object shown in Fig. 4–58 full size with your instruments. Show all dimensions and notes as they appear in this figure. The outline of the part should be drawn with an F pencil. The dimension lines should be drawn with a 2H pencil. Refer to Fig. 4–14.

3 Make an instrument drawing of the cross section of the siding plank shown in Fig. 4–59. Use the $7\frac{1}{2}''$ dimension for your drawing. Omit the dimensions on your finished drawing.

4 Make a full-size instrument drawing of the part shown in Fig. 4–60. Show all dimensions and notes. Refer to Fig. 4–14.

ARCHITECTS' SCALE

EXAMPLE

4'-6'	SCALE: 1"=1'-0"	⊢——————— 4'-6" ———————⊣
1. 6'-3'	SCALE: $\frac{1}{2}$"=1'-0"	⊢—
2. 1'-3$\frac{1}{4}$"	SCALE: 3"=1'-0"	⊢—
3. 14'-3'	SCALE: $\frac{1}{4}$"=1'-0"	⊢—
4. 8$\frac{1}{4}$"	SCALE: 6"=1'-0"	⊢—
5. 6'-2"	SCALE: $\frac{3}{4}$"=1'-0"	⊢—
6. 3'-3$\frac{1}{2}$"	SCALE: 1"=1'-0"	⊢—

ENGINEERS' SCALE

800'	SCALE: 1"=200'	⊢————— 800' —————⊣
7. 141.0'	SCALE: 1"=40'	⊢—
8. 2.3'	SCALE: 1"=5.0'	⊢—
9. 89.0'	SCALE: 1"=30'	⊢—
10. 3.40'	SCALE: 1"=1.0'	⊢—
11. 4,100'	SCALE: 1"=1000'	⊢—
12. 1650'	SCALE: 1"=600'	⊢—
13. 0.73'	SCALE: 1"=0.2"	⊢—
14. 0.105'	SCALE: 1"=0.03'	⊢—

Fig. 4–57 Problem 1: Use of scales.

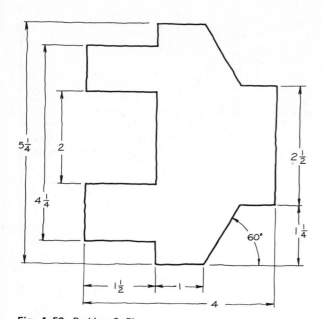

Fig. 4–58 Problem 2: Plate cover.

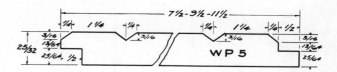

Fig. 4–59 Problem 3: Cross section of siding plank. (Courtesy of Western Pine Association.)

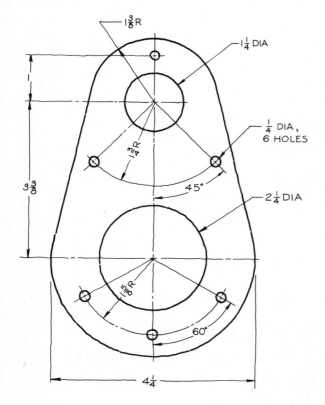

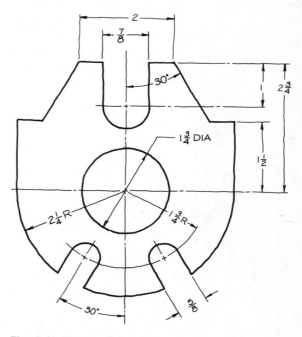

Fig. 4–61 Problem 5: Head piece.

Fig. 4–60 Problem 4: Gear plate. (Courtesy of Ford Motor Company.)

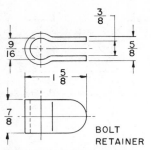

$\frac{3}{8}$

$\frac{9}{16}$ $\frac{5}{8}$

$1\frac{5}{8}$

$\frac{7}{8}$

BOLT
RETAINER

Fig. 4–62 Problem 6: Bolt retainer.
(Courtesy of Universal Engineering
Corporation.)

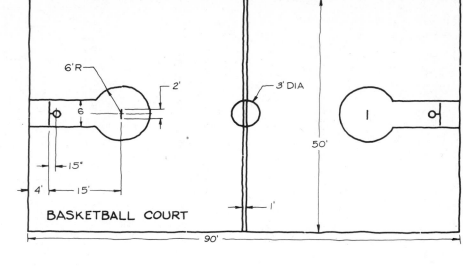

6'R

2'

3' DIA

6

50'

15"

4' 15'

1'

BASKETBALL COURT

90'

Fig. 4–63 Problem 7: Basketball
court.

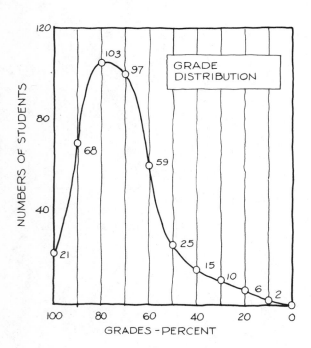

120

103

97

GRADE
DISTRIBUTION

80

68

59

40

25

21

15

10

6 2

100   80   60   40   20   0

GRADES–PERCENT

NUMBERS OF STUDENTS

Fig. 4–64 Problem 8: Grade distribution graph.

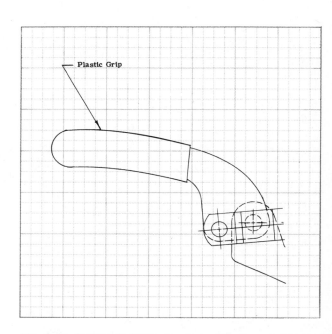

Plastic Grip

Fig. 4–65 Problem 9: Clamp handle. (Courtesy of Universal
Engineering Corporation.)

5 Make a full-size instrument drawing of the part shown in Fig. 4–61. Show all dimensions and notes. Refer to Fig. 4–13.

6 Make a double-size instrument drawing of the bolt retainer shown in Fig. 4–62. Show all dimensions and notes. Refer to Fig. 4–14.

7 Make an instrument drawing of the basketball court shown in Fig. 4–63. Scale: 1″ = 10′. Show all dimensions and notes.

8 Make an instrument drawing of the grade distribution shown in Fig. 4–64. Plot the points, using small circles for each plotted point as shown in the example. Draw a smooth curve through these points with your irregular curve.

9 Make an instrument drawing of the clamp handle shown in Fig. 4–65. Plot each of the points on a sheet of grid paper or plain paper. Each square on the grid represents $\frac{1}{4}″$. Complete the drawing with your irregular curve.

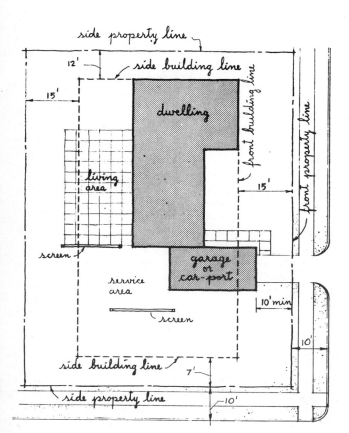

Fig. 4–66 Problem 10: Plot plan. (Courtesy of Federal Housing Administration.)

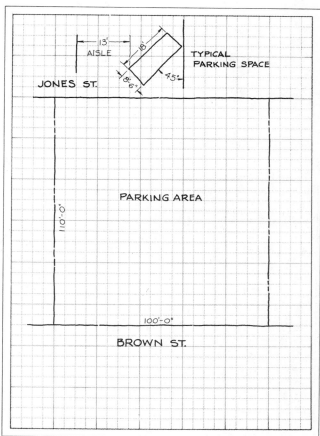

Fig. 4–67 Problem 12: Parking lot design.

TYPICAL SHAPES AND SIZES OF CONCRETE MASONRY UNITS

Dimensions shown are actual unit sizes. A 7⅝" x 7⅝" x 15⅝" unit is commonly known as an 8"x 8"x 16" concrete block.
Half length units are usually available for most of the units shown below. See concrete products manufacturer for shapes and sizes of units locally available.

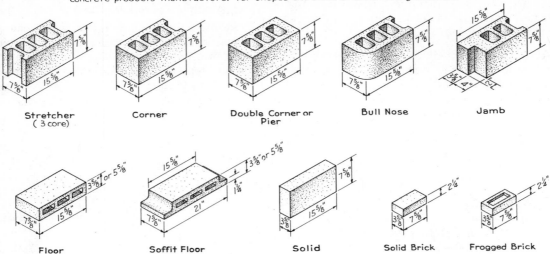

Stretcher (3 core) Corner Double Corner or Pier Bull Nose Jamb

Floor Soffit Floor Solid Solid Brick Frogged Brick

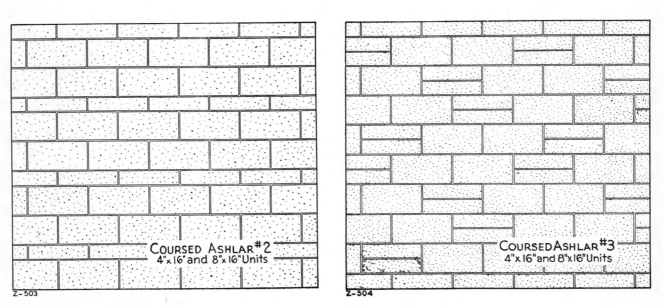

Fig. 4–68 Problem 13: Concrete block wall patterns. (Courtesy of Portland Cement Association.)

Design Problems

10 Make a drawing of the plot plan (Fig. 4–66) so that it will fit on an $8\frac{1}{2}'' \times 11''$ sheet. Select a scale such that the drawing will be as large as possible. Estimate the dimensions not shown to complete your layout.

11 Using Fig. 4–66 as a guide, make a drawing of a similar lot. Locate a house on the lot and show patios, driveways, and other features of the lot.

12 The lot shown in Fig. 4–67 is bounded on two sides by Jones Street and Brown Street. This lot is to be used for a parking lot with 45° parking. The areas and dimensions of the parking spaces are given in the example. Make a scale drawing of this lot with the parking spaces arranged so that the lot will hold as many cars as possible. Exits and entries can be on both streets. Select the best scale for your drawing.

13 Using the blocks and the patterns shown in Fig. 4–68, make scale drawings of the two patterns shown. Determine the thickness of the mortar joints between the blocks.

14 Using the block shown in Fig. 4–68, design other wall patterns for an exterior wall of a house, for a patio, and for a fence. Select the most appropriate scale that would be large enough for an accurate representation of your ideas.

15 Make a scale drawing of your classroom. Locate the drawing tables, blackboards, and cabinets in the room to give a scale floor plan.

16 Using the plan drawn in Problem 15, make a drawing to show how the room could be rearranged to give a better layout.

17 Prepare an instrument drawing of each of the five views of the boat bed shown at the right of Fig. 4–69. Estimate dimensions that are not given. This bed is made of $\frac{1}{4}''$, $\frac{1}{2}''$, and $\frac{3}{4}''$ plywood. Use as many sheets of Size B paper as necessary to complete the drawings.

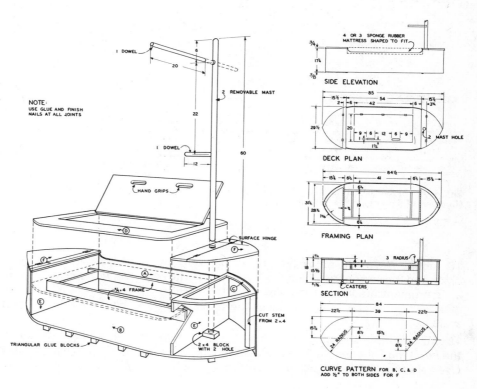

Fig. 4–69 Problem 17: Boat bed plan. (Courtesy of the American Plywood Association.)

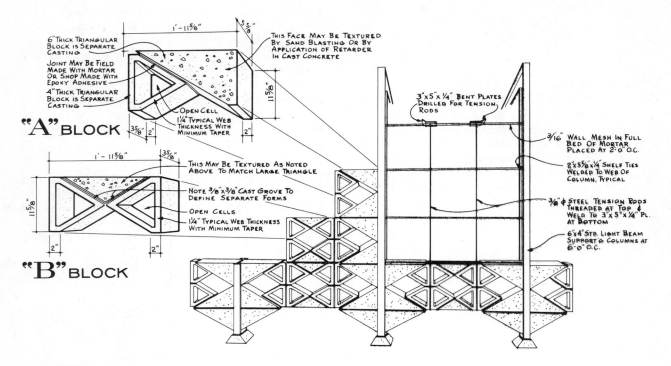

GENERAL NOTES

The entire screen wall is here developed from two block patterns in combination, allowing freedom of design.
All field mortar joints are vertical and horizontal for ease of laying, though final appearance is diagonal and free.
The 1'-0" x 2'-0" (nominal) block is adaptable to mass production on standard block-making machines with minimum
waste. All block should be made with lightweight aggregate; color aggregate and concrete mix is suggested.
Here the horizontal and vertical joints are provided 2'-0" o.c. for reinforcing in compliance with applicable code.
Horizontal joints at diamonds should be struck flush for concealment; joints at open diamonds should be raked.
This modular system is adaptable to integration with all other nominal sizes of masonry units for flexibility.

Fig. 4–70 Problems 18 through 21: Swimming pool screen.
(Courtesy of Kaiser Permanente Cement.)

18 Figure 4–70 illustrates two types of concrete block and the screen for which they were used. Make an instrument drawing of the elevation (front view) of a section of the screen. Select the appropriate scale.

19 Make a triple-size instrument drawing of each of the two types of concrete block shown in Fig. 4–70. Use a sheet of $8\frac{1}{2}'' \times 11''$ paper. Omit dimensions.

20 Design a block similar to those shown in Fig. 4–70 that can be used to give a variety of patterns for screens of this type. Draw your design large so it can be clearly understood. Show dimensions.

21 Design a screen of a different pattern from the one shown in Fig. 4–70. Use the blocks given in Fig. 4–70 or those that you designed in Problem 20.

Fig. 4–70 (Continued)

22 A floor plan of a weekend cottage is shown in Fig. 4–71. Make an instrument drawing of this plan on Size A paper at a scale of $\frac{1}{4}'' = 1'\text{-}0''$. The plan is converted to this scale by transferring measurements from the plan with your dividers to the scale printed under the plan where full-size dimensions can be determined. Convert this full-size dimension to $\frac{1}{4}'' = 1'\text{-}0''$ using your architects' scale.

Fig. 4–71 Problem 22: Weekend cottage floor plan. (Courtesy of U. S. Department of Agriculture.)

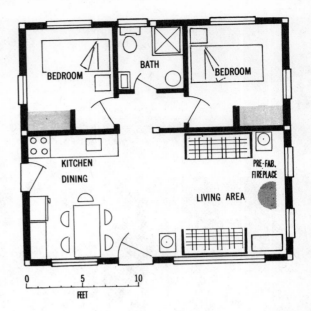

23 A side view of the fuselage of a model of a P-51 Mustang fighter plane is shown in Fig. 4–72. Make an instrument drawing of the outline of the fuselage, omitting dashed lines and lines representing structural members. For a full-size model drawing ($23\frac{1}{2}$″), each square of the grid is equal to $\frac{1}{4}$″; for a half-size model ($11\frac{3}{4}$″), each square is equal to $\frac{1}{8}$″. Draw a grid with each square either $\frac{1}{8}$″ or $\frac{1}{4}$″ that will be large enough for the drawing. Overlay this with tracing paper and plot points on this larger grid by transferring points at intervals from Fig. 4–72.

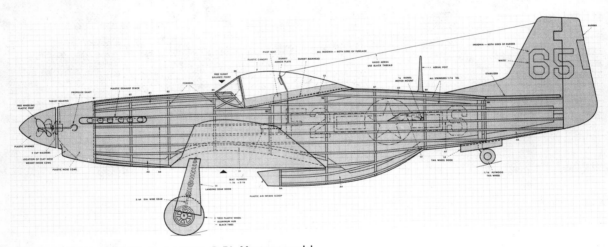

Fig. 4–72 Problem 23: North American P-51 Mustang model. (Courtesy of Paul K. Guillow, Inc., Wakefield, Mass. 01880. This model and many others are available from Guillow's and most hobby stores.)

The use of instruments   **Chap. 4**

Photo courtesy of U. S. Steel Corporation

5
GEOMETRIC
CONSTRUCTION

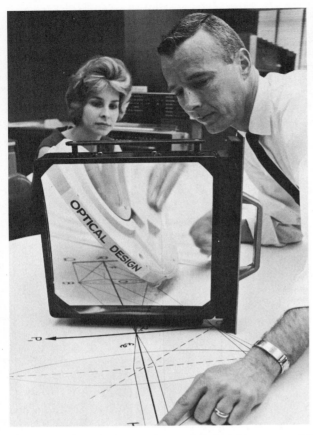

Fig. 5–1 This photo-enlarger lens was designed by a computer, but the principles of geometric construction had to be applied before the computer could be programmed. (Courtesy of IBM.)

5–1 INTRODUCTION

Many problems of drafting and graphics can be solved only by the application of geometry and geometric construction. In addition, engineering and technical problems are often solved by geometric construction during the design and completion of a project.

Such problems may be very complex, requiring the use of a computer; an example is the design of a photo-enlarger lens (Fig. 5–1). Yet the designer must have a thorough understanding of the basic concepts of geometry before he can apply them to the solution of a problem by computer. Despite

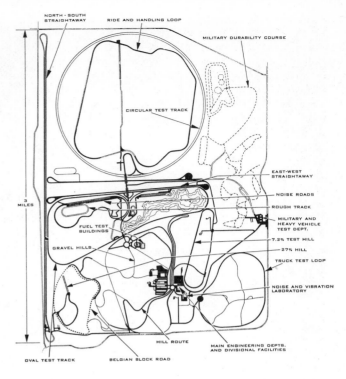

Fig. 5–2 This General Motors Proving Ground was designed with the aid of many applications of geometric construction. The diagram at the top shows the roads and facilities of the GM Proving Ground at Milford, Michigan. Below, the J-turn test at the Proving Ground checks the car, the tires, and the wheels under extreme side loads. (Courtesy of General Motors Corporation.)

increases in the capabilities of computers, computer solutions are still often checked by means of graphical constructions to ensure that the design is correct.

Another problem requiring geometric constructions was the General Motors Proving Ground track (Fig. 5–2), which is used to test the performance of automobiles, wheels, and tires. This track is composed of a variety of curves, arcs, and straightaways. Most of the initial design work on this track was developed graphically before the application of mathematical techniques to the design.

Mathematics was an outgrowth of graphical constructions; consequently, there is a close relationship between geometric construction and mathematics. Geometric construction is closely related to *plane geometry* and to *trigonometry;* indeed, proofs of many of the principles of these two disciplines can be developed graphically. Graphical methods can also be applied to *algebra* and *arithmetic*, and virtually all problems of *analytical geometry* can be solved graphically.

The principles discussed in this chapter will give some idea of the variety of graphical solutions to technical problems that are possible. An understanding of these principles will help improve one's understanding of mathematics.

5–2 CONSTRUCTION TECHNIQUES

Geometric construction problems should be solved in a uniform manner with very accurately drawn lines. Accuracy is important because graphical methods are used as a substitute for a mathematical solution. Without accuracy, a correct solution is impossible.

Construction lines should be drawn with a 4H pencil. These lines should be dark, but very thin for accuracy. The centers of arcs should be marked with a cross formed by short ($\frac{1}{8}''$ long) vertical and horizontal lines. Important points should be numbered or lettered. Tangency points should be located by constructing thin lines with a 4H pencil from the centers of arcs to the tangent lines, or from center to center in the case of tangent arcs.

The arcs that are drawn to complete tangency problems should be constructed to match the given lines, which are usually drawn with an F pencil. There should be no overlap at the points of tangency. Your construction should be neat so that it need not be erased. If your construction lines are neatly drawn, it will be easy for you to review the methods of solution at a later date.

5–3 BISECTING A LINE

Finding the midpoint of a line or the perpendicular bisector of a line is a basic technique of geometric construction. Two methods are illustrated in Fig.

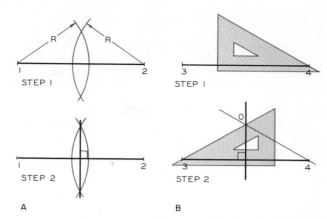

Fig. 5–3 Two methods of finding the perpendicular bisector of a line.

5–3. The first method involves the use of a compass to construct a perpendicular bisector of line 1–2 (Fig. 5–3A).

Step 1. Any radius R that is greater than half of the length of line 1–2 is used to construct arcs with centers at 1 and 2.

Step 2. A straight line is drawn through the points at which the two arcs cross. This line is the perpendicular bisector of line 1–2.

If an arc of a circle were substituted for the line 1–2, the same procedure would be used to find the midpoint. Arcs would be drawn using the two end points of the original arc as centers. The line drawn through the points where the arcs crossed would bisect the original arc.

The midpoint of line 3–4 is found on Fig. 5–3B by using a triangle and a straightedge.

Step 1. The triangle is placed so that a line can be drawn from point 4 making an angle of 30° with the line 3–4.

Step 2. Then the triangle is placed so that a line can be drawn through point 3 making a 30° angle with the line 3–4. To locate the midpoint of the line 3–4, a line is drawn from the point of intersection, O, perpendicular to the line 3–4.

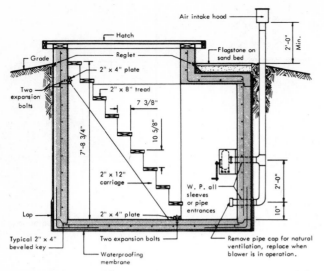

Fig. 5–4 This stairway was designed with the aid of geometric construction to divide the carriage into an equal number of divisions. (Courtesy of the Department of Defense.)

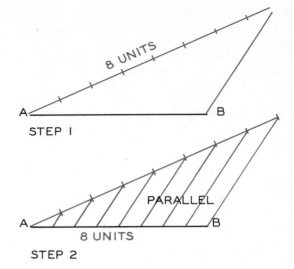

Fig. 5–5 Division of a line into equal segments by geometric construction.

This procedure is based on the principle that the altitude of an equilateral triangle is perpendicular to its base at the midpoint. A 45° triangle could have been used instead of the 30° triangle shown in the example.

5–4 DIVIDING A LINE INTO EQUAL PARTS

It is often necessary to divide a line into a number of equal parts, and a convenient scale may not be available that can be used for this purpose. Dividing a line into equal parts may be necessary in laying out a graph or a parking lot or in drawing threads on a bolt. For example, suppose a 1″ line is to be divided into seven equal parts. No scale is available that is divided into sevenths, and the mathematical units involve hard-to-measure decimals. However, this problem can be solved easily using geometric construction.

The stairway shown in Fig. 5–4 is divided into a number of equal divisions so that the steps will be equal and uniform. Many combinations of dimensions are possible, since the steepness of the stairway can be varied. A problem of this type is solved in Fig. 5–5.

Step 1. A line is drawn at a convenient angle through point *A*. This line is divided into eight equal segments using dividers or an available scale. The eighth division mark is connected to point *B* with a construction line.

Step 2. Lines are drawn from each division mark parallel to the construction line through point *B*. These lines intersect line *AB*, dividing it into eight equal segments.

5–5 BISECTING AN ANGLE

The barrel hooks attached to the ends of the barrel in Fig. 5–6 form an angle between the two chains. If one wanted to replace these two chains with a single chain attached to the middle of the barrel, it would be necessary to bisect the angle between the two chains. The single chain would be placed along the line of this bisector. The method of construction is illustrated in Fig. 5–7.

Step 1. An arc with radius R_1, with its center at *A*, is drawn to locate points *D* and *E*.

Step 2. Arcs with radius R_2 and centers at *D* and *E* are drawn to locate point *O*. The bisector can be drawn from *A* to *O*.

Fig. 5–6 The support cable attached to the eye of the barrel hooks must lie along the bisector of the angle formed by the two chains. (Courtesy of Air Technical Industries.)

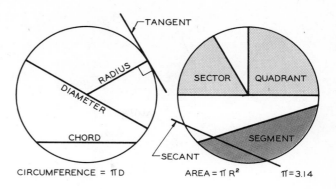

Fig. 5–8 The elements of a circle.

CIRCUMFERENCE = πD   AREA = π R²   π = 3.14

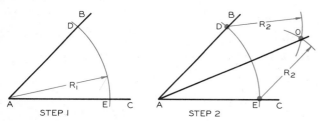

Fig. 5–7 Bisecting an angle by geometric construction.

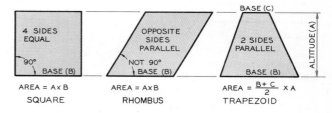

AREA = A x B   AREA = A x B   AREA = $\frac{B+C}{2}$ x A
SQUARE   RHOMBUS   TRAPEZOID

Fig. 5–9 Three quadrilaterals (four-sided figures).

5–6 THE CIRCLE

The circle is a figure that is common to many of the geometric constructions discussed in this chapter. The elements of a circle are defined in Fig. 5–8.

The circle is a conic section. In other words, if an imaginary plane were passed through a right cone perpendicular to its altitude, the cut would form a circle. Also, a plane passed perpendicular to the axis of a cylinder would cut a circular section.

You should become familiar with the terminology of the circle by studying Fig. 5–8. The terms found in this figure will be used throughout this book.

5–7 GEOMETRIC FIGURES

A number of plane figures are defined according to their characteristics to enable these shapes to be described verbally. The figures shown in Fig. 5–9 are *quadrilaterals;* that is, they are four-sided figures. A figure composed of four equal sides making a 90° angle at each corner is called a *square*. If the sides are equal but do not make a 90° angle at each corner, the figure is a *rhombus*. Both the square and the rhombus are special types of *parallelogram;* a parallelogram is defined as a figure with opposite sides that are equal and parallel.

A *trapezoid* is a four-sided figure two of whose sides are parallel but unequal. A *trapezium* is a four-sided figure with no two sides parallel or equal.

Triangles are plane figures that are used frequently in engineering and technology; a triangle is a rigid, strong shape that has many structural applications. The triangle is also the fundamental figure of trigonometry.

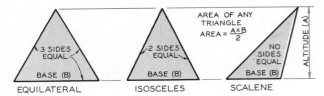

Fig. 5–10 Three general types of triangles.

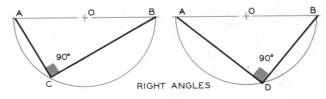

Fig. 5–13 Inscribing a right angle in a semicircle.

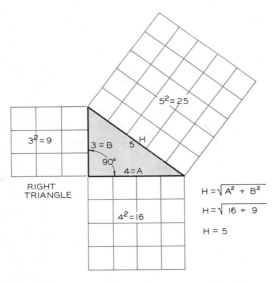

STEP 1   STEP 2

Fig. 5–11 Construction of a triangle from three given sides.

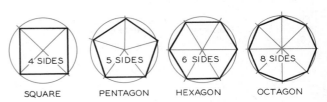

Fig. 5–14 Regular polygons inscribed in a circle.

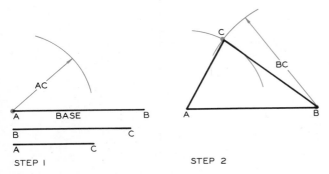

Fig. 5–12 A right triangle which illustrates the Pythagorean Theorem.

Three basic types of triangles are shown in Fig. 5–10. The *equilateral* triangle is composed of three equal sides. The *isosceles* has two equal sides. The *scalene* is composed of three sides each of a different length.

5–8 CONSTRUCTING A TRIANGLE

When the lengths of the three sides of a triangle are given, only one triangle can be constructed from these sides. The procedure is illustrated in Fig. 5–11.

Step 1. One side is selected as the base—line AB in this case. An arc with radius AC is drawn using point A as the center.

Step 2. The third side, BC, is used as the radius of an arc drawn with point B as the center. The point of intersection of the two arcs locates the vertex of the triangle at point C. Points A, B, and C are connected to form the triangle ABC.

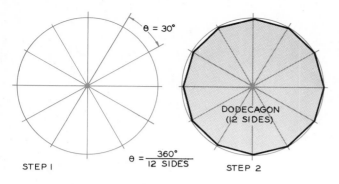

STEP 1

$\theta = 30°$

$\theta = \dfrac{360°}{12 \text{ SIDES}}$

DODECAGON
(12 SIDES)

STEP 2

Fig. 5–15 The method of constructing any regular polygon with any number of sides.

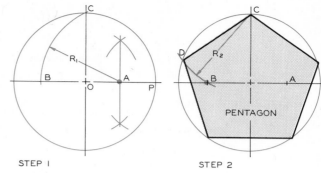

STEP 1

STEP 2

PENTAGON

Fig. 5–16 Construction of a pentagon.

5–9 THE RIGHT TRIANGLE

The right triangle is a triangle with one 90° angle. It was found to have unique characteristics that set it apart from other types of triangles, and was therefore used as the basis of most of the principles and relationships of trigonometry.

Pythagoras, a Greek philosopher who lived in the sixth century B.C., discovered that the two sides forming the 90° angle, when squared and summed, were equal to the square of the longest side, the hypotenuse. This relationship, called the Pythagorean Theorem, is illustrated in Fig. 5–12.

Another principle of geometry can be used to construct a right triangle. Any angle inscribed in a semicircle is a 90° angle, i.e., a right angle. Two examples of such angles are illustrated in Fig. 5–13.

5–10 REGULAR POLYGONS

A regular polygon is a many-sided figure composed of equal sides. Several basic polygons are shown in Fig. 5–14. These polygons are *inscribed* in a circle: this means that they are drawn *inside* of the circle. A polygon constructed on the outside of a circle is called *circumscribed*. Not shown are the following regular polygons: *heptagon* (seven sides), *nonagon* (nine sides), *decagon* (ten sides), and *dodecagon* (twelve sides).

Any regular polygon can be either circumscribed or inscribed in a circle as illustrated in Fig. 5–15. In this example, a twelve-sided figure, a dodecagon, is inscribed in a circle.

Step 1. The circle is divided into twelve equal sectors. Since 360°/12 = 30°, each sector has an angle of 30°.

Step 2. The sides are drawn from point of intersection to point of intersection on the circumference of the circle. The polygon could have been circumscribed by drawing the sides tangent to the circle between the sectors, but that is a less accurate method.

5–11 THE PENTAGON

The pentagon is a regular polygon with five sides. This geometric shape is sometimes used as the structural basis of a building. The Pentagon building in Washington, D.C., is an example of the use of this form. The construction of a pentagon is illustrated in Fig. 5–16.

Step 1. A circle of any diameter is drawn in which the pentagon is to be inscribed. The radius, *OP*, is bisected to locate point *A*. With *A* as the center and the distance *AC* as the radius R_1, point *B* is located on the diameter.

Step 2. With point *C* as the center and *BC* as the radius R_2, point *D* is found on the circle. The chord *CD* is one side of the pentagon, and can be used to locate the other equally spaced points on the circle that can be used as the corners of the pentagon.

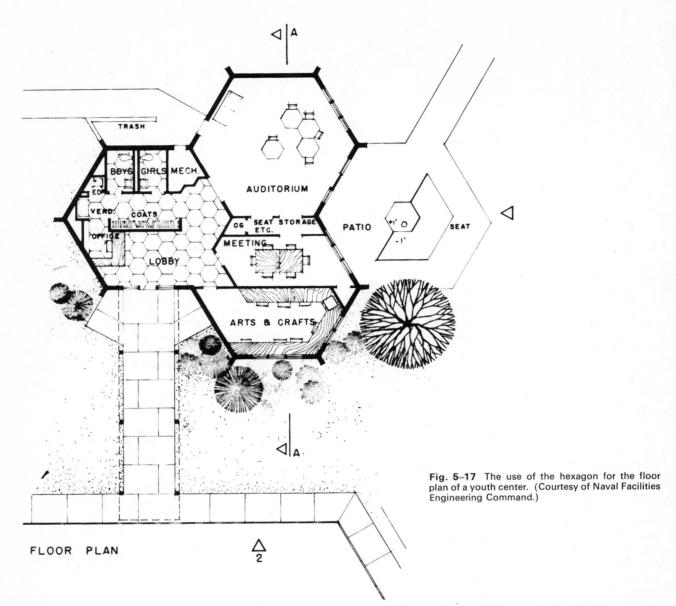

TRASH

BOYS | GIRLS | MECH.

ED

VEND. COATS

OFFICE

LOBBY

AUDITORIUM

SEAT STORAGE
ETC.
CG

MEETING

PATIO

SEAT

+1' O
-1'

ARTS & CRAFTS

A

A

FLOOR PLAN

△
2

Fig. 5–17 The use of the hexagon for the floor plan of a youth center. (Courtesy of Naval Facilities Engineering Command.)

5–12 THE HEXAGON

The hexagon is used as the basic shape for the floor plan shown in Fig. 5–17. It is also the structural unit used in the dome of the U. S. Pavilion at Expo '67 shown in Fig. 5–18. The hexagon is composed of six equal sides.

A method of inscribing a hexagon in a circle using a compass and a straightedge is illustrated in Fig. 5–19.

Step 1. A circle is drawn to represent the distance from corner to corner across the hexagon. The radius of the circle is used as radius to draw two arcs; the

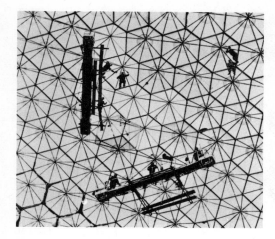

Fig. 5–18 This geodesic dome erected as the U. S. Pavilion at Expo '67 is composed of hexagons as a structural unit. (Courtesy of Rohn and Haas Company.)

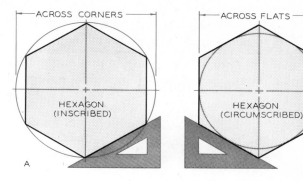

Fig. 5–20 A hexagon inscribed and circumscribed in a circle with the aid of a 30° triangle.

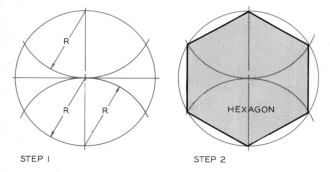

Fig. 5–19 Construction of a hexagon with a compass and a straightedge.

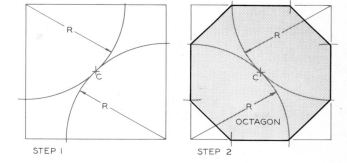

Fig. 5–21 Inscribing an octagon in a square.

centers of these arcs are the points of intersection of the circle and a diameter. The intersections of the arcs with the circle establish four of the corners of the hexagon.

Step 2. The four points found in Step 1 and the two points used for centers to construct the arcs are connected in sequence to form the hexagon.

Alternative methods of constructing a hexagon with a triangle and T-square are shown in Fig. 5–20. In Fig. 5–20A the hexagon is inscribed in a circle by means of a 30° triangle. In Fig. 5–20B the hexagon is circumscribed around a circle by means of a 30°

triangle. In the first method, the circle represents the distance across the corners of the hexagon; in the second, it represents the distance across the flats of the hexagon.

5–13 THE OCTAGON

The octagon is a regular polygon composed of eight equal sides. The construction of an octagon is shown in Fig. 5–21; in the method illustrated here, a square is the basic figure in which the octagon is inscribed.

Step 1. The center of the square is found at the intersection of diagonals. The distance from one

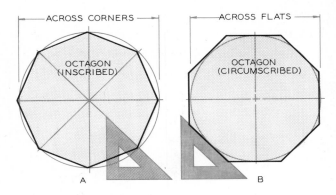

Fig. 5-22 An octagon inscribed and circumscribed in a circle with the aid of a 45° triangle.

Fig. 5-23 The design of this advanced traffic interchange was based on the application of geometric constructions. (Courtesy of the Texas Highway Department.)

corner to the center *C* is used as the radius for two arcs drawn with centers at opposite corners.

Step 2. The same radius is used to construct two arcs using the other two corners as centers. The points where the arcs intersect the sides of the square are connected in sequence to form an octagon.

An octagon can be drawn by either inscribing or circumscribing a circle with the aid of a 45° triangle, as shown in Fig. 5-22. In Fig. 5-22A the circle represents the distance across the corners; in Fig. 5-22B the circle represents the distance across the flats of the octagon.

5-14 TANGENCY CONSTRUCTION

One of the most common types of geometric construction is that of tangencies. The applications are numerous. The highway interchange shown in Fig. 5-23 is composed of a number of arcs and straight lines which form the total layout of the system. The curves are smooth, permitting the straight segments of road to join curves gradually with no abrupt changes caused by sharp angular intersections.

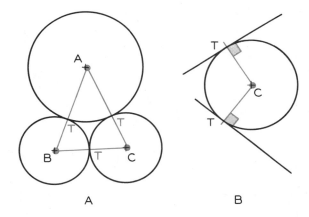

Fig. 5-24 The location of tangent points between tangent circles and between lines and a circle.

The basic principle of tangency problems is the location of the points of tangency between arcs or between arcs and straight lines. The point of tangency between arcs can be found by constructing a line from the center of one tangent arc to the center of the other (Fig. 5-24A). The points of tangency of an arc with two lines can be found by constructing

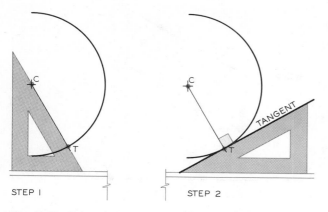

STEP I   STEP 2

Fig. 5–25 Construction of a line through point *T* that is tangent to the circle.

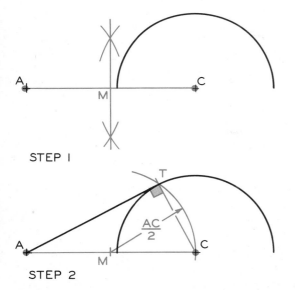

STEP I

STEP 2

Fig. 5–26 Location of the point of tangency between a line and an arc.

lines perpendicular to the tangent lines from the center of the arc (Fig. 5–24B). In both cases thin lines, drawn with a 4H or 3H pencil through the points of tangency, should be shown on the drawing. These lines are especially helpful in preparing finished drawings, since they indicate where arcs drawn with a compass should begin and end.

5–15 LINE FROM A POINT TANGENT TO AN ARC

Most people can approximate a line from a point tangent to an arc without the use of instruments; however, the exact location of such a line can be found by geometric construction.

A convenient method of constructing a line tangent to an arc through a given point is shown in Fig. 5–25.

Step 1. A triangle is positioned against a T-square to draw a thin line from the center of the arc through the point of tangency *T*.

Step 2. While the straightedge is held in position, the triangle is repositioned for drawing a line perpendicular to the line *CT*. This line is tangent to the arc at point *T*.

This procedure can be reversed to find the point of tangency of an arc and a tangent line. The triangle is first aligned with the tangent line, then turned to draw a line from the center of the arc perpendicular to the tangent line. The point of intersection of this line and the arc is the point of tangency.

Although the above method of constructing a line tangent to an arc is convenient, a more formal type of construction can be used to solve the same problem. This type of solution is illustrated in Fig. 5–26.

Step 1. A line is drawn from point *A* to the center of the arc, point *C*. This line is bisected to find its midpoint, *M*.

Step 2. With the midpoint *M* as the center and half the length of *AC* as the radius, an arc is drawn to locate *T*, the point of tangency. The line drawn from *A* to *T* is tangent to the arc. The accuracy of this construction can be checked by drawing a line from the center *C* perpendicular to the line *AT*. This line should intersect at point *T*.

5–16 ARCS TANGENT TO TWO LINES

Observation of any man-made product will reveal many applications of arcs that are tangent to straight lines. This rounding of sharp corners usually makes a design more functional and more attractive. An example of a simple device with many tangencies is shown in Fig. 5–27.

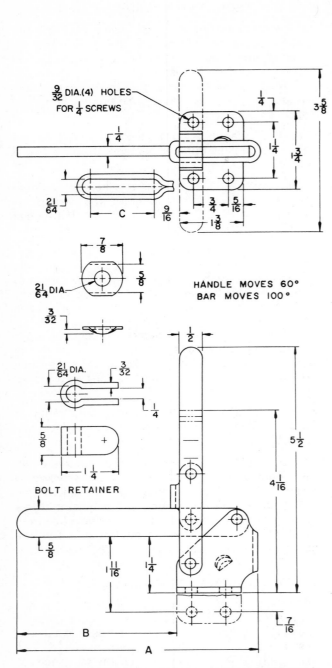

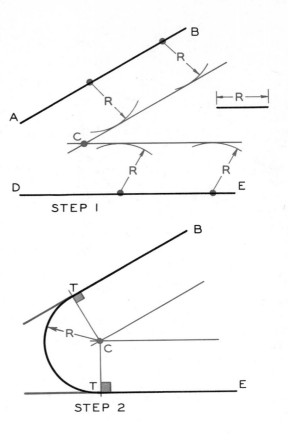

Fig. 5–28 Construction of an arc tangent to two lines.

Fig. 5–27 Several examples of tangency problems can be seen in this industrial drawing. These constructions were necessary in the design of each component. (Courtesy of De-Sta-Co Corporation.)

In Fig. 5–28 two lines, *AB* and *DE*, are given, and radius *R* is to be used to construct an arc tangent to the lines. For a problem of this type to have a single solution, the radius of the tangent arc must be given; otherwise, many solutions will be possible.

Step 1. A compass is used to construct arcs with radius *R* at two intervals along each line. Lines parallel to *AB* and *DE* are then constructed tangent to the arcs. These lines are extended to locate point *C* at a distance *R* from each line.

Step 2. Thin lines are drawn from point *C* perpendicular to lines *AB* and *DE* to locate two points of tangency. With point *C* as center and radius *R*, an arc is drawn tangent to the two lines.

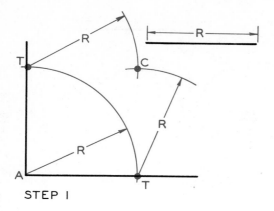

STEP I

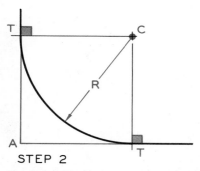

STEP 2

Fig. 5–29 Construction of an arc tangent to two perpendicular lines.

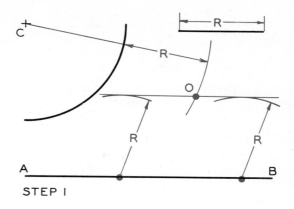

STEP I

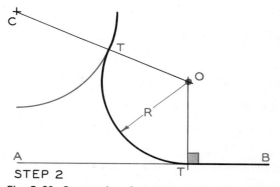

STEP 2

Fig. 5–30 Construction of an arc tangent to a line and an arc.

A special case of the same type of problem is solved in Fig. 5–29, where the lines are perpendicular. It is required that an arc of a given radius be drawn to be tangent to the two perpendiculars. The following method cannot be applied when the lines are not perpendicular.

Step 1. The given radius, *R*, is used to draw an arc with its center at point *A*, the intersection of the two perpendiculars. The arc will intersect the two lines to locate the points of tangency, *T*. Arcs are drawn with each point *T* as the center to locate point *C*.

Step 2. Thin lines are drawn from point *C* perpendicular to the given lines. These thin lines are centerlines, since they are perpendicular and in the conventional position of centerlines. The final arc, tangent to the lines, is drawn with radius *R* and with its center at point *C*.

In all cases, the points of tangency should be shown as part of the construction. These points are indicated either by short, thin lines or by centerlines drawn from the center through the points of tangency and extending past them about $\frac{1}{16}''$. These lines are useful in construction and provide a visual means of inspecting the construction to verify its correctness.

5–17 ARC TANGENT TO AN ARC AND A LINE

It is often necessary for an arc to be drawn with a given radius tangent to an arc and a straight line. Since an infinite number of solutions may be obtained by varying the radius, it is necessary for the radius to be given.

Step 1. A compass is adjusted to the given radius, *R* (Fig. 5–30). The approximate position where the center of the tangent arc should be located is deter-

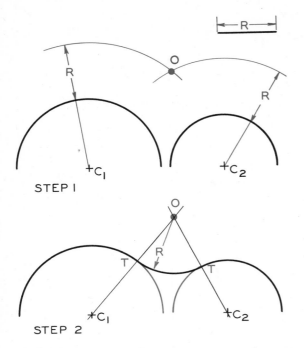

Fig. 5–31 Construction of an arc tangent to two given arcs.

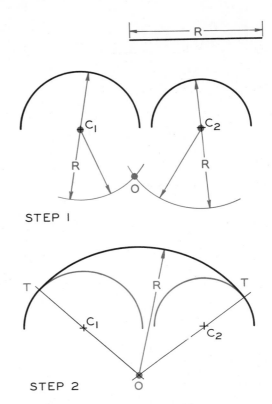

Fig. 5–32 Construction of an arc tangent to two given arcs.

mined by inspection or by trial and error, to help in checking the construction. A radius of the given arc with its center at C is extended in some convenient direction. Radius R is added to this radius and the total radius is used to draw an arc with its center at C. Two arcs of radius R are drawn from line AB to find a line parallel to AB and a distance R from it. The intersection of this line and the previously constructed arc establishes point O at a distance R from the arc and line AB.

Step 2. A thin line is drawn from point O to center C to locate the point of tangency between the two arcs. A second line is drawn from point O perpendicular to the line AB to locate the second point of tangency. With point O as the center, an arc is drawn with radius R that is tangent to the arc and the straight line.

5–18 ARC TANGENT TO TWO ARCS

The detail drawing shown in Fig. 5–27 illustrates several examples of tangency problems, including the construction of arcs tangent to given arcs. It was necessary to solve these geometric construction problems before arriving at the finished design. The method of construction is illustrated in Fig. 5–31.

Step 1. A compass adjusted to radius R is used to find the approximate location of the center of the arc that will be drawn tangent to the given arcs. This will serve as a check on the final construction. Radii from C_1 and C_2 are then extended in some convenient direction, and radius R is added to these radii. The total radii are used to construct arcs with centers C_1 and C_2 which intersect at point O.

Step 2. Thin lines are drawn from point O to C_1 and C_2 to locate the points of tangency T. With point O as center and radius R, an arc is constructed tangent to the given arcs.

Alternative solution. In cases where the given radius is sufficiently long, an alternative method is available for constructing an arc tangent to two given arcs. This method is illustrated in Fig. 5–32.

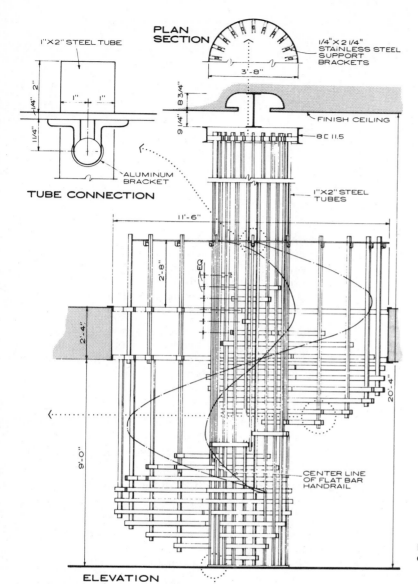

PLAN SECTION

1"X2" STEEL TUBE

1/4"X 2 1/4" STAINLESS STEEL SUPPORT BRACKETS

3'-8"

8 3/4"

9 1/4"

FINISH CEILING

8 C 11.5

ALUMINUM BRACKET

TUBE CONNECTION

1"X2" STEEL TUBES

11'-6"

2'-8"

EQ

2'-4"

20'-4"

CENTER LINE OF FLAT BAR HANDRAIL

9'-0"

ELEVATION

Fig. 5–33 A helix formed by a stairway. (Courtesy of U. S. Steel Corporation.)

Step 1. A radius is extended from each arc through the centers C_1 and C_2 in a convenient direction. The given radius R is measured from the arcs along the extended radii. The distance from points C_1 and C_2 to the ends of the extended radii of length R are used to form two arcs that intersect at point O.

Step 2. Thin lines are drawn from point O through centers C_1 and C_2 to locate the tangent points. With

radius R and point O as its center, an arc is drawn tangent to the two given arcs.

5–19 THE HELIX

A helix is a curve that coils around a cylinder at a constant angle or rise. Examples of helixes are a corkscrew and the threads on a screw. The handrail of the stairway in Fig. 5–33 also forms a helix.

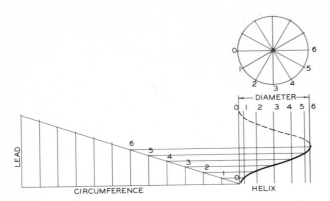

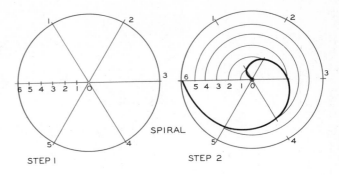

Fig. 5–34 Construction of a helix.

Fig. 5–36 Construction of the spiral of Archimedes.

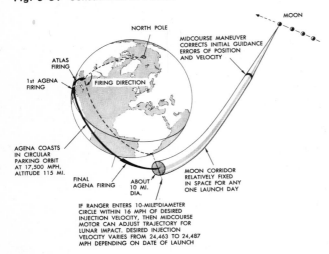

Fig. 5–35 A portion of the Ranger launch to the moon is a spiral. (Courtesy of the Jet Propulsion Laboratory.)

Step 1. The construction of a helix begins with the construction of the top and front views of the cylinder around which the helix will coil (Fig. 5–34). The top view of the cylinder is divided into a number of equal divisions which are numbered and projected to the front view of the cylinder as elements.

Step 2. The circumference of the cylinder is laid out perpendicular to the axis of the cylinder. Elements of the cylinder are spaced along this line by taking measurements from the top view with dividers. The circumference should be divided into the same number of divisions as the top view of the cylinder, and these divisions should be numbered to corre-

spond to the top view. The total rise the helix will make in 360° is laid off perpendicular to the circumference at its end; this line is called the lead. The hypotenuse of the right triangle which has the lead and the laid-out circumference as two of its sides represents a rolled-out view of the helix.

Step 3. The points where the elements intersect the hypotenuse of the rolled-out helix are projected to their respective elements in the front view of the cylinder. Point 1 is projected to element 1, point 2 to element 2, etc. The ends of the projection lines are then joined with an irregular curve.

The result of this construction is one complete 360° helix. The same procedure can be used to construct a helix of several revolutions.

5–20 SPIRAL OF ARCHIMEDES

A spiral is a coil that begins at a point and becomes larger as it travels around the center or origin. A spiral lies in a single plane. A portion of the path of the Ranger's route to the moon is a spiral (Fig. 5–35). The construction of a spiral is shown in Fig. 5–36.

Step 1. A circle is drawn and its circumference is divided into equal divisions. A radius of the circle is divided into the same number of equal divisions—six in this case. The divisions are numbered from the center outward.

Step 2. An arc whose radius is equal to one of the equal divisions of the radius of the circle is drawn from the radius O–6 to the radius O–1 with O as center. Then an arc whose radius is equal to two of

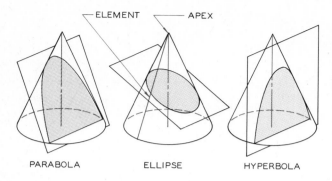

ELEMENT   APEX

PARABOLA   ELLIPSE   HYPERBOLA

Fig. 5–37 Three conic sections.

Fig. 5–38 This tracking antenna sends radio signals millions of miles into space and receives signals from satellites. Its cross section is a parabola. (Courtesy of Ryan Aeronautics.)

the equal divisions of the radius of the circle is drawn from the radius O–6 to the radius O–2 with O as center. This procedure continues until five arcs have been drawn. The points of intersection of the arcs with their corresponding radii are then joined with an irregular curve.

5–21 CONIC SECTIONS

Conic sections are plane figures that can be described graphically and mathematically. A conic section is formed by passing an imaginary cutting plane through a right cone. The resulting cut is a conic section.

When the plane is passed perpendicular to the axis of the cone, the conic section is a *circle*. When the cutting plane passes vertically through the axis of the cone, the conic section is a *triangle*. The other three types of conic sections are illustrated in Fig. 5–37.

A *parabola* is formed when the cutting plane makes the same angle with the base of the cone as do the elements of the cone. When the plane makes a greater angle with the axis of the cone than do the elements, the resulting conic section is an *ellipse*. When the cutting plane makes a smaller angle with the axis than do the elements, the conic section is a *hyperbola*.

The mathematical description of these conic sections is used extensively in analytical geometry and higher mathematics. The mathematical definitions are derived from the geometric construction that will be described in the following articles.

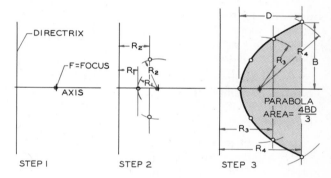

Fig. 5–39 The construction of a parabola.

5–22 THE PARABOLA

The parabola is defined mathematically as a plane curve, each point of which is equidistant from a *directrix* (a straight line) and its focal point. The cross section of the antenna in Fig. 5–38 is a parabolic curve. The parabola is also the cross-sectional shape of headlight reflectors, with the light bulb located at the focus. The construction of a parabola is described in Fig. 5–39.

Step 1. An axis is drawn perpendicular to a line called a directrix. The point F on the axis is chosen as the focus of the parabola.

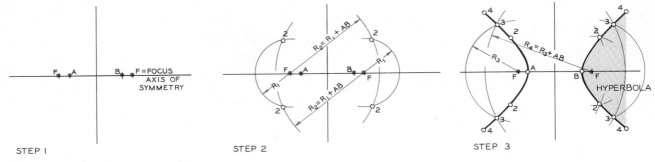

Fig. 5–40 The construction of a hyperbola.

Step 2. The midpoint of the line from the directrix to the focus is located using distances R_1; this point is a point on the parabolic curve. A radius R_2, slightly greater than R_1, is then used to construct a line a distance R_2 from the directrix and parallel to it. An arc with radius R_2 and center at F is drawn to intersect this line at two points. These two points are also points on the parabolic curve.

Step 3. Additional radii, R_3, R_4, etc., are used to find a series of points on the parabola. These points are connected with an irregular curve to complete the parabola.

All light and sound waves that enter the open end of a parabola parallel to its axis will be reflected to the focal point. Likewise, rays that are emitted from the focal point will be reflected parallel to the axis of symmetry. This characteristic makes this figure ideal as the cross section of an antenna or a headlight reflector.

5–23 THE HYPERBOLA

The hyperbola is defined as the path of a point which moves in such a way that the difference of its distances from two focal points is a constant. This definition is used to construct a hyperbola in Fig. 5–40.

Step 1. An axis of symmetry is constructed and a perpendicular line is drawn through it. Two focal points F are located on the axis equidistant from the perpendicular line. Two more points, A and B, are located equidistant from the perpendicular. The location of these points is either given or selected by the student. The points A and B are points on the hyperbolic curve.

Step 2. Radius R_1 is selected to draw arcs with the focal points F as the centers. Radius R_1 is added to AB (the distance between the nearest points on the two hyperbolas) to find R_2. The radius R_2 is used to draw arcs using the focal points as centers. The intersection of these arcs with the arcs of radius R_1 establishes the points 2 on the hyperbolic curve.

Step 3. Other radii are selected and added to AB to locate additional points in the same manner as described in Step 2. An irregular curve is used to complete the hyperbola.

Other methods can be used to construct hyperbolas and parabolas, but these methods are recommended because they are based on the mathematical definitions of the conic sections. The use of these methods will assist you in grasping the basic mathematical principles of conic sections.

5–24 THE ELLIPSE

The ellipse is formed by passing a plane through a cylinder or a cone at an angle. An example is shown in Fig. 5–41, where a sectional plane is passed through a cylindrical section of a fuselage.

The ellipse is defined as the path of a point which moves in such a way that the sum of its

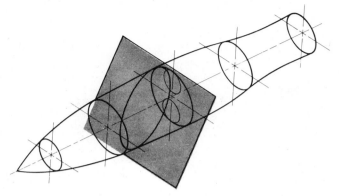

Fig. 5–41 A plane passed through a cylindrical fuselage forms an ellipse. (Courtesy of General Dynamics.)

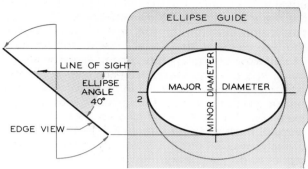

Fig. 5–43 Construction of an ellipse using ellipse guides.

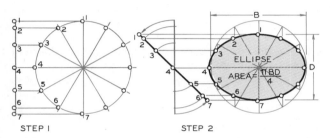

STEP I   STEP 2

Fig. 5–42 Construction of an ellipse.

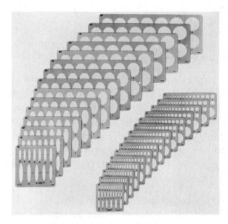

Fig. 5–44 Typical ellipse guides used for ellipse representation. (Courtesy of A. Lietz Co.)

distances from two focal points is a constant. The ellipse can be thought of as a view of a circle other than a perpendicular view. The construction of an ellipse is illustrated in Fig. 5–42.

Step 1. A circle is divided into a number of equal sectors. Projectors are drawn from the points at which the radii intersect the circle to an edge view of the circle. The projectors, which represent the reader's line of sight as he looks at the face view of the circle, are drawn perpendicular to the edge view, and the points where the projectors intersect the edge view are numbered to correspond to the points where they intersect the face view.

Step 2. The edge view of the circle is revolved into a new position so that the line of sight is not perpendicular to the edge view. The points on the revolved

edge are projected to the face view of the circle. Points are located on the ellipse by vertically projecting each of the numbered points on the face view of the circle to the projectors from the corresponding points on the edge view. The ellipse can be drawn with an irregular curve.

This same principle can be applied to the construction of an ellipse with the aid of an ellipse guide (template), as illustrated in Fig. 5–43. The edge view of the circle is revolved into the desired position. The angle between the line of sight and the edge view of the circle is the ellipse angle that is used for constructing the ellipse.

Note that one diameter of the ellipse is always equal to the diameter of the full circle. This is called the *major diameter*. The diameter perpendicular to the major diameter is the *minor diameter*, the shortest diameter that it is possible to measure. These two crossing lines are used to align the ellipse guide in a position for drawing the ellipse. Ellipse guides are usually graduated in intervals of 5°, with several sizes of ellipses at the same angle on a single template. The sizes of the ellipses are indicated in terms of the major diameter. In Fig. 5–43, the major diameter was 2" and the ellipse angle 40°. Typical sets of ellipse guides are shown in Fig. 5–44. When the ellipse angle and the major diameter are known, the guide can be aligned with the major and minor diameters for drawing an accurate ellipse with a minimum of effort.

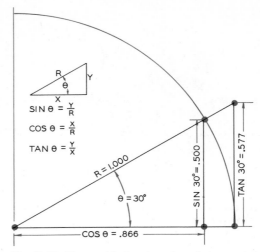

Fig. 5–45 The graphical construction of trigonometric functions.

5–25 GRAPHICAL TRIGONOMETRY

A trigonometric function is the relationship of a combination of the sides of a right triangle of a particular size. For example, the sine of 30° is equal to the length of one side divided by the length of another side and is always .500 for 30° right triangles. These functions can be taken from trigonometric tables, from a slide rule, or found graphically as described in the following steps.

Step 1. Draw a quarter of a circle with a radius of 1, 10, or a multiple of 10 with your engineers' scale (Fig. 5–45). Construct the angle whose functions you wish to know from the center; measure the angle from the horizontal.

Step 2. The sine of an angle is the numerical value of the opposite side (Y) divided by the hypotenuse (R). Since R was selected as 1.000, the length of Y is the

sine of the angle and can be measured in the drawing with an engineers' scale. It is found to be .500 for a 30° angle. This value will change for different angles.

The cosine of an angle is the adjacent side (X) divided by the hypotenuse (R); for a 30° angle a direct measurement of .866 is obtained. The tangent is the opposite side (Y) divided by the adjacent side (X). To find the tangent, similar triangles are used. The denominator (X) is extended to be equal to the radius R, which is 1.000. The length of Y can be measured as .577.

The other trigonometric functions—cotangent, secant, and cosecant—can be found with this same type of construction. They are not illustrated here. The graphical approach to trigonometry can assist you in understanding trigonometric functions.

PROBLEMS

Problems should be presented on $8\frac{1}{2}" \times 11"$ paper (Size A), grid or plain, using the format introduced in Article 3–15. Each grid square in the problem illustrations represents $\frac{1}{4}"$. All notes, sketches, drawings, and graphical work should be neatly prepared in keeping with the good practices

described in this book. Written matter should be legibly lettered with the aid of $\frac{1}{8}"$ guidelines.

General Problems
1 Use Fig. 5–46 for this problem. (A) Construct a perpendicular bisector of the line. (B) Construct the

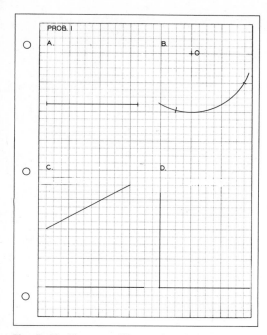

Fig. 5–46 Bisectors of lines and angles.

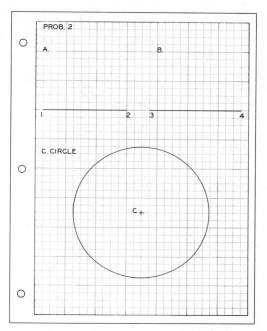

Fig. 5–47 Division of a line into equal parts and elements of a circle.

bisector of the arc between the two marks. (C) Construct a bisector of the angle. (D) Construct a bisector of the angle.

2 Use Fig. 5–47 for these problems and label all constructions. (A) Divide line 1–2 into seven equal parts by geometric construction. (B) Divide line 3–4 into nine equal parts by geometric construction. (C) Construct and label the following basic elements on the given circle: chord, radius, segment, sector, tangent, and secant.

3 Use Fig. 5–48 for this problem. (A and B) Using the given lengths of the sides, construct two triangles. (C) Inscribe two angles in the semicircle. Check the sizes of the angles thus formed to verify that they are right angles.

4 Graphically construct the areas formed by squaring the three sides of the triangle *ABC* in Fig. 5–49. This is an application of the Pythagorean Theorem. Determine the length of the hypotenuse both graphically and mathematically. Show all construction and calculations.

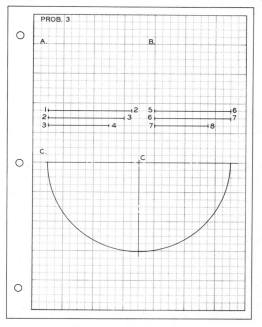

Fig. 5–48 Construction of triangles.

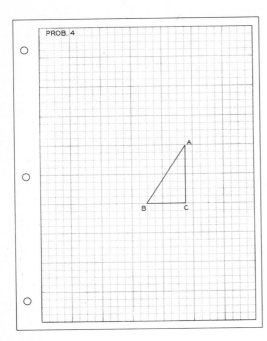

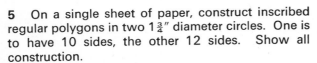

Fig. 5–49 Pythagorean Theorem problem.

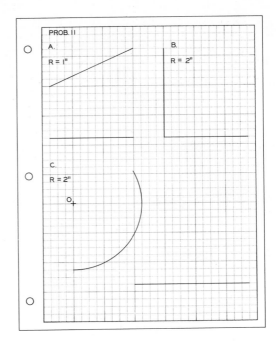

Fig. 5–50 Tangency constructions.

5 On a single sheet of paper, construct inscribed regular polygons in two $1\frac{3}{4}''$ diameter circles. One is to have 10 sides, the other 12 sides. Show all construction.

6 Construct an inscribed pentagon using a circle with a 3″ diameter.

7 On a single sheet, construct two hexagons using two $1\frac{3}{4}''$ diameter circles, a compass, and a straightedge. The first hexagon is to be circumscribed, the second inscribed.

8 On a single sheet, construct two hexagons using two $1\frac{3}{4}''$ diameter circles and a 30° triangle. Inscribe one and circumscribe the other.

9 Inscribe an octagon in a 5″ × 5″ square using a compass and a straightedge.

10 On a single sheet, construct two octagons using two $1\frac{3}{4}''$ diameter circles and a 45° triangle. Inscribe one and circumscribe the other.

11 Use Fig. 5–50 for this problem. (A) Using the radius indicated, construct an arc tangent to the two lines. (B) Using the radius indicated, construct an arc tangent to the two perpendicular lines. (C) Using the radius indicated, construct an arc tangent to the arc and the line. Show all construction on these problems and mark points of tangency with thin lines.

12 Use Fig. 5–51 for this problem. (A) Using the radius indicated, construct an arc tangent to the two arcs, with its center below the given centers. (B) Construct a line by geometric construction from point *A* that is tangent to the circle. Find the point of tangency by construction. (C) Using the radius indicated, construct an arc tangent to the given arcs. The center of this arc should be above the given arcs. Show all construction and mark points of tangency in these problems.

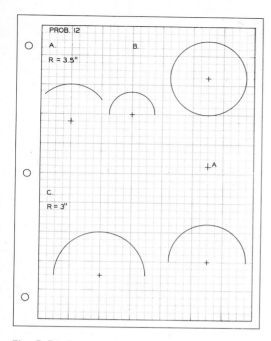

Fig. 5-51 Tangency constructions.

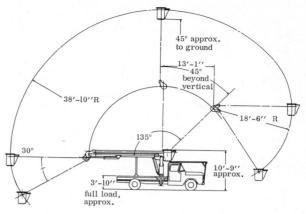

Fig. 5-52 Geometric path of an aerial lift. (Courtesy of Hughes-Keenan Division.)

13 Construct a helix with a 3″ diameter and 3″ lead. Lay out this problem on a sheet as shown in Fig. 3-31. Show all construction.

14 Construct a spiral in a 6″ diameter circle. Divide the circle into 15° sectors. Show all construction.

15 Make a drawing of the path of the aerial lift shown in Fig. 5-52 using the given radii. Draw the arcs to be tangent. Locate and mark the points of tangency.

16 Construct a parabola using the specifications given in Fig. 5-53. Draw the parabola as large as your sheet will permit. Find its area and show your calculations.

17 Construct two hyperbolas using the specifications given in Fig. 5-54. Draw the hyperbolas as large as your sheet will permit.

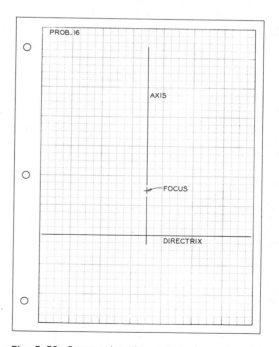

Fig. 5-53 Construction of a parabola.

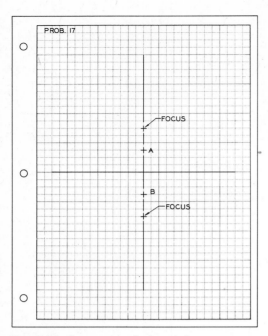

Fig. 5–54 Construction of a hyperbola.

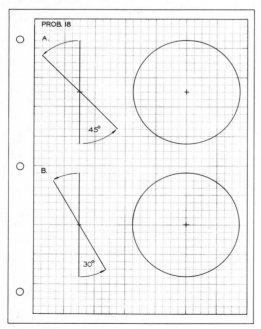

Fig. 5–55 Construction of ellipses.

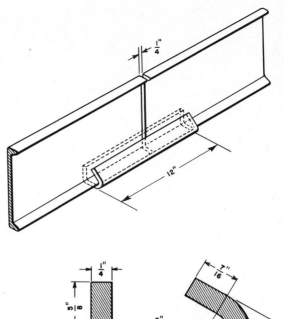

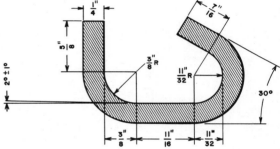

Fig. 5–56 A detail of a formed-steel clip used for aligning curb-facing panels. (Courtesy of Bethlehem Steel Company.)

18 Construct elliptical views of the circle when revolved as shown in Fig. 5–55A and B. Show all construction. Use an ellipse guide on one of the ellipses, if available. Label the major and minor diameters and the ellipse guide angle that should be used for drawing the ellipses.

19 Using a quadrant of a circle with a 5″ radius, construct the sine, cosine, and tangent functions of 35°. Show and label all construction. Check your graphical results with a trigonometry table to determine your accuracy. Select another angle on the same quadrant and determine its functions using these same procedures.

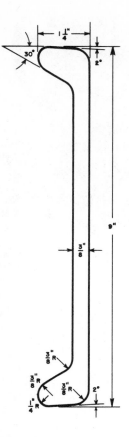

Fig. 5–57 A detail of a cross section through a curb-facing panel. (Courtesy of Bethlehem Steel Company.)

Fig. 5–58 A link of a chain. (Courtesy of Link-Belt Company.)

Design Problems

20 The curb facing shown in Fig. 5–56 was designed to protect concrete curbs at the edge of a street. Make a double-size drawing of the clip that was designed to align the joints. Show all construction and points of tangency.

21 Make a triple-size drawing of one end of the curb facing section (Fig. 5–57) using the given dimensions. Show all construction and points of tangency.

22 The link shown in Fig. 5–58 is used in a chain similar to the one in Fig. 5–59. The distance between the centers of the holes is $1\frac{1}{2}''$. Make a design drawing of the link using geometric construction principles. The holes are $\frac{3}{8}''$ in diameter. Your solution should be similar to the link in the photograph. Show all construction, mark points of tangency, and show overall dimensions.

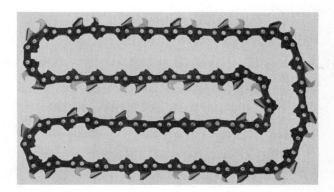

Fig. 5–59 A sawing chain composed of metal links. (Courtesy of Omark Industries.)

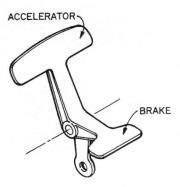

Fig. 5–60 An accelerator-brake for a golfing cart. (Courtesy of Versal, Inc.)

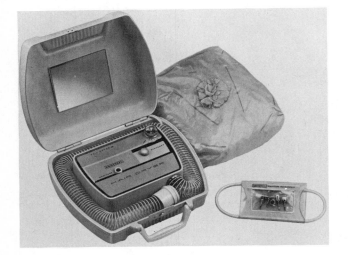

Fig. 5–61 A portable hair dryer. (Courtesy of General Electric.)

Fig. 5–62 Two 7″ movie reels shown attached to a Caralux projector. (Courtesy of Kodak.)

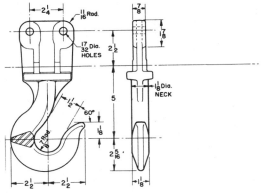

Fig. 5–63 A forged-steel hook attachment, weight 7.5 lb. (Courtesy of Mechanical Handling Systems, Inc.)

23 Draw true-size views of the foot pads on the golf cart accelerator-brake shown in Fig. 5–60. Design the pads to accommodate all foot sizes. You must determine all dimensions and radii. Indicate the overall dimensions of the designs on your completed drawing. Show all construction and points of tangency.

24 Make a design drawing of the top view of the portable hair dryer case shown in Fig. 5–61. The overall dimensions are 12″ × 10″. Select arcs to approximate the shape of the case shown in the photograph. Show all construction and locate points of tangency.

25 Redesign the spokes of the 8-mm movie reel shown in Fig. 5–62 using arcs or straight lines. The diameter of this reel is 7″. Show all construction and points of tangency.

26 Make a full-size design drawing of the front view of the hook attachment shown in Fig. 5–63. Select arcs that will approximate the shape of the hook shown. Show all construction and mark points of tangency.

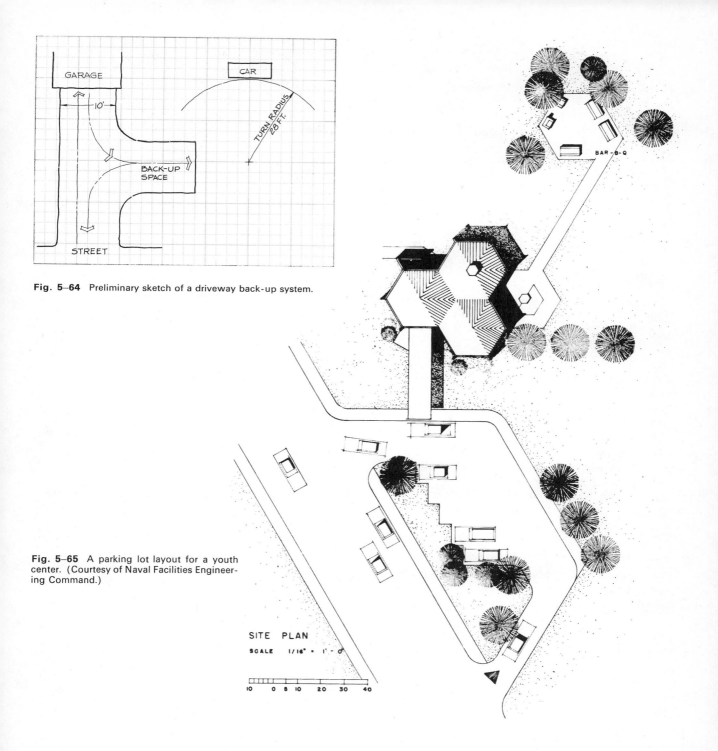

Fig. 5–64 Preliminary sketch of a driveway back-up system.

Fig. 5–65 A parking lot layout for a youth center. (Courtesy of Naval Facilities Engineering Command.)

GARAGE

CAR

10'

TURN RADIUS 28 FT.

BACK-UP SPACE

STREET

BAR - B - Q

SITE PLAN

SCALE 1/16" = 1' - 0"

10   0   5 10   20   30   40

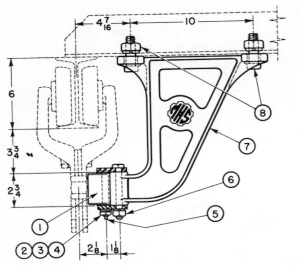

Fig. 5–66 A roller turn segment for an overhead conveyor system. (Courtesy of Mechanical Handling Systems, Inc.)

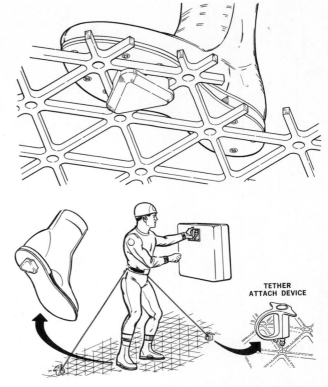

TETHER ATTACH DEVICE

Fig. 5–67 An experimental design for a foot restraint to be used in the S-IVB Orbital Workshop Project. (Courtesy of the National Aeronautics and Space Administration.)

27 Using the inside turning radius for an automobile, make a design layout of a one-car garage with a back-up space as shown in Fig. 5–64. Determine the dimensions of this space. Select an appropriate scale. Show all construction and points of tangency.

28 Using the turning radius of Problem 27, make a scale drawing of the parking lot shown in Fig. 5–65. Each parking space should be 8.5′ × 18′. Use a Size B sheet as shown in Fig. 3–33.

29 Make a half-size design drawing of the front view of the roller turn segment shown in Fig. 5–66. Show all construction and mark points of tangency. Estimate all dimensions not given.

30 Experimental boots have been designed (Fig. 5–67) to keep astronauts in contact with a floor grid when they are experiencing weightlessness in space.

Make drawings to illustrate the triangular pads under the boots and also the grid on which the boots will be used. The pads must be designed to a size that will fit any size of boot. Show all construction and mark points of tangency.

31 Design a better method of keeping an astronaut in contact with a surface of an orbital workshop when in space.

"Imagination is more important than knowledge . . .," said the famous physicist, Albert Einstein

6
THE DESIGN PROCESS

Fig. 6–1 This penholder was the product of the work of a designer and the application of his imagination. (Courtesy of Koh-I-Noor Corporation.)

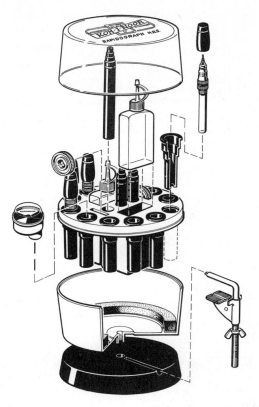

Fig. 6–2 Each part of this design had to be considered separately before the finished product could be constructed. (Courtesy of Koh-I-Noor Corporation.)

6–1 WHAT IS DESIGN?

Have you ever thought of how products and machines originate? For example, have you wondered how it is possible for you to turn on a switch and see a live television program from another country or even from the moon? You should consider the products and appliances you use daily. Perhaps you take them for granted and do not fully appreciate them.

By today's standards, the penholder shown in Fig. 6–1 is a simple device. Its purpose is to hold a number of inking pens and to reduce the tendency of

the ink to dry in the pens and clog them. However, like any well-designed product, a great deal of thought was necessary to develop this device. The number of pens to be held and the types of accessories had to be determined. These factors influenced the size of the container and the materials that could be used.

Many rough ideas were sketched, discussed, evaluated, accepted or rejected, and if accepted then refined and tested. With the formulation of each idea, it was necessary to develop details of construction and assembly. Other important considerations were the market appeal of the finished product, its selling price, and how it would be marketed. As you can see, the overall process of arriving at a solution involves many related problems.

This process of arriving at the best solution of a problem that has many possible solutions is called *design*. The term design will be used in this sense throughout this textbook, and frequent reference will be made to design and to the application of drafting principles to design.

It is design that gives us a product such as the penholder of Fig. 6–1. Design has both broad and detailed aspects. For instance, the first approach to the penholder design was very broad, being concerned with developing the overall concept—how many pens, what size, for whom, what price, etc. But as each of these problems was solved, the designer became more concerned with details and specifics. How will the base look? What materials should be used? What manufacturing processes? You can see in Fig. 6–2 that each part had to be considered as a single unit and as part of the overall design. Working drawings and specifications had to be prepared for each part before production was possible.

In any design, the primary concern is getting as many advantages as possible with the fewest disadvantages. We want a car that is as powerful as needed, but that uses as little gasoline as possible. We want an airplane as strong and yet as light as possible. The process of balancing a design's characteristics to achieve the optimum (the best balance) is called *optimization*.

6–2 WHO DESIGNS?

Since design can be defined as the solution of problems with many possible solutions to give an optimum result, we see that many people can be classified as designers. In some cases, design is the primary function of an individual; and in other cases, design is a secondary assignment. The people most commonly involved in design are discussed in the following paragraphs.

Fig. 6–3 This lunar vehicle was designed by engineers in cooperation with scientists and technicians. (Courtesy of Ryan Aircraft Corporation.)

The engineer. The engineer is responsible for the conversion of raw materials and power sources into needed products and services. He applies scientific and academic principles to the solution of problems and to the fulfillment of needs. This is the process of designing. It is design that distinguishes the engineer from the scientist. Most new products, processes, and contributions to technology come from the efforts of engineers through their ability to design. The lunar vehicle in Fig. 6–3 was developed by engineers working in conjunction with scientists and technicians.

The architect. The architect is a designer of buildings, environments, and even cities. He must take the best from the existing technology and organize it into the most efficient building or development possible. His primary role is that of designing, perhaps in a more artistic way than the engineer. The principles of designing a small

Fig. 6–4 The architect is a designer of buildings and the environment that surrounds them. (Courtesy of architects G. T. Rockrise and Associates and Red Cedar Shingle and Handsplit Shake Bureau.)

development (like the one shown in Fig. 6–4) are no different from those involved in designing an entire city.

The designer. Some industries and companies employ a specialist called a designer who is responsible for developing new ideas, products, or appliances. This person has a special talent for creating solutions to technological problems. Often he is an engineer, but this is not necessarily the case. The designer should not be thought of as a person interested only in the appearance of a product; instead, he is interested in its complete development from an idea into a functional device. The designer has inventive talents, but he is primarily a systematic problem solver.

Thomas A. Edison is the classic example of a designer with no formal training (Fig. 6–5). From

Fig. 6–5 Thomas A. Edison had no formal education, but he gave the world some of its most creative designs.

Fig. 6–6 The stylist is more concerned with the outward appearance of a product than the functional aspects of its design. (Courtesy of Ford Motor Company.)

his genius came the phonograph, the light bulb, and the motion picture camera; in all, he is responsible for 1100 patents. Each of Edison's designs was the result of extensive experimentation and trial-and-error testing to develop the optimum solution to the problem at hand.

The stylist. The person who is concerned with the outward appearance of a product is a *stylist*. A stylist may be concerned with the body configuration of an automobile or an electric iron (Fig. 6–6). The stylist must have a high degree of artistic awareness and a feeling for the consumer's reaction to a design. The automobile stylist, for example, is interested in the functional requirements of the body, driver vision, enclosure of passengers, space for the engine, etc. However, he does not involve himself with the design of items such as the engine, steering linkages, or suspension systems. He is concerned primarily with the outward appearance of the automobile.

The technician. The technician is not so closely involved with design as the engineer. His job is to test the engineer's designs, construct models of the designs, and assist in the final construction of the

product. He has considerable opportunity to apply his own imagination to the problems he encounters. Talented technicians who have demonstrated an ability to develop creative solutions to problems may become designers. This is especially true for design drafting technicians and mechanical engineering technicians.

6–3 WHAT IS CREATIVITY?

The term creativity is used to describe a person who has a talent for designing. Creativity has broad applications. A person may be a creative writer, composer, wood-carver, or dancer. However, in this book we are concerned primarily with creativity as it applies to the field of technology and engineering.

In technology, creativity is the application of inventiveness and imagination to a design that is different from previous solutions to a problem. The fact that the solution is different does not make it desirable, but does indicate a degree of creativity on the part of the designer.

In many respects, a designer in the world of technology must be more inventive than the artistically creative person. The designer has many

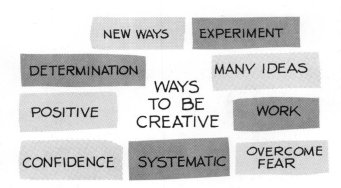

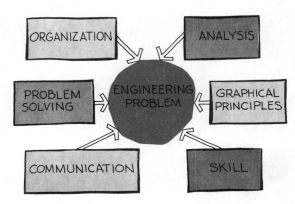

Fig. 6–7 Points that are helpful in developing creativity.

Fig. 6–8 Problems in engineering require a total approach employing all aspects of graphics and drafting.

restrictions of materials, economics, optimization, size, and function. The artist, on the other hand, has the minimum of restrictions. His primary purpose is to develop an attractive painting or piece of sculpture.

Many people claim that creativity cannot be taught; however, research has indicated that this ability, like most other personal talents, can be developed. Creativity is probably the most valuable trait a person can possess, for it is through creativity that new industries are born and ways of living are changed.

6–4 HOW CAN YOU DEVELOP CREATIVITY?

Creativity is a more dominant part of some personalities than of others. Some people exhibit an aptitude for design and creativity, but are unwilling to apply this talent. Such a person can be compared to the talented athlete who is unwilling to practice and work in his sport.

The following points may help you to recognize ways in which you can become more conscious of creativity. This will assist you in developing your own creative talents (Fig. 6–7).

1. Solve problems in a new way. Develop an awareness of the products that you use. Look for faults in design and ways in which faulty products could be improved. You cannot improve a design unless you are aware of its shortcomings. Can you design a better drafting stool, a better tape dispenser, or a better handle for an automobile door?

2. Experiment. A designer must be an experimenter. He usually likes to try many varied solutions to a problem. Often, an approach to a problem may be similar to an approach used for previous problems. A truly creative person will consider many solutions which may be quite different from one another. For example, instead of designing a new automobile wheel, why not consider other methods of propulsion such as skis, tracks, or a hovering system?

3. Determination. Seldom does success come accidentally. Pursue a problem using your talents as completely as possible. Accept each problem as a challenge.

4. Fear of failure. Fear of failure or criticism restricts many creative people from fully expressing their ideas or attempting a unique solution to a problem. The first automobiles were ridiculed by horse-and-buggy owners.

5. Try many ideas. The more ideas you consider, the more likely you are to find a creative solution to a design problem. Studies have indicated that a person capable of suggesting a large number of solutions is usually a creative person. Collect as many ideas as possible before deciding what the final solution will be.

6. Confidence. If you have a worthy idea, you should be confident enough to develop it and discuss it. Confidence is important since many new ideas are

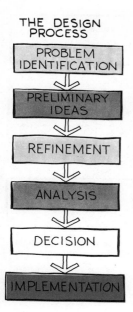

THE DESIGN PROCESS

PROBLEM IDENTIFICATION

PRELIMINARY IDEAS

REFINEMENT

ANALYSIS

DECISION

IMPLEMENTATION

Fig. 6–9 The steps of the design process.

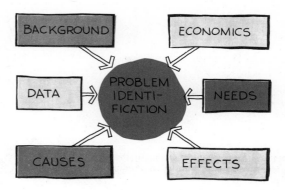

BACKGROUND   ECONOMICS

DATA → PROBLEM IDENTIFICATION ← NEEDS

CAUSES   EFFECTS

Fig. 6–10 Problem identification requires an accumulation of as much information concerning the problem as possible before a solution is attempted by the designer.

first rejected and only later reassessed and accepted. You must be confident enough to support an idea you believe in.

7. Be positive. It is easier to find poor features in a design than it is to suggest better ones. Do not look for reasons why a design idea will not work, but exhaust all possibilities for making it work before rejecting an idea.

8. Be systematic. Creativity should be applied as systematically as possible. Effort should be organized rather than haphazard. This will prevent duplication of effort and will result in better solutions.

9. Work. As in any endeavor, work is necessary for success in design. With work will come development of skills and valuable experience.

6–5 THE DESIGN PROCESS

The design process is a systematic approach to the solution of a design problem. This systematic approach can be applied to almost any type of problem. Many people have the misconception that

designs come in an "inspirational flash." In fact, most designs result from a disciplined attack on a problem in a systematic manner. Engineering and technological problems require a total approach to a problem, employing a number of subject areas (Fig. 6–8).

The design process that is suggested as a guide for you to follow is illustrated in Fig. 6–9. The steps in the process are (1) problem identification, (2) preliminary ideas, (3) refinement, (4) analysis, (5) decision, and (6) implementation. The designer usually finds that he must recycle his efforts and repeat some of the previous steps instead of completing each step in sequence. These steps will be defined in the following paragraphs.

Problem identification. The designer assumes that there is a need for anything that he is to design. A doorstop is designed to hold a door in a certain position. A washing machine has a special need to fill. Once the general need is established, the scope of the problem must be completely defined before an attempt can be made to develop its solution (Fig. 6–10).

Air pollution is a complex problem that needs to be solved. We must identify just what causes air pollution and the degree of pollution caused by each source. We must decide whether the problem is the control of atmospheric conditions, the control of the sources of impurities, the elimination of impurities, or

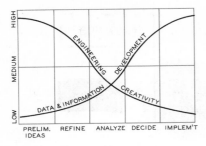

Fig. 6–11 Creativity is highest during the initial stages of the design process; data and information development increase during the final stages.

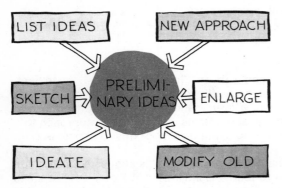

Fig. 6–12 Preliminary ideas are developed after the identification step has been completed. All possibilities should be listed and sketched to give the designer a broad selection of ideas from which to work.

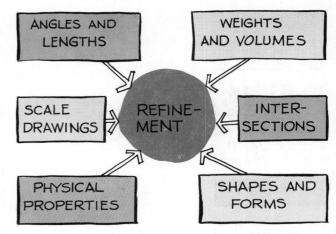

Fig. 6–13 Refinement involves the development of preliminary ideas into scale drawings from which additional information about the designs can be determined.

the creation of an artificial atmosphere free of polluted air. This is problem identification.

Preliminary ideas. Once we have sufficient information to clearly identify the problem, we are ready to accumulate as many preliminary ideas as possible. This is the most creative step of the design process (Fig. 6–11). Ideas should be as varied as possible. All ideas should be recorded with notes and sketches. No idea should be rejected at this point (Fig. 6–12).

Refinement. The better preliminary ideas are selected for more detailed study and development. Rough sketches are converted into scale drawings for space analysis, critical measurements, and the calculation of areas and volumes affecting the design (Fig. 6–13).

Analysis. The better refined designs are analyzed to determine their comparative merits with respect to cost, strength, function, and market appeal. This is the step where engineering and scientific principles are used most. Laboratory tests may be conducted to determine how well a design actually functions. Scale models may be constructed and tested (Fig. 6–14).

Decision. In every project, a stage is reached when a decision must be made based on a study of the design and the judgment of the designer or his associates. One of the designs must be decided on or a decision must be made to reject all designs developed so far (Fig. 6–15). It is as important to recognize a design that should be rejected as it is to accept a good design. An automobile that was produced but would not sell could prove extremely costly to a company. The final decision concerning a design may result in a combination of features from several designs.

Implementation. This step includes the preparation of the final drawings and specifications of the final design, as well as its fabrication (Fig. 6–16). Implementation involves the engineer, the techni-

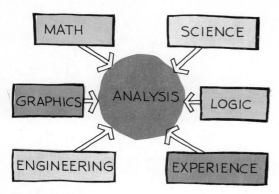

Fig. 6–14 The analysis phase of the design process is the application of all available technological methods from science to graphics in evaluating the refined designs.

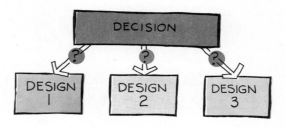

Fig. 6–15 Decision is the selection of the best design or design features to be improved.

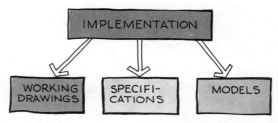

Fig. 6–16 Implementation is the final step of the design process, where drawings and specifications are prepared from which the final product can be constructed.

cian, and the craftsman. Modifications can still be made in the design by this team if they become aware of better methods and solutions. These changes will probably be rather minor and will relate to the manufacturing process. Implementation includes also the final production, manufacture, and fabrication of the finished design.

6–6 GRAPHICS AND THE DESIGN PROCESS

What is the relationship between design and drafting? Drafting is usually thought of as the phase of design in which the finished working drawings are prepared. This is the implementation stage, the last step and the least creative (Fig. 6–11). However, if we think in terms of graphics rather than simply drafting, the importance of these skills to each step of the design process becomes clear.

Data are gathered to define a problem and they are usually plotted on a graph in order to be interpreted. Freehand drawing, usually called sketching, is the designer's most important tool for developing ideas and recording them for study. Scale drawings are used to refine preliminary ideas. Graphical principles can even be used to analyze certain aspects of design—forces in structural members,

mathematical test data, clearances and sizes of components. Descriptive geometry and engineering graphics are applied to many of these problems; however, the basic drafting principles covered in this textbook will be sufficient for most design problems.

Graphics and drafting principles are probably more important to the design process than any other single field of study. The following sections will illustrate how graphics is applied to real problems. This will help you understand the relation of graphics to the solution of a design problem.

All design work, including notes and sketches, should be kept in a neat, easy-to-read format. It is advisable to use grid sheets that will assist with notes and sketching. Note that these worksheets are labeled and endorsed to serve as a permanent record of the designer's work.

6–7 A SIMPLE DESIGN PROBLEM

A simple example is given to illustrate the steps of the design process in the solution of a real problem. The application of graphics to each of the steps will be emphasized.

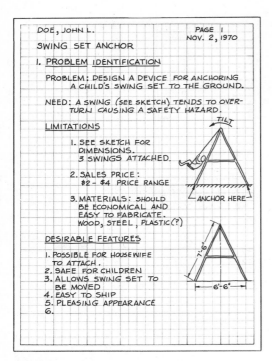

Fig. 6–17 Problem identification work sheet.

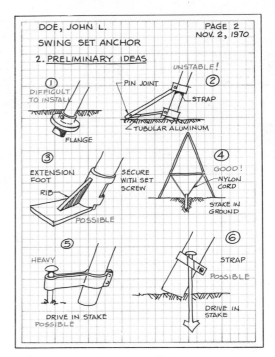

Fig. 6–18 Preliminary ideas are sketched with the necessary notes.

Swing set anchor. A child's swing set has been found unstable during the peak of the swing. The momentum of the swing causes the A-frame to tilt, with the possibility of overturning and causing injury. The swing set has swings to accommodate three children at one time. Design a device that will eliminate this hazard and have a market appeal for owners of swing sets of this type.

Problem identification. As a first step, the designer writes down the problem statement (Fig. 6–17) and a statement of the need. This simple action stimulates a flow of thought and assists him in taking action toward a solution. The desirable features and requirements are listed on a work sheet. Often it is easier to describe thoughts in the form of sketches than in words. Much of the information that is being written down will be obvious to the designer, but simply writing it down will help him get off "dead

center"—the situation that often occurs at the beginning of the creative process.

This problem is a simple one requiring more common sense than engineering, but common sense should not be overlooked as an important part of the design process. Many highly technical people tend to become too involved with sophisticated methods and overlook simple, direct solutions.

Another part of problem identification could be a market survey to determine the number of swing sets sold, to whom and by whom. This could give an approximation of the available market. Data of this type should be plotted on a graph for visual interpretation.

Preliminary ideas. A second work sheet is used to sketch preliminary ideas that may lead to a possible solution (Fig. 6–18). This is the most creative part of the design process, and it places the fewest re-

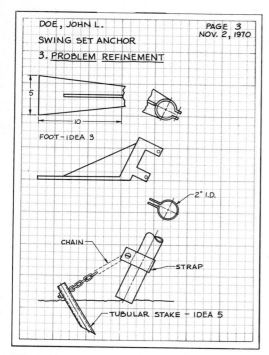

Fig. 6–19 The better preliminary ideas are refined by making scale drawings.

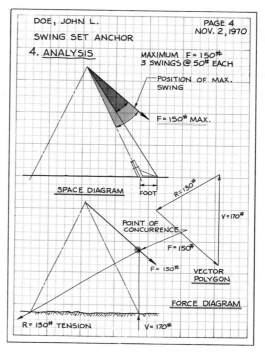

Fig. 6–20 The refined designs are analyzed by graphical methods.

straints on the designer. He must make many sketches and notes to describe his preliminary thoughts, without dwelling on a single design. After several ideas have been sketched, he can review them and make notes in colored pencil to indicate the better points of each design, narrowing his preliminary ideas to those that have the most merit.

Refinement. The two or three best designs are drawn to scale in a general working drawing as a means of refining the preliminary ideas. Sufficient notes are used to describe the design without becoming too involved with details (Fig. 6–19). Refinement provides the physical properties and dimensions that must be considered during the early stages of the design process.

Orthographic projection, working drawing principles, and descriptive geometry may be used according to the needs of the particular problem being refined. These topics will be discussed in greater detail in the following chapters. In this example (Fig. 6–19), simple orthographic views with auxiliary views depict the two designs. These drawings, even though they have been refined, are still subject to change throughout the entire design process.

Analysis. Once a preliminary design has been refined to establish fundamental dimensions and relationships, the designs must be analyzed to determine their suitability. The maximum angles of the swing need to be established by observation of a child swinging under average conditions. The force, F, at the critical angle can be calculated mathematically or estimated by observation (Fig. 6–20). Since three swings may be used at once, the maximum force will be applied when all three swings are in phase, causing a triple pull (150 lb in this example).

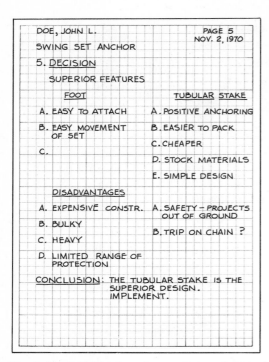

Fig. 6–21 A decision is made as to the best design to implement.

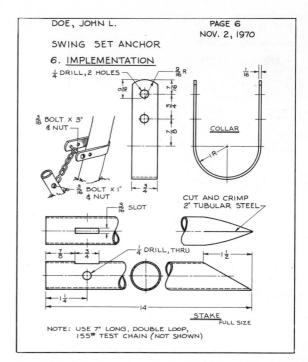

Fig. 6–22 A final working drawing is prepared from which the finished design can be implemented.

The danger zones are indicated graphically in the space diagram to show the effects of the foot design and to establish the dimension that it must have in order to eliminate the tilting tendency at the maximum angle. The force diagram is drawn to scale to analyze the reaction forces at the extreme condition. This diagram gives the direction of reaction, R, but not its magnitude. A vector polygon is drawn with the vectors parallel to the forces in the force diagram, where the only known force is $F = 150$ lb. The magnitude of the resultant R is found to be 130 lb, which is the maximum force that must be overcome at the base of the swing set.

Decision. The designs must be evaluated and the best one selected for implementation. The designer may wish to repeat the previous process at any point, and develop an entirely different approach to the problem if he sees a need for it. In this example (Fig.

6–21), the superior features of each design are listed for easy comparison. The disadvantages of each are also listed to prevent any design weakness from being overlooked. These tabulated lists are reviewed and a final conclusion is reached. A decision is made to implement the tubular stake design.

Implementation. The tubular stake design is presented in the form of a working drawing, in which each individual part is detailed and dimensioned, and from which the parts could be made. All principles of graphical presentation are used, including a freehand sketch illustrating how the parts will be assembled (Fig. 6–22). Note that changes have been made since the initial refinement of this design. These changes were believed to improve the design by making it more operational and economical while serving the desired function. Standard parts, such as nuts, bolts, and the chain, need not be drawn but

Fig. 6–23 The completed swing set anchor.

Fig. 6–24 This photograph shows the camera coverage an experimental spacecraft will have as it approaches the moon's surface during its last 15 minutes of flight. (Courtesy of the National Aeronautics and Space Administration.)

merely noted, since they are parts that will not be specially fabricated. With this drawing the designer has implemented his design as far as he can without actually building a prototype, a model, or the actual part (Fig. 6–23). He may later modify his design, but each such modification is a separate design process very similar to the one reviewed here.

6–8 A COMPLEX DESIGN PROBLEM

One of the most complex design problems in history was the design of a vehicle and support system to carry man to the moon. The same steps that we used in designing a swing set anchor were applied to this problem, but many more sophisticated and complex problems were solved. Graphics and drafting principles were just as important to this problem as to the simple problem. The following paragraphs will briefly illustrate how these steps of the design process were applied to the mission to the moon.

Problem identification. Once a decision had been made that there should be a mission to the moon, it was necessary to identify the problems related to the mission. Scientific data, such as photographs of the moon's surface, helped in locating a suitable landing site (Fig. 6–24). Criteria such as the distance from the earth to the moon, the gravitational fields of each, the availability of propulsion for

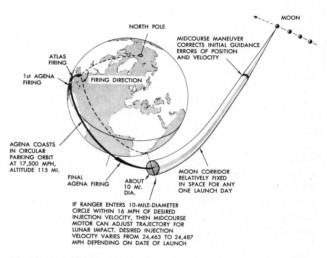

Fig. 6–25 This graphical schematic illustrates a proposed test flight to the moon by an unmanned spacecraft, Ranger, prior to manned flight. Information gained from this mission will be valuable to later manned missions. (Courtesy of the National Aeronautics and Space Administration.)

the spacecraft, the number of crew required, their living conditions during flight, the method of returning to the earth, and guidance systems had to be investigated. A preliminary, unmanned launch to the moon is illustrated in Fig. 6–25 with notes to identify details of the mission.

Information pertaining to the identification of a problem can be more easily understood and inter-

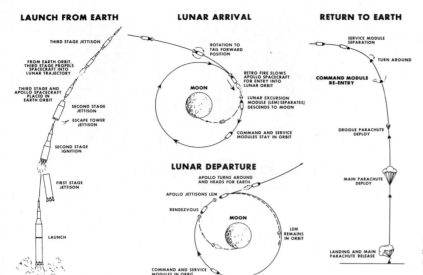

LAUNCH FROM EARTH

THIRD STAGE JETTISON

FROM EARTH ORBIT,
THIRD STAGE PROPELS
SPACECRAFT INTO
LUNAR TRAJECTORY

THIRD STAGE AND
APOLLO SPACECRAFT
PLACED IN
EARTH ORBIT

SECOND STAGE
JETTISON

ESCAPE TOWER
JETTISON

SECOND STAGE
IGNITION

FIRST STAGE
JETTISON

LAUNCH

LUNAR ARRIVAL

ROTATION TO
TAIL FORWARD
POSITION

RETRO FIRE SLOWS
APOLLO SPACECRAFT
FOR ENTRY INTO
LUNAR ORBIT

MOON

LUNAR EXCURSION
MODULE (LEM) SEPARATES;
DESCENDS TO MOON

COMMAND AND SERVICE
MODULES STAY IN ORBIT

LUNAR DEPARTURE

APOLLO TURNS AROUND
AND HEADS FOR EARTH

APOLLO JETTISONS LEM

RENDEZVOUS

MOON

LEM
REMAINS
IN ORBIT

LANDING AND MAIN
PARACHUTE RELEASE

COMMAND AND SERVICE
MODULES IN ORBIT

RETURN TO EARTH

SERVICE MODULE
SEPARATION

TURN AROUND

COMMAND MODULE
RE-ENTRY

DROGUE PARACHUTE
DEPLOY

MAIN PARACHUTE
DEPLOY

Fig. 6–26 A four-stage sketch is used to identify specific problems that must be solved in landing a man on the moon and returning him safely to earth. (Courtesy of the National Aeronautics and Space Administration.)

preted if presented graphically, as in Fig. 6–26. Tables of numbers showing variations in related factors can be graphed for evaluation. The reduction of gravitational force with distance from the earth is an example of this type of information. In the mission to the moon, estimates of the funds required for the project had to be tabulated and graphed. A further extension of the cost of the mission, the determination of a source of funds, and a decision on the method of gaining necessary financing were required. The fact that the project was being carried out by a government-supported system introduced problems of a political nature which had to be identified.

Preliminary ideas. The complexity of the problems involved in travelling to the moon required preliminary ideas in a large number of separate areas. The primary problem was that of providing a power unit to propel the spacecraft. The design of the spacecraft itself and its systems was the next problem. The method of landing the vehicle on the lunar surface and returning it to the earth also had to be determined.

The sketches shown in Figs. 6–27, 6–28, and 6–29 were used to develop ideas for a spacecraft. (These Mercury sketches were preliminary only and

do not reflect the final specifications.) Many of these ideas were considered too radical and extreme a few years ago to be anything more than comic-strip material.

Preliminary ideas that could be used to test the effects of space flight on animals were sketched (Fig. 6–30). These ideas led to the development of the command module (Fig. 6–31) and the final seating arrangement.

Thousands of sketches of this type were required in order to develop ideas that would contribute to man's trip to the moon. All significant ideas and sketches were saved for reference in succeeding steps of the design process.

Fig. 6–27 An early sketch suggests a method of separating the retro-motors from the Mercury spacecraft following their use in slowing down the craft upon reentering the earth's atmosphere. (Courtesy of the National Aeronautics and Space Administration.)

Fig. 6–28 This sketch depicts the capsule's deceleration by a parachute as it reenters the earth's atmosphere. (Courtesy of the National Aeronautics and Space Administration.)

Fig. 6–29 A final step is illustrated: the capsule safely afloat awaiting pick-up. (Courtesy of the National Aeronautics and Space Administration.)

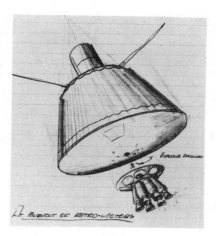

6–27

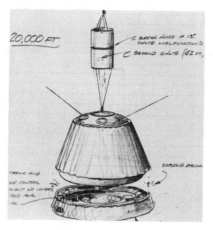

6–28

6–29

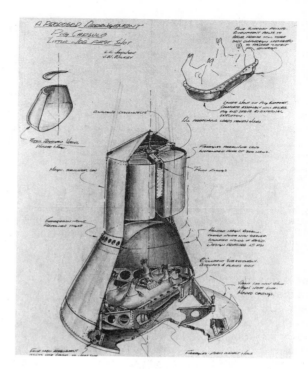

Fig. 6–30 A preliminary sketch of the spacecraft for Project Mercury illustrates a possible configuration for the capsule. A pig was initially considered for experimental tests, but was later rejected. (Courtesy of the National Aeronautics and Space Administration.)

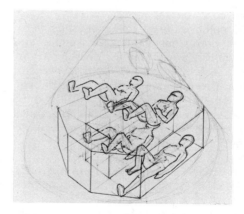

Fig. 6–31 This sketch was a preliminary idea for the seating arrangement for Project Apollo. (Courtesy of the National Aeronautics and Space Administration.)

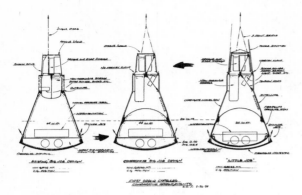

Fig. 6–32 The drawings were made as refinements of preliminary ideas for spacecraft designs. (Courtesy of the National Aeronautics and Space Administration.)

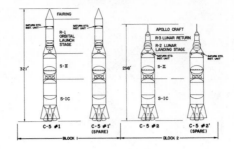

FUELING MODE LAUNCH PREPARATION

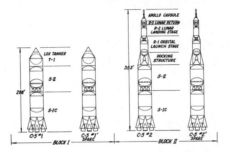

Refinement. Preliminary ideas were developed and drawn as scale drawings as a step toward refinement. Three configurations of the command module are illustrated in Fig. 6–32. A figure such as this allows a comparison of several solutions to a design problem.

The design for the Apollo Control Capsule was refined graphically by a series of auxiliary views (Fig. 6–33). These drawings were helpful in giving an understanding of the space requirements during the flight. Scale drawings permitted the designers to measure critical dimensions, establish weights, volumes, and areas, and study the function of the craft in relation to its passengers.

Graphical methods are the designer's most helpful tool in developing a design. Rough sketches and diagrams aid him in arranging his ideas in a preliminary form. Scale drawings assist the process of evolution from a rough idea to a refined concept. Descriptive geometry and spatial analysis can be employed to determine from scale drawings critical information that will influence the further development of the design.

Analysis. The analysis of the mission to the moon required a detailed study of scientific principles, utilizing advanced mathematics and other disciplines. The thrust of the rocket had to be tested extensively. Communications and guidance systems had to be analyzed through field tests, simulated missions, and

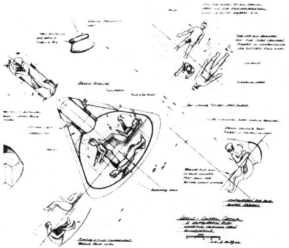

Fig. 6–33 Scale drawings were used to refine the final design of the spacecraft and to study the clearance and working areas within the Apollo capsule. By refining his drawings to scale, the designer can determine critical measurements and estimate weights and volumes. (Courtesy of the National Aeronautics and Space Administration.)

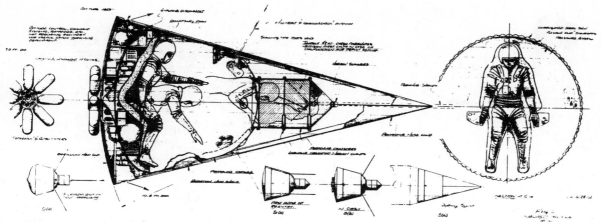

Fig. 6–34 The Mercury spacecraft is presented graphically to analyze the relationships between various interior units and human factors that are required for effective functioning. (Courtesy of the National Aeronautics and Space Administration.)

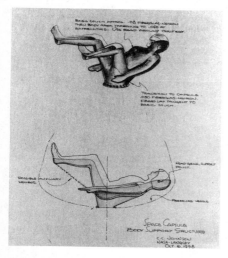

Fig. 6–35 An analysis of a couch support for an astronaut is shown in this sketch and scale drawing. This position was adopted, but the method of fabrication was discarded. (Courtesy of the National Aeronautics and Space Administration.)

unmanned missions. Environmental systems had to be tested with animals to determine the systems' ability to maintain the conditions required for manned flight.

A graphical analysis of the interior design of a proposed spacecraft is shown in Fig. 6–34. This drawing was used in analyzing the configuration and function of the interior of the capsule. The controls and other manually operated systems were analyzed to determine the feasibility of their location and function. The size of the astronaut was a primary factor affecting the size of the craft. Further analysis of human factors can be seen in the sketch shown in Fig. 6–35. When the astronaut's position was analyzed and tested, it was found that an astronaut could withstand the required *g*-loads present at launch and at reentry at the end of the flight.

The other analyses conducted on the space program are far too numerous even to mention. The proposed designs were tested and evaluated by hundreds of engineers, scientists, and technicians working as members of different teams.

Decision. Decisions must be made continually throughout the design process. Each individual component, system, and design concept for the trip to the moon had to be decided on by a number of groups and individuals. The decision process in a relatively new, experimental field such as this is more crucial to the outcome than it is in a routine design project, since there are more unknowns in an unexplored field. A wrong decision can hinder the program and disrupt the entire planning schedule.

Fig. 6–36 The decision step of the design process requires written and oral reports accompanied by graphical aids.

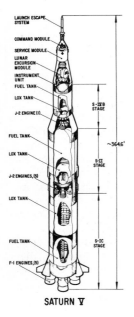

SATURN V

Fig. 6–37 Implementation requires that designs be presented in the form of working drawings and specifications; however, supplementary pictorials, models, and other techniques can be used to improve communications. (Courtesy of the National Aeronautics and Space Administration.)

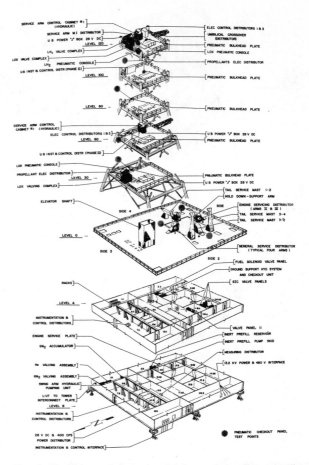

Fig. 6–38 This exploded pictorial is used to show details of construction of the launch tower of Complex 39, Cape Kennedy. (Courtesy of the National Aeronautics and Space Administration.)

All decisions had to be made by groups of experts qualified in specialized areas. No single individual or group was capable of making all the decisions required. The diversity of the backgrounds of the scientists, engineers, and other specialists made communication of concepts a much more critical factor in this project than among a group working within a small industry. If the best use was to be made of all talents involved in the project, these specialists had to be able to communicate their ideas to one another. Here again graphics was a useful tool. It was used in conferences to illustrate concepts by means of visual aids, such as flip charts.

Important decisions are usually made on the basis of oral presentations which may follow written reports. Design concepts are presented and discussed by the reviewing panel to enable its members to understand the design better and to make a reliable decision (Fig. 6–36). It is difficult to present technical ideas without the use of graphics.

Fig. 6–39 The final result of the design process is the accomplishment of the mission. Man lands on the moon and returns safely home. (Courtesy of the National Aeronautics and Space Administration.)

Implementation. Once the design was completed, manufacturers located in different parts of the nation were made responsible for producing the many parts that were needed. These parts had to be produced within close tolerances so that each manufacturer's parts would function properly when assembled with components produced by other manufacturers. This required that all designs be presented in great detail and with the maximum of clarity. The designers had to use every method at their disposal—working drawings, pictorials, scale models (Fig. 6–37)—to communicate their ideas. It would have been impossible to achieve unity of design without employing working drawings and graphical methods in the presentation of details and specifications. Figure 6–38 is an exploded pictorial, intended to show the construction of a launch tower.

As a final result of the design process, the designer sees his plans and specifications implemented and become a reality (Fig. 6–39). Only at this final stage, when the actual product is tested, does the designer know whether his design will function well enough to be considered satisfactory. Knowledge is gained through failure as well as success. Failure at the implementation stage should not be taken to mean the entire project was a failure; instead, it should provide suggestions for areas to be reevaluated.

6–9 APPLICATION OF DESIGN PRINCIPLES

The previous articles have discussed the process of design and given examples of this process applied to a simple and to a complex problem. An important point that should be emphasized concerning the design process is that the process should not be carried through from start to finish without deviation. Several times during the process the designer may revert to his initial steps and take a different approach. He may even reevaluate his initial problem identification to be sure that he is not overlooking an important factor. He may select a different preliminary idea after having gone through most of the process with other ideas. The possibility of using different ideas should be considered at each step. A good designer looks for the best possible solution and is willing to exhaust all possibilities to achieve this goal.

The following chapters of this book present basic drafting techniques. In these chapters reference will be made to the design process to emphasize the application of each topic to it. It is hoped that this approach will help you to make the best use of your creative talents and imagination.

PROBLEMS

Problems should be presented on $8\frac{1}{2}'' \times 11''$ paper (Size A), grid or plain, using the format introduced in Article 3–15. All notes, sketches, drawings, and graphical work should be neatly prepared in keeping with the good practices described in this book. Written matter should be legibly lettered with the aid of $\frac{1}{8}''$ guidelines.

1 Write a short report on the engineering achievement of the man who you feel has exhibited the highest degree of creativity. Justify your selection by outlining the creative aspects of your choice. Your report should not exceed three typewritten pages.

2 Take the following objects and construct a useful item from them: three sheets of $8\frac{1}{2}'' \times 11''$ paper, five paper clips, two rubber bands, three pencils, a piece of string (36" long), and a rubber eraser.

3 Make a list of uses for the following items (any use at all is acceptable): a brick, an old tire, a bucket of water, a sack of cotton, a nail, a vacuum cleaner, a stack of newspapers.

4 List some projects that could be assigned to your drafting class and would be an interesting exercise in design and the application of drafting at the same time.

5 Can you think of products that are not available on the market but are needed? What are these items and what are they needed for? Make a list of them. If you think of more than one, you are more creative than the average person.

6 Do you know people that you consider creative? If you do, write several paragraphs to identify the characteristics of these people as best you can. Give reasons to explain why you consider them creative.

7 Test your creativity in recognizing needs for new designs. List as many improvements for the typical automobile as possible. Make suggestions for implementing these improvements. Follow the same procedure in another area of your choice.

8 Make a list of new products that have been introduced within the last five years with which you are familiar.

9 Assume that you are a safety engineer charged with the responsibility of reducing schoolground accidents. By generally applying the design process, outline your plan for accomplishing this assignment.

10 Can you think of a better way to dispose of household garbage than the present method? This is a serious problem that must be solved. Consider this problem and make a list of ideas that could be considered. Identify the problem as clearly as you can.

11 Old tires have become a problem. In some cities as many as 30,000 old tires are discarded each day. If they are burned the air is polluted; on the other hand, they do not rot. List several methods of solving this problem.

12 Try to describe an object and its features to a classmate without giving its name or use. Have him draw a sketch of the object from your verbal description. Objects that can be used include an eraser, a compass, a tape dispenser, an ink bottle, a thumbtack, and a T-square.

13 Athletic fields are used for football games and track meets. This means that they are used only eight to ten times a year for about three hours each time. Make a list of other uses for a football stadium that would be beneficial to your school.

14 Using your own school as an example, study the need for additional bicycle racks. Determine whether there is a need and the types of features that would be desirable. Consider the complete problem: where the racks should be located, how many, and special features.

15 Can you describe an idea for a teaching device that would assist your teacher in demonstrating a certain method of geometric construction? Make sketches and notes to describe your ideas for the device.

16 Assume that you have been assigned the responsibility for organizing and designing a Go-Kart installation on your campus. This must be a self-supporting enterprise. Write a paragraph on each of the six steps of the design process to explain how the steps could be applied to the problem. For example, what action would you take to identify the problem?

17 You are responsible for designing a motorized wheelbarrow to be marketed for home use. Write a paragraph on each of the six steps of the design process to explain how the steps could be applied to the problem. For example, what action would you take to identify the problem?

18 List several items that you consider to be well designed. Explain your reasons and point out the better features.

19 Assume that you are marooned on a desert island with no tools, supplies, or anything. Identify major problems that you would be required to solve. List factors that would identify the problems in detail. *Example:* Need for food. Determine (a) available sources of food on island, (b) method of storing food supply, (c) method of cooking, (d) method of hunting and trapping or otherwise obtaining food, etc. Although you are not in a position to gather data or supply answers to these questions, list factors of this type that would need to be answered before a solution could be attempted.

20 Can you design a device for holding a fishing pole in a fishing position while you are fishing in a rowboat? This could be a simple device that will allow you freedom while performing other chores in the boat. Make notes and sketches to describe your design.

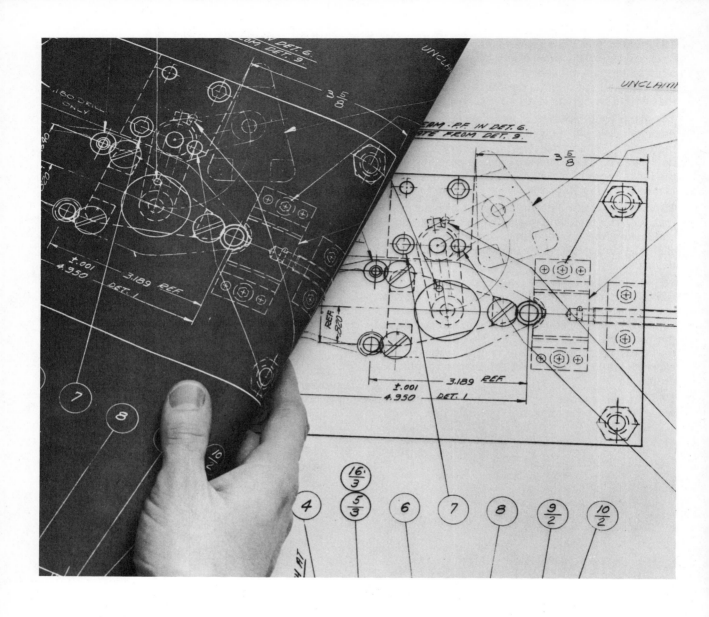

7
ORTHOGRAPHIC
PROJECTION

Fig. 7–1 Charles A. Lindbergh's plane, *Spirit of St. Louis*, is an example of an important contribution to aviation that was built from engineering drawings. This was the plane used for the first successful flight across the Atlantic in 1927. (Courtesy of Ryan Aeronautical Co.)

Fig. 7–2 A pictorial cutaway drawing illustrates the structural framework and the location of the gasoline tanks of the *Spirit of St. Louis*. (Courtesy of Ryan Aeronautical Co.)

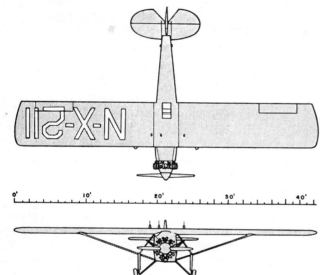

Fig. 7–3 The *Spirit of St. Louis*. is shown in three orthographic views. When these views are studied at the same time, the plane's shape can be understood. (Courtesy of Ryan Aeronautical Co.)

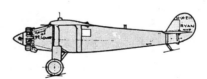

7–1 INTRODUCTION

The previous chapters were concerned with the development of skills, knowledge of drawing, and the use of instruments. These skills must be employed in the performance of any form of drafting or design assignment. This chapter deals with the methods that are commonly used to describe three-dimensional objects by a series of views.

The design of any object begins with a drawing. The final design is presented as a completed working drawing from which the design is fabricated. An example of a significant design is the *Spirit of St. Louis* which was built to attempt the first crossing of the Atlantic Ocean in 1927 (Fig. 7–1). This was the most famous airplane since the Wright brothers' first model. The *Spirit of St. Louis* was flown by Charles A. Lindbergh, who left New York on May 20, 1927, and arrived at Paris, France $33\frac{1}{2}$ hours later. This was the beginning of wide-scale aviation.

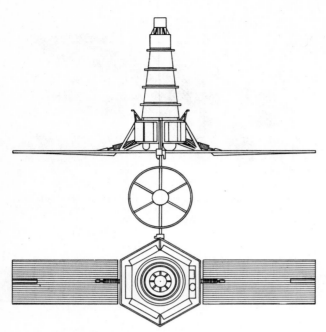

Fig. 7–4 A modern counterpart to the *Spirit of St. Louis* is the Ranger Spacecraft, which made one of the first voyages to the moon. Its shape is described by two orthographic views. (Courtesy of Jet Propulsion Laboratory, California Institute of Technology.)

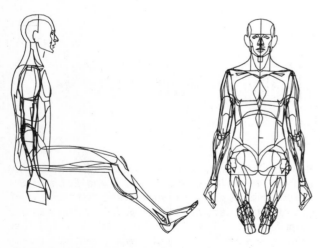

Fig. 7–5 Orthographic projection can be used to depict a man by the same principles that were used in illustrating technological products. The side and front views of this man were drawn by a computer. (Courtesy of the Boeing Company.)

This airplane has some unusual features. A pictorial of its construction is shown in Fig. 7–2. Note that the front portion of the plane was designed to contain the fuel for this 3610-mile flight. The tanks were positioned under the wings and over the landing gear to make the plane more stable. Because of their size, the tanks completely filled the front of the plane, making it impossible for Lindbergh to have a front window.

The top, front, and right side views of the *Spirit of St. Louis* are shown in Fig. 7–3. Note that when you look at these views, you can visualize how the plane will look in three dimensions. A single view by itself does not provide enough information for you to understand the shape of the plane. Also, the views are placed in a logical sequence so that it is easy to relate one view to another. This method of drawing a series of views of an object is called *orthographic projection* or *multi-view projection*. This method is used to construct all working drawings used in industry.

In contrast to the *Spirit of St. Louis* is the Ranger Spacecraft that was designed to travel to the moon during the early stages of moon exploration. The two views of the Ranger shown in Fig. 7–4 enable you to understand the shape of the craft. A man can also be drawn in orthographic projection (Fig. 7–5). By referring to the front view and the left side view you can easily understand the position of the man. This drawing was made by a computer at the Boeing Company.

This chapter will present the various techniques used to describe the shape of objects by orthographic projection. Although most examples given in textbooks of this type use small machine parts as examples, you should be aware that orthographic projection is used to represent all projects from large bridges to the small parts in your wristwatch. A thorough understanding of orthographic projection is necessary to solve advanced problems of graphics and descriptive geometry.

7–2 ORTHOGRAPHIC PROJECTION

The construction of orthographic views is the method by which the draftsman prepares multi-view drawings to represent an object. Views of the object are projected perpendicularly onto projection planes with parallel projectors. This basic definition of orthographic projection is illustrated in Fig. 7–6.

An orthographic view of an object is a view that shows how it looks from only one direction. The Model T Ford in Fig. 7–7, introduced in 1908, is an approximate orthographic view. Except in the drawing of the wheels and the folded top, there is no indication of the third dimension, which is perpendicular to the plane of the paper. Only two dimensions are seen in a single orthographic view, in this case, the dimension from the front of the car to the back and the height of the car. The third dimension, the dimension from one front wheel to the other front wheel, could be seen in the top view or the front view if these views were shown. Thus, an object that does not lie in a single plane is a three-dimensional object. Though you may think of your triangles and templates as two-dimensional objects, they are actually three-dimensional since they have a thickness.

Another important aspect of orthographic projection is the placement of the views in relation to one another. It is important that the views be arranged so that the reader of the drawing can understand and interpret the views with the least amount of difficulty. The following sections will discuss the arrangement for six-view drawings and drawings requiring fewer than six views.

7–3 THE SIX-VIEW DRAWING

In orthographic projection there are six principal views that can be drawn of any object. The planes on which these views are projected are perpendicular to each other where they are joined together. The set of planes can be thought of as a glass box which surrounds the object being drawn (Fig. 7–8).

Each view is projected onto the projection plane with parallel projectors that are perpendicular to the projection plane. This procedure constitutes the definition of orthographic projection. You can see that it is best if the object is positioned with its sides parallel to the projection planes. This will make it possible for the sides that are parallel to the projection planes to be seen in their true shape in the orthographic views.

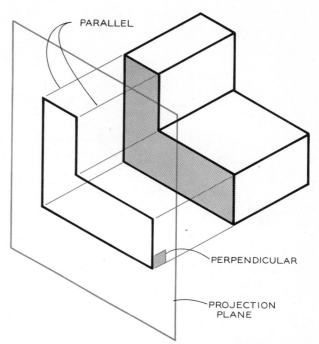

Fig. 7–6 Orthographic projection is defined as the projection of a view onto a projection plane with parallel projectors. The projectors are perpendicular to the projection plane.

Fig. 7–7 This view of a 1909 Ford Model T approximates an orthographic view. This view is almost the same as the view of the car that would appear on a working drawing. (Courtesy of Ford Motor Company.)

The six views resulting from orthographic projection are called: front view, top view, bottom view, rear view, left side view, and right side view. These names simply describe the views of the object

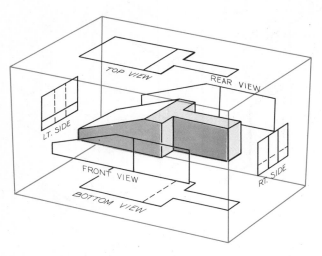

Fig. 7–8 Six principal views of an object can be drawn in orthographic projection. You can assume that the object is in a glass box with the views projected onto the six planes of projection.

rather than the object itself. Many objects do not have a view that is obviously a front view. When this is the case, the most descriptive view—the one that shows the shape of the object best—is usually selected to be the front view.

The glass box in which the object is contained can be thought of as being opened up (Fig. 7–9) into one plane. This plane is the plane of your drawing paper. When this is done, the six views are located in a logical, easy-to-understand arrangement. The top view is over the front view, the bottom view under the front view, the right side view to the right of the front view, and the left side view to the left of the front view (Fig. 7–10). The only remaining view is the rear view, which is drawn to the left of the left side view. Each of these views could be seen in succession if you moved about the object to the six positions; orthographic projection simply provides a composite of the six views in a conventional arrangement. Analysis of the composite views makes it possible to understand the shape of the object.

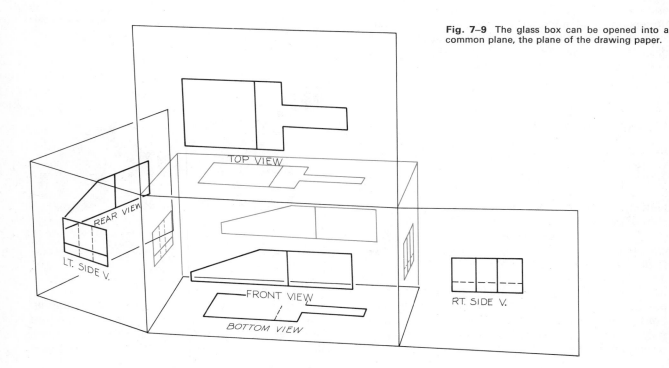

Fig. 7–9 The glass box can be opened into a common plane, the plane of the drawing paper.

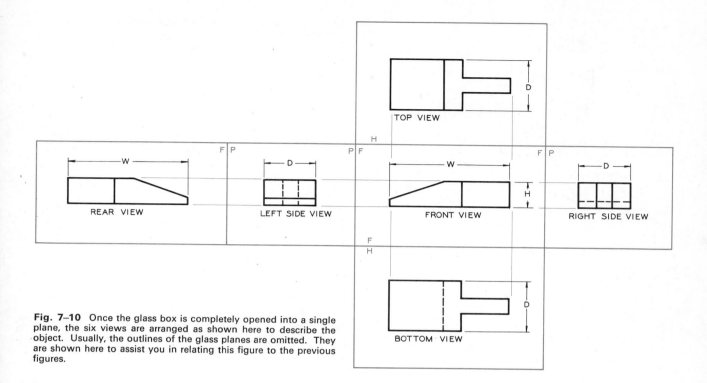

Fig. 7–10 Once the glass box is completely opened into a single plane, the six views are arranged as shown here to describe the object. Usually, the outlines of the glass planes are omitted. They are shown here to assist you in relating this figure to the previous figures.

The outlines of the planes of the glass box are shown in Fig. 7–10 to help you relate the projection planes to the glass box. However, in actual practice, the outlines of the planes are omitted since it is understood that orthographic projection principles are used.

Aside from providing a standard arrangement that is universally understood, orthographic projection provides an easy method of laying out the views with the minimum of construction. The top, front, and bottom views each have the same width, which need be measured only once and can be projected to the other views since they are aligned directly over each other. The rear, left side, front, and right side views have the same height, which can be measured once and projected to the other views. Now only the depth dimensions and the width of the rear view have to be measured separately. The dimensions height, width, and depth are indicated by the letters *H*, *W*, and *D* in Fig. 7–10.

The six views of another object are shown pictorially in Fig. 7–11. Note that the planes of projection are labeled *F*, *H*, and *P*. These letters represent the three principal planes of projection: *frontal*, *horizontal*, and *profile*. Since the planes on which the front and rear views are projected are parallel, both are given the same name, *frontal* planes. The planes on which the top and bottom views are projected are parallel and are called *horizontal* planes. The side views are projected onto parallel planes called *profile* planes. You can see that these planes are labeled in Fig. 7–10 also by the letters *F*, *H*, and *P* at the hinge lines between the planes of the glass box.

The six views of the object in Fig. 7–11 are shown in Fig. 7–12. The three dimensions present in a three-dimensional object—*height, width,* and *depth*—are shown on each view. These dimensions are mutually perpendicular. The dimensions are normally represented by numerals indicating specific measurements, but at this stage it is well to become

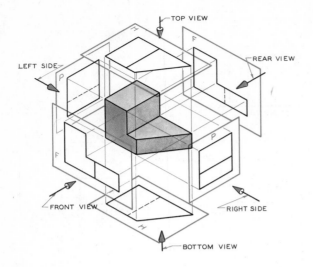

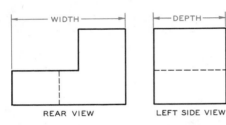

TOP VIEW

REAR VIEW

LEFT SIDE

FRONT VIEW

RIGHT SIDE

BOTTOM VIEW

Fig. 7–11 The six positions for viewing the principal views of an object are shown here.

TOP VIEW

DEPTH

WIDTH

WIDTH

DEPTH

HEIGHT

REAR VIEW

LEFT SIDE VIEW

FRONT VIEW

RIGHT SIDE VIEW

DEPTH

BOTTOM VIEW

Fig. 7–12 The standard arrangement for the six principal views of orthographic projection. Compare these views with the pictorial representation in Fig. 7–11.

familiar with their general definition. A six-view drawing of the type shown in Fig. 7–12 is dimensioned with two rows of dimension lines arranged to give the most simple and readable arrangement. Extension lines are drawn from only one view, even though some dimensions are common to a number of views (such as height, which is common to four views). Since it is understood that these views have common dimensions, the dimensions need not be repeated on each view.

Note that some lines in Figs. 7–10 and 7–12 are drawn as dashed lines. These are called *hidden lines*; they represent lines or planes that are invisible in a specific view. Showing the lines as hidden lines clarifies details that might otherwise be overlooked. The technique of drawing these lines will be discussed in Article 7–4.

Seldom is it necessary to use six views to describe an object. Three or four views are usually adequate. The most fundamental requirement of orthographic projection is the placement and arrangement of the views. The top view must be placed above the front view, for example. Drawing a correct top view, but placing it where the right side view

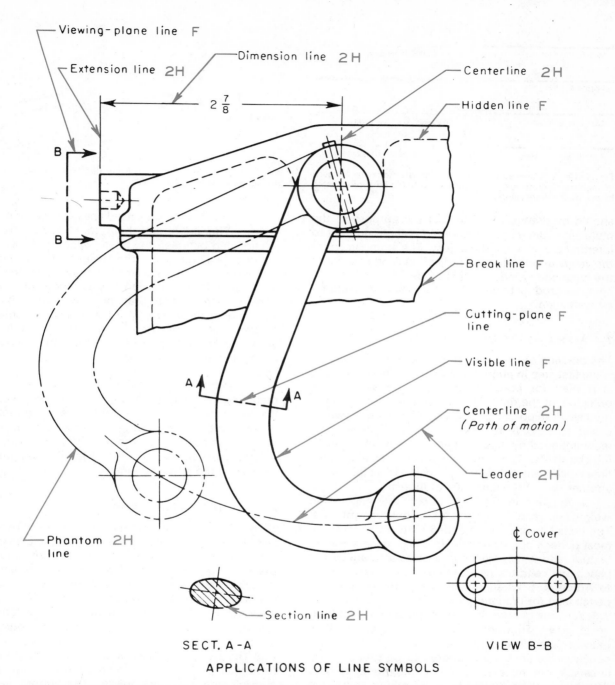

Viewing-plane line F

Dimension line 2H

Extension line 2H

Centerline 2H

Hidden line F

$2\frac{7}{8}$

B

B

Break line F

Cutting-plane F
line

Visible line F

A

A

Centerline 2H
(Path of motion)

Leader 2H

Phantom 2H
line

₵ Cover

Section line 2H

SECT. A-A

VIEW B-B

APPLICATIONS OF LINE SYMBOLS

Fig. 7–13 The alphabet of lines showing the types of lines recommended for engineering drawings and the pencil grades that should be used. (Courtesy of ANSI; Y14.2-1957.)

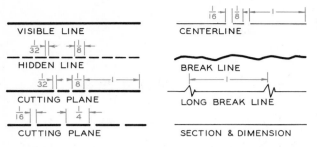

VISIBLE LINE

$\frac{1}{32}$ |← →| $\frac{1}{8}$

HIDDEN LINE

$\frac{1}{32}$ |← →| $\frac{1}{8}$

CUTTING PLANE

$\frac{1}{16}$ |← →| $\frac{1}{4}$

CUTTING PLANE

$\frac{1}{16}$ →| |← →| $\frac{1}{8}$ |← |→ 1 →|

CENTERLINE

BREAK LINE

LONG BREAK LINE

SECTION & DIMENSION

Fig. 7–14 A comparison of the line weights for lines that are used in engineering drawings. The dimensions should be approximated by eye by the draftsman.

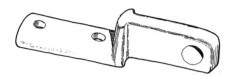

Fig. 7–15 This is a sketch of a part that is illustrated with four orthographic views in Fig. 7–16.

should be drawn, would defeat the purpose of the multi-view drawing. This would make it difficult to interpret the shape of the object. The arrangement of the views in orthographic projection is one aspect of the language of industry that makes it possible for a complex product to be understood and manufactured by craftsmen.

7–4 ALPHABET OF LINES

The drawing of the views of orthographic projection is the first step in preparing a working drawing which is a plan for construction. Remember that the objective of the drawing is communication with the greatest ease possible. One way of making drawings easier to read is to use the proper line weights recommended by industrial and governmental drafting standards. These recommended lines are sometimes called the "alphabet of lines"; this alphabet is another part of the language of industry.

A drawing in Fig. 7–13 shows the relative line weights that should be used for various types of lines. The pencil leads recommended here are suitable for most general applications. However, papers vary in texture, and it may become necessary to adjust the pencil grades to the type of paper being used. Refer to Article 4–5 when selecting the proper grade of pencil lead for preparing a working drawing.

All lines of a working drawing should be black, never gray. Thin lines should be just as black as heavier lines such as visible lines. Only light construction lines are permitted to be gray. These lines are not necessary to the interpretation of a drawing, but are merely light guidelines that were not erased.

The most commonly used lines are shown in Fig. 7–14. The important thing to remember is the relationship between the lines. When a drawing is made at a large scale, the weight of the lines is usually heavier than in a small drawing. The length of the segments of a hidden line is longer in a large drawing than in a small drawing. The dimensions and line weights given in Fig. 7–14 are only representative of the *average* drawing. The lines used in ink drawings are usually a little heavier than those in pencil drawings, but this difference is hardly noticeable.

You should refer to Figs. 7–13 and 7–14 when preparing instrument drawings or sketches, because the use of the proper line weights is very important to the preparation of a drawing. These lines will be used in the examples of orthographic projection that follow. Note the relationship of the line weights as the size of the drawing varies.

7–5 THE FOUR-VIEW DRAWING

Some objects may require more than three views, but seldom does an object require six views to explain its shape. Regardless of the number of views required, the same general rules of orthographic projection apply. Views are selected that will give the most characteristic features of the object. The object shown in Fig. 7–15 is an example of an object that is conveniently represented by four orthographic views.

The most characteristic view is selected as the front view (Fig. 7–16). The top view and the right and left side views are drawn. The bottom view is omitted since it will not add any clarifying details to

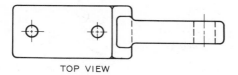

TOP VIEW

Fig. 7–16 Most parts can be illustrated using fewer than six principal views. This object is shown with four views.

L. SIDE VIEW   FRONT VIEW   R. SIDE VIEW

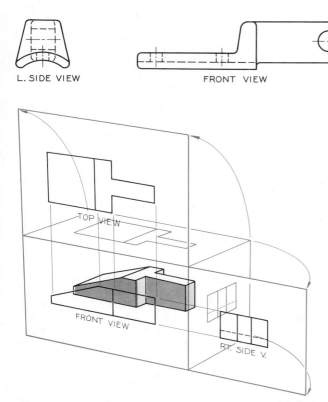

Fig. 7–17 Three-view drawings are commonly used for describing machine parts and designs. The glass box is used to illustrate how the views are projected to their projection planes.

TOP VIEW

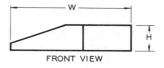

FRONT VIEW   RIGHT SIDE VIEW

Fig. 7–18 The three orthographic views of the part in Fig. 7–17 are shown.

the drawing. The rear view is the same as the front view and is therefore omitted.

Orthographic views should be selected to have the fewest possible number of hidden lines. A view composed mostly of visible lines is easier to interpret and to understand than one containing many hidden lines.

The draftsman should eliminate as much unnecessary work as possible. If fewer views are adequate to explain the shape of an object, the unnecessary views should be omitted.

7–6 THE THREE-VIEW DRAWING

The most commonly used orthographic arrangement is the three-view drawing composed of the front, top, and right side views. The reason is that three views are usually adequate to explain the shape of an object; in addition, the top, front, and right side views are so positioned that it is easy for the draftsman to lay them out.

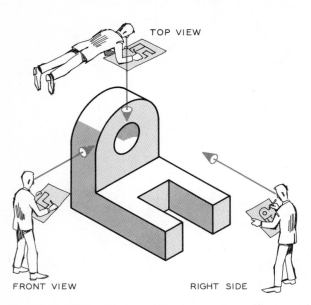

Fig. 7–19 When preparing a three-view drawing, you can assume that you move about the object and draw the views that are visible to you.

TOP VIEW

FRONT VIEW   RIGHT SIDE

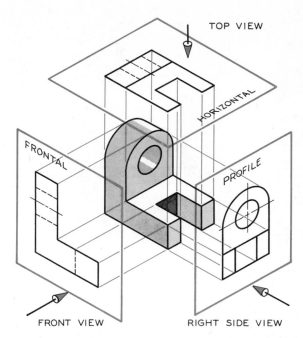

Fig. 7–20 The orthographic projection of three views onto the principal planes—horizontal, frontal, and profile.

TOP VIEW

HORIZONTAL

FRONTAL   PROFILE

FRONT VIEW   RIGHT SIDE VIEW

The same glass box theory is applied to three views as to six views (Fig. 7–17). The two nonfrontal planes are opened into the frontal plane, which represents the drawing surface on the drafting table. The resulting three views can then be drawn as shown in Fig. 7–18. The outlines of the projection planes are omitted in actual practice.

Another way of thinking of the three-view orthographic projection is illustrated in Fig. 7–19. Instead of opening a glass box that contains the object, you can assume that you yourself are moving about the object to the three positions shown. In each position you draw the object as you actually see it. When you place yourself in front of the object, you see the front view. At the right, you see the right side view. When looking down on the object, you see its top view.

The three views that you would see are projected onto the three principal planes—horizontal, frontal,

and profile (Fig. 7–20). When drawn as orthographic views, they are shown as in Fig. 7–21. Note that the most representative views with the fewest hidden lines have been selected. The left side view would have had more hidden lines than the right side view. If the views had been selected as shown in Fig. 7–22, the resulting right side view would have had hidden lines because of a poor choice of views.

It is not necessary for the three views always to be the top, front, and right side views. It is only necessary that the three views selected be in the proper sequence so that they are adjacent to each other. For example, the rear, bottom, and top views are not adjacent and cannot be easily related. It is easy to select any view of the object as the front view that is descriptive of its shape so that the other two adjacent views will be descriptive and have the fewest possible hidden lines. The following are combinations of orthographic views often used: top,

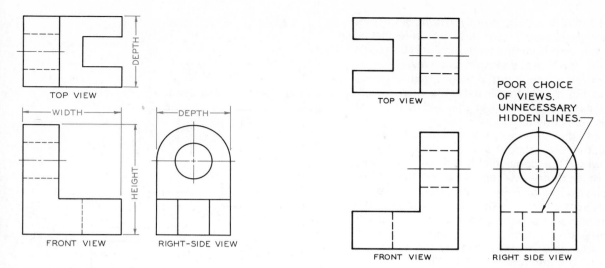

Fig. 7–21 The standard arrangement for a three-view orthographic drawing.

Fig. 7–22 When three views of an object are drawn, you should select the three best views with the fewest hidden lines. The selection of views here is not as good as the selection in Fig. 7–21.

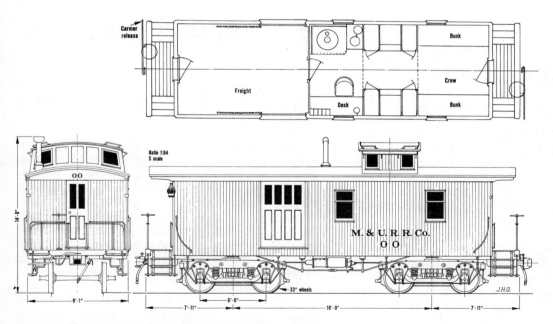

Fig. 7–23 The three-dimensional shape of this Middletown and Unionville caboose can be easily understood by referring to this three-view drawing. (Courtesy of *Model Railroader Magazine*.)

front, and left side views; front, bottom, and right side views; or bottom, front, and left side views. However, the most common arrangement is that used in Fig. 7–21: top, front, and right side views.

A three-view drawing of a freight train caboose is shown in Fig. 7–23. In this case, the view usually thought of as the side view was selected as the front view. This was done to conserve space. If the front, or end, of the caboose were selected as the front view, the total amount of space required by the drawing would be considerably greater. Another example of a three-view arrangement that saves space is shown in Fig. 7–24. When the side view is projected directly from the top view, as shown, the drawing requires less width and makes better use of the available space. Whichever location is chosen, the right side view is drawn exactly the same; the only difference is the arrangement. The three-view drawing of a P-51 Mustang (Fig. 7–25) requires less space when the side view is projected from the top view rather than from the front view.

7–7 BASIC TYPES OF LINES

The previous paragraphs were concerned with defining orthographic projection and the principles of depicting three-dimensional objects. In these examples three basic types of lines were used— visible lines, hidden lines, and centerlines.

Visible lines are often called object lines, since they are lines on the object that would be visible if you were to look at the actual object. When two planes intersect, a line of intersection is formed that must be shown as a visible line. The outline of a drawing is always a visible line. Figure 7–13 illustrates visible lines.

Hidden lines are object lines also, but they are invisible when viewed from some directions. To clarify the drawing, these hidden lines are drawn to ensure that the reader of the drawing does not overlook a feature simply because it is not visible in the particular view he is looking at. Examples of hidden lines can be seen in Fig. 7–26, where they are used to depict holes that would not be seen otherwise. The

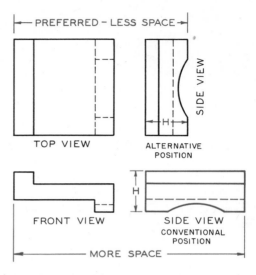

Fig. 7–24 The side view can be projected from the top view as shown in the alternative position. This conserves space. (Courtesy of ANSI; Y14.3-1957.)

weight of hidden lines is almost half the weight of visible lines (Fig. 7–13).

Centerlines are lines that are used to call attention to circular shapes and especially to circular holes. You will note in Fig. 7–26 that centerlines are very thin lines drawn with long dashes and short dashes. In the circular view, the centerlines are crossing perpendicular lines, with the short dashes crossing at the exact center of the circle or arc. The crossing of the short dashes locates the center for drilling a hole or drawing the circular feature. Centerlines should extend about $\frac{1}{8}$" beyond the arc to which they apply in the circular view.

The rectangular view of the circular hole or feature cannot be interpreted as being cylindrical without a centerline. Consequently, centerlines are very helpful in clarifying a drawing. Centerlines are

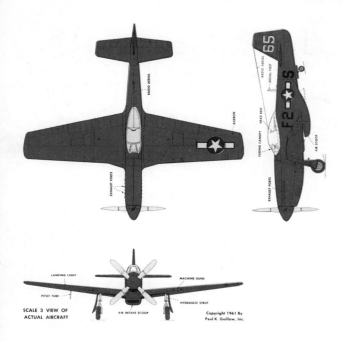

Fig. 7–25 Space was saved by projecting the right side view of this P-51 Mustang from the top view rather than from the front view. (Courtesy of Paul K. Guillow, Inc.)

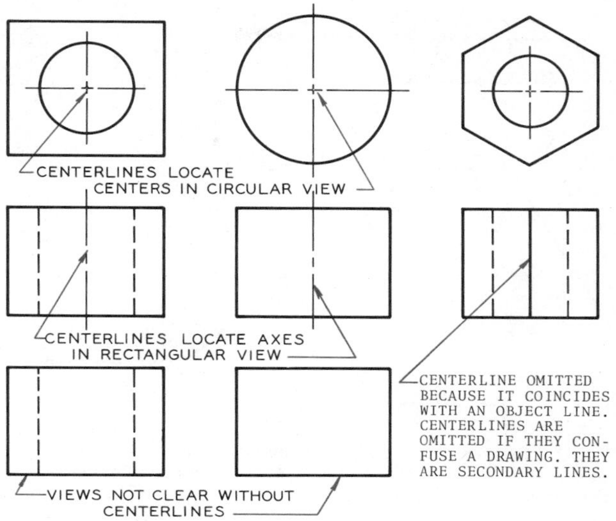

CENTERLINES LOCATE CENTERS IN CIRCULAR VIEW

CENTERLINES LOCATE AXES IN RECTANGULAR VIEW

CENTERLINE OMITTED BECAUSE IT COINCIDES WITH AN OBJECT LINE. CENTERLINES ARE OMITTED IF THEY CONFUSE A DRAWING. THEY ARE SECONDARY LINES.

VIEWS NOT CLEAR WITHOUT CENTERLINES

Fig. 7–26 Centerlines are used to define cylindrical shapes, both external cylinders and interior holes.

secondary lines; that is, they are not absolutely necessary to a drawing. Therefore, they should be omitted if they confuse the drawing in any way. Note that the centerline in the front view of the hexagon (Fig. 7–26) was omitted since it coincided with an object line. An object line always takes precedence over a secondary line such as a centerline. Use centerlines wherever possible, but do not allow them to confuse a drawing.

7–8 INTERSECTING LINES

Orthographic views are frequently composed of many intersections of hidden and visible lines, as illustrated in Fig. 7–27. It is customary to follow standardized procedures in joining these lines to give the best effect. Enlarged examples of intersections

are shown in the figure. These conventions for showing intersections, which are based on considerations of appearance and function, have become standard and should be used wherever possible. A close study of these intersections will enable you to recognize the logic behind these rules.

7–9 VIEWS OF A PLANE

In orthographic projection, a plane can be seen in one of three ways. It can appear as an edge, as a true-size plane, or as a foreshortened view. These three ways of viewing a plane are illustrated in Fig. 7–28.

You will note examples of these three ways of seeing a plane in Fig. 7–29, where three views of the object are drawn. A plane will appear true size when your line of sight is perpendicular to the plane—in the top view in this case. When a plane of an object is

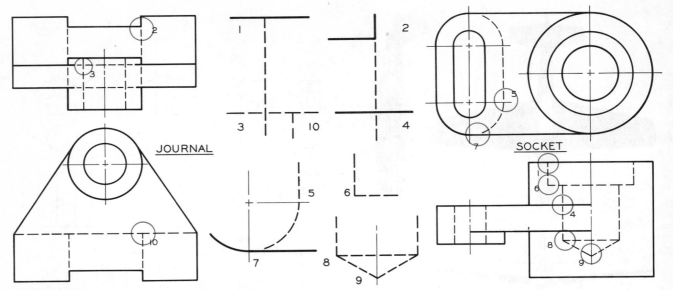

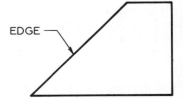

Fig. 7–27 Examples of recommended intersections between hidden and visible lines. These standard intersections should be used to improve the clarity of a drawing.

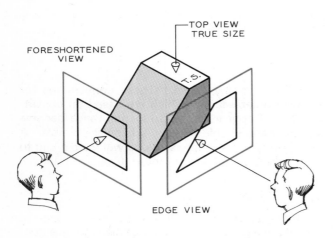

Fig. 7–28 In orthographic projection a plane may project as a true-size plane, as an edge, or as a foreshortened plane.

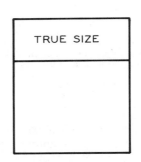

Fig. 7–29 A plane is shown in three views: as an edge, foreshortened, and true size.

TRUE SIZE

FORESHORTENED

EDGE

positioned to be perpendicular to a projection plane, the plane will appear as an edge on that projection plane, the side view in this case. When the plane is not parallel or perpendicular to the projection plane, the result will be a foreshortened view.

These terms are used to describe a plane verbally when a three-dimensional object is being discussed. You should become familiar with these terms, since they will be used to describe planes throughout this book.

FIGURE 7–30. TRANSFERRING DEPTH DIMENSIONS

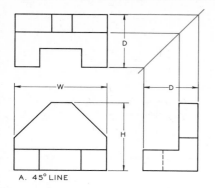

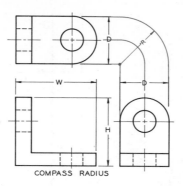

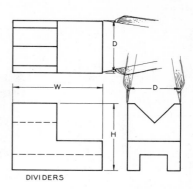

A. 45° LINE

COMPASS RADIUS

DIVIDERS

A. The depth dimension can be projected from the top view to the right side view by constructing a 45° line positioned as shown.

B. The depth dimension can be projected from the top view to the side view using a compass and a common center.

C. The depth dimension can be transferred from the top view to the side view using dividers or a scale.

7–10 PROJECTION OF DEPTH DIMENSION

You have noticed by now that certain dimensions in a multi-view drawing are common to more than one view. Height is common to the front and right side views, and depth is common to the top and right side views. Height can be projected directly from the front view to the right side view; in the case of depth, however, a straight projection is not possible.

Three common methods of projecting depth from the top view to the right side view are shown in Fig. 7–30. In A, a 45° line is used to permit the depth dimensions to be projected horizontally to the 45° line and then downward to the right side view. The second method (B) is a radial method; a compass is used to transfer the depth dimension to the side view. The third method (C) is direct transfer of the depth dimension by means of dividers or other measuring devices from view to view. This method is used most by the professional draftsman. Each of these methods can be used to good advantage in certain situations.

7–11 LAYOUT OF A THREE-VIEW DRAWING

The draftsman must have either a freehand sketch of an object that he is to draw in orthographic projection or a mental picture of what the object is to look like. The designer develops mental pictures more often than the draftsman, since the designer actually

designs the part to fit the needs of a situation. The draftsman, on the other hand, is more concerned with assisting the designer by representing his ideas in the form of finished drawings; in doing this, the draftsman works from the designer's rough sketches.

Once the draftsman understands the object that he is to draw, he begins by blocking in the overall dimensions of each of the three views (Step 1 in Fig. 7–31). This will ensure that the views are properly located on the sheet and that adequate room is available. In Step 2 a notch is removed from the front view, and lines in the top and side views are drawn to indicate this removal.

The triangular notch and the two notches at the bottom of the side view are removed and are projected to the top and front views (Step 3). These lines are strengthened to complete the drawing. The dimensions of W, D, and H are positioned as shown to represent the overall dimensions.

The dimension and extension lines used in the drawing are very thin lines of the same weight as the centerline. Arrows are drawn at each end of the dimension lines to call attention to the dimensions being indicated.

Another example of the completion of a three-view drawing is shown in Fig. 7–32. The primary shapes of the views are given, but lines are missing from each view. In Step 1, the planes shown in the

FIGURE 7–31. CONSTRUCTION OF A THREE-VIEW DRAWING

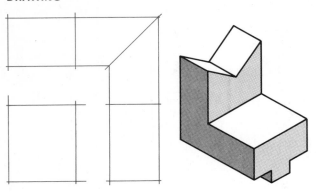

Step 1. To draw three views of the object, begin by "blocking in" the overall dimensions of each view.

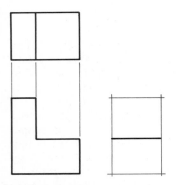

Step 2. Remove the major portions of the object and project to the other view.

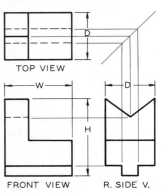

TOP VIEW

W

D

H

FRONT VIEW   R. SIDE V.

Step 3. Remove the portions in the right side view and project to the top and front views. Show hidden lines and add dimensions W, D, and H.

FIGURE 7–32. COMPLETING MISSING LINES

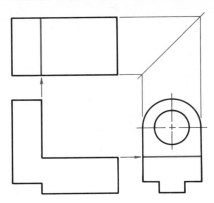

Step 1. Partially completed views must be completed by analyzing each view and projecting to the other views.

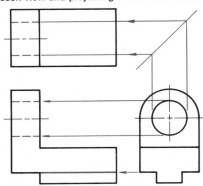

Step 2. The hole is projected to the top and front views and centerlines are shown. The lower plane in the side view will appear as an edge in the front view.

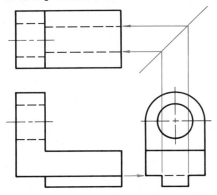

Step 3. The remaining hidden lines are shown in the top and side views to complete the views of the drawing.

front view are projected to the top and side views, where the planes appear as edges. In Step 2, the circular hole is shown in the front and top views with hidden lines and centerlines. Also, the edge view of the plane is projected to the front view from the side view as a visible line. In Step 3, the two vertical planes shown in the side view are projected to the top view, where they appear as edges that are hidden. The addition of these lines completes the drawing.

7–12 NUMBERING POINTS

It should be understood that the interpretation of a drawing often requires a great deal of analysis. Do not think that you are supposed to look at several views of an object and have an image of the object suddenly appear in your mind. The term *visualize* implies that you have the ability to analyze the views of a drawing in a systematic manner and then to interpret the shape of the object. Some drawings require much more analysis than others before they can be understood or visualized.

One method of analysis that will assist you in understanding the views of a drawing or in drawing an object is *point numbering*. This is a process whereby the points of intersection of lines in a drawing are numbered using the same numbers in each view. This enables you to analyze one line at a time by reading the numbers.

A simple prism (Fig. 7–33) illustrates a method of numbering points on a drawing. Note in the top view that points 1, 2, 3, and 4 are numbered on the outside of the view. This is done because these points are on top of the prism and are therefore visible. The points on the bottom of the prism— 5, 6, 7, and 8—are lettered in the inside of the top view since they would not be visible in the top view. The same method of numbering points is applied to all the views in this example. This procedure is not a rigid rule, but is simply another attempt to provide a systematic method of reading and preparing drawings that will make it easier to interpret them.

Seldom is it necessary to letter all the points in a drawing. It is recommended that numbering or lettering of points be used only when this method is helpful to you in the preparation or reading of a drawing. Numbers will assist in the analysis of the views of a drawing.

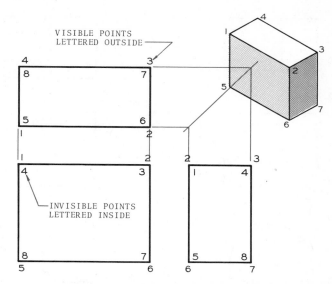

Fig. 7–33 A numbering system is helpful in analyzing the views of a complicated drawing. General rules are shown here on a simple prism.

7–13 MISSING-LINE PROBLEMS

Missing-line drawings, as illustrated in Fig. 7-34, are helpful to the student in understanding orthographic projection. Certain features were given in these drawings, but the views were not complete. In Fig. 7–34 the missing lines have been added in color and the key points have been numbered.

These examples should be reviewed, since they will be helpful to you in solving missing-line problems that will be assigned from your problem book or from the end of the chapter. These exercises will improve your ability to analyze the views of a drawing.

7–14 CURVE PLOTTING

Not all drawings are composed of straight lines and planes. Often it is necessary to plot an irregular curve on a view of a drawing.

An example of curve plotting is shown in Fig. 7–35. The front and side views are complete, but the top view is incomplete. In Step 1, a series of points is projected from the front view to the side view and the points are numbered. In Step 2, points 1, 2, and 3 are

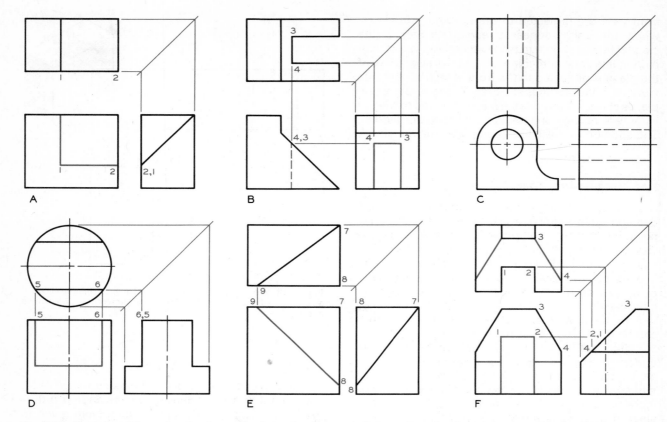

Fig. 7–34 Examples of three-view drawings with missing lines in one or all views. Note that the points are numbered to help in analyzing and completing the three views.

FIGURE 7–35. PLOTTING CURVED LINES

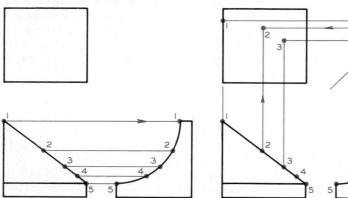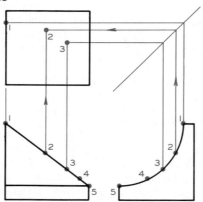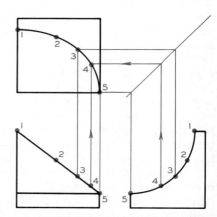

Step 1. To plot curved lines in orthographic projection, begin by locating and numbering points in two views.

Step 2. The two views of each point are projected to the third view, where the projectors intersect to locate the points.

Step 3. All points are projected in this manner. The points are connected with the aid of an irregular curve.

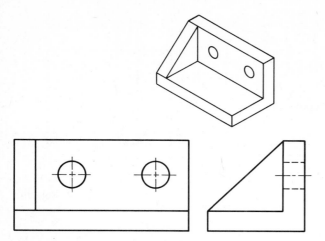

Fig.7–36 An example of a part requiring only two views to describe it completely.

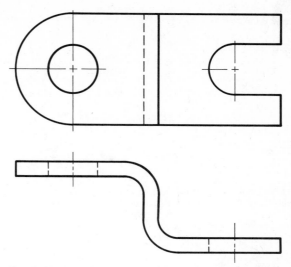

Fig. 7–37 A part requiring only two views to give its description.

projected from the front and side views to locate corresponding points in the top view. In Step 3, points 3, 4, and 5 are projected to the top view. The five points are then connected with the aid of an irregular curve to complete the drawing.

A greater degree of accuracy could have been achieved if the points had been placed closer together. It can be seen in this case that the numbering of points is very helpful to the draftsman. The points should be projected one at a time; if all points were projected to the top view in one operation, the projectors would become confusing. Each point should be projected from the front and side views to the top view and numbered before the next point is considered.

7–15 TWO-VIEW DRAWINGS

Whereas some objects require three views to adequately describe their shape, other objects require only two views. The part shown in Fig. 7–36 is an example of an object which requires only two views. The top view would add nothing to the understanding of the object that was not already given in the two views shown here.

A similar example is shown in Fig. 7–37. A side view is unnecessary since the two views given are completely descriptive. Cylindrical parts need only two views to completely describe them (Fig. 7–38).

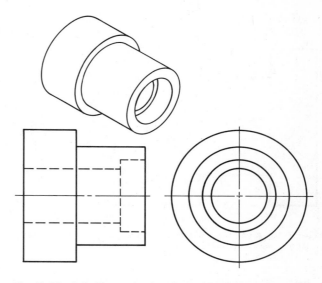

Fig. 7–38 Cylinders can be described with only two orthographic views.

A two-view drawing of a coal loader is shown in Fig. 7–39. These views are drawn only to show the general shape of this piece of equipment. Many hidden lines and other details have been omitted since they are not required for the purposes of this drawing.

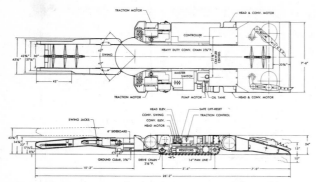

Fig. 7–39 Two views of this coal loader are adequate to give a general idea of its form. (Courtesy of Joy Manufacturing Company.)

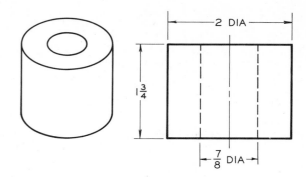

Fig. 7–41 A cylinder can be described with one view. Note that "DIA" is used to emphasize its circular characteristic.

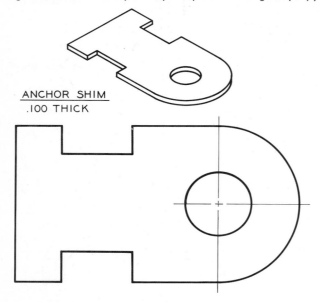

ANCHOR SHIM
.100 THICK

Fig. 7–40 A part made of material of a uniform thickness requires only one view and a note to describe its shape.

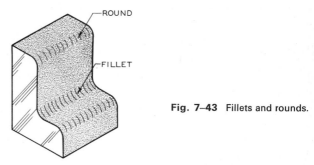

HUFFY RAIL

Fig. 7–42 One view is sufficient to describe most of the details of this bicycle's frame. (Courtesy of Huffy.)

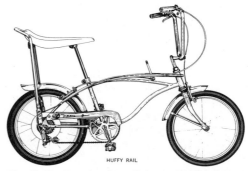

ROUND

FILLET

Fig. 7–43 Fillets and rounds.

7–16 SINGLE-VIEW DRAWINGS

Objects made of sheet metal or other materials of a uniform thickness can be described with only one view and a note to indicate thickness. An example of this type is the anchor shim shown in Fig. 7–40.

Cylinders can also be depicted with one view provided the diameters are labeled "DIA" to call attention to the circular feature that is not shown. An example of a cylinder depicted in this way is shown

in Fig. 7–41. The frame of the bicycle shown in Fig. 7–42 is essentially a structure of uniform thickness. This view is adequate for most of its fabrication.

7–17 CONVENTIONAL INTERSECTIONS

For the sake of improved clarity, it is sometimes necessary to utilize practices that may be violations of the strict rules of orthographic projection. The violation of rules to clarify a drawing is called *conven-*

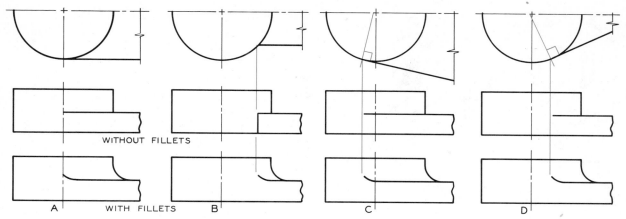

Fig. 7–44 Examples of intersections between parts of objects with and without fillets.

WITHOUT FILLETS

WITH FILLETS

A   B   C   D

FIGURE 7–45. PLOTTING A RUNOUT

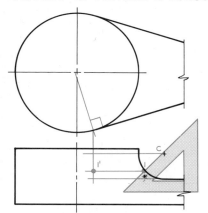 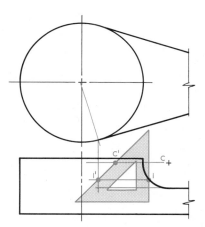 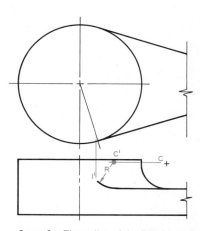

Step 1. The point of tangency between the circular part and the edge is found in the top view and projected to the front view. A 45° triangle is used to find point 1, which is projected to locate point 1'.

Step 2. A 45° triangle is used to locate point **C′**, which is on the horizontal projector from the center of the fillet, C.

Step 3. The radius of the fillet is used to draw the runout with **C′** as the center. The runout arc is equal to one-eighth of a circle.

tional practice. Examples of conventional practice will be discussed in the following paragraphs.

In orthographic views, many of the lines of intersection between planes are obscured because the joints are rounded. The rounded corners, inside and outside, that are usually found on metal parts are illustrated in Fig. 7–43. A *round* is a rounded exterior corner; a *fillet* is a rounded interior corner. Fillets and rounds add strength to a part, are easy to produce,

and make the part attractive.

Four examples of intersections are shown in Fig. 7–44 in which the front views are drawn both with and without fillets. Note that at the intersections between the features without fillets straight lines of intersection are drawn. Where there are fillets, the line of intersection at the point of tangency in each problem ends with a curved line called a *runout*. The runout is drawn as illustrated in Fig. 7–45.

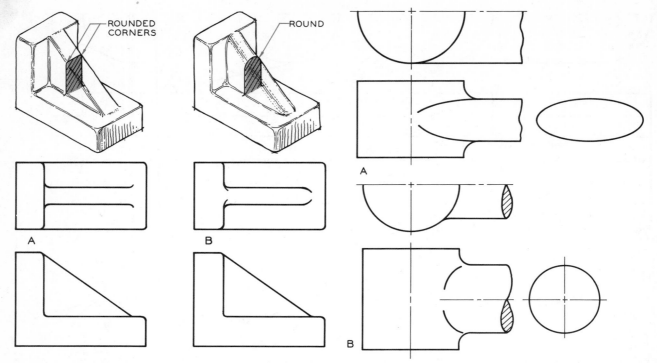

Fig. 7–46 Conventional intersections of ribs with rounded corner (A) and ribs with a completely rounded cross section (B).

Fig. 7–47 Conventional methods of representing intersections of elliptical and cylindrical shapes. These intersections are drawn by approximation.

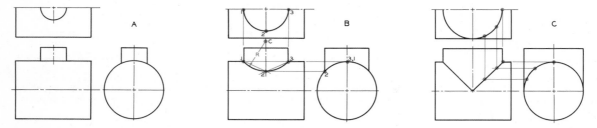

Fig. 7–48 Conventional intersections of cylindrical shapes.

The runout is drawn with the same radius as the fillet. The length of the arc forming the runout is one-eighth of a total circle. A 45° triangle can be used to perform this construction as shown in Fig. 7–45.

The draftsman will find that most of the parts that are made in the foundry by casting have fillets and rounds on most corners. It is helpful if his draw-

ings describe these features that might otherwise be overlooked. The part in Fig. 7–46A is designed to have fillets and rounds on each edge as illustrated in the pictorial sketch. The top and front views show how these fillets and their runouts are drawn. You may approximate these by eye instead of attempting the tedious process of plotting each point. A circle template can be used advantageously for drawing the runouts, thus saving drafting time.

You will note that the object shown in Fig. 7–46B varies somewhat from the example in A. In this case the rib has a rounded cross section, not just rounded corners. The runouts in this example are shown differently so that this feature can be recognized by looking at the top and front views.

Some parts are designed to have cylindrical or elliptical cross sections. Two examples are shown in Fig. 7–47 with fillets at the intersections. In part A, the horizontal member is elliptical in cross section and intersects the vertical cylinder. The line of intersection is approximated as shown with the aid of an irregular curve. In part B, both members are cylindrical. Since the intersection is filleted, there will be no sharp line of intersection. To approximate the intersection, only partial lines are drawn with an irregular curve as shown in the figure.

When cylinders intersect without fillets, the line of intersection will be a visible line, as shown in the examples in Fig. 7–48. When a relatively small cylinder intersects a larger cylinder, the line of intersection is conventionally shown as in part A, with no attempt made to plot the line of intersection. For intersecting cylinders of approximately the same size (part B), the line of intersection is drawn as an arc that passes through points 1, 2, and 3. The center can be found by extending the perpendicular bisectors of chords 1–2 and 2–3 to their point of intersection. The intersection shown in part C is a true projection, since the cylinders have equal diameters and would actually intersect in this manner. Points are plotted to illustrate the method of finding the line of intersection.

Some conventional practices for illustrating the intersections of circular and rectangular holes in cylindrical shapes are shown in Fig. 7–49. Where the hole is narrow or small, as in parts A and C, the intersection is merely shown as a hole in the outer wall of the cylinder. A wider rectangular hole would be conventionally drawn as shown in part B. A medium-sized circular hole intersecting a cylinder would be constructed with circular arcs passing through the three points, as shown in part D. The construction of this example is similar to that of part B of Fig. 7–48.

The intersections discussed here are approximate intersections that are sufficient for most drafting applications; they involve a minimum expendi-

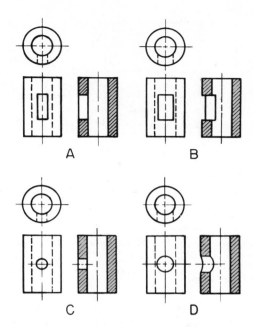

Fig. 7–49 Conventional intersections of holes in cylindrical shapes. The views with the crosshatching represent cross sections through the objects. (See Chapter 11.)

ture of time. Exact intersections for larger parts and objects fabricated from sheet metal will be covered in Chapter 17. Accurate intersections must be plotted point by point.

7–18 CONVENTIONAL PRACTICES

As previously defined, a conventional practice is a method of preparing a drawing that has been found to be effective even though the method may deviate from rules in the strict sense. Many of the conventional practices are described in drafting standards, but some situations will require the draftsman to use his own judgment to prepare the most readable drawing.

An example of conventional practices is shown in Fig. 7–50. In general, when planes intersect with a large curve, the line of intersection between the planes is not visible to the eye and therefore no lines of intersection are shown in the view (part B). In part A, two lines are shown to represent the two vertical planes that appear as edges in the top view. The view in part C has a single line to represent the

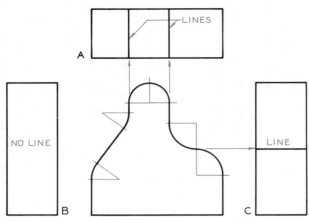

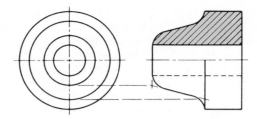

Fig. 7–51 It is a conventional practice to represent the circular view with circles that would not be shown if the strict rules of orthographic projection were followed. These circles make the view more descriptive.

Fig. 7–50 Examples of the use of visible lines to complete a view.

point where the two arcs of the object are tangent. This intersection forms a very thin horizontal plane that must be shown with a line.

A conventional practice for drawing parts with curved intersections is shown in Fig. 7–51. Since there are no sharp intersections at the corners of the object, by strict application of the rules the circular view would have no lines. The circular view would not be very descriptive if this rule were followed; consequently, conventional practices are followed instead. The imaginary corners of the object in the right side view are drawn as if they were not rounded, and these imaginery intersections are projected to the circular view where circles are drawn to represent these intersections. Thin extension lines are drawn on the right side view to locate the imaginary corners.

7–19 PARTIAL VIEWS

Some parts can be more easily understood if the drawing consists of partial views. A partial view is a view in which some of the lines, usually hidden lines, are omitted to add clarity to the drawing.

Figure 7–52 is an example of a part that is represented with a front view and two side views that are partial views. In this case the views are more effective in describing the object than the complete views would be. When an object can be drawn in

such a way as to facilitate the interpretation of the drawing, the draftsman should use whatever technique will make this possible.

7–20 HALF VIEWS

When drawing cylindrical objects, draftsmen usually choose the circular view as one of the views to describe the shape of the object. When the circular view does not have unique features about its circumference, it is permissible to show only half of the circular view (Fig. 7–53).

The full circular view (part A) requires considerably more space than the half view. The half view (part B) is just as descriptive as the full view, but drawing time and space are saved. When a half view is drawn, the rounded portion of the half view should be nearest the other view. In other words, the half of the view farthest away from the adjacent view is the half that is removed. Note that a centerline is used at the dividing diameter rather than a visible line, to emphasize that the view is a half view and not a view that is truly semicircular in shape.

7–21 REVOLVED VIEWS

A part may have an inclined feature that can be drawn more easily and more descriptively if the part is revolved and projected to the adjacent view. An example is given in Fig. 7–54. The inclined arm is revolved into the horizontal position and then is projected to the top view, where it is drawn as if the arm were truly horizontal. This makes it easier to read the top view.

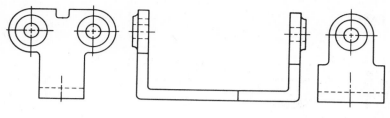

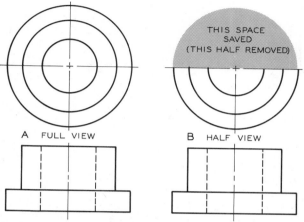

Fig. 7–52 This is a conventional method of describing an object with views that omit certain hidden and visible lines that might be confusing.

A FULL VIEW

THIS SPACE SAVED (THIS HALF REMOVED)

B HALF VIEW

Fig. 7–53 Cylindrical and symmetrical shapes may be shown with half views to conserve space and drafting time. The half that is away from the adjacent view is the half that is omitted.

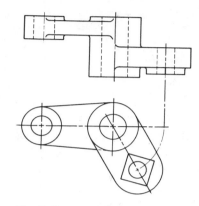

Fig. 7–54 It is conventional practice to draw the top view of a part of this type as if it were revolved in line with the horizontal member. This makes the top view easier to draw and to read.

This conventional practice applies to parts made of thin material with slight curves or bends. The curb facing shown in Fig. 7–55 is not drawn as a true orthographic projection. Instead, the front view represents the true size of the curb facing as if it were not curved at all but a flat plane. Views of this type are helpful to the user of the drawing and are easily drawn by the draftsman.

7–22 LEFT-HAND AND RIGHT-HAND PARTS

Two parts are often required that are very similar to each other, but one part is actually a "mirror image" of the other. Two parts of this type are shown in Fig. 7–56. Your first impression is that the parts are interchangeable, but the parts are actually as different as a pair of shoes. These two parts are similar in every way except that one is a left-hand part and the other is a right-hand part.

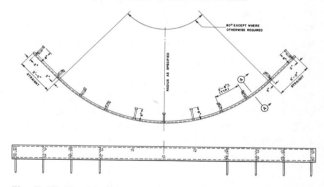

Fig. 7–55 The front view of a curb facing is drawn as a full-size, developed view. This is not a true projection, but is a conventional practice representation. (Courtesy of Bethlehem Steel Corporation.)

The draftsman can reduce his drawing time by drawing views of only one of the parts and labeling these views as shown in Fig. 7–56B. A note can be added to indicate that the other mating part has the

FIGURE 7–56. LEFT-HAND AND RIGHT-HAND PARTS

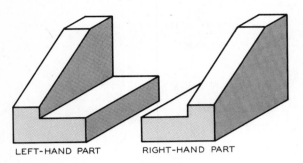

LEFT-HAND PART   RIGHT-HAND PART

A. Some parts are required to be similar except that one is a left-hand part and the other is a right-hand part.

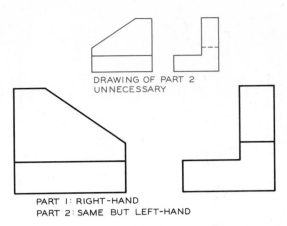

DRAWING OF PART 2 UNNECESSARY

PART 1: RIGHT-HAND
PART 2: SAME BUT LEFT-HAND

B. One of the parts can be drawn and labeled, right-hand in this case. The other part need not be drawn, but merely indicated by a note.

same dimensions, but that it is a left-hand version of the right-hand part that is drawn. If the views of part 2 were drawn, they would appear as shown in the figure.

7–23 RELATIONSHIP TO DESIGN

You have learned that there are many principles and rules that must be followed in representing three-dimensional objects. These rules are very important to the draftsman in performing his role as a member of the technological team, and they are equally important to the designer and the engineer. The designer may not prepare all the completed drawings that will be used by the craftsman in the shop, but he must be familiar with orthographic projection before he can communicate his ideas to his associates. He must be able to prepare a rough, freehand sketch before a draftsman can understand his design.

Graphical methods are very important to the designer; these methods are his most important tool for developing his design ideas. The following chapter will discuss the application of sketching to the preparation of orthographic views of designs. Sketching is a method of rapidly communicating designs and thinking with one's pencil.

Design problems are given at the end of the chapter in addition to conventional problems. These will enable you to develop your ability to think as a designer would in solving a problem. Draftsmen usually perform design functions to a certain degree. Those who develop their ability to design will find more job opportunities than will those who limit themselves to preparing the designer's drawings from his sketches.

PROBLEMS

These problems are to be solved in accordance with Article 3–15 and the specifications of your instructor. Most problems are to be drawn on standard Size A paper ($8\frac{1}{2}$" × 11") in ink or pencil.

Many of the problems given for this chapter are laid out on grid paper where each grid is equal to $\frac{1}{4}$". The drawings can be transferred to grid paper of the same type, or else drawn on blank paper with the aid of your architects' scale. Use Size A paper (Fig. 3–32) with the endorsement, title strip, and border shown in Article 3–15. Some problem sheets are to have a vertical and others a horizontal format. Refer to specific articles in this chapter when necessary to assist you in the solutions.

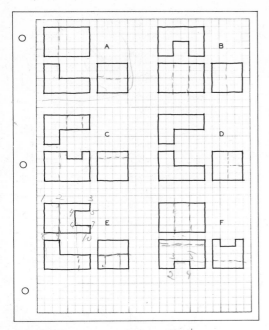

Fig. 7–57 Problem 1: Orthographic projection.

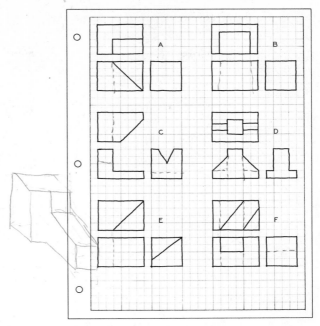

Fig. 7–58 Problem 2: Orthographic projection.

General Problems

1–3 Using instruments, lay out the given views of the objects shown in Figs. 7–57, 7–58, or 7–59 as assigned. At least one view has missing lines that are to be completed in keeping with the rules of orthographic projection. Use the proper alphabet of lines.

4–39 Pictorials (Figs. 7–60, 7–61, 7–62) are drawn on a pictorial grid where each grid is equal to $\frac{1}{2}$" when drawn on Size A paper. Using instruments, draw three views of the problems assigned by your instructor. Two problems will fit on each Size A sheet. Do not overlook centerlines. Number the points in each view (Article 7–12) of the problems assigned by your instructor.

40–54 Using instruments, lay out the views given in Figs. 7–63 through 7–77 as assigned. Use Size A sheets with title strips and borders (Article 3–15). Lines or entire views may be missing in these three-view drawings. Complete these views and apply the principles of orthographic projection and conventional methods. Note that several problems are to be laid out using a horizontal format.

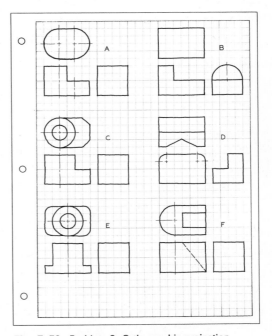

Fig. 7–59 Problem 3: Orthographic projection.

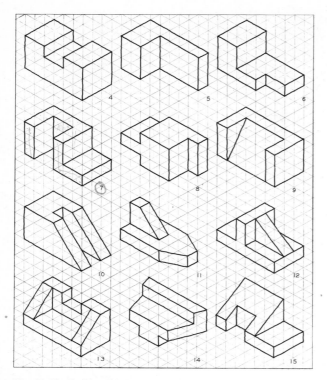

Fig. 7–60 Problems 4 through 15.

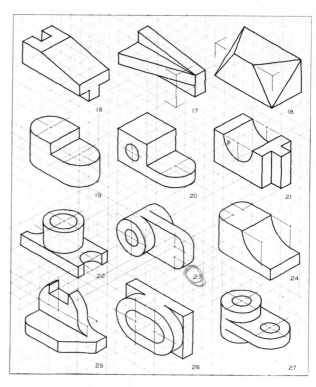

Fig. 7–61 Problems 16 through 27.

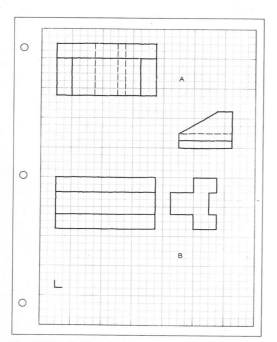

A

B

L

Fig. 7–63 Problem 40.

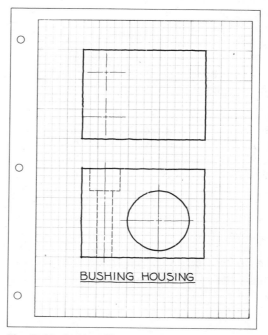

BUSHING HOUSING

Fig. 7–64 Problem 41.

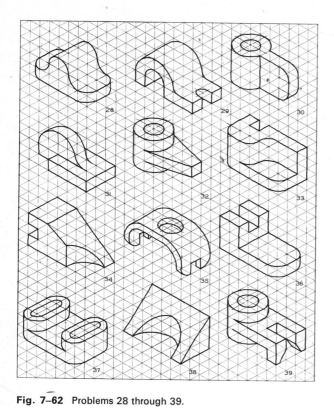

Fig. 7–62 Problems 28 through 39.

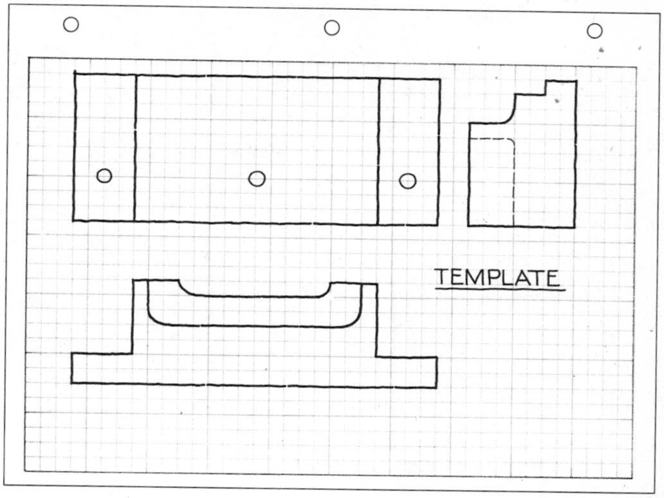

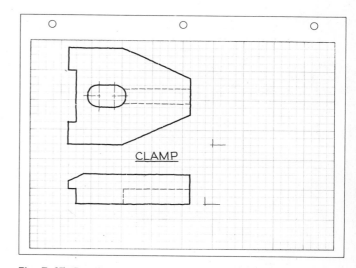

TEMPLATE

Fig. 7–66 Problem 43.

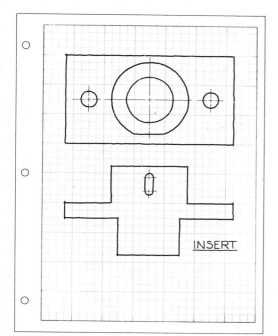

INSERT

Fig. 7–65 Problem 42.

CLAMP

Fig. 7–67 Problem 44.

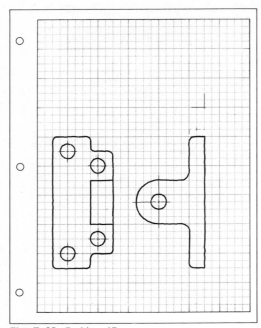

Fig. 7–68 Problem 45.

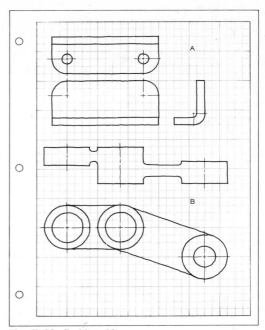

Fig. 7–69 Problem 46.

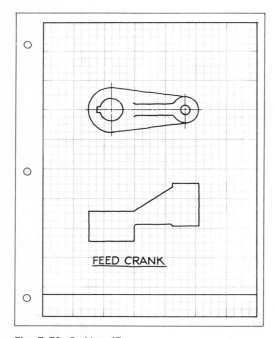

FEED CRANK

Fig. 7–70 Problem 47.

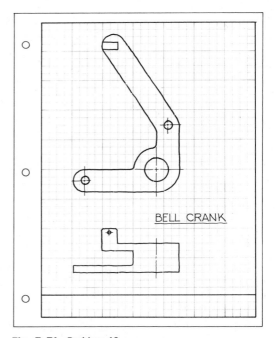

BELL CRANK

Fig. 7–71 Problem 48.

Orthographic projection **Chap. 7**

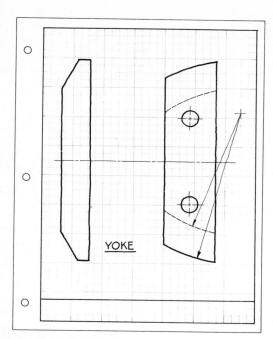

Fig. 7–72 Problem 49.

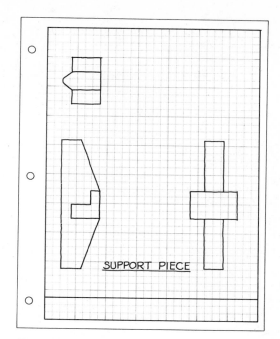

Fig. 7–73 Problem 50.

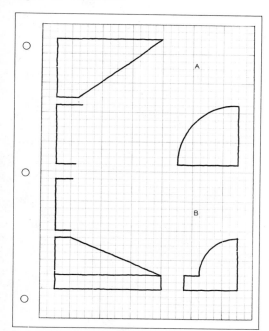

Fig. 7–74 Problem 51.

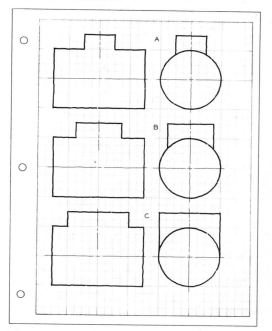

Fig. 7–75 Problem 52.

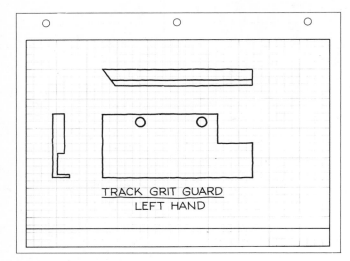

Fig. 7–76 Problem 53.

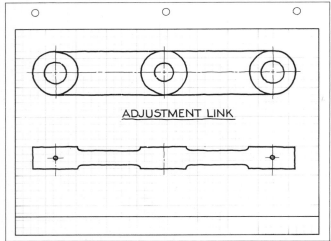

Fig. 7–77 Problem 54.

55–60 These problems (Figs. 7–78 through 7–83) are to be drawn as orthographic views. Use only the number of views necessary to describe the objects. These are to be drawn on the size of paper assigned by your instructor. Size A or B will be adequate with one object per sheet. Select the proper scale for each problem and indicate the scale on your drawing. Use instruments to solve these problems. Give the title of each part on the completed sheet.

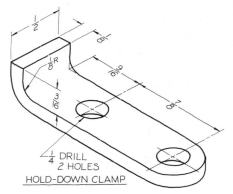

HOLD-DOWN CLAMP

Fig. 7–78 Problem 55.

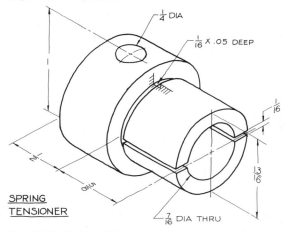

SPRING TENSIONER

Fig. 7–79 Problem 56.

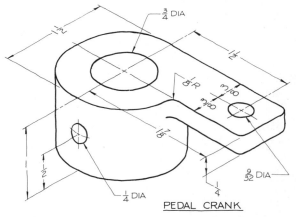

PEDAL CRANK

Fig. 7–80 Problem 57.

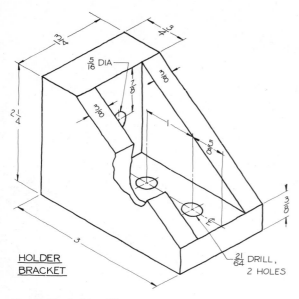

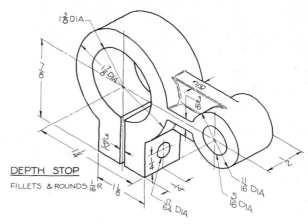

HOLDER
BRACKET

Fig. 7–81 Problem 58.

DEPTH STOP

FILLETS & ROUNDS $\frac{1}{16}$ R

Fig. 7–83 Problem 60.

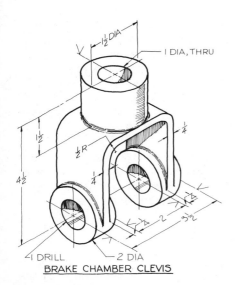

BRAKE CHAMBER CLEVIS

Fig. 7–82 Problem 59.

Design Problems

Design problems are more realistic examples of the type of work that must be performed by draftsmen. Design problems require that you use your own judgment to supply missing dimensions and details that are not clearly indicated. In some cases, only several important dimensions are given; the other details are left for you to design and to present in the form of orthographic drawings. Today's draftsman must be able to assist the designer by making minor decisions for his approval. Learn to develop your logic and to use the graphical process to present your ideas. Design problems can be presented on Size A or B paper using instruments or as assigned by your instructor. You must be responsible for selecting the proper scale. Always try to make your drawings as large as possible while still maintaining adequate space on the drawing sheet.

61 Make a three-view drawing of the assembled saw-horse (Fig. 7–84) on a Size A sheet with instruments.

62 The illustration of a garden caddy (Fig. 7–85) gives a designer's idea for the method of construction and the materials that are to be used. Large parts are to be made from $\frac{3}{4}''$ thick plywood. The caddy

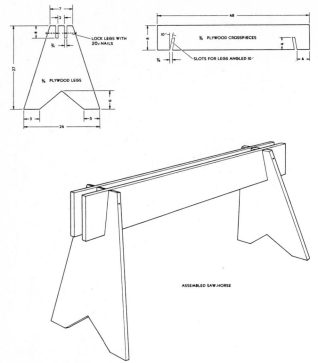

Fig. 7–84 Problem 61. (Courtesy of American Plywood Association.)

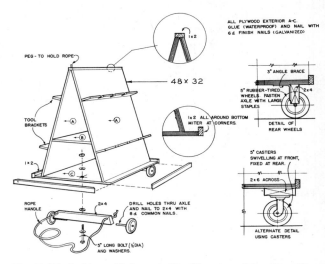

Fig. 7–85 Problems 62 through 65. (Courtesy of American Plywood Association.)

must hold rakes and garden tools with handles that are 1″ to 1½″ in diameter. Using instruments, make a two-view drawing of the assembled and completed caddy. Use Size A paper.

63 Using instruments, select a scale that will allow you to make the necessary views of all parts of the caddy (Fig. 7–85). Each part should be handled separately as an independent part but on the same sheet. Show all parts on a single Size B sheet. Dimensions can be omitted, but all parts should be drawn to scale.

64 Make a bill of materials for the parts that will be required for the construction of the caddy (Fig. 7–85). The bill of materials should be lettered on a Size A sheet using four columns with the following headings: Part No., Part Name, Number Required, and Size. The four columns might read for one part: A, Side, 2, 48″ × 32″. Give information in the table for the wheels and other parts of the caddy.

65 Since plywood comes in 4′ × 8′ sheets, it is important that the designs be laid out with the minimum of waste. Make a drawing of a 4′ × 8′ sheet of plywood and show how the parts of the garden caddy (Fig. 7–85) can be most economically cut from the sheet with the least waste. This may cause you to modify your first design to make better use of materials. Use a Size A sheet.

66 Using instruments, make a three-view orthographic drawing to describe the shape of the table shown in Fig. 7–86 on a sheet of Size A paper. Label the views and indicate the scale used.

67 Repeat Problem 66 but make drawings of the bench in Fig. 7–86.

68 Repeat Problem 66 but make drawings of the barbecue cabinet in Fig. 7–86.

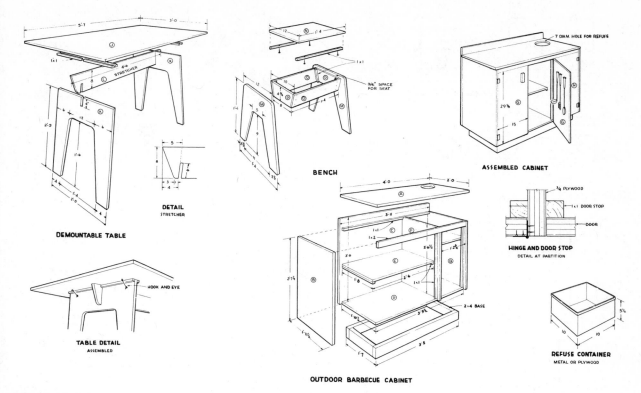

Fig. 7–86 Problems 66 through 77. (Courtesy of American Plywood Association.)

69 Using instruments, make the necessary orthographic views to describe each individual part of the table in Fig. 7–86. Each part should be treated separately as an independent part, but all parts should appear. For example, all the parts of the unassembled table should be drawn on the same sheet as individual parts. Use a Size B sheet.

70 Repeat Problem 69 but make drawings of the bench in Fig. 7–86.

71 Repeat Problem 69 but make drawings of the barbecue cabinet in Fig. 7–86.

72 Follow the instructions of Problem 64 to make a bill of materials for the table in Fig. 7–86.

73 Follow the instructions of Problem 64 to make a bill of materials for the outdoor barbecue cabinet in Fig. 7–86.

74 Follow the instructions of Problem 64 to make a bill of materials for the bench in Fig. 7–86.

75 Follow the instructions of Problem 65 to make a cutout pattern for the table in Fig. 7–86.

76 Follow the instructions of Problem 65 to make a cutout pattern for the bench in Fig. 7–86.

77 Follow the instructions of Problem 65 to make a cutout pattern for the barbecue cabinet in Fig. 7–86.

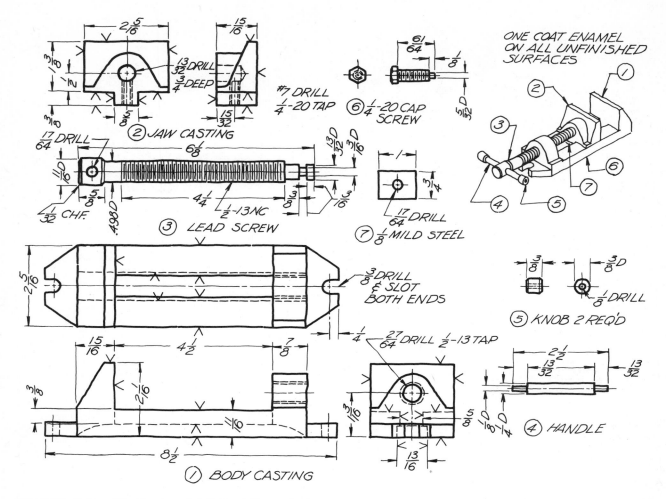

Fig. 7–87 Problem 78. (Courtesy of C. F. Struck Corporation.)

78 The parts shown in Fig. 7–87 are parts of a drill press vise. Most parts are sufficiently dimensioned to assist the machinist in finishing the rough casting after the parts have been made in the foundry. However, you will find that many of the parts are not completely dimensioned. Draw views of these parts with instruments on Size A sheets. Several parts will fit on each sheet, but at least two sheets will be required to show all the parts. The dimensions can be omitted, but they should be used to lay out the drawings. Where dimensions have been omitted, use

your judgment to arrive at the size of the undimensioned feature. Check each view to see that no lines or details have been omitted. Note: The V's are *finish marks* that are shown on the edge views of the surfaces that are to be finished (machined to a smooth surface).

79 The cobbler's bench shown in Fig. 7–88 is a toy made of wood. A small child uses a mallet to drive the pegs through the centerboard; the bench is then

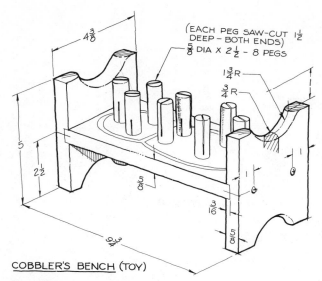

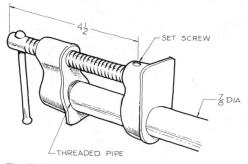

(EACH PEG SAW-CUT 1½
DEEP — BOTH ENDS)
⅝ DIA X 2½ – 8 PEGS

1¾R

¾ R

4⅜

5

2½

⅝

3/16

⅝

9¾

COBBLER'S BENCH (TOY)

Fig. 7–88 Problems 79 through 81.

4½

SET SCREW

⅞ DIA

THREADED PIPE

Fig. 7–89 Problem 82.

turned over and the pegs driven in from the other side. Make a three-view orthographic drawing of the assembled toy with instruments on a Size A sheet. Dimensions can be omitted. Indicate the scale that was used on your drawing.

80 Using instruments, make the necessary orthographic views of each part of the toy shown in Fig. 7–88 to completely describe it. All parts can be depicted on the same Size B sheet.

81 Make detail drawings (omitting dimensions) of the parts of a wood mallet that could be used on the

cobbler's bench in Fig. 7–88. Use a Size A sheet and instruments.

82 A clamping device is illustrated in Fig. 7–89. This assembly fits on a $\frac{7}{8}$" diameter pipe that is threaded at one end and is used for clamping parts that are being glued. Using instruments, make the necessary orthographic views of each part on a Size C sheet. All parts should be shown individually but on the same sheet. Do not show threads at this point unless required by your instructor. You must estimate the dimensions and design the parts of this assembly using your judgment.

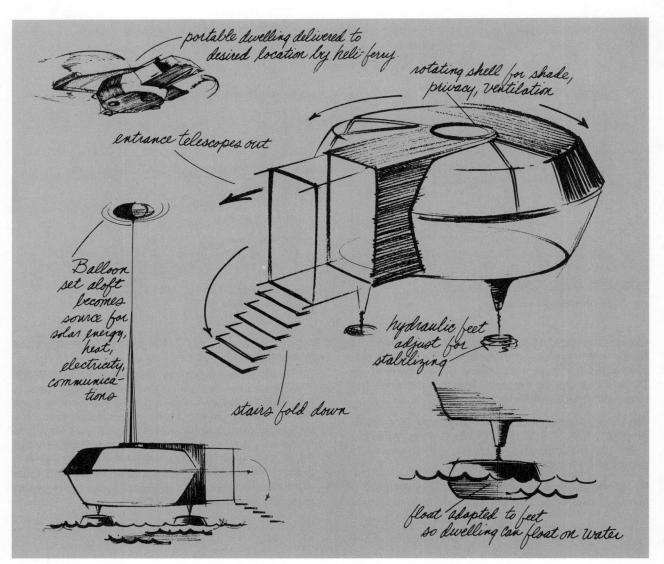

portable dwelling delivered to desired location by heli-ferry.

rotating shell for shade, privacy, ventilation

entrance telescopes out

Balloon set aloft becomes source for solar energy, heat, electricity, communications

hydraulic feet adjust for stabilizing

stairs fold down

float adapted to feet so dwelling can float on water

Courtesy of Lippincott and Margulies, Inc., and Charles Bruning Company

8
ORTHOGRAPHIC SKETCHING

Fig. 8–1 Freehand sketching is a necessary means of discussing technical problems. The engineers here are sketching their ideas pertaining to a refinery problem. (Courtesy of Standard Oil of New Jersey.)

Fig. 8–2 The development of a revolutionary design such as Craig Breedlove's *Spirit of America* requires an efficient method of communication. Sketching is the method used to develop and to communicate new design ideas of this type. (Courtesy of Goodyear Tire and Rubber Company.)

8–1 INTRODUCTION

Freehand sketching is a very important tool used by the designer and the engineer to originate and develop their ideas. Many sketches are made in the process of solving a design problem before an instrument drawing is prepared. When the instrument drawings are made, the designer's freehand sketches will be his means of communication with the draftsman who will make the drawings. Sketching is essential throughout the design process, but it is especially important during the earlier stages of solving a problem.

Technical problems associated with industry and engineering are usually difficult to discuss verbally in conversation. It is necessary to refer to illustrations or drawings to make sure that the points being discussed are understood. A team of engineers will often resort to freehand sketching and schematic diagrams to aid in their communication of ideas (Fig. 8–1). Without the ability to rapidly sketch his ideas, the engineer's communication is hampered.

The more complex or unusual the design, the more difficult it will be to describe its details to an associate. Objects that are familiar to others can be described verbally, since there is a basis of understanding when the object is familiar. For example,

you could verbally describe your drawing compass to another student in your class with a minimum of difficulty, since he is familiar with compasses and has a mental picture of the instrument when you mention its name. On the other hand, the early design concepts for a unique vehicle like *The Spirit of America* (Fig. 8–2) require a considerable degree of explanation. This is where freehand sketching assists in describing ideas.

This chapter will be concerned with freehand sketching as it relates to orthographic projection, covered in Chapter 7. The principles of constructing and arranging views will apply to sketching in the same manner as they applied to instrument drawing. The primary difference is that the objective of freehand sketching is speed. A draftsman or a designer can think more quickly than he can draw, and he can draw more quickly freehand than with instruments. Freehand drawing speeds his communication and thinking processes.

Pictorial sketching is equally important to the presentation of technical ideas. Pictorials can be understood by everyone, and do not require a familiarity with orthographic projection or graphical principles. A designer's pictorial sketch of an auto-

Fig. 8–3 Freehand sketches can be effective as a means of preparing pictorials. This designer's sketch of a new body style is easily understood even though it is a freehand sketch. (Courtesy of Ford Motor Company.)

mobile is shown in Fig. 8–3. Not only can the man in the plant understand his idea, but so can the business manager, the stockholder, and the potential customer. Pictorial sketching will be covered in Chapter 9, but many of the same techniques discussed here will apply.

8–2 SKETCHING FOR COMMUNICATION

Without the ability to prepare rapid freehand sketches, the designer could not function. Sketching is his means of communicating with others and with himself. It may sound strange to say that a person communicates with *himself*, but this is indeed true in the design process. Designing is a series of decisions: an idea is developed; part of it is good and this part is identified; the design is modified to keep the good and eliminate the bad; a new concept is introduced into the design and other decisions for addition and elimination are made.

The process of identifying good and bad aspects of an idea requires the designer to review each idea and sketch a modified solution. This procedure is

almost impossible to perform without a pencil in hand; thus freehand sketching is a means of thinking and communicating with oneself. Every sketch that you make is an idea that has been saved, while fleeting ideas that are not sketched may be forgotten and lost.

Do not think of sketching as an artistic process that only the talented can perform. If you learn to use the many different guides and aids available, you will be able to prepare freehand sketches that will express your ideas clearly. Remember that it is important to develop speed. If you cannot sketch more quickly than you can draw with instruments, you are defeating the purpose of freehand sketching. Practice making rapid freehand sketches, but do not assume that fast sketches should be sloppy or difficult to read.

8–3 A DESIGN CASE STUDY

The best way to describe the role of freehand sketching in the design of a solution to a technical problem is to present an actual case. As an example we shall use the connector shown in Fig. 8–4. The following

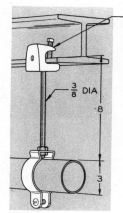

NEED A NEW DESIGN FOR A CONNECTOR THAT WILL RECEIVE A $\frac{3}{8}$" DIA HANGER ROD AND WILL ALLOW SWING OF PIPE CAUSED BY CONTRACTION OR EXPANSION. PRESENT DESIGN TOO RIGID. PIPE WILL CARRY WATER (10.8 LBS. PER FOOT).

CONNECTOR SHOULD BE DESIGNED TO FASTEN TO SIDE OR BOTTOM OF AN OVERHEAD BEAM.

EACH CONNECTOR SHOULD CARRY 100 LBS. HOW FAR APART SHOULD THEY BE SPACED ?

Fig. 8–4 A case study of a problem requiring the design of a new piece of hardware. (Courtesy of Midland Ross Corporation.)

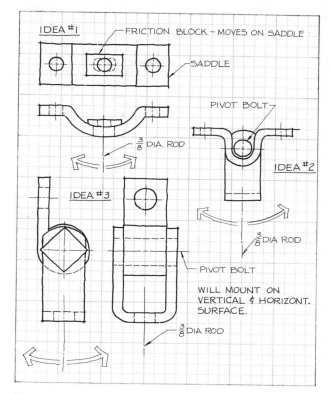

Fig. 8–5 A number of ideas are sketched freehand. Sketching allows the designer to work rapidly without retarding his thought process by making instrument drawings.

paragraphs will allow you to review the steps leading to the design of this simple connector. Remember to refer to Chapter 6, which outlines the design process.

Problem identification. A connector is needed which can be attached to an overhead beam to support a water pipe 3″ in diameter. Because of the change of temperature of water in long pipes, there is a high degree of contraction and expansion. The present connector (Fig. 8–4) does not provide adequately for this variation in the length of the pipe. A connector is needed that will allow the $\frac{3}{8}$″ diameter hanger rod to move as the length of the pipe changes with temperature.

It would be helpful if the connector were designed so that it could be connected to a vertical column as well as to a horizontal beam. Each connector should be designed to carry a maximum load of 100 lb. The allowable load of each connector will determine how far apart the connectors must be spaced when installed.

Note that the designer has made a start toward the solution by simply writing down the problem statement; he has identified several of the requirements considered. A pictorial sketch is helpful in keeping the problem situation before him.

Preliminary ideas. The next step is the most creative step of the design process and is the step

that uses freehand sketching to the greatest extent. This step is the development of creative ideas.

Several ideas are sketched on a work sheet which has a printed grid to assist with freehand drawing (Fig. 8–5). The grid can be used to assign a scale to the sketches, but this is less important than sketching rapidly to stimulate your thought process. Notes are made on the sketches to point out the various features that should be considered. A few of the more critical dimensions are indicated where necessary.

Refinement. Idea 3 is selected as the best idea to refine and study further (Fig. 8–6). Freehand orthographic views are sketched in an attempt to make the

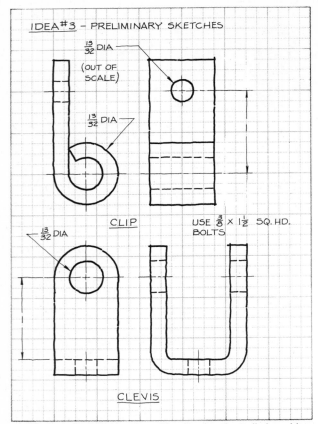

IDEA #3 — PRELIMINARY SKETCHES

$\frac{13}{32}$ DIA

(OUT OF SCALE)

$\frac{13}{32}$ DIA

CLIP

USE $\frac{3}{8}$ × $1\frac{1}{2}$ SQ. HD. BOLTS

$\frac{13}{32}$ DIA

CLEVIS

Fig. 8–6 A good idea is selected from among the preliminary ideas and developed in the form of more accurate orthographic sketches. Dimensions are kept to a minimum at this point.

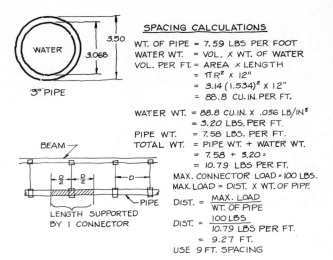

SPACING CALCULATIONS

3.50

WATER

3.068

3" PIPE

WT. OF PIPE = 7.59 LBS PER FOOT
WATER WT. = VOL. × WT. OF WATER
VOL. PER FT. = AREA × LENGTH
   = πR^2 × 12"
   = 3.14 (1.534)^2 × 12"
   = 88.8 CU.IN. PER FT.

WATER WT. = 88.8 CU.IN. × .036 LB/IN^3
   = 3.20 LBS. PER FT.
PIPE WT. = 7.58 LBS. PER FT.
TOTAL WT. = PIPE WT. + WATER WT.
   = 7.58 + 3.20 =
   = 10.79 LBS PER FT.
MAX. CONNECTOR LOAD = 100 LBS.
MAX. LOAD = DIST. × WT. OF PIPE
DIST. = $\frac{\text{MAX. LOAD}}{\text{WT. OF PIPE}}$
DIST. = $\frac{100\,\text{LBS}}{10.79\,\text{LBS PER FT.}}$
   = 9.27 FT.
USE 9 FT. SPACING

BEAM

PIPE

LENGTH SUPPORTED BY 1 CONNECTOR

Fig. 8–7 The analysis of the spacing of the connectors is shown in these calculations. Can you follow the procedure used in arriving at the answer?

engineering procedures required to analyze this design. An analysis of the spacing of the pipe supports is shown in Fig. 8–7. Note that graphics is important to an organized analysis of the problem.

You can analyze several features of this design graphically. If this connector were connected to a horizontal beam, it would be necessary for the clevis to revolve without making contact with the bottom of the beam and thereby causing it to bind. The radius of curvature and the dimensions of the clevis are analyzed to permit adequate clearance under the vertical and horizontal conditions mentioned in the problem identification step.

Decision. After reviewing the various aspects of the connector design, the designer and the technicians in the shop agree that the connector should function as intended. A decision is made on the basis of the preliminary ideas and the refinement drawings. The connector will be made, tested, and produced in large quantities if preliminary tests are successful.

Implementation. To implement the design, a detailed working drawing is necessary to communicate the details and specifications to the craftsmen who will fabricate the connector. The draftsman

drawing more to scale than the freehand preliminary sketches were. Scale is important at the refinement stage, since the refinement drawing will assist the designer in making his final decision. Only the more important dimensions are given on the refinement sketch.

Analysis. A complete analysis of Idea 3 would require an understanding of materials and manufacturing processes to ensure that the design would safely support 100 lb and that the proper bolts were selected for the design conditions. However, you can apply your common judgment to the design proposed at this step, since you are probably unfamiliar with the

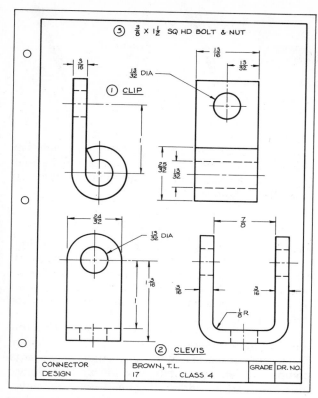

③ $\frac{3}{8}$ X 1$\frac{1}{2}$ SQ HD BOLT & NUT

① CLIP

$\frac{13}{32}$ DIA

② CLEVIS

$\frac{13}{32}$ DIA

| CONNECTOR DESIGN | BROWN, T.L. 17 | CLASS 4 | GRADE | DR. NO. |

Fig. 8–8 The completed working drawing of the parts of the finished design for the connector.

Fig. 8–9 A photograph of the completed connector. (Courtesy of Midland Ross Corporation.)

drawings are shown in Fig. 8–8. The bolt is not drawn because it is a common part available in standard sizes, and therefore does not have to be designed.

A photograph of the finished connector can be seen in Fig. 8–9. The steps of the design process used in arriving at this design of a rather simple part are the same steps that are used for more complex designs. Freehand sketching is equally important to all types of design problems.

8–4 TYPES OF LINES

The alphabet of lines discussed previously in Chapter 7 is applied to freehand sketching also. Using the proper line weights makes it possible to communicate clearly with a minimum of misunderstanding.

The pencils used most often in freehand sketching are in the soft-to-medium range: B, HB, and F. It is possible to use only one pencil weight for all lines whether they are heavy visible lines or thin construction lines. This requires that the pencil point be sharpened differently for each type of line. For example, light construction lines could be made first with a sharp point (Fig. 8–10D), and then the point could be rounded to give a heavy line such as the

prepares instrument working drawings by referring to the designer's freehand sketches. These sketches reduce the time required for the designer to communicate his ideas to the draftsman and thereby free the designer for other responsibilities while the drawings are being completed.

The draftsman makes sure that his drawing is to scale and that the proper sizes of the parts are specified. He must rely on his past experience and the standards of the company in completing the finished drawings. He also makes changes in the designer's sketches where necessary, since it is very possible that certain features may not have been sketched to scale accurately. The finished working

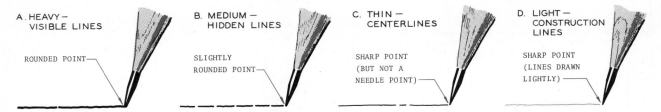

A. HEAVY—
VISIBLE LINES

ROUNDED POINT

B. MEDIUM—
HIDDEN LINES

SLIGHTLY
ROUNDED POINT

C. THIN—
CENTERLINES

SHARP POINT
(BUT NOT A
NEEDLE POINT)

D. LIGHT—
CONSTRUCTION
LINES

SHARP POINT
(LINES DRAWN
LIGHTLY)

Fig. 8–10 The types of pencil points required to make the various types of lines used in freehand sketching. Practice sharpening your pencil to give these types of lines.

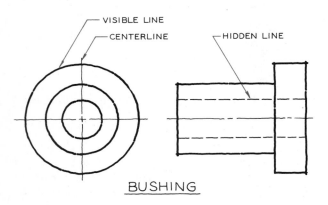

VISIBLE LINE

CENTERLINE

HIDDEN LINE

BUSHING

Fig. 8–11 The application of the standard line weights to an orthographic drawing.

visible line in A. All lines of the same type should be made at the same time for the sake of uniformity.

All freehand lines should be uniformly black with the exception of construction lines, which are very light gray lines used to lay out the sketch. The various types of lines used in most drawings are illustrated in Fig. 8–10. In A, a rounded point is used for visible lines; in B a slightly rounded point for medium-weight lines; and in C a sharp point is used for drawing thin lines such as centerlines and dimension lines. Do not use a needle point, because the point will break.

The example in Fig. 8–11 illustrates the application of the various line weights in an orthographic sketch. Note that it is obvious at a glance that the sketch is a *freehand sketch* and *not* an instrument drawing. It is not the purpose of a freehand sketch to look like an instrument drawing. You should not try to conceal the fact that your sketch was made free-

hand, but instead, emphasize the freehand qualities of your sketches. Note that there are wiggles in the lines (Fig. 8–10) and other irregularities that are common in freehand sketches.

8–5 FREEHAND TECHNIQUES

Speed is the primary purpose of freehand sketching, but speed is of little value if the completed sketch does not communicate as intended. Consequently, you should develop speed without sacrificing good drawing principles and rules of orthographic projection.

Freehand lines cannot be drawn very long without a degree of waviness or other form of variation. The reason for this is that the arm is much like a large compass which pivots at the shoulder and the elbow; thus any long line drawn freehand tends to curve. Consequently, it is easier to draw longer lines if they are drawn as a sequence of short strokes as illustrated in Fig. 8–12A. It may even add to the appearance of your drawing if these strokes are separated by a small space without an overlap of the lines.

Freehand lines can be drawn as continuous lines, but care must be taken to prevent the lines from varying as they get longer. Continuous lines are shown in Fig. 8–12A.

A poorly drawn sketch is shown in Fig. 8–12B. In general, the sketch appears to have been drawn too hurriedly and carelessly. When a designer is preparing a sketch merely as a communication with himself, the quality of the sketch is not as important as it would be if he were planning to use it to communicate with a draftsman or one of his associates.

The use of the proper techniques of intersecting lines at the corner of an object adds greatly to the attractiveness of a freehand sketch (Fig. 8–13). In

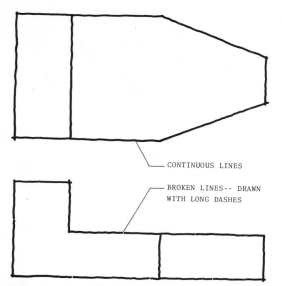

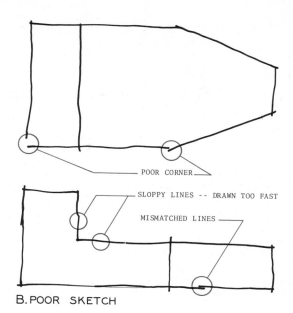

CONTINUOUS LINES

BROKEN LINES-- DRAWN WITH LONG DASHES

A. GOOD SKETCH

POOR CORNER

SLOPPY LINES -- DRAWN TOO FAST

MISMATCHED LINES

B. POOR SKETCH

Fig. 8–12 The sketch in A is a good freehand sketch. Lines may be continuous or drawn as short strokes with small gaps between them. The sketch in B is a poor sketch because it was drawn too hurriedly. This type of sketch is acceptable for use by the designer to communicate with himself when he is developing ideas.

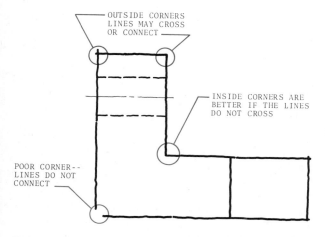

OUTSIDE CORNERS LINES MAY CROSS OR CONNECT

INSIDE CORNERS ARE BETTER IF THE LINES DO NOT CROSS

POOR CORNER-- LINES DO NOT CONNECT

Fig. 8–13 Techniques of sketching intersecting lines to give the best effect.

general, a corner should be distinctly defined with crossing lines or at least a continuous intersection where the lines butt together. It is more important that the corners be clearly defined than other details in a sketch. The intersecting lines can cross at exterior corners, but the sketch will look better if the interior corner lines do not cross, but merely butt into each other.

8–6 FREEHAND STROKES

An important rule of freehand sketching is to be comfortable when you are sketching. If you are uncomfortable, it is likely that you will not make a good sketch.

Since your arm has a natural left-to-right movement, you will be able to draw horizontal lines more easily than vertical lines. However, since it is unnecessary to tape your drawing to a table top, you may turn your drawing sheet to a position that affords the greatest comfort when sketching.

FIGURE 8–14

A. Horizontal strokes can be made in a natural left-to-right direction.

B. Vertical lines can be made more comfortably if your sheet is turned so that you can use the same strokes as you used in part A.

C. Angular lines can be made more easily if the sheet is turned so that you can take advantage of the most comfortable position for drawing straight lines.

Fig. 8–15 If you prefer to leave your paper in one position while sketching, you should draw vertical lines with a downward stroke.

Fig. 8–16 This orthographic sketch is made with lines having an artistic quality. This technique comes only with practice. (Courtesy of Ford Motor Company.)

Three positions of a drawing are shown in Fig. 8–14. In A, the horizontal lines are drawn left-to-right in a natural stroke. To draw vertical lines (B), the sheet was revolved 90° and the lines sketched with the same left-to-right strokes. Lines at an angle (C) are drawn in the same manner by turning the sheet as shown.

If you prefer to leave your sheet in one position while sketching, then vertical lines should be drawn with a downward stroke (Fig. 8–15). This is usually the best direction for most people, but the important thing is to draw lines in a manner that is most natural for *you*. Develop your own style and techniques that will give the best results.

8–7 ARTISTIC STROKES

Some designers have a flair for making sketches with an artistic quality and an unusual line technique. An example of a freehand orthographic view of an automobile design is shown in Fig. 8–16. Note that the strokes have an artistic character. These lines are a combination of pencil lines and lines made with a felt-tip marker.

The sketch of the auditorium in Fig. 8–17 has an artistic appearance even though the lines are very typical of technical sketches. Another example of pictorial and orthographic sketches with an artistic quality is shown in Fig. 8–18.

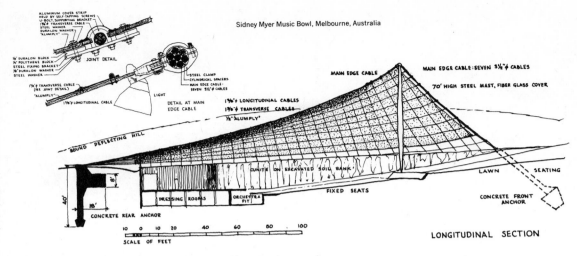

Sidney Myer Music Bowl, Melbourne, Australia

LONGITUDINAL SECTION

Fig. 8–17 This freehand sketch illustrates the structure and details of a theater. (Courtesy of U.S. Steel Corporation.)

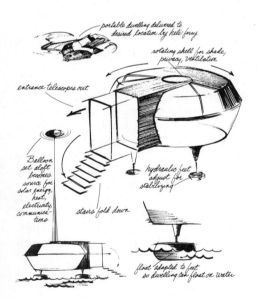

Fig. 8–18 These sketches of a "Transportable Uni-Lodge" for the future have an artistic flair and give the appearance of the work of a professional designer. (Courtesy of Lippincott and Margulies, Inc., and Charles Bruning Company.)

As you become more skilled in sketching, you will develop your own "style" of drawing. A style and skill will come to some more quickly than to others, but practice is the best way of improving your technique.

8–8 SKETCHING MATERIALS

It is important that you keep your sketches throughout your course or during your assignment on a job. These will be helpful to you in noting your improvement and also in reviewing the ideas that you have developed and filed away.

You should do most of your sketches on $8\frac{1}{2}$" × 11" paper. This is a standard sheet size (Size A) that is available in pads (Fig. 8–19) or in individual sheets. Some papers have a grid printed on the sheet that can be used as a guide in sketching. It is preferable that the grid be printed in a light color so as not to be confused with the lines that are drawn on the sheet. An example of a sheet of paper that is adequate for sketching is shown in Fig. 8–20. The squares on this sheet are spaced $\frac{1}{4}$" apart.

Fig. 8–19 The materials for freehand sketching and the accumulation of ideas.

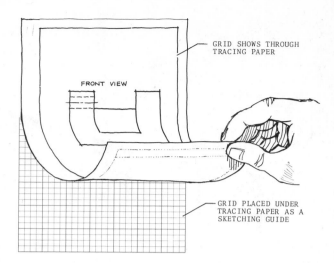

GRID SHOWS THROUGH TRACING PAPER

FRONT VIEW

GRID PLACED UNDER TRACING PAPER AS A SKETCHING GUIDE

Fig. 8–21 A grid sheet can be used under a sheet of tracing paper as a guide for freehand sketching.

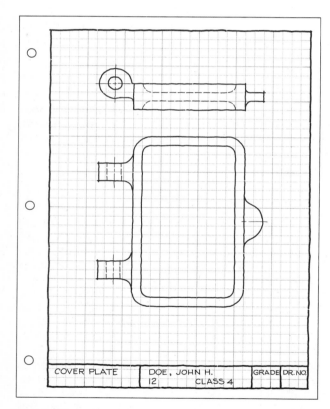

COVER PLATE   DOE, JOHN H.   GRADE DR. NO.
12   CLASS 4

Fig. 8–20 Paper is available with a printed grid for freehand sketching. Some tracing papers have a light blue grid that will not reproduce when run through a diazo machine.

Some tracing paper sheets are available with a grid printed in light blue. Such a grid enables the designer to make blue-line prints of his sketches using the diazo machine. The light blue lines will not reproduce on the print; only the sketched lines will be visible.

Since tracing paper is transparent enough to be seen through, a grid sheet can be placed under the sketching sheet and used as a guide. This removes the necessity of having a grid printed directly on the sketch sheet (Fig. 8–21).

To keep your sketches in an orderly file for future reference, use either an envelope or a ring notebook. Periodically, you should compare your latest sketches with those made earlier in the course to determine your progress. You should also compare your sketches with those made by classmates. This will be helpful in improving your technique and style.

8–9 SKETCHING ARCS

It is more difficult to sketch circles or arcs than straight lines. However, you can improve your sketching of circles if you use construction lines as a guide. Construction lines are gray lines that are

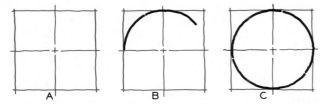

Fig. 8–22 The box method of sketching circles.

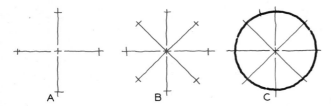

Fig. 8–23 The radius method of sketching circles.

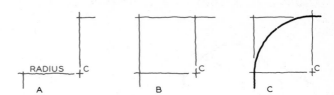

Fig. 8–24 A method of sketching arcs.

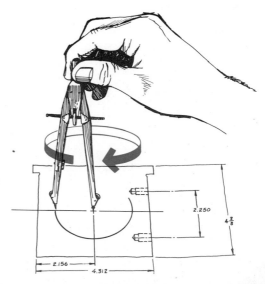

Fig. 8–25 Templates can be used for lightly drawing in circles which can later be darkened by a freehand technique.

Fig. 8–26 A compass can be used for drawing arcs which can later be darkened with freehand strokes.

drawn lightly so that it will be unnecessary to erase them when the drawing is completed.

A method of sketching circles is illustrated in Fig. 8–22 in a sequence of steps. The vertical and horizontal centerlines are sketched (A) and a box is blocked in with construction lines. The distance across this square box is the diameter of the circle to be sketched. The circle is drawn in segments (parts B and C) which are tangent to the box at the four points where the centerlines cross.

Another method is illustrated in Fig. 8–23, where the centerlines are drawn and the radius measured from the center along each line (part A). Two 45° lines are drawn and the radius of the circle is measured along these lines (part B). The points located by this method are used as a guide in sketching the circle (part C).

The same principles can be used to draw only a portion of a circle, an arc. In Fig. 8–24, the centerlines of a quarter-circle are sketched (part A), measured, and a square drawn to enclose the quarter-circle (part B). In part C, the quarter-circle is sketched to be tangent to the box at the points where the centerlines cross.

You can see how these guidelines will be helpful to you in sketching arcs. With added practice you will

FIGURE 8–27. LAYOUT OF A THREE-VIEW SKETCH

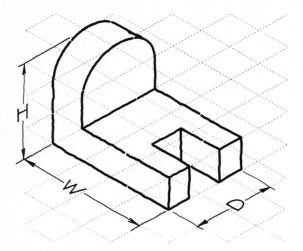

Given: A pictorial sketch of an object.
Required: Lay out a three-view sketch that will describe this object. Indicate general dimensions and label all views.
Reference: Article 8–10.

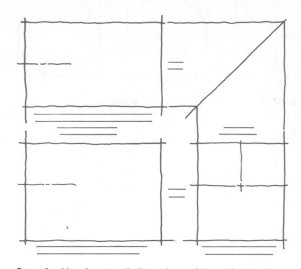

Step 1. Use the overall dimensions of the object to block in the general proportions of the part. Leave space between the views for labels and dimension lines. Project the depth of the top view to the side view as shown. Guidelines for lettering should be made with a straightedge.

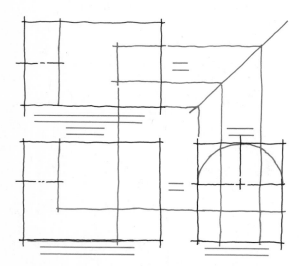

Step 2. Sketch in the remaining features, observing the proportions of the views. Project these lines to each view. Draw all construction lines lightly so that erasure will be unnecessary.

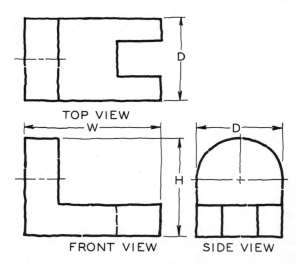

TOP VIEW

FRONT VIEW   SIDE VIEW

Step 3. Darken the lines with a medium-weight pencil (F or HB) to conform to the standard line weights. Add dimension lines, using D, W, and H to represent depth, width, and height. Label the views with $\frac{1}{8}''$ letters. Centerlines aid in the interpretation of the views.

develop an ability to make better arcs and circles without guidelines. However, the best designers and draftsmen use guidelines even though they may have many years of experience, simply because guidelines improve their drawings.

If you fail to become reasonably skilled at sketching circles, do not let this reduce your speed of sketching. You may use a circle template (Fig. 8–25) to lightly draw the circle or the arc, then darken the line freehand to match the other lines of your sketch. A compass can be used in the same manner (Fig. 8–26), the instrument lines being darkened freehand.

Develop any time-saving techniques that will give satisfactory results, because time is an important factor in any aspect of technology. Strive to become as rapid as possible without sacrificing the quality of your work.

8–10 THE THREE-VIEW SKETCH

The three-view sketch should be approached in the same manner as the instrument drawing. The steps of preparing a three-view sketch of an object are illustrated in Fig. 8–27. A pictorial sketch of a part is given, and we are required to construct three orthographic views. It is important that the proper proportions be maintained to give a realistic representation of the part in the three-view sketch. Since the views will be labeled and dimensioned, space must be provided between the views for this information. The dimensions—height, depth, and width—are blocked in to indicate the general overall proportions of the part in Step 1, with construction lines. Guidelines for lettering are drawn with a straightedge for the labels and dimensions. The depth in the right side view can be projected from the top view to a 45° construction line. This line is usually drawn with instruments to give more accuracy.

Additional details are sketched in Step 2. The notch is drawn in the top and projected to the front view. The circular shape in the side view is sketched using centerlines and construction lines as guides for the arc. The lines are darkened to the proper weight in Step 3 to complete the views. The views are labeled and dimensions W, D, and H are indicated between the views as shown.

FIGURE 8–28. LAYOUT OF A SKETCH

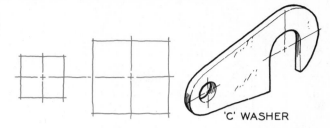

Step 1. The outside circles of the "C" washer are blocked in with centerlines as shown.

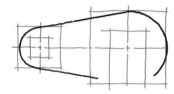

Step 2. Circles are sketched in the blocked-in squares and connected with tangent lines. The internal arcs are blocked in with construction lines.

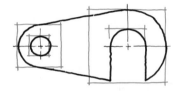

Step 3. The remaining features are sketched in the blocked-in areas. Light construction lines are not erased.

8–11 LAYOUT OF A SKETCH

A freehand sketch can be drawn with greater accuracy if construction lines are used to "block in" the view before it is drawn. An example is shown in Fig. 8–28, where a "C" washer is sketched in three steps.

The external circles are blocked in to represent both ends of the view (Step 1). The circles are sketched and connected with tangent lines in Step 2. The smaller circles are blocked in also in Step 2 and these circles are sketched in Step 3 to complete

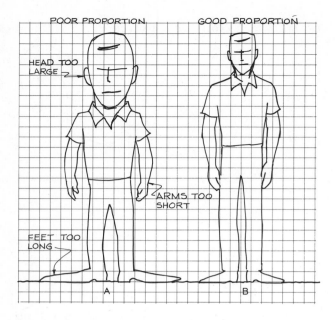

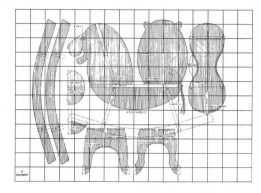

Fig. 8–29 The importance of proper proportion can be seen in these two sketches.

Fig. 8–30 Irregular shapes can be enlarged or reduced if a grid is used to establish the shapes of the parts. (Courtesy of the American Plywood Association.)

the view. The use of construction lines is essential to this type of sketch in order to maintain the proper proportion.

The construction lines are not erased when the sketch is complete. These are very light lines that will not detract from the drawing if they are properly drawn.

8–12 PROPORTION

A very important part of sketching is maintaining the proper proportion. Of course, at the very earliest step of the design process proportion is not a very important concern because the only objective at the outset is the development of ideas. Later, as several ideas emerge, it is helpful if the proportions of the design sketched are as accurate as possible. It may be found that a good design will not work when it is

drawn to scale, because allowance was not made for the sizes of certain details and standard parts.

Two sketches of a man are shown in Fig. 8–29. Note that the features of the man in A are out of proportion when the man is viewed in his entirety. The sketch of the man in B is better and is acceptable to our sense of proportion. This same sense of proportion should be applied to drawing any object —a chair, a shop project, or a machine part.

8–13 PROPORTION BY GRID

It is often necessary to make a drawing of an irregular shape that you may think calls for artistic talent. Or it may be necessary to enlarge a given drawing to a larger scale. One method of enlarging or reducing a drawing is the use of a grid as illustrated in Fig. 8–30.

A shop project, a rocking lion, is drawn on a grid. The drawing is small in Fig. 8–30, but it is shown

3" squares

Fig. 8–31 This is an enlargement of Fig. 8–30 that was made by drawing a larger grid for a guide. (Courtesy of the American Plywood Association.)

enlarged in Fig. 8–31. By simply using a larger grid (3" per grid), the drawing of these irregular shapes can be sketched freehand using the grid as a guide. You can see how this same layout can be drawn full size and cut out and assembled as a shop project by using $\frac{3}{4}$" plywood with a 3" grid drawn on the plywood.

Once the freehand lines have been sketched, instruments can be used to smooth the curves to the degree required by the application.

8–14 FREEHAND WORKING DRAWINGS

Since saving time is important in industry, freehand sketches are sometimes used instead of instrument drawings when the parts are relatively simple. An example is the gland shown in Fig. 8–32. This freehand sketch was prepared on a sheet which had a light blue grid printed on it.

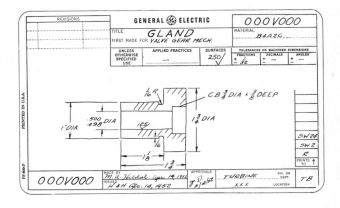

Fig. 8–32 Simple parts can be detailed as freehand sketches without the necessity for instrument drawings. (Courtesy of the General Electric Company.)

For an object of this degree of simplicity, there is no need for an instrument drawing of the part. Consequently the engineer's sketch can be used in the shop as effectively as an instrument drawing.

More complicated parts will require the use of instrument drawings in order to show the numerous notes and details that are necessary. Whether a free-hand sketch or an instrument drawing is used, good lettering is always essential because the lettering gives the specifications that the shop will follow. Even if your drawing is out of scale and in poor proportion, if the lettering, notes, and dimensions are clearly understandable, it will be possible for the shop to fabricate the part.

PROBLEMS

These problems are to be solved in accordance with Article 3–15 and the specifications of your instructor. Most problems are to be drawn on standard Size A paper ($8\frac{1}{2}'' \times 11''$) in ink or pencil.

Many of the problems of this chapter are laid out on grid paper where each grid is equal to $\frac{1}{4}''$. The drawings can be transferred to a grid paper of a similar type or else drawn on blank paper with proportions estimated by eye. Use Size A paper (Fig. 3–32) with the endorsement, title strip, and border (drawn freehand) shown in Article 3–15. Refer to the text of this chapter to assist you in your solutions.

General Problems

1 Referring to the pictorial view of the decorative wall (Fig. 8–33A), prepare a freehand sketch which shows the front view of the wall (orthographic view). Lay out this sketch on Size A paper (plain or with a grid).

2 Repeat Problem 1, referring to Fig. 8–33B.

3–5 Using Size A paper, prepare freehand sketches that will duplicate those shown in Figs. 8–34, 8–35, and 8–36. Estimate the dimensions that are not given. Strive to keep the same general proportions. Use Size A paper.

6–14 Using one sheet of Size A paper per connector, make the necessary freehand sketches that will fully describe the connectors in Fig. 8–37. Estimate the dimensions not given. Draw the sketches by eye, rather than with a scale, to improve your ability to represent proper proportions.

15 Prepare orthographic freehand sketches of the driving cup in Fig. 8–38 which completely describe it. Use Size A paper.

16 Prepare orthographic freehand sketches of the lever in Fig. 8–39 which completely describe it. Use Size A paper.

17–22 Each of the objects shown in Fig. 8–40 is either a single part or an assembly of parts. Using Size A paper, make freehand orthographic sketches of the individual parts. Problems 17, 19, 20, and 22 are composed of several parts. Sketch the necessary views of the individual parts to describe them. You may show more than one part on a sheet if they are parts of the same assembly.

23 Prepare the necessary orthographic freehand sketches to describe the adapter fitting (part 10) at B in Fig. 8–41. Use Size A paper.

24 Prepare the necessary orthographic freehand sketches to describe the brackets that support the adapter, part 10, shown at B in Fig. 8–41. Use Size A paper.

25 Prepare the necessary orthographic freehand sketches to describe the positioning bracket, part 8, in Fig. 8–41.

26 Prepare the necessary orthographic freehand sketches to describe the midbody attaching insert, part 9, in Fig. 8–41.

27 The handwheel in Fig. 8–42 is composed of three parts. Prepare orthographic freehand sketches of these three parts using your judgment as to how they are connected. Use Size A paper.

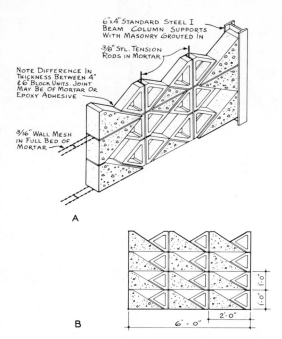

A

B

Fig. 8–33 Problems 1 and 2: A decorative wall made of concrete blocks. (Courtesy of Kaiser Permanente Cement; designed by Architect Loch Crane.)

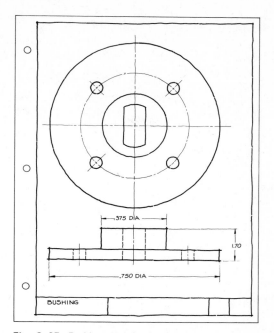

Fig. 8–35 Problem 4: A freehand sketch of a bushing.

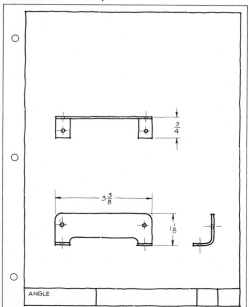

Fig. 8–34 Problem 3: A freehand sketch of an angle.

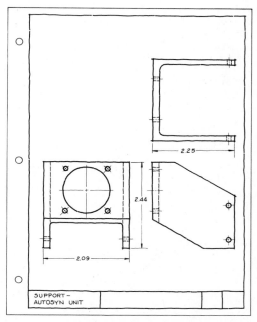

Fig. 8–36 Problem 5: A freehand sketch of a support for an autosyn unit.

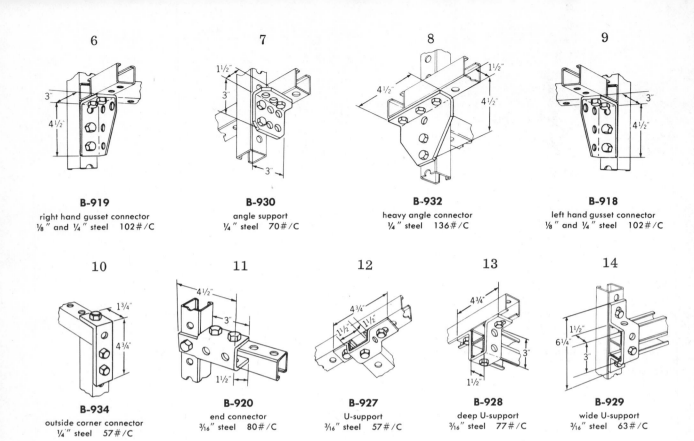

6

B-919
right hand gusset connector
⅛″ and ¼″ steel   102#/C

7

B-930
angle support
¼″ steel   70#/C

8

B-932
heavy angle connector
¼″ steel   136#/C

9

B-918
left hand gusset connector
⅛″ and ¼″ steel   102#/C

10

B-934
outside corner connector
¼″ steel   57#/C

11

B-920
end connector
³⁄₁₆″ steel   80#/C

12

B-927
U-support
³⁄₁₆″ steel   57#/C

13

B-928
deep U-support
³⁄₁₆″ steel   77#/C

14

B-929
wide U-support
³⁄₁₆″ steel   63#/C

Fig. 8–37 Problems 6 through 14. (Courtesy of Midland Ross Corporation.)

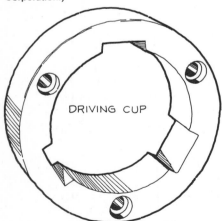

Fig. 8–38 Problem 15: Driving cup.

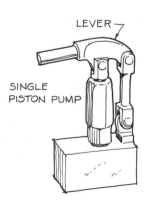

Fig. 8–39 Problem 16: Single piston pump.

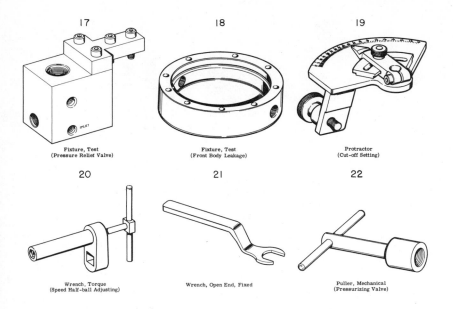

17
Fixture, Test
(Pressure Relief Valve)

18
Fixture, Test
(Front Body Leakage)

19
Protractor
(Cut-off Setting)

20
Wrench, Torque
(Speed Half-ball Adjusting)

21
Wrench, Open End, Fixed

22
Puller, Mechanical
(Pressurizing Valve)

Fig. 8–40 Problems 17 through 22. (Courtesy of the Bendix Corporation.)

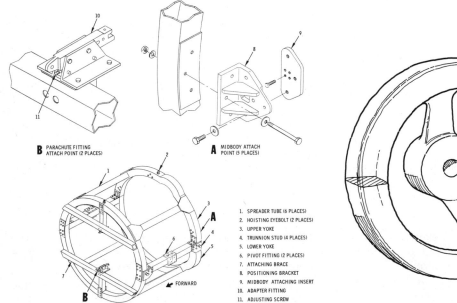

B PARACHUTE FITTING
ATTACH POINT (2 PLACES)

A MIDBODY ATTACH
POINT (5 PLACES)

1. SPREADER TUBE (6 PLACES)
2. HOISTING EYEBOLT (2 PLACES)
3. UPPER YOKE
4. TRUNNION STUD (4 PLACES)
5. LOWER YOKE
6. PIVOT FITTING (2 PLACES)
7. ATTACHING BRACE
8. POSITIONING BRACKET
9. MIDBODY ATTACHING INSERT
10. ADAPTER FITTING
11. ADJUSTING SCREW

← FORWARD

Fig. 8–41 Problems 23 through 26. (Courtesy of Lockheed Aircraft Corporation.)

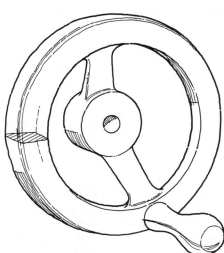

Fig. 8–42 Problem 27: Handwheel.

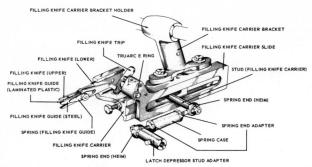

Fig. 8–43 Problem 28: Portion of loom assembly. (Courtesy of Draper Corporation.)

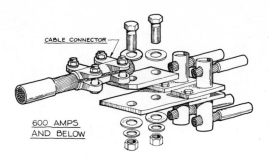

Fig. 8–45 Problem 35: An electrical cable connector. (Courtesy of Toledo Edison Company.)

Type "C-1" Ball Valve Lever Operated

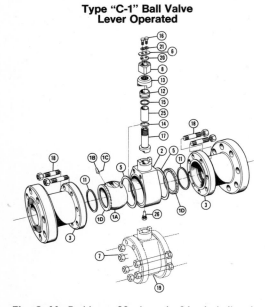

Fig. 8–44 Problems 29 through 34: A ball valve assembly. (Courtesy of Cameron Iron Works.)

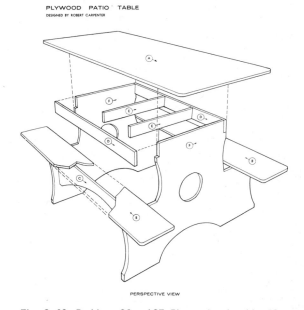

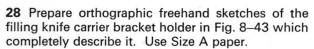

Fig. 8–46 Problems 36 and 37: Plywood patio table. (Courtesy of American Plywood Association.)

28 Prepare orthographic freehand sketches of the filling knife carrier bracket holder in Fig. 8–43 which completely describe it. Use Size A paper.

29–34 Prepare the necessary orthographic freehand sketches to describe parts 2, 3, 17, 12, 13, and 8 shown in Fig. 8–44. Show each individual part on a sheet of Size A paper.

35 Prepare the necessary orthographic freehand sketches to describe the upper portion of the cable connector in Fig. 8–45. Use Size A paper.

36 An exploded assembly of a plywood patio table is shown in Fig. 8–46. Draw the necessary orthographic freehand sketches to describe the assembled table. Use Size A paper.

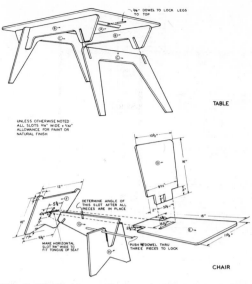

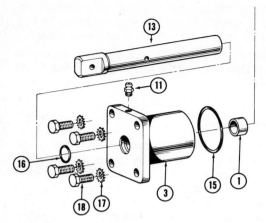

Fig. 8–47 Problem 38: Valve assembly. (Courtesy of Cameron Iron Works.)

Fig. 8–49 Problems 40 through 43: Plywood table and chair. (Courtesy of American Plywood Association.)

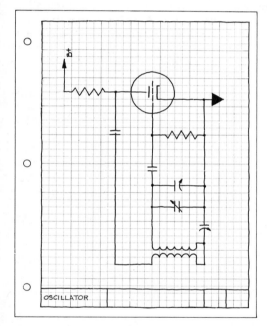

Fig. 8–48 Problem 39: Sketch of an oscillator circuit.

38 Prepare the necessary orthographic freehand sketches to describe parts 13 (shaft) and 3 (carrier) shown in Fig. 8–47. Use Size A paper.

39 Using grid or plain paper, sketch the layout of the oscillator circuit in Fig. 8–48.

40 A partially exploded assembly of a plywood table is shown in the upper half of Fig. 8–49. Prepare the necessary freehand sketches to describe the assembled table. Use Size A paper.

41 Prepare the necessary orthographic views of each individual part of the table in Fig. 8–49. All parts are made of $\frac{3}{4}''$ plywood. Use Size A paper.

42 A partially exploded assembly of a plywood chair is shown in the lower half of Fig. 8–49. Prepare the necessary freehand sketches to describe the assembled chair. Use Size A paper.

43 Prepare the necessary orthographic views of each individual part of the chair in Fig. 8–49. All parts are made of $\frac{3}{4}''$ plywood. Use Size A paper.

44 Prepare a freehand sketch that illustrates the floor plan for the weekend cabin shown in Fig. 8–50. Use Size A paper.

37 Prepare the necessary orthographic freehand sketches to describe the individual parts of the plywood patio table in Fig. 8–46. The table is made of $\frac{3}{4}''$ plywood. Use Size B paper.

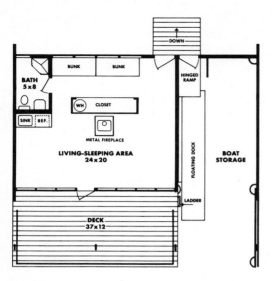

Fig. 8–50 Problem 44: Sketch of a floor plan of a weekend cabin. (Courtesy of American Plywood Association.)

45 Lay out a grid spaced $\frac{3}{4}''$ apart with instruments on a Size B sheet. Draw the rocking horse in Fig. 8–51 on this grid. This is to be a freehand sketch.

46 Lay out a grid spaced $\frac{3}{4}''$ apart with instruments on a Size B sheet. Draw the rocking lion in Fig. 8–30 on this grid.

Design Problems

Design problems are more typical applications of freehand sketching, since this is the method used by a designer in developing his ideas. The following problems require that you use your judgment to a greater extent than the previous problems of this chapter. In general, these problems are easy to solve, but the difficulty is devising the *best* solution or the *optimum*.

In solving design problems, make a number of sketches to express your ideas; do not feel that you are limited to only one possible solution. Select the

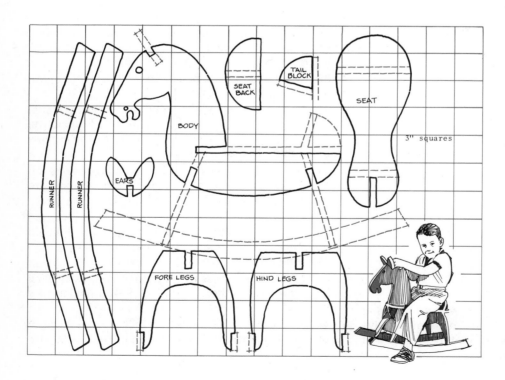

Fig. 8–51 Problem 45: Layout for a rocking horse on $\frac{3}{4}''$ plywood. (Courtesy of American Plywood Association.)

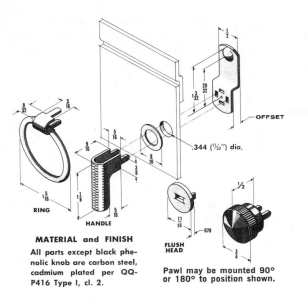

RING

HANDLE

.344 (¹¹⁄₃₂'') dia.

OFFSET

FLUSH HEAD

MATERIAL and FINISH

All parts except black phenolic knob are carbon steel, cadmium plated per QQ-P416 Type I, cl. 2.

Pawl may be mounted 90° or 180° to position shown.

Fig. 8–52 Problem 50: Design of a locking mechanism. (Courtesy of Southco Corporation.)

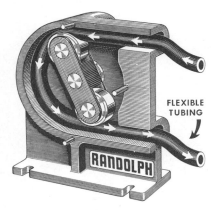

FLEXIBLE TUBING

RANDOLPH

Fig. 8–53 Problem 51: A pump design. (Courtesy of the Randolph Company.)

proper scale for your drawings if dimensions are important. Remember, the more ideas you can produce, the more likely you are to come up with a creative solution.

47 Design a doorstop that can be attached to a wall or to a floor to prevent the door from hitting the wall when it is opened. Show several ideas for solving this design problem. Prepare orthographic sketches of your better ideas. Indicate the one solution that you think is the very best.

48 Make a series of freehand orthographic sketches of a design for a cup and toothbrush holder that could be attached to your bathroom wall. First you must determine the sizes of cups and toothbrushes to be sure your design is in the correct proportion.

49 Make freehand sketches of the faucet handles in your bathroom that are used for turning water on and off at the lavatory. Using these as a guide, design a better faucet handle and communicate your design in a series of freehand orthographic sketches. Develop several ideas and specify the design that you think is the best.

50 The locking assembly illustrated in Fig. 8–52 is used to lock metal cabinets. Three types of hand grip are shown—a ring, a handle, and a knob. Design a better handle or ring than those shown. Prepare orthographic freehand sketches of your design. Also illustrate how the parts would be assembled together.

51 An illustration of a Randolph pump, in which a liquid is pumped through a flexible tube by rotating rollers, is shown in Fig. 8–53. The tubing has an outside diameter of $\frac{3}{8}$''. Study this pump and make freehand sketches to describe the parts of the pump, including the cover plate which is not shown in the illustration. Use your judgment to determine the shape and the description of the parts that are not visible to you in this assembly. Use as many sheets of Size A paper as necessary.

52 Design a book rest that will hold your textbook in a position on your desk that is convenient for you when you are referring to it. Show your designs as a series of freehand orthographic sketches. Use Size A paper.

53 Design a floor plan for a dormitory room that you would like to have when you go to college. Show your ideas as a series of freehand sketches of floor plans. Keep your plan as practical as possible.

54 Design a rocking toy similar to those shown in Figs. 8–30 and 8–51. You may redesign the toy completely or simply change the type of animal represented. Show your completed design as freehand sketches on Size A or B paper.

Fig. 8–54 Problem 58: A rotating pencil pointer.

55 Design a mailbox that could be used at your home. Can you think of new features or a new material from which the mailbox could be made? Show your ideas as orthographic freehand sketches on Size A paper.

56 Make a freehand sketch of a project that you would like to make in the shop. Show your ideas as orthographic freehand sketches.

57 Design a locker unit that could be used in your classroom for storing the drafting supplies used either by the entire class or by you alone. Show your ideas as freehand orthographic sketches.

58 The device in Fig. 8–54 is a rotating pencil pointer that is designed to fit a holder attached to a desk top. Design the holder into which the $\frac{1}{4}''$ dia. × 2'' post will fit. Show your ideas as a series of orthographic freehand sketches. Use Size A paper.

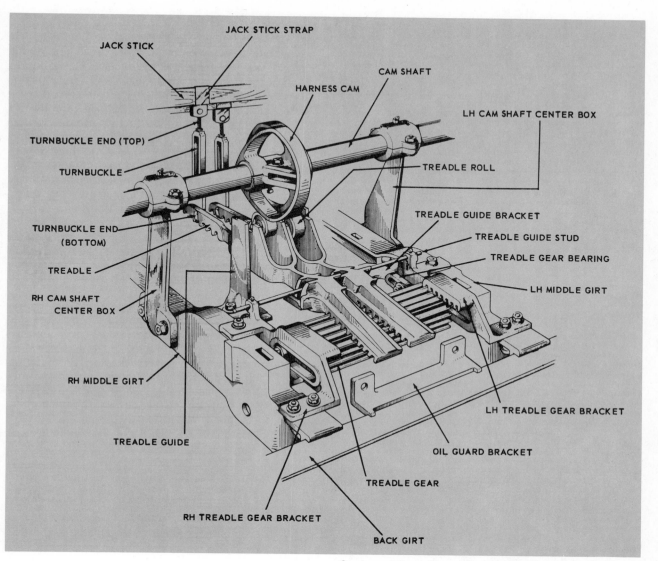

JACK STICK STRAP

JACK STICK

HARNESS CAM

CAM SHAFT

LH CAM SHAFT CENTER BOX

TURNBUCKLE END (TOP)

TURNBUCKLE

TREADLE ROLL

TREADLE GUIDE BRACKET

TURNBUCKLE END (BOTTOM)

TREADLE GUIDE STUD

TREADLE GEAR BEARING

TREADLE

LH MIDDLE GIRT

RH CAM SHAFT CENTER BOX

RH MIDDLE GIRT

LH TREADLE GEAR BRACKET

TREADLE GUIDE

OIL GUARD BRACKET

TREADLE GEAR

RH TREADLE GEAR BRACKET

BACK GIRT

Courtesy of Draper Corporation, Hopedale, Massachusetts

9
PICTORIALS

9-1 INTRODUCTION

A working drawing prepared according to graphic principles may be correct in every detail yet difficult to read, even to the skilled technician. This is not the fault of the designer, the draftsman, or the craftsman using the drawings; it simply reflects the fact that the object being shown in the drawing is complicated.

Pictorials can be used effectively to describe an object that is difficult to depict in a working drawing. A pictorial is a drawing that shows the three dimensions of an object in much the same manner as an object is shown in a photograph. Pictorials are helpful in communicating ideas in such a way that a minimum of effort is required for interpretation.

An example of the value of a pictorial drawing can be seen in a pictorial of an assembly of a golf car (Fig. 9-1). This car is composed of many individual parts that must fit together in a specific manner. It is difficult to explain the relationship between the parts by a drawing or even by telling someone orally. However, a maintenance and operation catalog must explain this assembly as simply and completely as possible. The illustration in Fig. 9-2 shows an exploded assembly of the front and rear suspension systems. By referring to this drawing, an untrained person can understand the assembly of the various parts and their relationship. Each part is drawn as a pictorial so that each is recognizable and appears much the same as it would if photographed.

Pictorials can be used to advantage in many types of communication, from technical reports to oral presentation. Pictorials may be line drawings, freehand sketches, or artists' renderings with a high degree of realism. This chapter will discuss the fundamental mechanics required for preparing the types of pictorials most often used by the draftsman and technician in engineering applications.

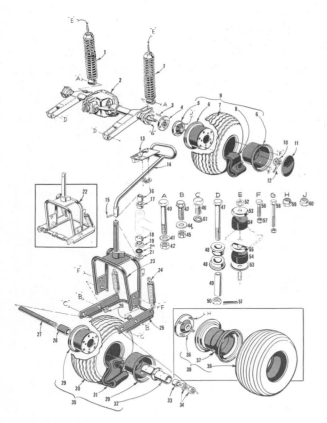

Fig. 9-2 This exploded pictorial illustration clearly explains the relationship of various parts of the front and rear suspension of the Viking golf car shown in Fig. 9-1. (Courtesy of Versal, Inc.)

9-2 TYPES OF PICTORIALS

The three basic types of pictorial are used to illustrate the same object in Fig. 9-3. The three types are (A) *isometric*, (B) *oblique*, and (C) *perspective*.

The isometric drawing is the most commonly used pictorial system. Obliques have special applications which make them advantageous at certain times. The perspective will be discussed in Chapter

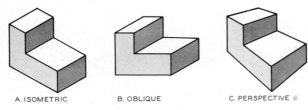

A. ISOMETRIC   B. OBLIQUE   C. PERSPECTIVE

Fig. 9–3 The three basic types of pictorials.

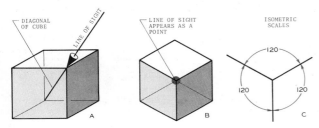

Fig. 9–4 An isometric drawing will result when the line of sight is parallel to the diagonal of a cube (A). The line of sight will appear as a point in the isometric drawing (B), and the surfaces will be equally foreshortened. The three axes will be separated by 120° (C).

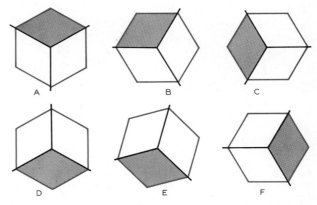

Fig. 9–5 Various positions of the axes of isometric drawings.

18, since it is used extensively in *technical illustration*. Perspectives are the most realistic pictorials, but they are more difficult to prepare than isometrics and obliques.

9–3 ISOMETRIC DRAWING PRINCIPLES

An isometric drawing is an effective method of illustrating an object with the minimum of difficulty. However, the principles of isometric drawing are based on principles of orthographic projection. When a cube is drawn in isometric, the three visible surfaces of the cube appear equal in size and shape. This is so because in an isometric drawing the line of sight is assumed to be parallel to the diagonal of a cube (Fig. 9–4A). The result is that the diagonal appears as a point (part B) and the three surfaces are equally fore-shortened. The three axes of the isometric drawing are spaced 120° apart (part C). These axes may be referred to as *isometric scales*.

The fact that the three planes of a cube are equally foreshortened is the basis for the term *isometric*. This word means "equal measurement."

The three isometric axes (or scales) must be positioned 120° apart, but the object being drawn in isometric can be positioned in any manner that will show the details properly. Several positions of a cube are illustrated in Fig. 9–5. Note that in all cases the axes are separated by 120° even though each object is positioned differently.

9–4 ISOMETRIC LINES AND PLANES

The three isometric axes are important in the construction of an isometric pictorial. These lines, and other lines that are parallel to them, are called *isometric lines*. True measurements can be made along these lines using any scale desired. You cannot make true measurements along lines that are *not* isometric lines.

For example, the isometric lines labeled in Fig. 9–6A can be measured just as in an orthographic view. However, a nonisometric line, one that is not parallel to one of the axes, cannot be measured to determine its length, since the scale changes as the

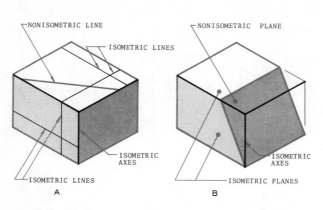

Fig. 9–6 (A) True measurements can be made only along isometric lines (lines that are parallel to the three axes). Lines not parallel to the axes are nonisometric and cannot be measured. (B) Nonisometric planes are planes that are inclined to any of the three planes of a cube in an isometric drawing.

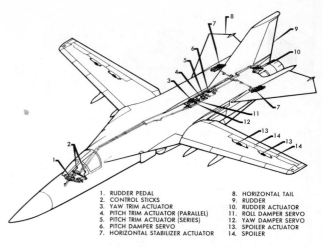

1. RUDDER PEDAL	8. HORIZONTAL TAIL
2. CONTROL STICKS	9. RUDDER
3. YAW TRIM ACTUATOR	10. RUDDER ACTUATOR
4. PITCH TRIM ACTUATOR (PARALLEL)	11. ROLL DAMPER SERVO
5. PITCH TRIM ACTUATOR (SERIES)	12. YAW DAMPER SERVO
6. PITCH DAMPER SERVO	13. SPOILER ACTUATOR
7. HORIZONTAL STABILIZER ACTUATOR	14. SPOILER

Fig. 9–7 An isometric drawing of the F-111 aircraft. (Courtesy of General Dynamics.)

FIGURE 9–8. CONSTRUCTION OF AN ISOMETRIC DRAWING

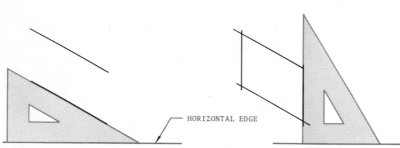

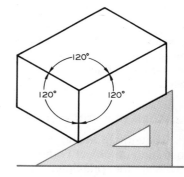

Step 1. A 30°-60° triangle is used in combination with a horizontal straightedge for drawing the initial lines of an isometric.

Step 2. Vertical lines are drawn. Note that parallel lines appear parallel in isometric as well as orthographic views.

Step 3. The final side of the isometric is drawn and the lines are strengthened. The 30°-60° triangle automatically separates the axes of the drawing by 120°.

direction of the line in relation to the isometric axes changes.

The three surfaces of a cube drawn in isometric are called *isometric planes* (Fig. 9–6B). Planes that are not parallel to these planes are *nonisometric* planes. Measurements on nonisometric planes must be handled differently from measurements on isometric planes.

9–5 CONSTRUCTING AN ISOMETRIC DRAWING

An isometric drawing can be used to illustrate various kinds of objects, from a simple part to a complex project such as the airplane in Fig. 9–7. The same principles are used in all cases. The examples in this chapter have been kept simple to explain these principles as clearly and directly as possible.

FIGURE 9-9. LAYOUT OF AN ISOMETRIC DRAWING

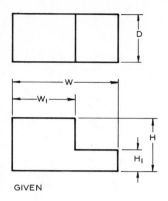

GIVEN

Step 1. The object is blocked in: a box is drawn using the overall dimensions—height, width, and depth—from the orthographic views.

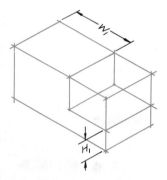

Step 2. The notch is removed by using dimensions W_1 and H_1. All lines are drawn as light construction lines to this point.

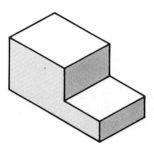

Step 3. The final lines are strengthened. If the construction lines were made lightly, they need not be erased in the final isometric since they will hardly be visible.

The basic tools for constructing an isometric drawing are the 30°-60° triangle and the straight-edge. Since the isometric axes are 120° apart, the 30-60° triangle will automatically give this separation when used with a horizontal base line (the horizontal edge) as shown in Fig. 9–8. Usually the vertical lines of an object are drawn as vertical lines in isometric (Step 2). The completed isometric drawing of a block is shown in Step 3 of Fig. 9–8.

When working from a multi-view drawing such as a working drawing, you can transfer actual dimensions to the isometric drawing to make sure that the proper proportions are maintained. It is easier to construct an isometric drawing if you draw a block first using the overall height, width, and depth dimensions (Fig. 9–9, Step 1). Other dimensions can be used to establish notches or parts that must be removed from the "blocked-in" drawing (Step 2) to give the completed pictorial (Step 3).

A comparison between a plan view of a concrete wall with a built-in duct and a pictorial of the same feature can be seen in Fig. 9–10. This detail is more understandable in isometric form than in orthographic form.

An object that is somewhat more complicated—two notches must be removed—is shown in Fig. 9–11. In Step 1, the object is "blocked in" using the overall dimensions and one notch is removed using

FIGURE 9–11. LAYOUT OF AN ISOMETRIC DRAWING

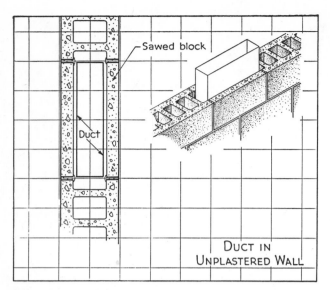

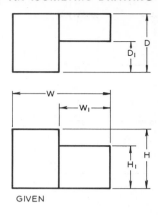

GIVEN

Fig. 9–10 A comparison of an orthographic view and an isometric pictorial of the same detail. (Courtesy of Portland Cement Association.)

dimensions W_1 and D_1. In Step 2, the second notch is removed using dimensions H_1 and W_1. The completed isometric drawing is shown in Step 3.

9–6 ANGLES IN ISOMETRIC

Angles formed with nonisometric lines cannot be measured as true angles, nor can nonisometric lines be measured as true-length lines. The two 30° angles shown in the orthographic views in Fig. 9–12A do not appear as 30° angles in the isometric drawing in B. In B one of the angles is more than 30° and the other is less than 30°.

This fact is further illustrated in Fig. 9–13, where an object with nonisometric planes is drawn in isometric. The lines that appear true length in orthographic projection appear longer and shorter than true length in isometric. The only way of locating points A and B is by using measurement D along the isometric axis. Remember that only measurements parallel to isometric axes can be measured as true length. Angles cannot be measured in isometric.

An object with an inclined surface is shown in Fig. 9–14. The method of constructing an isometric drawing of this object from the two orthographic views is shown in three steps. In Step 1, the object is blocked in pictorially, and the notch is removed using dimensions from the given views. In Step 2 the inclined plane is drawn from its extreme ends. Note that any two lines of an object which are parallel in orthographic views will project parallel in the pictorial view as well. The completed pictorial, strengthened with heavier lines, is shown in Step 3. If the construction lines are kept very light, they need not be erased because they will not be noticeable when the object lines are strengthened. In addition, to obtain a neater drawing, the pictorial can be traced or transferred to a clean sheet after construction has been completed.

The column detail in Fig. 9–15 is shown in isometric to clarify its details of construction. Hidden lines are usually omitted in pictorials, but in this case they are used to point out details that might be overlooked. Note that the metal shoe has angular flanges at each corner.

FIGURE 9–11 (CONTINUED)

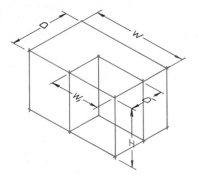

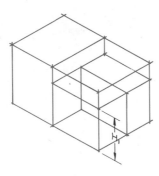

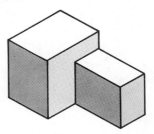

Step 1. The overall dimensions of the object are used to lightly block in the object. One notch is removed by using dimensions taken from the given views.

Step 2. The second notch is removed using dimension H_1.

Step 3. The final lines of the isometric are strengthened.

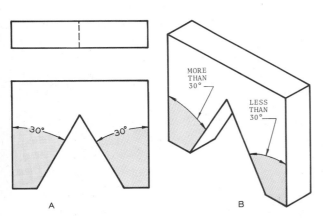

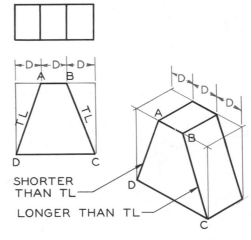

Fig. 9–12 Angular measurements cannot be made in isometric drawings. Angles drawn in isometric are greater and less than the true angles.

Fig. 9–13 Angular lines can be located in isometric by measuring only along the isometric axes. Note that angled lines are less and greater than true length (TL) in isometric.

FIGURE 9–14. CONSTRUCTION OF AN ISOMETRIC DRAWING WITH AN INCLINED PLANE

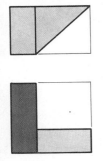

GIVEN

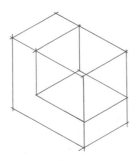

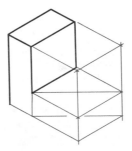

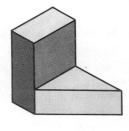

Step 1. The object is blocked in using the overall dimensions. The notch is removed.

Step 2. The inclined plane is located by establishing its end points.

Step 3. The lines are strengthened to complete the drawing.

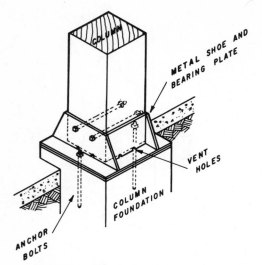

Fig. 9–15 An isometric drawing of a column detail; the support shoe has inclined planes. (Courtesy of American Plywood Association.)

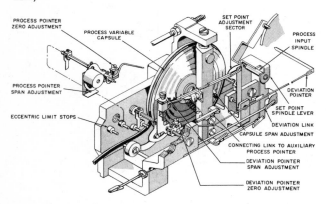

Fig. 9–16 A pictorial of a scale instrument where circular features are drawn in isometric as ellipses. (Courtesy of Fischer and Porter Company.)

9–7 CIRCLES IN ISOMETRIC

The most difficult problem of pictorial drawing is that of representing circles by means of ellipses. The pictorial assembly shown in Fig. 9–16 is composed of several circular shapes that are drawn as ellipses.

There are three methods of constructing circles in isometric drawings: (1) point plotting, (2) four-center ellipse construction, and (3) ellipse templates.

FIGURE 9–17. PLOTTING CIRCLES

GIVEN

Step 1. The cylinder is blocked in using the overall dimensions. The centerlines locate the points of tangency of the ellipse.

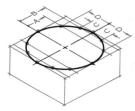

Step 2. Coordinates are used to locate points on the circumference of the circle.

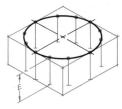

Step 3. The lower ellipse is found by dropping each point a distance equal to the height of the cylinder *E*.

Step 4. The two ellipses can be drawn with an irregular curve and connected with tangent lines to complete the cylinder.

These three methods will be discussed in the following articles.

9-8 CIRCLES: POINT PLOTTING

When a series of points is located along the circumference of a circle, these points can be located in an isometric pictorial by using two dimensions parallel to the isometric axes. These two dimensions are called *coordinates*. Examples of coordinates are shown in Fig. 9–17 in the given views of the cylinder.

First the cylinder is blocked in and drawn pictorially, with the centerlines added as shown in Step 1. The points where the centerlines intersect the box are the points of tangency through which the ellipse must pass. Coordinates *A*, *B*, *C*, and *D* are used in Step 2 to locate points on the ellipse that can be joined with the aid of an irregular curve. The ellipse shown here is a *true ellipse*.

The lower ellipse that is located on the bottom plane of the cylinder can be found without using a second set of coordinates for each point. Since the upper plane is parallel to the lower plane, the height *E* can be measured below each point on the upper plane (Step 3). The completed ellipses can be connected with parallel vertical lines tangent to both ellipses to give the completed drawing in Step 4.

This true ellipse corresponds to the ellipse found in ellipse templates. The ellipse template used for true ellipses in isometric drawings is the 35° template.

9-9 CIRCLES: FOUR-CENTER ELLIPSE CONSTRUCTION

A handwheel used in an orbital workshop that will be launched into space is shown in Fig. 9–18 as an isometric drawing. The circular features were constructed using the four-center ellipse method to give an *approximate* ellipse. This is a method that is satisfactory for most applications, even though the ellipse is not a true ellipse since it is formed from arcs drawn with a compass.

The construction of a four-center ellipse is shown in four steps in Fig. 9–19. The top view of the circle is blocked in with a square which is tangent to the circle at four points. The isometric drawing of the square results in a rhombus (Step 1). We find the centerlines by locating the midpoints of the sides of the rhombus. In Steps 2 and 3, perpendicular construction lines are drawn from the midpoints of the

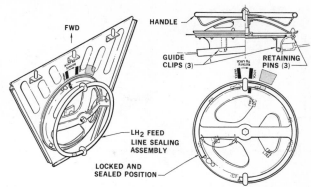

Fig. 9–18 An example of parts that have been drawn using ellipses in isometric to represent circles. This is a handwheel that is proposed for use in an orbital workshop to be launched into space in the future. (Courtesy of the National Aeronautics and Space Administration.)

sides of the rhombus to locate center points for drawing the four arcs that will be tangent to the sides and will form the ellipse. This construction is based on the principle that the perpendicular bisectors of the chords of a circle intersect at the circle's center.

The radii for the arcs are found by measuring from the center points to the midpoints of the sides of the rhombus. The four arcs are drawn separately to give the completed four-center ellipse in Step 4. This method can be used on any of the three isometric planes, since all isometric planes are equally foreshortened.

9-10 CIRCLES: ELLIPSE TEMPLATES

Circles in pictorial can be drawn by using ellipse templates, which were discussed in Chapter 5. In order to use an ellipse guide effectively, it is necessary that you understand ellipses and their elements.

When a circle is blocked in (Fig. 9–20A), the diameter of the circle is equal to the length of one of the sides of the rhombus. Note that the longest diameter of the ellipse is greater than the true diameter of the circle. This diameter is called the major diameter (Fig. 9–20B). The minor diameter is the smallest diameter that can be measured. The minor diameter is perpendicular to the major diameter and, like the major diameter, passes through the center of the ellipse.

FIGURE 9–19. CONSTRUCTION OF THE FOUR-CENTER ELLIPSE

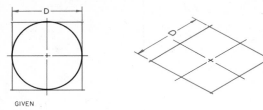

GIVEN

Step 1. The diameter of the circle is used for construction of a rhombus that is tangent to the ellipse.

Step 2. Perpendicular lines are drawn from the midpoints of two intersecting sides of the rhombus to locate the center of an arc for drawing one segment of the ellipse. The procedure is repeated on the opposite sides of the rhombus to yield a second segment of the ellipse.

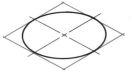

Step 3. The centers for the two remaining arcs are located.

Step 4. When the four arcs have been drawn, the final result is an approximate ellipse.

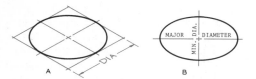

Fig. 9–20 The diameter of the circle is measured along the isometric axes. The major diameter of an ellipse in isometric is greater than the actual diameter of the circle, since it is the diagonal of the rhombus. The minor diameter is perpendicular to the major diameter.

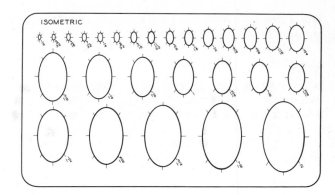

Fig. 9–21 The isometric ellipse template is a special template designed to reduce drafting time. Note that the true diameters of the circles are not the major diameters of the ellipses, but the diameters that are parallel to the isometric axes.

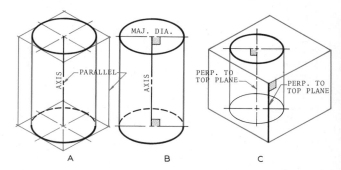

Fig. 9–22 Two methods of drawing cylinders in isometric are shown in A and B. Construction of a cylindrical hole in isometric is shown in C.

A special isometric ellipse template is available for drawing ellipses that lie in isometric planes (Fig. 9–21). Marks are given around the elliptical holes in the template for aligning the guide with the major and minor diameters or the isometric centerlines of the circles in isometric.

Two methods of using the isometric ellipse template are illustrated in parts A and B of Fig. 9–22. In A, the cylinder is blocked in and the isometric centerlines are drawn. The centerlines are used for aligning the ellipse template. The diameter of the circle shown in isometric is shorter than the major diameter of the ellipse. This shorter diameter is the dimension that is labeled on the ellipse template. For example, if the true diameter of the circle is $1\frac{1}{2}''$, then the $1\frac{1}{2}''$ ellipse template is used.

FIGURE 9–23. CYLINDERS IN ISOMETRIC

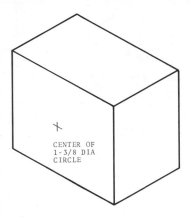

CENTER OF
1-3/8 DIA
CIRCLE

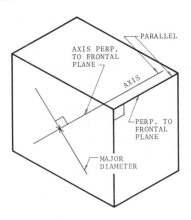

PARALLEL

AXIS PERP.
TO FRONTAL
PLANE

AXIS

PERP. TO
FRONTAL
PLANE

MAJOR
DIAMETER

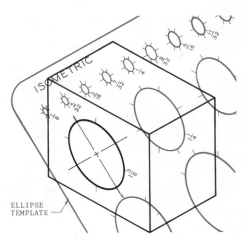

ISOMETRIC

ELLIPSE
TEMPLATE

Step 1. The center of the hole with a given diameter is located on a face of the isometric drawing.

Step 2. The axis of the cylinder is drawn from the center parallel to that isometric axis which is perpendicular to the plane of the circle. The major diameter is drawn perpendicular to the axis of the cylindrical hole.

Step 3. The 1⅜″ ellipse template is used to draw the ellipse by aligning the major and minor diameters with the guidelines on the template.

In Fig. 9–22B, the major diameter of the ellipse and the axis of the cylinder are used for constructing the cylinder. The axis of a right cylinder is always perpendicular to the major diameter of the elliptical ends. In this case, the ellipse guide's major diameter is aligned to be perpendicular to the axis. As in part A, you must use the size of ellipse that corresponds to the true diameter of the circle measured in the direction of the isometric axes. The reason for this is that the major diameter of the isometric ellipse is not labeled on the template. The major diameter is greater than the actual diameter of the circle.

You can use these principles very conveniently to construct a cylindrical hole through an isometric drawing of a part. Since one isometric axis will always be perpendicular to the plane formed by the other two axes, the axis of a cylindrical hole will be parallel to one of the axes if it is perpendicular to one of the isometric planes. The elliptical view of the cylinder is drawn by placing the major diameter of the ellipse template perpendicular to the axis of the cylinder (Fig. 9–22C).

An example of constructing a cylindrical hole through an isometric view is shown in three steps in Fig. 9–23. The isometric is drawn in Step 1 and the center is located on the desired plane (which we shall

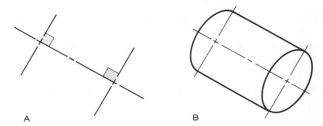

A

B

Fig. 9–24 A cylinder can easily be constructed in isometric by drawing the axis to the proper length and constructing major diameters perpendicular to the axis at each end (A). The ellipse templates are selected for the proper size and the circular ends are drawn by aligning the major and minor diameters with the template (B).

call the frontal plane). In Step 2, the axis of the cylinder is drawn parallel to that isometric axis which is perpendicular to the plane of the circle (i.e., the frontal plane). The minor diameter will be located on this axis. The major diameter is then drawn perpendicular to the axis of the cylinder through its center. Now that the minor and major diameters have been established, an ellipse template can be used to complete the drawing (Step 3).

The isometric ellipse template can also be used conveniently to draw a cylinder when the length of

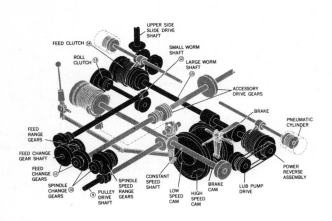

Fig. 9–25 Examples of ellipses drawn in schematic to illustrate gearing systems of a machine. (Courtesy of the National Acme Company.)

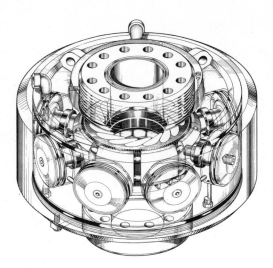

Fig. 9–26 This diaphanous view of a blowout preventer was drawn using an ellipse template to illustrate the circular features. (Courtesy of Cameron Iron Works, Inc., and L. G. Whitfield.)

the axis and the diameter of the circle are known. The axis is drawn as an isometric line and measured to the proper length. The major diameters are drawn perpendicular to the axis at each end (Fig. 9–24A). The ellipse template's major diameter is aligned with the perpendiculars at each end and the ellipses are drawn (part B). If the circular end is 2″ in diameter, then the 2″ ellipse template is used. The elliptical ends of the cylinder are connected with isometric lines that are tangent to the ellipses.

Several examples of ellipses and axes are shown in isometric in Fig. 9–25. Note that the major diameters are perpendicular to their respective axes. The same principles were applied to the drawing in Fig. 9–26. The horizontal circles were drawn with isometric ellipse templates, but the cylindrical parts that face in different directions about the center were drawn with different ellipse templates, each with a different angle—30°, 15°, etc.

9–11 PARTIAL CIRCLES IN ISOMETRIC

Partial circles such as fillets and rounds are drawn in isometric using the principles discussed in the previous articles. Any of the methods can be used.

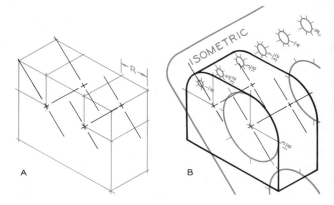

Fig. 9–27 Construction of rounded corners with an ellipse template. The four-center ellipse method could have been used equally well.

In Fig. 9–27A, an object with rounded corners is blocked in and the centerlines are located at each corner that is to be rounded. An ellipse template is used in B to construct the rounded corners on the front and back planes. These rounded corners could have been constructed by the four-center ellipse method or by plotting points on the circles.

FIGURE 9–28. MEASURING ANGLES WITH AN ELLIPSE TEMPLATE

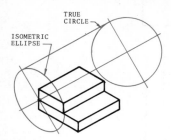

Step 1. An ellipse is drawn with the major diameter perpendicular to the hinge line of the two parts. Any size of ellipse could be used. A true circle is drawn with its center on the projection of the hinge line and with a diameter equal to the major diameter of the ellipse.

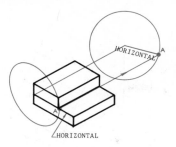

Step 2. Point *A* is projected to the circle to locate the direction of the horizontal in the circular view.

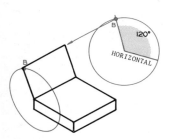

Step 3. The position of rotation is measured 120° from the horizontal to locate point *B*, which is then projected to the ellipse to locate the position of the revolved surface.

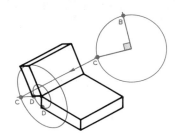

Step 4. To locate the perpendicular to the surface, a 90° angle is drawn in the circular view and the point *C* is projected to the ellipse; a line is drawn from point *C* on the ellipse to the center of the ellipse. A smaller ellipse is drawn to pass through point *D* on the lower part of the object. The point where this ellipse intersects the line from *C* to the center of the ellipse establishes the thickness of the revolved part. The drawing can now be easily completed.

9–12 REVOLVED FEATURES IN ISOMETRIC

Some objects are designed with surfaces that do not lie in isometric planes; hence their angles must be constructed with the aid of coordinates or an ellipse guide. Such an object is illustrated in Fig. 9–28, where one surface is hinged to another. Since the hinge line is perpendicular to the path of revolution, this path can be shown as an ellipse in Step 1, with the major diameter of the ellipse perpendicular to the hinge line. A true circle is drawn with a diameter that is equal to the major diameter of the ellipse.

In Step 2, point *A* is located on the ellipse and projected to the circle to locate the position of a horizontal line in the circle. To locate the position of the hinged part when it is revolved 120°, this angle is

measured in the construction circle (Step 3). The point *B* in the circle is then projected to the ellipse to locate the plane of the revolved surface.

To find the thickness of the revolved part, it is necessary to find the direction of the line that is perpendicular to the surface. In Step 4, point *C* is located on the circle 90° from point *B* and is projected to the ellipse. The line from the center of the ellipse to point *C* is perpendicular to the surface. To find the thickness, a smaller ellipse is drawn that passes through point *D* of the lower piece, which has the same thickness as the revolved part. The new position of point *D* is found on the line drawn to point *C*. The drawing is completed by drawing the edges of the surfaces parallel to the line through *D* on the revolved part and to the hinge line.

FIGURE 9–29. CONSTRUCTION OF ELLIPSES ON AN INCLINED PLANE

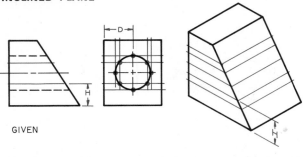

GIVEN

Step 1. Coordinates are established in the orthographic views and corresponding coordinates are located in the isometric drawing. All measurements are made parallel to the isometric axes.

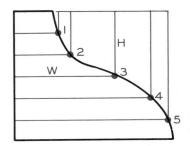

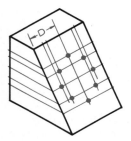

Step 2. The other coordinates are drawn to locate points on the ellipse.

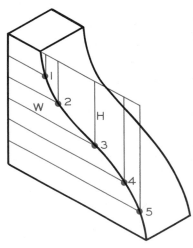

Fig. 9–30 The construction of an irregular curve in an isometric drawing by plotting points.

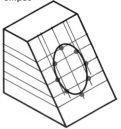

Step 3. The points are connected with an irregular curve, or an ellipse template angle can be selected by trial and error.

9–13 CIRCLES IN NONISOMETRIC PLANES

When a circle or an arc lies on a nonisometric plane, the circle must be plotted point-by-point, since the regular isometric ellipse guide can be used only on isometric planes. Two views of an object having an inclined plane are given in Fig. 9–29. The object is

drawn in isometric, and a series of coordinates is used to locate points corresponding to those in the given views. These coordinates are used in Step 1 and Step 2 to locate a number of points on the ellipse. The points are connected with an irregular curve (Step 3) to give the completed ellipse.

The ellipse could have been blocked in and the centerlines located on the nonisometric surface. An ellipse-guide angle (other than isometric) could have been determined by trial and error to approximate the

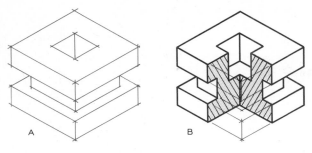

Fig. 9–31 The construction of an isometric half section. The imaginary cutting plane passes halfway through the object to show internal features.

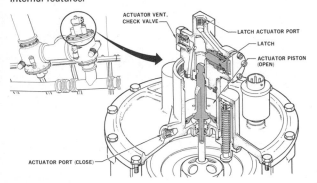

Fig. 9–32 A pictorial half section used to illustrate a vent control valve of an orbital workshop. (Courtesy of the National Aeronautics and Space Administration.)

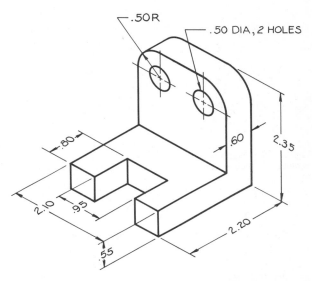

Fig. 9–33 An isometric drawing can be dimensioned to serve the same purpose as a working drawing.

ellipse that would be tangent to the blocked-in ellipse. In an isometric drawing, it is not essential that the ellipse be exactly drawn. After all, a pictorial is merely a representation of an object, and a high degree of accuracy is not essential in most cases.

9–14 IRREGULAR CURVES IN ISOMETRIC

Irregular curves that are not composed of arcs or circles must be plotted point-by-point using coordinates to locate each point. In Fig. 9–30 points 1 through 5 are located along the irregular curve in the given views with coordinates of width and height. These coordinates are transferred to the isometric drawing and are measured along the isometric axes.

The points are located and are connected with an irregular curve. The curve on the back side of the

isometric can be found by projecting each point on the front surface to the rear surface by a distance equal to the depth of the object.

9–15 ISOMETRIC SECTIONS

Sections will be covered in a later chapter, but isometrics can be applied to this form of drawing also. Since a section is a view of an object that has a portion removed in order to make the internal features visible, it is easy for this portion to be removed from an isometric drawing also.

A half section (in which the cutting plane passes halfway through the object) is shown pictorially in Fig. 9–31. The object is blocked in in part A and is completed in part B. To finish the drawing, the section lines are drawn on the surface that has been cut by the imaginary cutting plane.

FIGURE 9–34. CONSTRUCTION OF A CONE IN ISOMETRIC

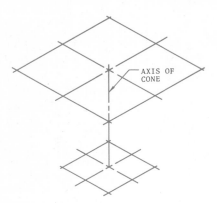

AXIS OF
CONE

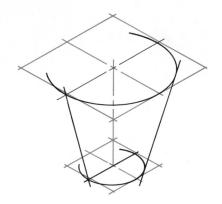

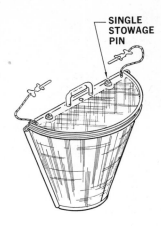

SINGLE
STOWAGE
PIN

Step 1. The axis of the cone is constructed. Each circular end of the cone is blocked in.

Step 2. An ellipse guide is used for constructing the circles in isometric at each end. These ends are connected to give the outline of the object.

Step 3. The remaining details of the screen storage provisions are added to complete the isometric. (Courtesy of the National Aeronautics and Space Administration.)

An example of an isometric half section is shown in Fig. 9–32 to illustrate a vent control valve of an orbital workshop. This drawing shows the internal and external features very clearly.

9–16 DIMENSIONED ISOMETRICS

The shape of a part may be more easily understood if it is drawn isometrically and dimensioned in the pictorial view. A part is shown dimensioned as an isometric drawing in Fig. 9–33.

The dimension lines are drawn as isometric lines with extension lines that locate the dimensions outside the object; this use of extension lines prevents the dimensions from overlapping and confusing the view. The numerals are positioned to lie in the same plane as the isometric plane that is being dimensioned. Note that dimensions that have leaders, such as the .50 DIA holes, use numerals constructed with horizontal guidelines rather than positioned in an isometric plane.

Dimensioned pictorials are excellent for reducing the time it takes for an untrained craftsman to read a complex drawing. The pictorial aids greatly in the understanding of the shape of a part.

9–17 CONSTRUCTION OF A CONICAL PART IN ISOMETRIC

Three steps in the preparation of an isometric drawing of a conical screen storage unit are illustrated in Fig. 9–34. In Step 1, the axis of the cone is measured true length and the rhombuses that enclose the upper and lower circles of the cone are constructed at either end of the axis. The centerlines of each circle are drawn as isometric lines.

In Step 2, the semicircular ends are drawn as ellipses with the aid of either the four-center ellipse method or an ellipse template. A line is drawn from the diameter of the upper circle to the diameter of the lower circle to divide the cone in half. Then a line is drawn tangent to the two ellipses to complete the general outline of the pictorial.

In Step 3, additional details and features are added to complete the pictorial. Lines are added to give a texture to the screen. This illustration fully describes an antivortex screen storage unit.

9–18 ISOMETRIC SCHEMATICS

Isometric drawings are helpful in explaining three-dimensional objects or systems that are difficult to understand in multi-view drawings. Isometric

high pressure steam system

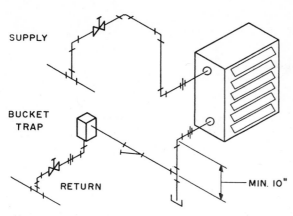

Fig. 9–35 Piping layouts can be illustrated effectively in isometric with single lines. (Courtesy of Grinnell Corporation.)

Fig. 9–36 A piping installation at a petroleum refinery is difficult to represent with orthographic views. (Courtesy of Pan American Petroleum Corporation.)

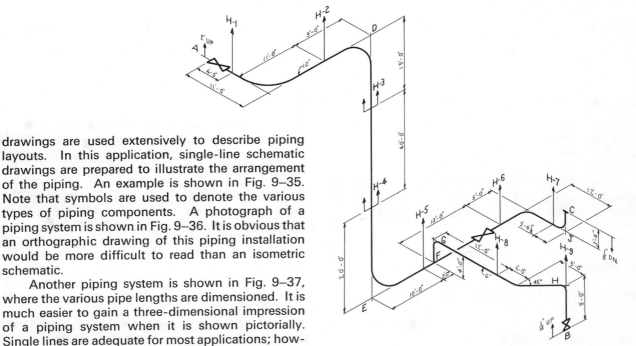

drawings are used extensively to describe piping layouts. In this application, single-line schematic drawings are prepared to illustrate the arrangement of the piping. An example is shown in Fig. 9–35. Note that symbols are used to denote the various types of piping components. A photograph of a piping system is shown in Fig. 9–36. It is obvious that an orthographic drawing of this piping installation would be more difficult to read than an isometric schematic.

Another piping system is shown in Fig. 9–37, where the various pipe lengths are dimensioned. It is much easier to gain a three-dimensional impression of a piping system when it is shown pictorially. Single lines are adequate for most applications; however, double-line drawings are sometimes used to give a more realistic impression.

Fig. 9–37 A dimensioned piping layout shown in isometric using single-line piping symbols. (Courtesy of Grinnell Corporation.)

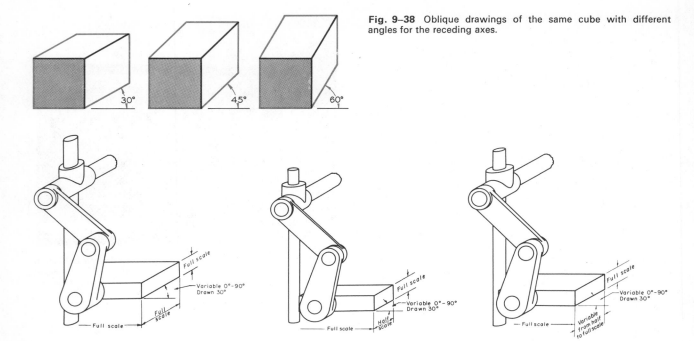

A OBLIQUE PROJECTION - CAVALIER

B OBLIQUE PROJECTION - CABINET

C OBLIQUE PROJECTION - GENERAL

Fig. 9–39 The three basic types of oblique drawings. (Courtesy of ANSI; Y14.4-1957.)

9–19 OBLIQUE DRAWINGS

Although there are similarities between oblique drawings and isometrics, the oblique drawing is based on a different set of principles. Instead of being a type of orthographic projection, as an isometric drawing is, the oblique is usually positioned so as to have one surface of a cube parallel to the projection plane; this surface will thus appear true size. The receding axis is projected to the picture plane—the plane represented by the sheet of paper on which the drawing is made—with projectors that are *oblique* to the picture plane. In the case of orthographic projection and isometric projection, the projectors are *perpendicular* to the picture plane.

Three oblique drawings of a cube are shown in Fig. 9–38. It is important to note that the receding axis can be at *any angle*. In each case, one face of the cube is drawn true size and the receding axis is oblique to the true-size surface.

9–20 TYPES OF OBLIQUES

There are three types of obliques: (a) cavalier, (b) cabinet, and (c) general. In all types, one surface usually appears true size and the receding axis can be drawn at any angle. The primary difference is the scale at which the receding axis is drawn (Fig. 9–39).

In *cavalier* obliques the measurements along the receding axis are true length and are equal to the same dimensions in the orthographic views. The reason for this is that the projectors form 45° angles with the picture plane. This does not mean that the angle between the receding axis and the horizontal must be 45°; this angle can vary from 0° to 90°, and in all cases the measurements along the receding axes will be full size (Fig. 9–39A).

In *cabinet* oblique drawings the measurements along the receding axis are half-length. This shortens the drawing and gives it a more realistic appearance (Fig. 9–39B).

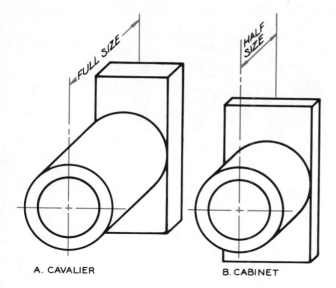

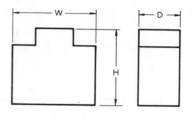

FIGURE 9-41. OBLIQUE CONSTRUCTION

A. CAVALIER

B. CABINET

Fig. 9-40 A comparison of cavalier and cabinet oblique.

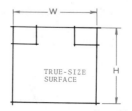

GIVEN

Step 1. The front surface of the oblique is drawn as a true-size plane. The corners are removed.

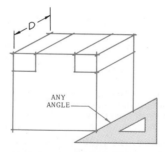

Step 2. The receding axis is selected and the true dimensions are measured along this axis.

In *general* obliques the measurements along the receding axes may be reduced to any proportion between half size and full size (Fig. 9-39C). The angle of the receding axis can vary between 0° and 90°.

A comparison of the most commonly used types of obliques—cavalier and cabinet—is shown in Fig. 9-40. It is apparent that objects with long depths appear excessively long when drawn as cavalier obliques. The cabinet oblique gives a much better appearance.

9-21 CONSTRUCTION OF AN OBLIQUE

As in drawing an isometric, it is advisable to construct an oblique by using the height, width, and depth dimensions to draw a box that contains the object. The front surface is drawn true size in Step 1 of Fig. 9-41. In Step 2, the receding axis is drawn at any angle—30° in this case. The depth is measured true length along the receding axis; therefore, this is a cavalier oblique drawing. The notches are removed from the blocked-in drawing and the lines are strengthened in Step 3 to complete the drawing.

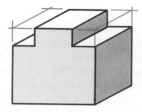

Step 3. The finished cavalier oblique is strengthened to complete the drawing.

9-21   Construction of an oblique   217

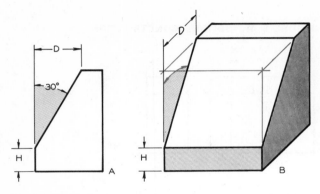

Fig. 9–42 Angles in oblique must be located by using coordinates. They cannot be measured true size.

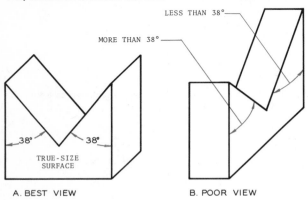

Fig. 9–43 The best view is the view that takes advantage of the ease of construction offered by oblique drawings. The view in B is less descriptive and harder to construct than the view in A.

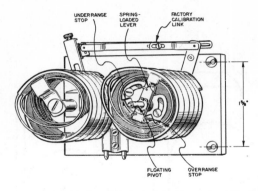

Fig. 9–44 An illustration of circles drawn in oblique as true circles. (Courtesy of Fischer and Porter Company.)

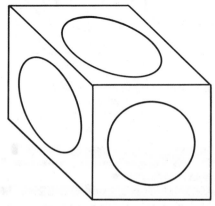

Fig. 9–45 Each of these three circles lies on one of the three planes of an oblique drawing.

The resulting cavalier oblique adequately describes the object in much the same manner as an isometric drawing would.

9–22 ANGLES IN OBLIQUE

Actual measurements can be made in any direction on the true-size plane of an oblique. But on the two other planes of the oblique, true measurements can be made only parallel to the axes of the drawing. In this respect obliques are similar to isometric drawings.

An inclined plane is shown in an orthographic view in Fig. 9–42A. The angle shown here cannot be measured as a 30° angle in the oblique (B). Instead, dimension *D* must be measured along the receding axis to establish the point where the inclined plane will intersect the upper plane of the drawing. Dimension *H* is used to establish the other end of the inclined plane.

Since angles and inclined planes cannot be measured as true angles and true lengths in oblique, it is wise for the draftsman to take advantage of the benefits of an oblique when laying out a drawing. For example, the oblique drawing in part A of Fig. 9–43 is drawn with the front view as a true-size plane where the true angles can be measured. The drawing in part B is correct, but this view requires more construction than does the drawing in A. In addition, the angles cannot be measured true size since they do not lie in a true-size plane. Nor does the position of the object illustrate its features as well in B as in A.

9-23 CIRCLES IN OBLIQUE

One side of a cube always shows true size in an oblique drawing; this means that angles and other measurements can be made true size on this surface in any direction. This feature is the greatest advantage of an oblique drawing. It means that circles can be drawn as true circles on the true-size plane. Figure 9–44 is an example of an oblique drawing of a gauging device composed of circular shapes. The circles are drawn as true circles rather than as ellipses. This advantage can also be seen in Fig. 9–39, where the circular ends of the cylinders are drawn as true circles.

Only one plane of an oblique can appear true size; consequently, the circles on the other two planes must be drawn as ellipses (Fig. 9–45). The four-center ellipse method is used to construct these ellipses as in isometric drawings.

The construction of a four-center ellipse to represent a circle on an oblique plane is shown in four steps in Fig. 9–46. The given circle is blocked in with a square that is tangent to the circle at four points. The square is constructed in Step 1 as a rhombus with the receding axis set at an angle which corresponds with the angle of the oblique plane on which the circle is drawn. The centerlines cross the side of the rhombus at the four points where the ellipse will be tangent. From these points, perpendicular construction lines are drawn to locate the center of an arc that will constitute one-quarter of the ellipse (Step 2). This method is again applied to construct the remaining arcs (Step 3). The completed ellipse is shown in Step 4.

Whenever possible, oblique drawings of objects with circular features should be positioned to have circles drawn on the true-size planes so that they can be drawn as true circles. Unless advantage is taken of this feature, the object might better be illustrated by an isometric drawing.

A wise use of the features of oblique drawings is shown in part A of Fig. 9–47. The circular features here are drawn as true circles. The drawing in part B requires the semicircular feature to be constructed by the four-center ellipse method. Not only does this method require more construction effort, but the view in part B is not as descriptive of the part as is the view in part A.

FIGURE 9-46. FOUR-CENTER ELLIPSE IN OBLIQUE

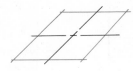

GIVEN

Step 1. The circle that is to be drawn in oblique is blocked in with a square which is tangent to the circle at four points. This square will appear as a rhombus on the oblique plane.

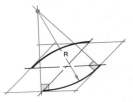

Step 2. Construction lines are drawn perpendicularly from the points of tangency to locate the centers for arcs for drawing two of the four segments of the ellipse.

Step 3. The centers for the two remaining arcs are located.

Step 4. When the four arcs have been drawn, the final result is an approximate ellipse.

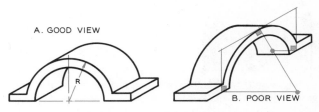

Fig. 9–47 An oblique view should be positioned to enable circular features to be drawn with the greatest of ease.

FIGURE 9-48. CONSTRUCTION OF AN OBLIQUE

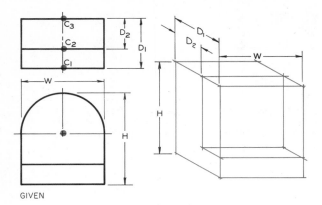

GIVEN

Step 1. The overall dimensions are used to block in the oblique pictorial. The notch is removed.

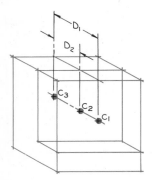

Step 2. The three centers C_1, C_2, and C_3 are located on each of the planes.

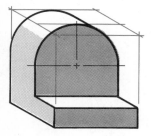

Step 3. The three centers found in Step 2 are used to draw the semicircular features of the oblique. Lines are strengthened.

9-24 CIRCULAR FEATURES IN OBLIQUE

An object with a semicircular end is given in Fig. 9-48. The object is drawn as a blocked-in oblique in Step 1 with the notch removed. Center C_1 is located on the front plane of the box in Step 2. This point is projected back parallel to the receding axis to represent the axis of the cylindrical feature. Center C_2 is located on the middle plane and C_3 is located on the rear plane.

These centers can be used in Step 3 for drawing the two arcs needed to represent the semicircular end. To complete the outline of the object, a line is drawn tangent to the two arcs and parallel to the receding axis. The lines are strengthened to complete the drawing. Note that the circular features are drawn as true circles to take advantage of the fact that true-size measurements can be made on one plane of an oblique pictorial.

9-25 IRREGULAR CURVES IN OBLIQUE

As in isometric drawings, irregular curves that do not lie in the true-size plane of an oblique must be plotted point-by-point. An example is shown in Fig. 9-49.

Coordinates are used to locate points along the curve in the orthographic view. These coordinates are transferred to the oblique drawing to locate the points. An irregular curve is used to draw the curving line. The more points that are used, the more accurate the irregular curve will be.

If the object is of a uniform thickness, the lower curve can be found by projecting vertically down from the upper points a distance equal to the height of the object. It is unnecessary to plot each point on the lower surface with coordinates.

9-26 DIMENSIONED AND SECTIONED OBLIQUES

Oblique drawings can be shown as sections and/or dimensioned as the need may arise to communicate an idea. In Fig. 9-50, a full section illustrates a fly-wheel. Dimensions have been added to make it possible for this pictorial to serve as a working drawing. Any such combination of features is permissible if it aids the interpretation and understanding of an idea.

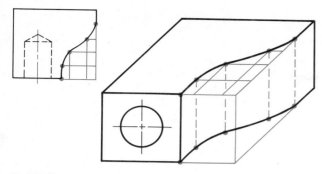

Fig. 9–49 Coordinates are used to establish irregular curves in oblique. The lower curve is found by projecting the points downward a distance equal to the height of the oblique.

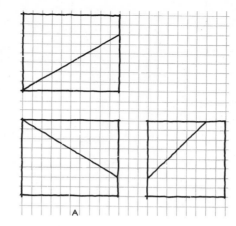

A

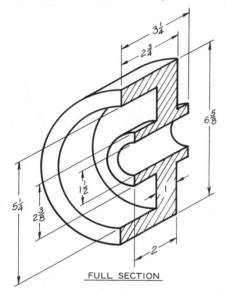

FULL SECTION

Fig. 9–50 Oblique pictorials can be drawn as sections and dimensioned to serve as working drawings.

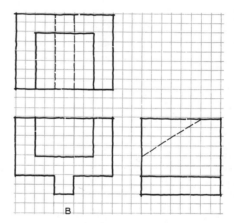

B

Fig. 9–51 Three-view sketches of two parts shown in orthographic projection that may be difficult to visualize.

9–27 PICTORIAL SKETCHING AND DESIGN

Pictorial sketching is used to prepare preliminary sketches to explain an idea that is being developed by a designer. It is also a useful means of communicating ideas from person to person in informal discussions when it becomes difficult to explain details verbally.

The student will find that pictorial sketches help him to visualize multi-view drawings. For example,

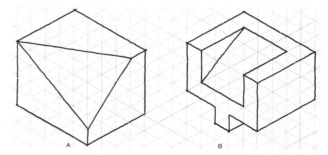

Fig. 9–52 Pictorials of the objects shown in Fig. 9–51. These sketches were made on isometric sketching paper.

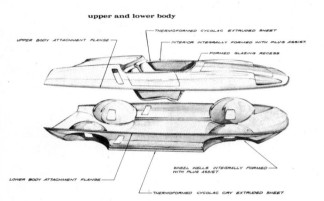

upper and lower body

UPPER BODY ATTACHMENT FLANGE

THERMOFORMED CYCOLAC EXTRUDED SHEET

INTERIOR INTEGRALLY FORMED WITH PLUG ASSIST

FORMED GLAZING RECESS

WHEEL WELLS INTEGRALLY FORMED WITH PLUG ASSIST

LOWER BODY ATTACHMENT FLANGE

THERMOFORMED CYCOLAC CRV EXTRUDED SHEET

Fig. 9–53 A pictorial sketch made by a designer to develop his ideas for the design of an experimental automobile. (Courtesy of Borg-Warner Corporation.)

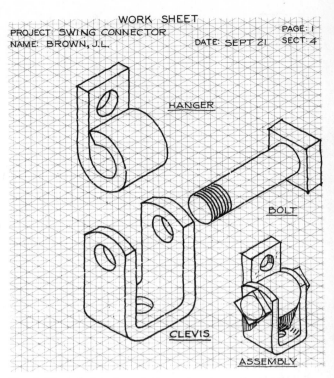

WORK SHEET

PROJECT: SWING CONNECTOR
NAME: BROWN, J.L.
DATE: SEPT 21
PAGE: 1 SECT: 4

HANGER

BOLT

CLEVIS

ASSEMBLY

Fig. 9–54 A designer's work sheet where isometric sketches are used to illustrate the components of a swing connector.

the two parts shown as three-view drawings in Fig. 9–51 may not be clearly understood. However, these parts can be sketched freehand using the principles of isometric drawings discussed earlier in this chapter. These sketches will assist you in determining whether or not the proper lines are shown in the orthographic view or whether lines are missing.

Note that the freehand isometrics in Fig. 9–52 are drawn on a special isometric paper with a printed grid to serve as a guide. One can actually count the numbers of grid lines on the rectangular grid used for the three-view drawings (Fig. 9–51) and then count corresponding numbers of grid lines on the isometric grid (Fig. 9–52). In this case, each grid on the iso-metric grid corresponds to two on the rectangular grid.

Isometric sketches can also be made on tracing paper that is laid over an isometric grid sheet. In this way the grid lines can be used as a guide but will not be seen on the completed pictorial.

Sketching is important in developing a design. Pictorial sketching is an effective method which the designer can use to communicate with himself. He may have difficulty in understanding the details of a design unless he can draw pictures of it in various positions to study it.

A design for the development of a sports car body is sketched in Fig. 9–53. This sketch is neither an isometric nor an oblique. It is closer to being a perspective. You should not become so restricted by the principles of pictorials that they hamper you in sketching ideas to improve your communication. Remember, rules of graphics and drafting are made to

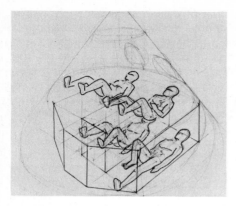

Fig. 9–55 This rapid sketch was useful in developing preliminary ideas for the seating arrangement for Project Apollo. (Courtesy of the National Aeronautics and Space Administration.)

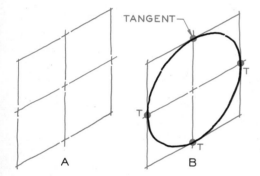

Fig. 9–56 A method of using guidelines for sketching a circle in isometric.

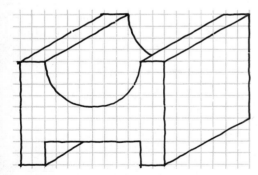

Fig. 9–57 An oblique pictorial sketch made on rectangular grid paper.

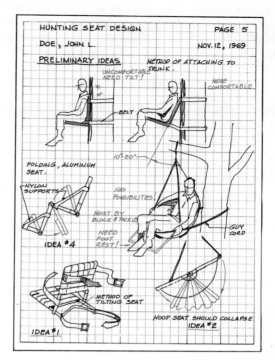

HUNTING SEAT DESIGN   PAGE 5
DOE, JOHN L.   NOV. 12, 1969
PRELIMINARY IDEAS   METHOD OF ATTACHING TO
                          TRUNK.
UNCOMFORTABLE
NEED TILT!   MORE
                                       COMFORTABLE
BELT
10°–20°
FOLDING, ALUMINUM
SEAT.
NYLON
SUPPORTS   HAD
                POSSIBILITIES
HOIST BY
BLOCK & TACKLE
NEED   GUY
FOOT   CORD
REST!
IDEA #4
METHOD OF
TILTING SEAT
HOOP SEAT SHOULD COLLAPSE
IDEA #1   IDEA #2

Fig. 9–58 An example of a designer's work sheet where freehand sketches were used to develop ideas as multi-view drawings and as pictorials.

serve you, not to restrict your communication.

Sketches of the swing connector discussed in Article 8–3 are shown on a work sheet in Fig. 9–54. Such sketches assist the designer in understanding the parts better than is possible when looking at orthographic drawings. He may modify the parts a number of times and draw each in pictorial to assist with his thinking process.

You should learn to develop speed in pictorial sketching. Your strokes should be light and fast as you develop the overall shape of an object, and then the lines should be darkened as the shape is finalized. A rapid sketch of a preliminary design of the Apollo capsule is shown in Fig. 9–55. Note that the lines are rapidly drawn to enable the designer to understand and to quickly communicate his ideas effectively. To sketch freehand effectively, you must have an understanding of the principles of pictorial drawings.

Ellipses in isometric or oblique pictorials can be sketched with greater ease if light guidelines are used to construct a rhombus on the surface on which the circle lies, as shown in Fig. 9–56. With experience you should be able to approximate an ellipse on a pictorial surface by eye without using an excessive number of guidelines.

Obliques can be sketched on rectangular grid paper as shown in Fig. 9–57 using the principles of oblique drawings discussed earlier. The grid can be used for the true-size surface, but the angle of the receding axis must be determined by eye since no guidelines for this axis are printed on the grid.

A combination of design sketches is shown in Fig. 9–58 to illustrate a designer's ideas for a hunting seat that can be attached to a tree. Note that these orthographic and pictorial sketches represent the designer's thinking process as he develops an idea step-by-step to arrive at the best solution. Notes and remarks are made on the sketches as ideas come to mind; these notes stimulate the designer's flow of ideas.

Learn to use pictorial sketching to communicate and develop your thoughts. This is a means of communication that will do the job when all other forms of oral and graphical communication fail.

PROBLEMS

These problems are to be solved in accordance with Article 3–15 and the specifications of your instructor. Most problems are to be drawn on standard Size A paper ($8\frac{1}{2}$" × 11") in ink or pencil.

Many of the problems are laid out on grid paper where each grid is equal to $\frac{1}{4}$". The drawings can be drawn as pictorials on paper with a printed $\frac{1}{4}$" isometric or rectangular grid. These pictorials may be sketched or drawn with instruments on blank paper or grid paper. Use Size A paper (Fig. 3–32) with the endorsement, title strip, and border shown in Article 3–15. More detailed pictorials, especially those with arcs and circular features, should be drawn on Size B paper, one problem per sheet. Less complicated objects can be drawn two to each Size A sheet, as shown in Fig. 9–59. Refer to the text of this chapter to assist you in the solutions.

General Problems

Isometrics

1–21 Using Size A paper, draw isometric pictorials (freehand or with instruments as assigned) of the objects shown in Figs. 9–60 and 9–61. Draw two problems on each sheet as illustrated in Fig. 9–59. Select the best view for each isometric drawing to describe the object.

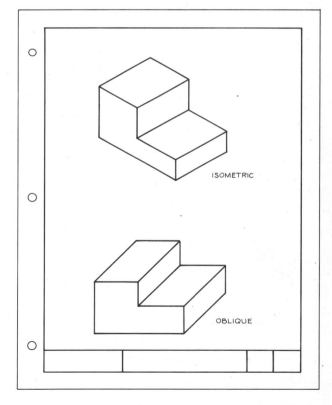

Fig. 9–59 A typical layout for problems drawn on Size A paper.

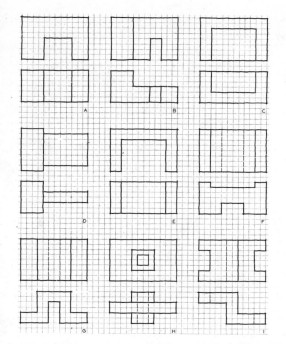

Fig. 9-60 Problems 1 through 9 and 46 through 54.

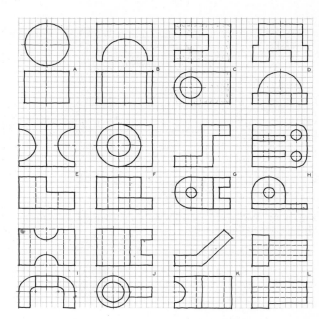

Fig. 9-62 Problems 22 through 33 and 67 through 78.

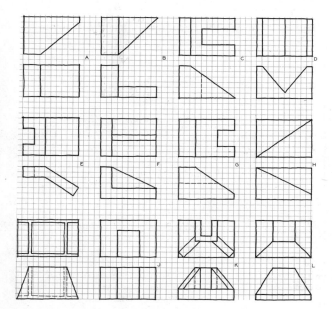

Fig. 9-61 Problems 10 through 21 and 55 through 66.

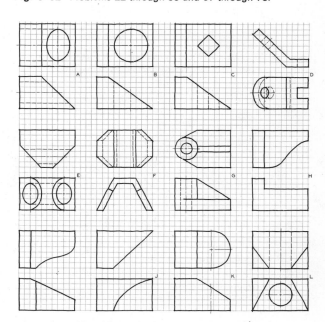

Fig. 9-63 Problems 34 through 45 and 79 through 90.

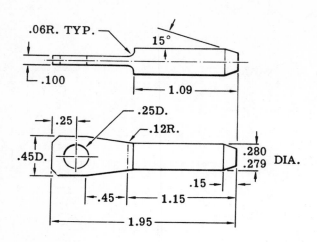

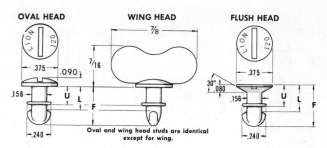

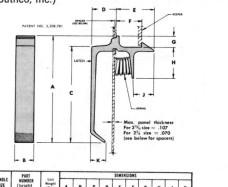

Fig. 9–64 Problems 91 and 92: Valve centering pin. (Courtesy of Bell Helicopter Corporation.)

Fig. 9–66 Problem 99: Quick-locking studs. (Courtesy of Southco, Inc.)

Fig. 9–67 Problem 100: Latch handle. (Courtesy of Southco, Inc.)

Fig. 9–65 Problems 93 through 98: Overhead conveyor attachments. (Courtesy of Mechanical Handling Systems, Inc.)

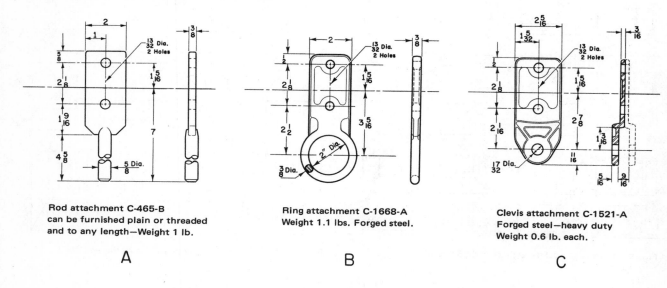

Rod attachment C-465-B
can be furnished plain or threaded
and to any length—Weight 1 lb.

A

Ring attachment C-1668-A
Weight 1.1 lbs. Forged steel.

B

Clevis attachment C-1521-A
Forged steel—heavy duty
Weight 0.6 lb. each.

C

22–45 Using Size B paper, draw isometric pictorials (freehand or with instruments as assigned) of the objects shown in Figs. 9–62 and 9–63. Draw one problem on each sheet. For these problems each grid represents $\frac{1}{2}$". Select the views that will best describe the objects.

Obliques

46–66 Using Size A paper, draw oblique pictorials (freehand or with instruments as assigned) of the objects shown in Figs. 9–60 and 9–61. Draw two problems on each sheet as illustrated in Fig. 9–59. Select the best view for each oblique drawing to describe the object. The receding axis can be drawn at any angle you choose. One problem on each sheet is to be drawn as a cavalier oblique and the other is to be drawn as a cabinet oblique.

67–90 Using Size B paper, draw oblique pictorials (freehand or with instruments as assigned) of the objects shown in Figs. 9–62 and 9–63. Draw one problem on each sheet. For these problems each grid represents $\frac{1}{2}$". Select the views that will best describe the objects. The receding axis can be drawn at the angle you think is best. The problems are to be drawn as cavalier obliques or as cabinet obliques, and the pictorials labeled to indicate the method used.

Obliques and Isometrics

91 Using Size A paper, draw an isometric pictorial of the valve centering pin in Fig. 9–64. Triple the dimensions in this drawing. Use instruments.

92 Using Size B paper, draw a cavalier oblique with a 45° receding axis of the valve centering pin in Fig. 9–64. Triple the given dimensions. Use instruments.

93–95 Using Size A paper (Fig. 3–30), draw isometrics of the attachments (A, B, and C) in Fig. 9–65 as assigned. Use full-size dimensions in these drawings with one part per page. Use instruments.

96–98 Using Size A paper, draw obliques of the attachments (A, B, and C) in Fig. 9–65 as assigned. Use full-size dimensions in these drawings with one part per page. Use instruments.

99 Using Size A paper, draw isometric sketches of the studs in Fig. 9–66 on the same sheet. These should be rapid sketches that describe the parts with the minimum of drawing time.

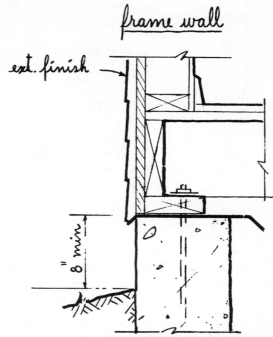

Fig. 9–68 Problem 101: Sill detail of a frame wall. (Courtesy of Federal Housing Administration.)

100 Using Size A paper, draw a cabinet oblique pictorial with a 30° receding axis of the latch in Fig. 9–67. Use instruments.

101 Using Size A paper, draw an isometric of the sill detail in Fig. 9–68 with instruments. The floor joists are 2" × 8" and are placed at intervals of 16" from center to center. The sill, which is bolted to the 10" thick concrete beam, is a 2" × 6" member. Your pictorial should explain the details of construction. You may wish to omit a portion of the floor in order to show the details. Select the scale to best show the construction.

102 Using Size B paper, draw a double-size isometric drawing of the jack lock assembly in Fig. 9–69. Use instruments.

103 Using Size B paper, draw full-size isometrics of the individual parts of the clamping fixture in Fig. 9–70. Use instruments. Draw as many parts on a

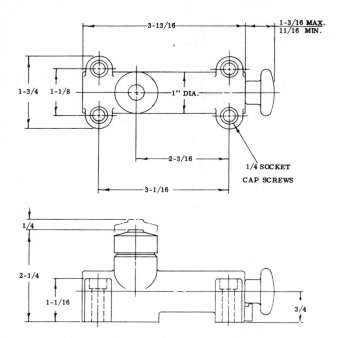

Fig. 9–69 Problem 102: Jack lock assembly. (Courtesy of Universal Engineering Corporation.)

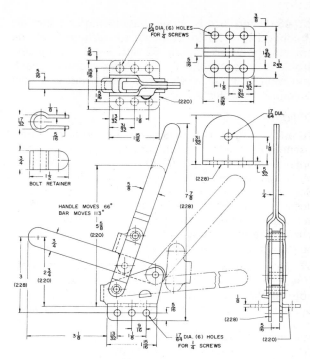

Fig. 9–70 Problem 103: Clamping fixture. (Courtesy of De-Sta-Co, Inc.)

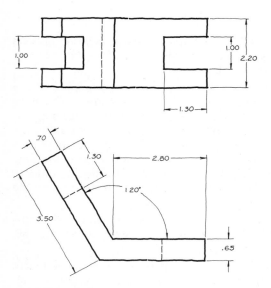

Fig. 9–71 Problem 104: Angle brace.

Fig. 9–72 Problems 105 and 106: Waffle maker. (Courtesy of General Electric Company.)

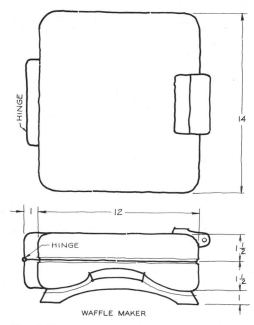

Fig. 9–73 Problems 105 and 106: Sketch of waffle maker shown in Fig. 9–72.

Fig. 9–74 Problem 107: Automatic coffee maker. (Courtesy of General Electric Company.)

Fig. 9–75 Problem 108: Automatic can opener. (Courtesy of General Electric Company.)

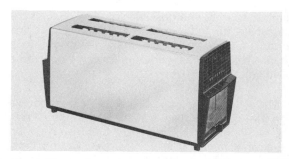

Fig. 9–76 Problem 109: Automatic toaster. (Courtesy of General Electric Company.)

single sheet as possible. More than one sheet may be required.

104 Using Size B paper, draw a full-size isometric of the angle brace in Fig. 9–71. Use instruments. Use an ellipse guide to establish the 120° angle. Show construction on your drawing.

105 Figure 9–72 shows a waffle maker which is sketched in two views in Fig. 9–73. Using Size B paper, draw an isometric of the waffle maker with its lid opened 60°. Use an ellipse guide to establish the 60° angle. Use instruments and select the best scale for your drawing.

Design Problems

Design problems are more typical applications of freehand sketching, since this is the method used by a designer in developing his ideas. The following problems require that you use your judgment to a greater extent than the previous problems of this chapter. In general, these problems are easy to solve, but the difficulty is devising the *best* solution or the *optimum*.

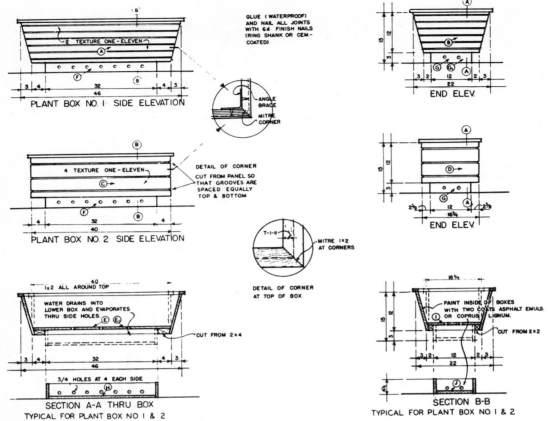

Fig. 9–77 Problem 110: Plant boxes. (Courtesy of American Plywood Association.)

In solving design problems, make a number of sketches to express your ideas; do not feel that you are limited to only one possible solution. Select the proper scale for your drawings if dimensions are important. Remember, the more ideas you can produce, the more likely you are to come up with a creative solution.

106 Make several pictorial sketches of a handle design that could be used instead of the one shown on the waffle maker in Fig. 9–72. Use Size A paper. Make several freehand sketches; develop your final solution as an instrument drawing. Use as many sheets as necessary.

107 (A) Make a freehand sketch of the coffeepot shown in Fig. 9–74. Your sketch should be as descriptive as possible of the pot as it appears in the figure. Use Size A paper. (B) Make several pictorial sketches of a new design for a coffeepot. Estimate dimensions.

108 Repeat Problem 107 for the automatic can opener in Fig. 9–75.

109 Repeat Problem 107 for the toaster in Fig 9–76.

110 Two plant boxes are shown in Fig. 9–77. (A) Draw pictorials of these boxes as they are at present designed. (B) Redesign these plant boxes using the

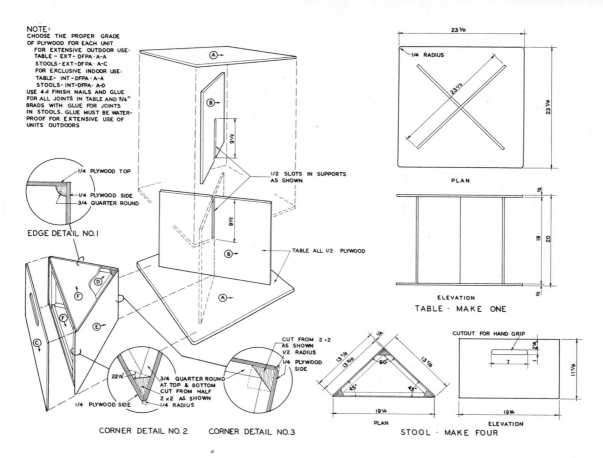

NOTE:
CHOOSE THE PROPER GRADE
OF PLYWOOD FOR EACH UNIT
FOR EXTENSIVE OUTDOOR USE:
TABLE – EXT– DFPA · A–A
STOOLS–EXT–DFPA A–C
FOR EXCLUSIVE INDOOR USE:
TABLE– INT –DFPA · A–A
STOOLS– INT–DFPA A–D
USE 4 d FINISH NAILS AND GLUE
FOR ALL JOINTS IN TABLE AND 3/4"
BRADS WITH GLUE FOR JOINTS
IN STOOLS. GLUE MUST BE WATER-
PROOF FOR EXTENSIVE USE OF
UNITS OUTDOORS

1/4 PLYWOOD TOP
1/4 PLYWOOD SIDE
3/4 QUARTER ROUND

EDGE DETAIL NO.1

1/2 SLOTS IN SUPPORTS AS SHOWN

TABLE ALL 1/2 PLYWOOD

CUT FROM 2 × 2
AS SHOWN
1/2 RADIUS
1/4 PLYWOOD SIDE

22½°
3/4 QUARTER ROUND
AT TOP & BOTTOM
CUT FROM HALF
2 × 2 AS SHOWN
1/4 PLYWOOD SIDE
1/4 RADIUS

CORNER DETAIL NO. 2   CORNER DETAIL NO.3

1/4 RADIUS

PLAN

ELEVATION
TABLE · MAKE ONE

PLAN

STOOL · MAKE FOUR

CUTOUT FOR HAND GRIP

ELEVATION

Fig. 9–78 Problem 111: A child's table and chair. (Courtesy of American Plywood Association.)

1/2 BLACK-IRON LEGS

END ELEVATION

SIDE ELEVATION

Fig. 9–79 Problem 112: End table. (Courtesy of American Plywood Association.)

same general dimensions as shown pictorially. Use Size B paper; select the best scale.

111 A child's table and chair are shown as exploded pictorials and as orthographic views in Fig. 9–78. (A) Draw pictorials of the assembled table and chair as they are at present designed. (B) Redesign the chair and table as a shop project and draw pictorially (with instruments or freehand). Use Size B paper.

112 An end table is shown in Fig. 9–79. (A) Draw a pictorial of the completely assembled table. (B) Make a pictorial drawing of the table legs, which are made of $\frac{1}{2}$" diameter bent rods.

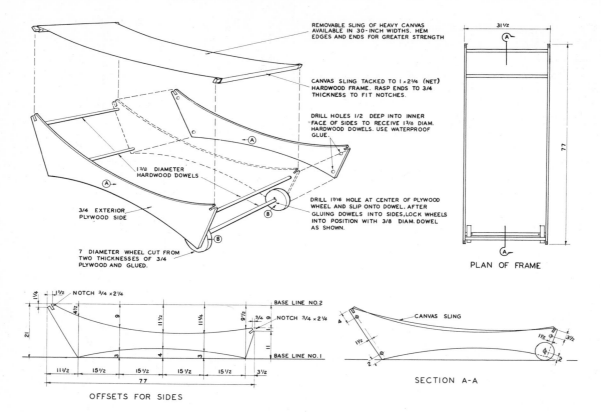

REMOVABLE SLING OF HEAVY CANVAS AVAILABLE IN 30-INCH WIDTHS. HEM EDGES AND ENDS FOR GREATER STRENGTH

CANVAS SLING TACKED TO 1 x 2¼ (NET) HARDWOOD FRAME. RASP ENDS TO 3/4 THICKNESS TO FIT NOTCHES.

DRILL HOLES 1/2 DEEP INTO INNER FACE OF SIDES TO RECEIVE 1⅜ DIAM. HARDWOOD DOWELS. USE WATERPROOF GLUE.

1⅜ DIAMETER HARDWOOD DOWELS

3/4 EXTERIOR PLYWOOD SIDE

DRILL 1⁷/₁₆ HOLE AT CENTER OF PLYWOOD WHEEL AND SLIP ONTO DOWEL. AFTER GLUING DOWELS INTO SIDES, LOCK WHEELS INTO POSITION WITH 3/8 DIAM. DOWEL AS SHOWN.

7 DIAMETER WHEEL CUT FROM TWO THICKNESSES OF 3/4 PLYWOOD AND GLUED.

31½

77

PLAN OF FRAME

NOTCH 3/4 x 2¼
BASE LINE NO. 2
NOTCH 3/4 x 2¼
BASE LINE NO. 1
77

OFFSETS FOR SIDES

CANVAS SLING

SECTION A-A

Fig. 9–80 Problem 113: Sunbathing sled. (Courtesy of American Plywood Association.)

113 A sunbathing sled is shown in Fig. 9–80. (A) Make an isometric instrument drawing of one of the plywood sides of the sled. (B) Make a pictorial of the assembled sled. (C) Redesign the sled and show your ideas as freehand sketches or with instruments.

114 A photograph of a steam and dry iron is shown in Fig. 9–81. (A) Make a freehand sketch of this iron as it is at present designed. (B) Redesign the handle of this iron and show your ideas in the form of free-hand pictorial sketches.

Fig. 9–81 Problem 114: Steam and dry iron. (Courtesy of General Electric Company.)

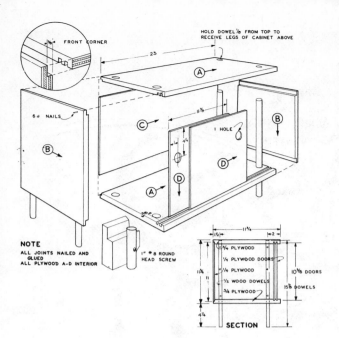

FRONT CORNER

HOLD DOWEL ⅛ FROM TOP TO
RECEIVE LEGS OF CABINET ABOVE

23

6 d NAILS

1 HOLE

NOTE
ALL JOINTS NAILED AND
GLUED
ALL PLYWOOD A-D INTERIOR

1" # 8 ROUND
HEAD SCREW

1½   11¾   2

¾ PLYWOOD
¼ PLYWOOD DOORS
¼ PLYWOOD
½ WOOD DOWELS
¾ PLYWOOD

11¾   11   10⅞ DOORS   15⅝ DOWELS

4¼

SECTION

Fig. 9–82 Problem 115: Stacking cabinet. (Courtesy of American Plywood Association.)

115 A stacking cabinet is shown in Fig. 9–82. These cabinets are designed to stack on top of each other to the height desired. (A) Make a pictorial (oblique or isometric as assigned) of the assembled cabinet. (B) Redesign this cabinet and show your ideas as pictorials, freehand or with instruments.

10
AUXILIARY VIEWS
AND REVOLUTIONS

Fig. 10–1 The inclined display panel of the Videx receiver is an example of a plane that must be found true size by means of a primary auxiliary view. (Courtesy of ITT Industrial Laboratories.)

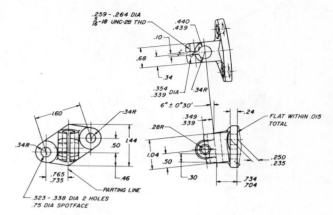

Fig. 10–2 An example of a primary auxiliary view used in a working drawing. (Courtesy of General Motors Drafting Standards.)

10–1 INTRODUCTION

The principles of orthographic projection were discussed in Chapter 7. These principles are fundamental to all graphical methods whether used for a simple sketch or a complex working drawing. This chapter illustrates the application of principles of orthographic projection in the construction of auxiliary views and revolutions.

The principal views of an object, such as the top, front, and side views, are usually drawn in such a position that their planes are parallel to the principal projection planes. This makes it possible for the surfaces to be drawn with their true size and shape in these principal views. However, if the surfaces of the object are not mutually perpendicular, all cannot be parallel to the principal planes. This means that at least one plane will be inclined to one of the principal planes. For example, the display panel of the Videx receiver in Fig. 10–1 is an inclined plane that is not parallel to either the frontal or the profile plane, and cannot be drawn true size in either the front or the side view. To draw this plane true size requires the use of an auxiliary view or a revolution of the surface.

This chapter will discuss auxiliary views and revolutions. Both of these methods are commonly used to construct supplementary views to describe objects that cannot be completely explained by means of the principal views. Figure 10–2 illustrates the use of an auxiliary view to describe a clamp for an automobile hand brake cable. Note that the auxiliary view, by projecting upward from the front view, provides a true, circular view of the hole.

10–2 PRIMARY AUXILIARY VIEWS

You will remember from Chapter 7 that the three principal planes of orthographic projection are the *frontal*, *horizontal*, and *profile* planes. These are the names of the planes of the imaginary glass box in which the object is placed for drawing its various views. When a surface of the object is parallel to one of these planes, it will project its true size onto that plane. The true size of a surface is important, because the dimensions of the surfaces of an object must be known before the object can be fabricated in the shop.

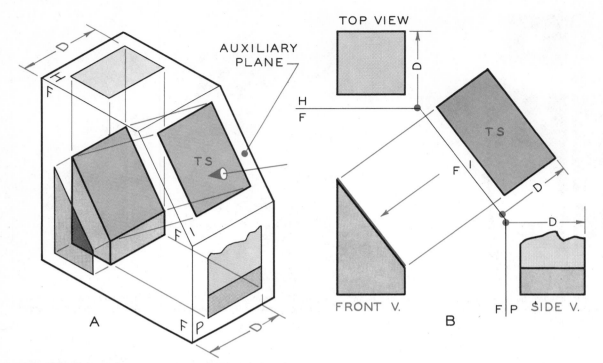

Fig. 10–3 Finding the true size of an inclined plane by projecting from the front view, using a frontal reference plane (*F*–1).

A plane that appears as a slanted edge in a principal view (such as the top, front, or side view) may be found true size in a primary auxiliary view (Fig. 10–3). By definition, a primary auxiliary view is an orthographic view that is projected from a primary or principal view. The purpose of a primary auxiliary view is usually to find the true size of a slanted surface or to obtain a circular view of a cylinder. However, a primary auxiliary view may be projected in any direction from any principal view. The following articles will discuss the three types of primary auxiliary views. These are views that are projected from (a) the front view, (b) the top view, and (c) the side views.

10–3 AUXILIARIES PROJECTED FROM FRONT VIEWS

A plane that appears as an edge in the front view (Fig. 10–3) can be found true size in a primary

auxiliary view projected from the front view. Reference line *F*–1 is drawn parallel to the edge view of the plane at any convenient location. It is drawn to conform to the pictorial in part A of the figure in this case, to make the orthographic views in part B easier to understand. Note that primary auxiliary plane 1 (labeled 1 for primary or first) is perpendicular to the auxiliary plane. Also, the line of sight is parallel to the frontal plane. When you look at the object in the direction indicated by the line of sight, you will see the frontal projection plane as an edge, and consequently, you will see the measurements that are perpendicular to the frontal plane true length. These dimensions are those of depth, represented by *D*, which are perpendicular to the frontal plane and appear true length in the top and side views of part B.

The inclined plane is projected from the front view perpendicularly to the *F*–1 line. Depth *D* is measured in the top or side view and transferred to the auxiliary view with dividers. Each of the four

FIGURE 10-4. CONSTRUCTION OF A PRIMARY AUXILIARY VIEW

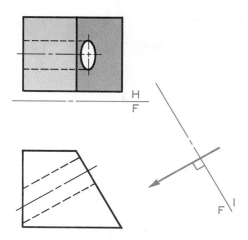

Given: The top and front views of a block with an inclined surface which appears as an edge in the front view.
Required: Find a true-size view of the inclined surface.
Reference: Article 10-3.

Step 1. Construct a convenient *H–F* reference plane between the top and front views that is perpendicular to the projectors between the views. Draw a line of sight perpendicular to the edge view of the inclined surface. Draw the edge view of the auxiliary plane perpendicular to the line of sight and parallel to the inclined surface.

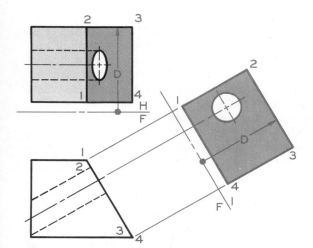

Step 2. Number points in the top and front views. Project the points perpendicularly from the inclined edge to the auxiliary plane. Transfer the dimensions from the *H–F* plane to the auxiliary view, e.g., dimension *D*. Connect the points obtained to give a true-size view of the surface.

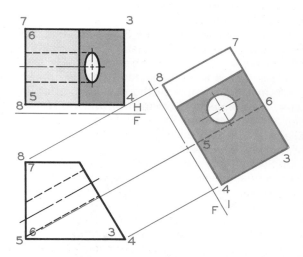

Step 3. Number the remaining points of the object in the top and front views and project them to the auxiliary view to complete the auxiliary view of the object. Line 5–6 is a hidden line. Measure all dimensions perpendicularly to the reference planes used.

Fig. 10–5 An object that requires an auxiliary view projected from the front view to find the true size of the inclined surface.

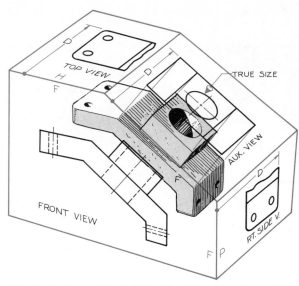

Fig. 10–6 A pictorial showing the relationship of the projection planes used to find the true size of the inclined plane.

corners of the surface is found in this manner and then all four corners are connected to give the true size of the inclined plane.

You can see in part A of Fig. 10–3 that the primary auxiliary plane is the plane upon which the auxiliary view is projected. It is positioned parallel to the surface that is to be projected true size onto it.

A four-step example of the construction of an auxiliary view projected from the front view is shown in Fig. 10–4. The same steps apply to any primary auxiliary view, regardless of the view from which the auxiliary view is projected.

In Step 1, a reference plane is conveniently located between the two adjacent views and perpendicular to the projection lines between the views. The line of sight is drawn perpendicular to the edge view of the inclined (slanted) surface. Then the edge view of the auxiliary plane is drawn perpendicular to the line of sight and parallel to the inclined surface in the front view. In Step 2, the true-size view of the inclined plane is found by projecting from the front view parallel to the line of sight and transferring the depth dimension from the top view as indicated. The

cylindrical hole appears as a true circle in the auxiliary view, where it can be accurately located with dimensions that are true length.

In Step 3, the remaining points on the object are numbered in the top and front views and are projected to the auxiliary view. These points are connected by lines, and visibility is determined to complete the view. It is seldom necessary in practice to include all details in the auxiliary view, since the auxiliary view is used as a supplement to the principal views. Therefore, many hidden lines may be omitted in the auxiliary view, and only the important features shown that are not true size in the principal views.

10–4 APPLICATION OF AN AUXILIARY PROJECTED FROM THE FRONT VIEW

A machine part, a shaft socket, is shown in Fig. 10–5. This part has an inclined surface with a cylindrical hole drilled through it. It is not possible to find the true size of the inclined surface in the top or side views. However, it appears as an edge in the front view; consequently, an auxiliary view can be

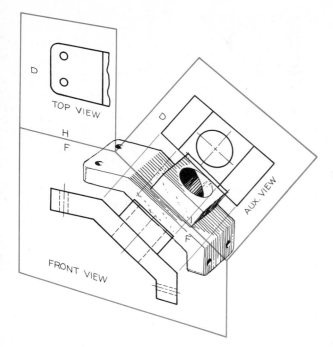

Fig. 10–7 The projection planes are opened into a common plane to represent the plane of the drawing paper.

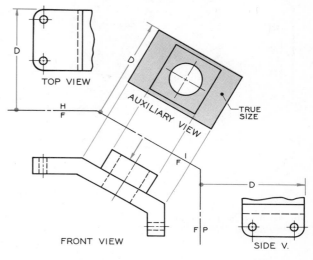

Fig. 10–8 Construction of an auxiliary view of the object shown in Figs. 10–5, 10–6, and 10–7 as it would appear on your drawing paper.

projected from the front view to find a true-size view of the inclined surface and a circular view of the hole.

A pictorial showing the three principal views and the auxiliary view is given in Fig. 10–6. Note that the auxiliary plane is perpendicular to the frontal plane. The top and side views are drawn as partial views, with conventional break lines used to indicate that the views are incomplete. The pictorial model is opened into one common plane (the plane of the drawing paper) in Fig. 10–7. Note that in this illustration the projectors are perpendicular to the fold line F–1.

The proper method of constructing the necessary views of the object as a sequence of orthographic views is shown in Fig. 10–8. Compare this figure with the three-dimensional pictorial of the views in the previous figures. Note that the depth dimension is measured from the frontal plane in the top, side, and auxiliary views.

The auxiliary view is a true-size view of the inclined plane that can be measured to locate the circular hole. The hole can be drawn easily since it is

a true circle in this view. If the top and side views were complete, they would contain many hidden lines and the hole would be elliptical in each view. Obviously, the auxiliary view is easier to draw and is more effective in describing the part.

10–5 AUXILIARIES PROJECTED FROM TOP VIEWS

The slanted plane in Fig. 10–9 is inclined to the frontal and profile planes and is perpendicular to the horizontal plane. It will appear true size when projected onto an auxiliary plane that is parallel to the inclined plane.

In part B of the figure, reference line H–1 is drawn parallel to the edge view of the slanted plane. To obtain a true-size view of the inclined plane, the corners of the inclined surface are projected from the top view perpendicularly to the H–1 line, and then the distance H is transferred from the front view to

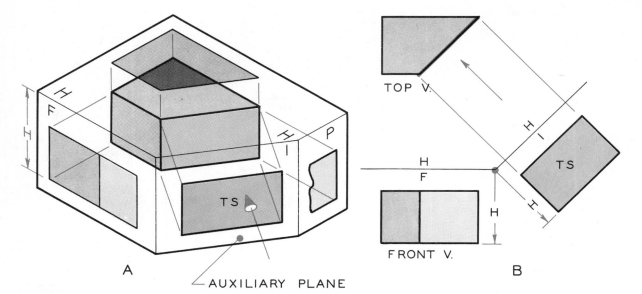

A

AUXILIARY PLANE

B

Fig. 10–9 A primary auxiliary view projected from a top view to give the true size of an inclined surface. A horizontal reference plane (*H*–1) is used.

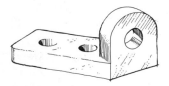

Fig. 10–10 An object with an inclined plane that appears as an edge in the top view. This plane can be found true size by a primary auxiliary view projected from the top view.

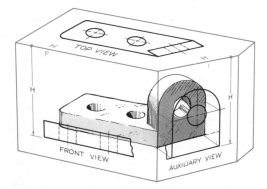

Fig. 10–11 A pictorial showing the relationship of the projection planes used to find the true size of the inclined plane.

the auxiliary view with dividers. The four corners are connected to give the true-size view of the inclined plane.

If you were to cut out the portion of the page on which part B of Fig. 10–9 appears, you could fold the paper along the *H–F* and *H*–1 reference lines to form a three-dimensional model. This model would look very much like the illustration in part A. This technique can be used as an aid in helping you understand the relationship of the various views and projection planes.

10–6 APPLICATION OF AN AUXILIARY PROJECTED FROM THE TOP VIEW

The part shown in Fig. 10–10 has a slanted surface with a cylindrical hole drilled through it. This slanted surface will not be seen true size in either the front or the side view. However, the surface will appear as an edge in the top view. Thus it is possible to construct a primary auxiliary view to find the true size of the slanted surface.

A pictorial model (Fig. 10–11) illustrates the relationship of the projection planes. Note that the auxiliary plane is parallel to the slanted surface and

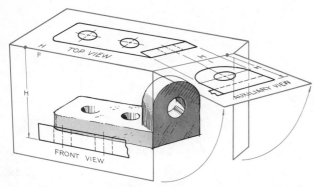

Fig. 10–12 The projection planes are opened into a common plane to represent the plane of the drawing paper.

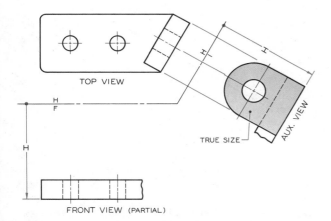

Fig. 10–13 Construction of an auxiliary view of the object shown in Figs. 10–10, 10–11, and 10–12 as it would appear on your drawing paper.

Fig. 10–14 The diagonal base supports that attach to the horizontal base of the orthicon camera could be found true length and true size in auxiliary views projected from the top view drawing. (Courtesy of ITT Industrial Laboratories.)

perpendicular to the horizontal plane of the box. The front view is shown as a partial view because the slanted surface would cause many hidden lines and ellipses to appear in a complete view. The auxiliary view supplements the portion of the front view that is omitted.

In Fig. 10–12 the auxiliary plane on which the auxiliary view is projected is swung into the horizontal plane. When an orthographic drawing of this part is made, this plane will represent the surface of the drawing paper. The dimension H will be seen true length in the auxiliary view and will be equal to the dimension H in the front view. Your line of sight is parallel to the horizontal plane in both the front and the auxiliary views, and consequently height (H) can be measured in both views since it is perpendicular to the horizontal plane.

The pictorial views of the object and the projection planes that were shown in the previous figures are given in the form of an orthographic drawing in

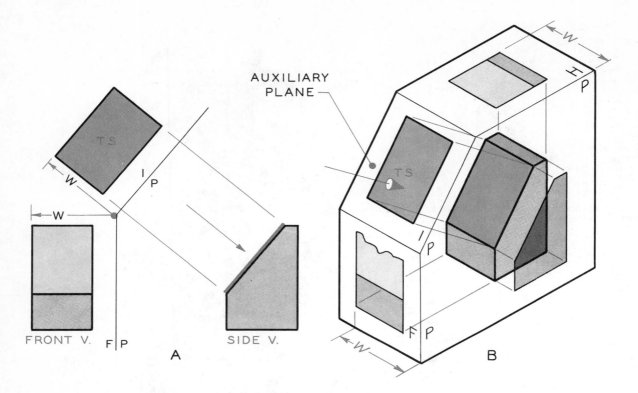

Fig. 10–15 A primary auxiliary view projected from a side view to give a true-size view of an inclined surface.

Fig. 10–13. You can assume that the planes of the model in Fig. 10–12 have been opened into a single plane, the plane of the drawing paper. The *H–F* and *H*–1 lines represent the hinge lines between the projection planes.

Since in the auxiliary view you are looking perpendicularly at the slanted surface, this view will show the circular features true size; they can therefore be drawn with a compass. When circular features are not true size, they appear as ellipses. Note that the auxiliary view, like the front view, is a partial view; the front view describes the portion that is omitted from the auxiliary view. The *H* dimensions are measured perpendicularly from the edge view of the horizontal plane, as was illustrated in Fig. 10–12.

The structural mount shown in Fig 10–14, used to attach a camera to a telescope, illustrates the need

for auxiliary views to find the true lengths of the base supports. Since the four supports will appear as edges in the top view, auxiliary views may be projected from the top view—that is, from the horizontal plane—to find their lengths and shapes. This is a necessary step in the design, which must be done before working drawings can be made to describe the details of fabrication.

10–7 AUXILIARIES PROJECTED FROM PROFILE VIEWS

The slanted plane in Fig. 10–15 appears on an edge in the side view. Thus it is inclined to the horizontal and frontal planes, but perpendicular to the profile plane. The auxiliary line *P*–1 is drawn parallel to the edge view of the inclined surface in the side view at a

Fig. 10–16 The bed of this Model 45 Haulpak truck was designed through the use of auxiliary views to determine the sizes of oblique planes. (Courtesy of LeTourneau-Westinghouse Company.)

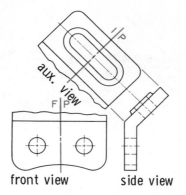

Fig. 10–17 Construction of a partial auxiliary view where the reference plane passes through the center of a symmetrical object. (Courtesy of ANSI; Y14.3-1957.)

convenient location (part A). When you look perpendicular to the auxiliary plane, you will see the profile plane as an edge. Consequently, width dimensions (W), which are perpendicular to the profile plane, will appear true length in the auxiliary view. Therefore, each measurement of W can be transferred from the front view to the auxiliary view to establish the corners of the inclined surface (part B). The corners are connected to give the true-size view of the inclined surface.

The truck bed shown in Fig. 10–16 is composed of slanting planes that can be found true size by auxiliary views. Any two orthographic views can be used to find the true size of the slanting planes by following the principles of auxiliary projection. Remember that to find the true size of a plane in a single primary auxiliary view, the plane must appear as an edge in one of the principal views.

10–8 LOCATION OF REFERENCE PLANES

The previous examples have introduced auxiliary-view methods by using a reference plane that is placed between the views. This position is easiest to understand when you are learning auxiliary-view methods, since it can represent the hinge line between adjoining projection planes.

Sometimes, however, it is more convenient if the reference plane is located at some other position. For example, in Fig. 10–17, where a true-size view of an inclined surface is projected from a side view, the reference plane is located through the center of the object in the front view. This procedure saves time, since the object is symmetrical and two measurements can be laid off at a time, one on each side of the reference plane, in the auxiliary view. In all cases, regardless of where the reference plane is placed, it must be perpendicular to the projectors between the two views to which the reference plane relates. Note that the $F–P$ reference plane is perpendicular to the projectors between the front and side views.

10–9 IRREGULAR CURVES

An auxiliary view of an object which has a curved edge is shown in Fig. 10–18. The auxiliary view projected from the front view is constructed by plotting a series of points located on the curved edge and projecting them to the auxiliary plane. These points are then connected with an irregular curve to give the true shape of the inclined surface. The projection principles are identical to those used to draw auxiliary views of surfaces composed of straight lines. Any irregularly shaped surface of any form can

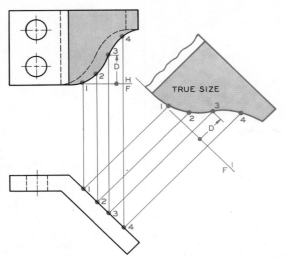

Fig. 10–18 An auxiliary view of an object containing an irregular curve.

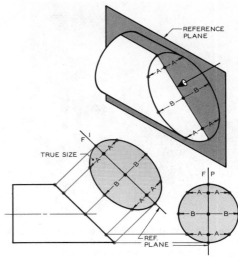

Fig. 10–19 Construction of an auxiliary view of an object requiring that a series of points be plotted. Since the object is symmetrical, the reference plane is positioned through its center.

be drawn true size in a primary auxiliary view if it appears as an edge in a principal view and if two views of the surface are given.

Note that the reference plane in Fig. 10–18 is located in the top view and is an extension of one of the lines in the top view. This is another variation in the placement of the reference plane, in addition to the one previously mentioned in Article 10–8.

The problem illustrated in Fig. 10–19 is that of a plotted curve in an auxiliary view that was constructed by the same procedure as used in Fig. 10–18. In this case the slanted surface appeared as an edge in the front view, making it possible to construct a true-size auxiliary view projected from the front view. Since the object is symmetrical, a reference plane is constructed through its center as described in Article 10–8.

Points are located on the edge view of the slanted surface and are projected to the side view (the circular view). Each point on the front view is then projected to the auxiliary view and is located by transferring distances *A* and *B* from the reference plane in the side view to the reference plane in the auxiliary view. The points in the auxiliary view are

connected with an irregular curve or an ellipse template to complete the ellipse.

The more points that are located on the ellipse, the more accurate the auxiliary view will be. Since the reference plane is located through the center of the side view, two dimensions at a time can be laid off in the auxiliary view. The elliptical view is true size, since your line of sight is perpendicular to the inclined surface.

10–10 AUXILIARY SECTIONS

Auxiliary views can be used to provide sectional views of objects should such views be necessary to describe their shapes and characteristics. A section is a "cross section" through a portion of the object to describe its form. Sections will be discussed in detail in Chapter 11.

An example of an auxiliary section is shown in Fig. 10–20. The heavy dashed line in the front view represents the edge view of a cutting plane that passes through the object. The cross section of the object is shown true size in the auxiliary section.

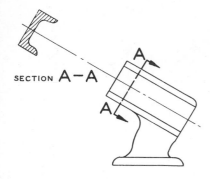

SECTION A–A

Fig. 10–20 An auxiliary section projected from a front view. (Courtesy of Chrysler Engineering Standards.)

10–11 SECONDARY AUXILIARY VIEWS

A secondary auxiliary view is an auxiliary view projected from a primary auxiliary view. You will remember that a primary auxiliary view is an auxiliary view projected from one of the principal views of an object. If several auxiliary views are projected from the same principal view (the front view, for example), all the auxiliary views are *primary* auxiliary views. A *secondary* view is the second successive auxiliary view and must be projected from the primary auxiliary view.

The end of a cutting tool is shown in Fig. 10–21 with a top and front view. The end of the tool is beveled with a plane that is inclined to the horizontal, frontal, and profile planes. This plane cannot be found true size in a primary auxiliary view, since the plane does not appear as an edge in one of the principal views. Therefore, a secondary view must be used to find the true size of the plane.

Line 1–2 is a horizontal line in the front view; it will therefore be true length in the top view, where the horizontal projection plane appears true size. If the line of sight is drawn parallel to the true length of 1–2 in the top view, the line will be seen as a point in the auxiliary view and the inclined plane will appear as an edge. Since the plane now appears as an edge, we can look perpendicularly at the edge and construct a secondary auxiliary view. The secondary auxiliary line 1–2 is drawn parallel to the edge of the surface and perpendicular to the line of sight.

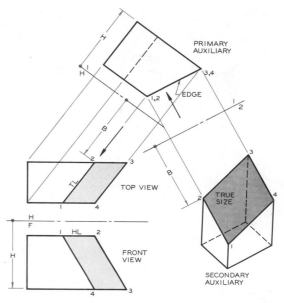

Fig. 10–21 The determination of the true size of a surface by a secondary auxiliary view.

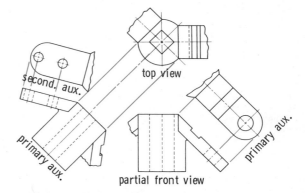

Fig. 10–22 An example of the use of two primary auxiliary views and a secondary auxiliary view.

A sample measurement *B* is shown in the secondary auxiliary view to show how the dimension is measured in the top view from reference line *H*–1. All dimensions are measured in this manner to locate the corner points of the tool. These points are connected to give the true-size view of the beveled plane

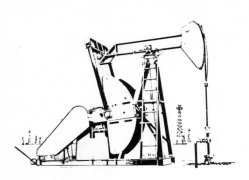

Fig. 10–23 A pump for removing oil from an oil well. (Courtesy of Link-Belt Company.)

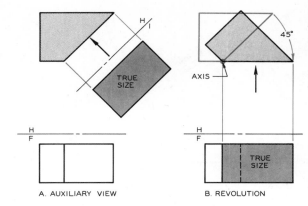

A. AUXILIARY VIEW

B. REVOLUTION

Fig. 10–25 A comparison of the auxiliary view with revolution to find the true size of a plane as it would appear on your drawing paper. This is the same object shown in Fig. 10–24.

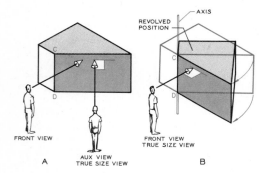

Fig. 10–24 For an auxiliary view, the observer moves his position; in revolution, the observer remains stationary and the object is revolved.

and the remainder of the tool. Usually, the true-size view of the secondary auxiliary plane is adequate, and the remainder of the object is not drawn unless there is a specific need for it.

Another example of a secondary auxiliary view is shown in Fig. 10–22. Two primary auxiliary views are drawn and a secondary auxiliary view is projected from one of the primary auxiliary views. In this example, reference planes are not drawn; however, measurements are taken in the same manner as in the previous examples where reference planes were shown.

10–12 REVOLUTIONS

Many designs involve parts and mechanisms that revolve or rotate about various pivot points and shafts. An oil pump is an example of a mechanism with a continuous revolving motion (Fig. 10–23). Many machines of this type must be graphically analyzed by the principles of revolution.

The construction of revolutions is very similar to that of auxiliary views. The method can be used to find the true size of a surface when the surface appears as an edge in one of the principal views. A comparison of an auxiliary view and a revolution is shown in Fig. 10–24. Imagine that you are positioned so as to have a front view of an object, and that this view contains a slanted surface. From this position you will not have a true-size view of the slanted surface. For an auxiliary view that will give the true size of the slanted surface, you can change your position so that your line of sight is perpendicular to the plane of the slanted surface (Fig. 10–24A).

However, you could obtain a true-size view of the slanted surface from the front-view position if the object were revolved until the slanted surface was perpendicular to your line of sight (Fig. 10–24B). To revolve this object, you may place a vertical axis of revolution anywhere you like. In this example, it passes through corner *CD* of the object. Note that,

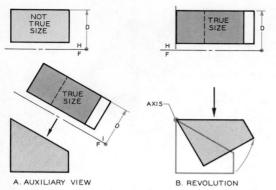

A. AUXILIARY VIEW   B. REVOLUTION

Fig. 10–26 Determination of the true size of a surface that appears as an edge in the front view by an auxiliary view and by revolution.

Fig. 10–27 This LeRoi drilling rig is designed to permit revolution about two axes to give a wide range of applications. (Courtesy of Westinghouse Air Brake Company.)

even though the width and depth dimensions of the object change as it is revolved, the height dimension remains the same. This is the dimension that is parallel to the axis of rotation.

The object shown pictorially in Fig. 10–24 is shown in orthographic views in Fig. 10–25. In part A, the slanted surface is found true size by an auxiliary view. In effect, you as an observer have changed your position so that your line of sight is perpendicular to the edge view of the slanted surface. In B, the slanted surface is found true size in the front view by revolving the object. In this case your front-view position remains unchanged. Since the axis of revolution is vertical, it appears as a point in the top view. The top view is revolved until the slanted surface is parallel to the frontal plane; the slanted surface is then projected to the front view. The height dimensions are shown to complete the true-size view. The other lines of the object are also shown.

10–13 REVOLUTION OF FRONT VIEWS

A slanted surface that appears as an edge in the front view can be found true size by a primary auxiliary view or by a single revolution. The comparison is shown in Fig. 10–26. Your position as an observer must be changed so that your line of sight is perpendicular to the slanted surface in the auxiliary view in A. However, in finding the true size of this slanted surface, it is possible to use the same line of sight that is used for finding the top view of an object. To do this, the front view is revolved (Fig. 10–26B).

An axis can be located in the front view as a point, and as a true-length line in the top view. The front view is revolved about the axis until the slanted plane appears as a horizontal edge in the front view; from this it is possible to project a true-size view in the top view.

As in the auxiliary view, the depth dimension (D) does not change. This makes it possible to use depth to find the true-size view by both methods.

The drilling rig shown in Fig. 10–27 is designed with structural arms that rotate about a vertical and a horizontal axis to give a wide range of positions. To establish the limits of these ranges requires the application of revolution principles.

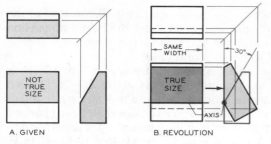

Fig. 10–28 Construction of a true-size view of a plane that appears as an edge in the side view by revolution.

Fig. 10–29 This Haulpak 40 truck was designed with a bed which revolves about an axis that appears as a point in the side view. (Courtesy of LeTourneau-Westinghouse Company.)

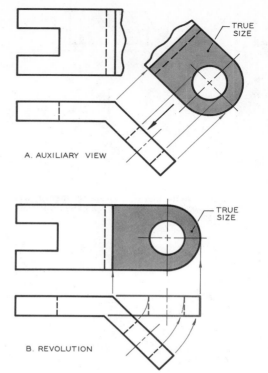

Fig. 10–30 A comparison of the auxiliary-view method and the revolution method.

10–14 REVOLUTION OF SIDE VIEWS

The slanted surface in Fig. 10–28 does not appear true size in either the front or the top view. Since it appears as an edge in the side view, it can be found true size by a primary auxiliary view or by a single revolution of the side view. The side view is shown revolved in Fig. 10–28B. The object is revolved 30° about an axis that appears as a point in the side view until the slanted surface is vertical and parallel to the frontal plane. When this surface is projected to the front view it will appear true size. Note that the width dimensions do not change, since these dimensions are parallel to the axis of revolution. The axis can be placed in any convenient location.

Your position for viewing the surface true size is the same position used for seeing any front view that is projected from the side view. To find an auxiliary view of this surface, you would have to change your position if the object were not revolved.

The truck in Fig. 10–29 has a bed which revolves about an axis that appears as a point in the side view. The same principles of revolution can be used to analyze its movement and positions.

10–15 APPLICATIONS OF REVOLUTIONS

A machine part can be described by using partial orthographic views and an auxiliary view as shown in Fig. 10–30A. The auxiliary view is a supplementary view that gives the true shape of the inclined plane.

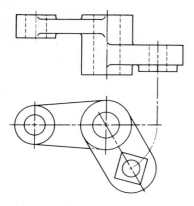

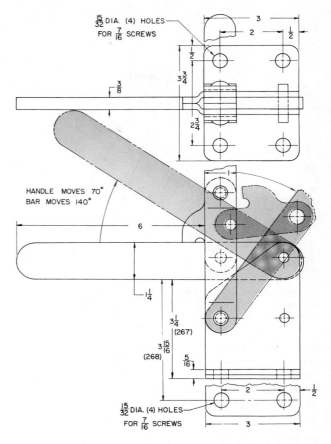

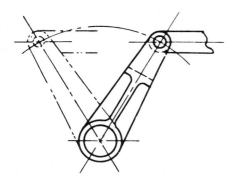

Fig. 10–31 A typical revolution of a part as it would appear on a working drawing.

Fig. 10–32 Alternative positions of revolved parts are shown with thin lines with two short dashes at intervals.

Fig. 10–33 An example of revolved members to illustrate alternative positions of a clamping device. (Courtesy of De-Sta-Co Corporation.)

An alternative method of describing an object of this type is shown in Fig. 10–30B. This is the use of revolution to find the top view as a true-size view. This is not a true top view in the strict sense of orthographic projection. However, the one shown here is an accepted one that is often used in practice. The slanted surface is revolved in the front view into a horizontal position and then projected to the top view, where the surface is shown true size.

It is standard practice not to show the revolved position in the front view since the use of revolution is understood. The revolution shown in Fig. 10–30B will assist you in understanding the procedure used to find the top view. A more typical example of a revolved view as it would appear on a working drawing is shown in Fig. 10–31.

Revolution is used to establish alternative positions of parts that revolve about pivot points. When alternative positions are shown, they are drawn with thin lines that are similar to centerlines except that they have two short dashes instead of one (Fig. 10–32). An example of this type of revolution is shown in Fig. 10–33, where the links of a clamping device are shown revolved. Note that

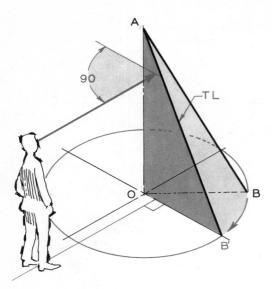

Fig. 10–34 The observer will see line *AB* true length when *AOB* has been revolved into position *AOB'*, where it is a frontal, true-size plane.

alternative-position lines have been used to distinguish the two positions that are shown. This method of graphical analysis is used to determine what length a structural member must be to function as required.

10–16 THE TRUE LENGTH OF A LINE BY REVOLUTION

You may wish to find the true length of a line on a drawing but not necessarily the entire plane on which the line lies. This line may be a corner of an object, the fold line of a piece of bent sheet metal, or the length of a section of pipe. Of course, if the line is parallel to a projection plane, it will appear true length in one of the principal views; but often a line will be oblique to all projection planes.

Any line can be found true length by a single revolution. For example, assume that you are looking at line *AB* in Fig. 10–34 from a front-view position. You will not see the line *AB* true length in this position, because your line of sight is not perpendicular to it. However, if you assume that a vertical axis passes through point *A*, you can revolve point *B* about the axis until you have a true-size view of the

FIGURE 10–35. TRUE LENGTH OF A LINE BY REVOLUTION

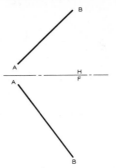

Given: The top and front views of line *AB*. This is the line that is shown pictorially in Fig. 10–34.

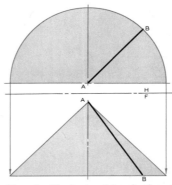

Step 1. The horizontal projection of line *AB* in the top view is used as a radius for drawing a half view of a cone. The front view of the cone is drawn with its axis passing vertically through point *A*.

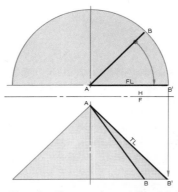

Step 2. The top view of line *AB* is revolved into position *AB'* where it is parallel to the frontal plane. In this position it is the outside element of the cone in the front view, where it can be measured true length.

plane *AOB'*. Since you see *AOB'* true size, you will see *AB'* true length, since it lies on this true-size plane.

This procedure is shown orthographically in Fig. 10–35. A vertical axis through point *A* appears as a point in the top view and as a true-length line in the front view. The horizontal distance from *A* to *B* can be used as a radius for drawing the top view of the cone which has *AB* as an element. Only half of the cone is shown in the top view to save space. The front view of the cone is found by projecting from the top view.

In Step 2, line *AB* is revolved to position *AB'* to be parallel to the frontal plane. In this position, *AB'* will project to the front view as an outside element of the cone, where it will be true length and can be measured.

This process can be used without the necessity of revolving an entire object or plane. Time and effort are saved by being concerned only with the line in question.

10–17 DOUBLE REVOLUTION

As in a primary auxiliary view, the plane that you wish to find true size with a single revolution must appear as an edge in one of the principal views. If a plane does not appear as an edge in one of the principal views, either a secondary auxiliary view or a double revolution is required to find its true size.

An example of the solution of a double-revolution problem is shown in Fig. 10–36. Three views and a pictorial of the block are given, with the requirement to find the true size of the slanted surface. In Step 1, line 1–2 (which appears true length in the top view) is revolved in the top view until it is parallel to the projectors between the top and front views. Thus line 1–2 will appear as a point in the front view and the plane 1–2–3 will be an edge in the front view. The axis of revolution appears as a point in the top view and as a vertical axis in the front view. The height does not change, since this dimension is parallel to the axis of revolution.

Now that plane 1–2–3 appears as an edge in the front view, this view can be revolved until the edge view is vertical. This will make it possible for the plane to be projected to the side view, where the

FIGURE 10–36. TRUE SIZE BY DOUBLE REVOLUTION

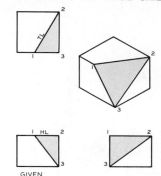

Given: Three views of a block with an oblique plane across one corner. It is required to find the plane true size by revolution.

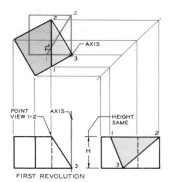

FIRST REVOLUTION

Step 1. Since line 1–2 is horizontal in the front view, it is true length in the top view. The top view is revolved into a position where line 1–2 can be seen as a point in the front view.

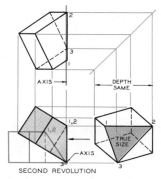

SECOND REVOLUTION

Step 2. Since plane 1–2–3 was found as an edge in Step 1, this plane can be revolved into a vertical position in the front view, so that it will appear true size in the side view. The depth dimension does not change, since it is parallel to the axis of revolution.

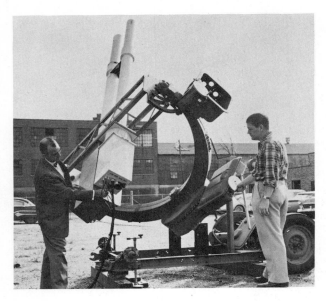

Fig. 10–37 The cradle of this orthicon camera was designed to permit revolution to any position for tracking space vehicles and astronomical bodies. (Courtesy of ITT Industrial Laboratories.)

Fig. 10–38 This 45° elbow requires an auxiliary view to find its flanges true size. (Courtesy of Johns Manville.)

true-size view can be found. In this revolution, the depth will remain the same, since this dimension is parallel to the axis that appears as a point in the front view. The entire object is found in this view by projecting dimensions from the top and front views.

An application of a double revolution is the cradle of the image orthicon camera shown in Fig. 10–37. This camera can be revolved about three axes to track vehicles and astronomical bodies. The camera thus has complete coverage of the heavens.

10–18 REVOLUTION AND AUXILIARY VIEWS IN COMBINATION

The 45° elbow shown in Fig. 10–38 is an example of an object that needs an auxiliary view to supplement the principal views. These views are shown in Fig. 10–39, where front, auxiliary, and partial bottom views are given. Note that the holes in the flanges do not lie on the centerlines of the bottom and auxiliary views; therefore, they will not project to the front view of the flanges to show the true radial distance of the holes from the centers of the flanges.

In order to give a better impression of the location of the holes, they are revolved in the auxiliary and bottom views to the respective centerlines of these views. This makes it possible for the holes to be projected to the front view and located their true radial distance from the centers of the flanges. This is a conventional method of combining auxiliary views and revolution to give a better descriptive front view of the object. Additional applications of conventional revolutions will be discussed in Chapter 11.

10–19 AUXILIARY VIEWS AND DESIGN

The designer must use auxiliary views to solve problems which involve inclined members and surfaces that cannot be shown in principal views. In some cases he must use both auxiliary views and revolutions to solve design problems.

Many applications of auxiliary views and revolutions can be seen in the construction of a sphere that was used as the symbol of the New York World's Fair of 1964 and 1965 (Fig. 10–40). Many planes, lengths, and angles were determined by the designers and engineers who worked on the project. Each con-

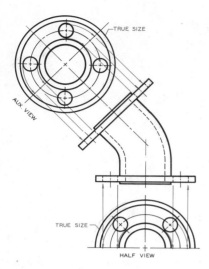

Fig. 10–39 A combination of an auxiliary view and a revolution used to describe the 45° elbow.

Fig. 10–40 The Unisphere® of the New York World's Fair contains many examples of design problems that were solved using auxiliary views and revolutions. (Courtesy of U. S. Steel Corporation.)

nector had to be specially designed to join the structural members correctly. This required the application of primary and secondary auxiliary views.

Each part of the structure was designed and detailed on paper. The drawings were then used for fabricating each part that was assembled on the site (Fig. 10–41). Because of the high degree of accuracy that was required, the designers had to have a thorough understanding of the relationships among the parts and connectors.

Note that straight members were used to represent the circles of revolution or parallels on the surface of the Unisphere®. These parallels represent lines that are parallel to the equator of the globe.

A more complex application of auxiliary views and revolutions to design is the four-wheel traction-drive mechanism of a vehicle to operate on the moon's surface. A pictorial illustration of the preliminary design is shown in Fig. 10–42. A refinement drawing of the assembly is shown in Fig. 10–43 in the form of orthographic views. Auxiliary views are projected from the principal views of the design (Fig. 10–43) to find the lengths and clearances of

Fig. 10–41 The designer had to design each member and connector of the sphere that could be assembled on the site with a high degree of accuracy. (Courtesy of U. S. Steel Corporation.)

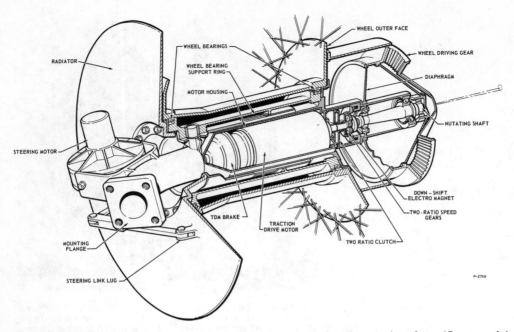

Fig. 10–42 A pictorial of a wheel assembly for a vehicle to be used on the moon's surface. (Courtesy of the Bendix Corporation.)

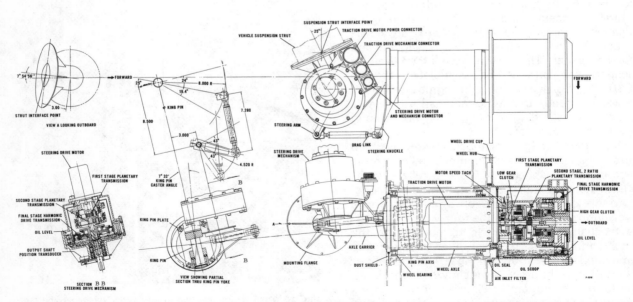

Fig. 10–43 The refinement of the design for the wheel mechanism uses primary, secondary, and revolved views to analyze the various members of the linkage assembly. Additional views were also used to finalize the design. (Courtesy of the Bendix Corporation.)

various structural members. Revolution is used to show the various positions of the linkage system for the analysis of its operation. In this case, the designer is using auxiliaries and revolutions to study and analyze his design.

The completed, deliverable wheel assembly is shown in Fig. 10–44. This problem is typical of the design problems that are encountered in industry. This design required the application of spatial relations and auxiliary views to determine the design characteristics. You should become aware of the products that you use in your daily activities, and try to identify applications that were probably developed with the use of auxiliary views and revolutions.

Fig. 10–44 A photograph of the completed, deliverable wheel assembly. (Courtesy of Bendix Corporation.)

PROBLEMS

These problems are to be solved in accordance with Article 3–15 and the specifications of your instructor. Most problems are to be drawn on standard Size A paper ($8\frac{1}{2}$" × 11") using ink or pencil.

Many of the problems are laid out on grid paper where each grid is equal to $\frac{1}{4}$". The drawings can be transferred to grid paper of a similar type, or else the problems can be drawn on blank paper (Fig. 3–32) with the endorsement, title strip, and border as shown in Article 3–15. Refer to the text of this chapter to assist you in the solution of the problems.

General Problems

Auxiliary Views

1–24 Refer to Fig. 10–45 for instructions for laying out each auxiliary view problem on Size A paper. Substitute various top views from Figs. 10–46 and 10–47 in place of the top view given in the example. Each grid square represents $\frac{1}{4}$". These views should be drawn with the aid of your instruments. Using the same outline shape of the front view given in Fig. 10–45, construct auxiliary views to find the true size of the inclined surface. The reference-plane lines can be positioned at your convenience. Show only the

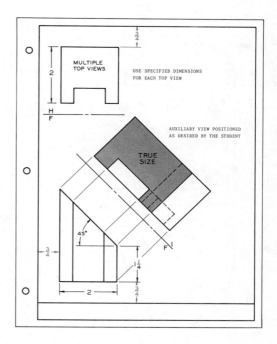

Fig. 10–45 Layout for Problems 1 through 24.

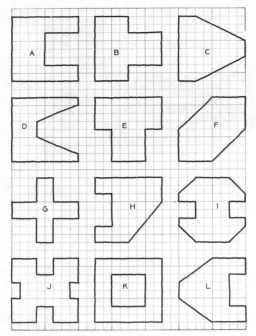

Fig. 10–46 Problems 1 through 12 and 69 through 80.

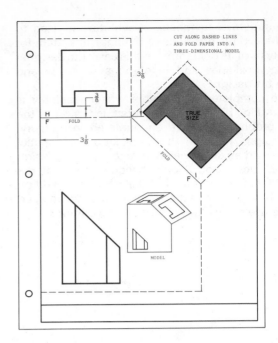

Fig. 10–48 Layout for Problems 25 through 48.

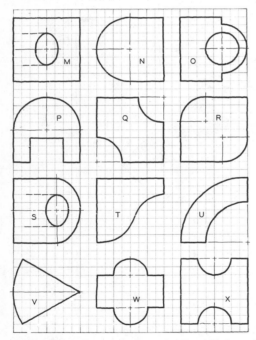

Fig. 10–47 Problems 13 through 24 and 81 through 92.

inclined surface unless your instructor asks you to draw the entire view of the object.

25–48 Refer to Fig. 10–48 for instructions for laying out each auxiliary view problem. Lay out the same problems that were shown in Figs. 10–46 and 10–47 using the same dimensions for the views as were given in Fig. 10–45. Draw reference planes in the position shown in Fig. 10–48. Once the auxiliary view has been constructed, cut the views out with scissors along the dashed lines and fold along the hinge lines that are given. This will form a three-dimensional model that will help you visualize the relationship between the principal planes and the auxiliary planes. Show only the inclined surface in the auxiliary view. Use instruments for all construction.

49 Draw the lifting eyes on a sheet of Size A paper with instruments positioned as shown in Fig. 10–49. Construct a partial auxiliary view of the inclined surface that will show its true size. Locate the circular hole on this surface with two dimensions.

50 Draw the floor flange on a sheet of Size A paper with instruments as shown in Fig. 10–50. Construct

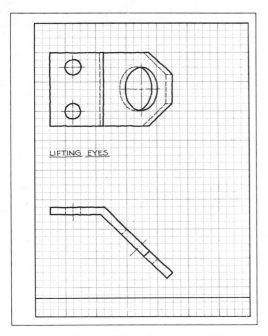

Fig. 10–49 Problem 49: Auxiliary view of lifting eyes.

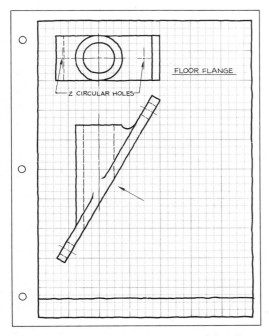

Fig. 10–50 Problem 50: Auxiliary view of floor flange.

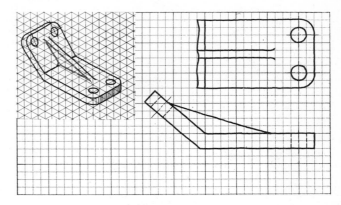

Fig. 10–51 Problem 51: Auxiliary view of angle connector.

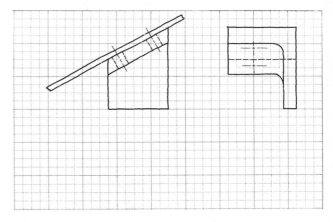

Fig. 10–52 Problem 52: Auxiliary view of a corner support.

an auxiliary view that will give a true-size view of the inclined plane in the direction of the line of sight. Show only the inclined surface and the two circular holes in the auxiliary view, omitting the elliptical hole.

51 Using instruments, draw the angle connector shown in Fig. 10–51 on a sheet of Size A paper with a horizontal layout (Fig. 3–33). Construct an auxiliary view from the front view that will show the inclined surface true size.

52 Using instruments, draw the corner support shown in Fig. 10–52 on Size A paper with a horizontal layout (Fig. 3–33). Construct an auxiliary view from the front view that will show the inclined surface true size. Show the circular holes in this view. Draw the entire object.

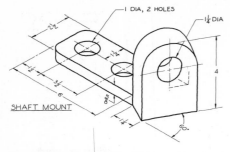

Fig. 10–53 Problem 53: Auxiliary view of a shaft mount.

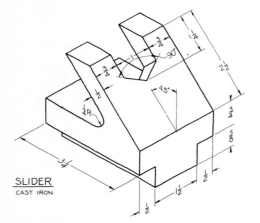

SLIDER
CAST IRON

Fig. 10–54 Problem 54: Auxiliary view of a slider.

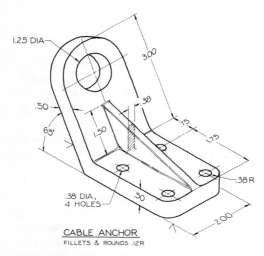

CABLE ANCHOR
FILLETS & ROUNDS .12R

Fig. 10–55 Problem 55: Auxiliary view of a cable anchor. Problem 93: Revolution.

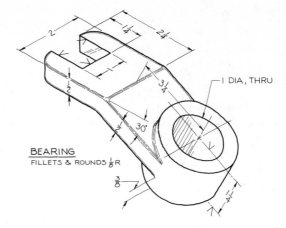

BEARING
FILLETS & ROUNDS $\frac{1}{8}$R

Fig. 10–56 Problems 56 and 94: Auxiliary view and revolution of a bearing.

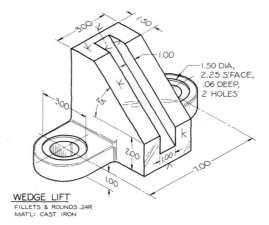

WEDGE LIFT
FILLETS & ROUNDS .24R
MAT'L: CAST IRON

Fig. 10–57 Problem 57: Auxiliary view of a wedge lift.

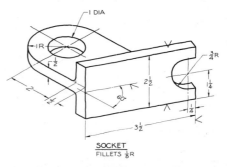

SOCKET
FILLETS $\frac{1}{8}$R

Fig. 10–58 Problem 58: Auxiliary view of a socket.

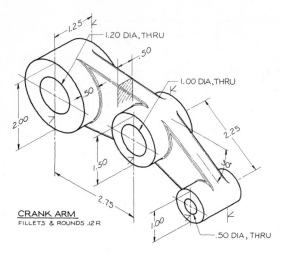

Fig. 10–59 Problem 59: Auxiliary view of a crank arm. Problem 95: Revolution.

CRANK ARM
FILLETS & ROUNDS .12 R

1.25
1.20 DIA, THRU
.50
1.00 DIA, THRU
.50
2.00
1.50
2.25
30°
2.75
1.00
.50 DIA, THRU

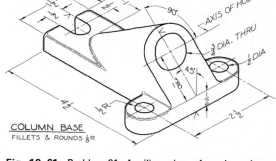

Fig. 10–61 Problem 61: Auxiliary view of a column base.

COLUMN BASE
FILLETS & ROUNDS ⅛ R

90°
AXIS OF HOLE
¾ DIA. THRU
½ DIA
45°
2½

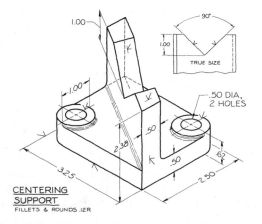

Fig. 10–60 Problem 60: Auxiliary view of a centering support.

CENTERING SUPPORT
FILLETS & ROUNDS .12 R

1.00
90°
1.00
TRUE SIZE
1.00
.50 DIA, 2 HOLES
.50
2.38
.62
.50
3.25
2.50

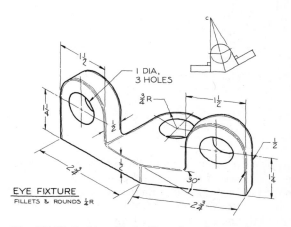

Fig. 10–62 Problem 62: Auxiliary view of an eye fixture.

EYE FIXTURE
FILLETS & ROUNDS ¼ R

1½
1 DIA, 3 HOLES
¾ R
1½
½
½
½
½
30°
2¾
2¾
½
1¼
C

53–62 Figures 10–53 through 10–62 are pictorial sketches that are dimensioned. These are designed to be laid out on Size A paper (either a vertical or horizontal layout) at half size or full size. Lay out the principal views of each object so that the inclined plane will appear as an edge in one of the views. Project an auxiliary view from the edge view of the inclined surface in order to find its true size. Proper layout of the views to make good use of the available space is an important aspect of the problem. A rough

layout or sketch will be helpful to you in determining the proper arrangement.

Secondary Auxiliary Views

63–67 Refer to Fig. 10–63 as a guide for laying out Problems 63 through 67. Problem 63 has been partially done in Fig. 10–63. For Problems 64 through 67, use the given views labeled A, B, C, and D respectively in Fig. 10–64. Number the points in the two

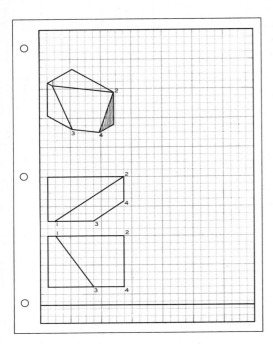

Fig. 10–63 Layout for Problems 63 through 67. Problem 63 is shown in the layout.

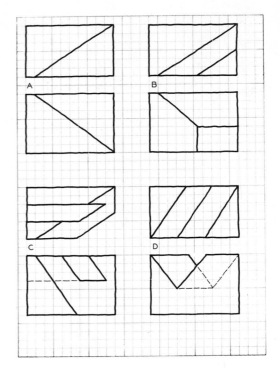

Fig. 10–64 Problems 64 through 67 and Problems 96 through 99: True size by auxiliary view and revolution.

given views to identify the inclined planes. Construct true-size views of the inclined planes by projecting from the top view. A secondary auxiliary view will be required. Refer to Article 10–11. Project the entire object in the auxiliary views. Use instruments.

68 Make a two-view drawing of the tie-rod base in Fig. 10–65 on Size A paper with instruments. Find the inclined plane true size by means of a secondary auxiliary view by projecting the primary auxiliary view from the top view.

Revolutions

69–92 Refer to Fig. 10–66 for laying out these problems. Use the same top views that were given in Figs. 10–46 and 10–47. Find the inclined surface true size in the top view by revolving the front view as shown in the example.

93 Lay out the top and front views of the cable anchor in Fig. 10–55 on Size A paper with instruments. Show the top view as a conventionally revolved view where the inclined surface appears true size. Refer to Fig. 10–30.

94 Repeat Problem 93 using the bearing in Fig. 10–56.

95 Repeat Problem 93 using the crank arm in Fig. 10–59. Refer to Fig. 10–31.

96–99 Lay out two views of the objects assigned in Fig. 10–64. Referring to Article 10–17, find the true-size views of the inclined planes by double revolution. Use Size A paper and position the problems on the sheet to make the best use of the available space.

100 Lay out the problems shown in Fig. 10–67 on Size A paper using instruments. (A) Find line 1–2

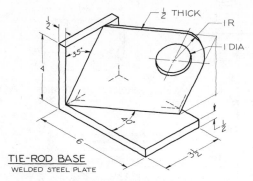

TIE-ROD BASE
WELDED STEEL PLATE

Fig. 10–65 Problem 68: Auxiliary view of a tie-rod base.

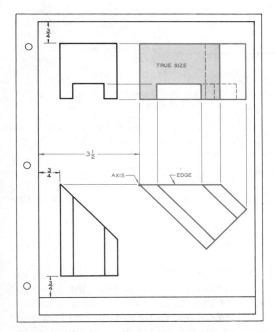

Fig. 10–66 Layout for Problems 69 through 92: True size by revolution.

true length in the front view by revolving the line about an axis through point 1. (B) Find line 3–4 true length in the top view by revolving the line about an axis through point 4. (C) Find line 5–6 true length in the top view by revolving the line about an axis through point 5. (D) Find the true lengths of lines 9–10 and 7–8 by revolution. These are the fold lines on a sheet metal part.

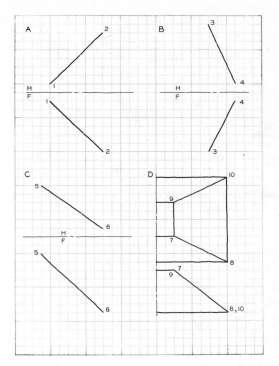

Fig. 10–67 Problem 100: True length of lines by revolution.

Design Problems

101 The dimensions of a fallout shelter are shown in Fig. 10–68. Construct the necessary principal views and auxiliary views to find the area of the inclined surfaces of the roof. Measure the roof and determine its area. How much would the roof cost at $1.29 per square foot for the material used? Show your construction and calculations on Size A paper. Use instruments.

102 Design a hinge bracket that will attach to the arch and the foundation pier in Fig. 10–69. Your design should be in two pieces as illustrated in the sketch, but you are encouraged to develop a different design. Show your design in principal views and auxiliary views as necessary to show all surfaces true size. The arch is 12″ × 12″ in cross section. Select the best scale and size of drawing paper to show your design.

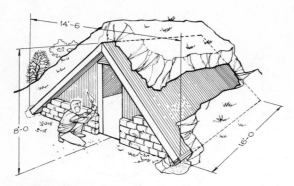

Fig. 10–68 Problem 101: Dimensions of a fallout shelter. (Courtesy of the Department of Defense.)

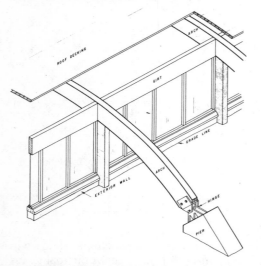

Fig. 10–69 Problem 102: Hinge bracket design. (Courtesy of American Plywood Association.)

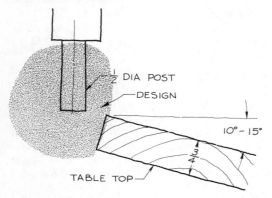

Fig. 10–71 Problem 104: Lamp socket design.

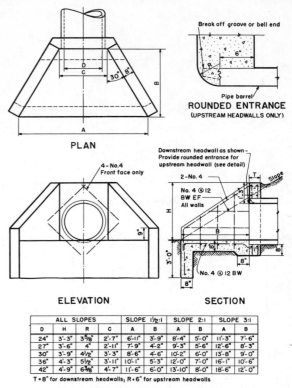

PLAN

ROUNDED ENTRANCE
(UPSTREAM HEADWALLS ONLY)

Break off groove or bell end

Pipe barrel

4 – No.4
Front face only

Downstream headwall as shown —
Provide rounded entrance for
upstream headwall (see detail)

2 – No. 4

No. 4 @ 12
BW EF
All walls

No. 4 @ 12 BW

ELEVATION

SECTION

ALL SLOPES				SLOPE 1½:1		SLOPE 2:1		SLOPE 3:1	
D	H	R	C	A	B	A	B	A	B
24"	3'-3"	3⅝"	2'-7"	6'-11"	3'-9"	8'-4"	5'-0"	11'-3"	7'-6"
27"	3'-6"	4"	2'-11"	7'-9"	4'-2"	9'-3"	5'-6"	12'-6"	8'-3"
30"	3'-9"	4½"	3'-3"	8'-6"	4'-6"	10'-2"	6'-0"	13'-8"	9'-0"
36"	4'-3"	5½"	3'-11"	10'-1"	5'-3"	12'-0"	7'-0"	16'-1"	10'-6"
42"	4'-9"	6⅜"	4'-7"	11'-6"	6'-0"	13'-10"	8'-0"	18'-6"	12'-0"

T = 8" for downstream headwalls; R + 6" for upstream headwalls

REINFORCED CONCRETE HEADWALL
TYPE "C"

Fig. 10–70 Problem 103: Headwall design. (Courtesy of the U. S. Navy.)

103 A design for a concrete headwall is shown in Fig. 10–70. It is necessary to determine the true size and shape of the trapezoidal sides of the reinforced headwall. Use a *D* of 36" (refer to table) and a slope of 2:1. Select a scale that will permit construction on a Size A sheet.

104 Design a bracket with a socket that will receive a $\frac{1}{2}$" diameter post of a desk lamp (Fig. 10–71). The bracket should clamp to the table top by some efficient method. Your design should be as simple as possible. (A) Sketch your design as freehand orthographic views on Size A paper. (B) Convert your freehand sketch to a finished instrument drawing that may utilize auxiliary views to describe your design.

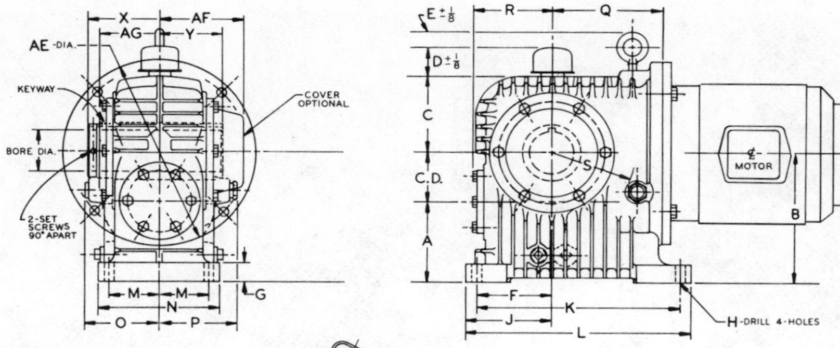

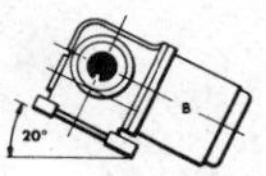

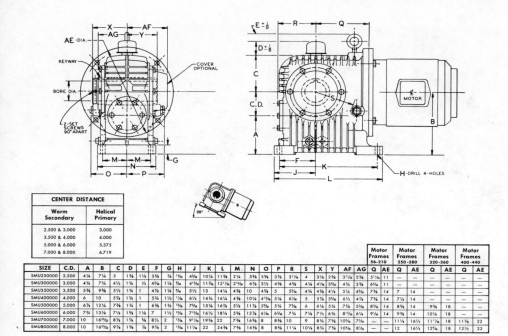

CENTER DISTANCE	
Worm Secondary	Helical Primary
2.500 & 3.000	3.000
3.500 & 4.000	4.000
5.000 & 6.000	5.375
7.000 & 8.000	6.719

																							Motor Frames 56-210		Motor Frames 250-280		Motor Frames 320-360		Motor Frames 400-440	
SIZE	C.D.	A	B	C	D	E	F	G	H	J	K	L	M	N	O	P	R	S	X	Y	AF	AG	Q	AE	Q	AE	Q	AE	Q	AE
SMU250000	2.500	4 1/4	7 1/4	5	1 3/8	1 1/8	3 5/8	7/8	15/32	4 3/16	10 1/4	11 3/8	2 1/4	5 5/8	3 5/8	3 7/8	3 11/16	4	3 1/8	2 5/8	3 11/16	2 3/8	5 11/16	11	—	—	—	—	—	—
SMU300000	3.000	4 3/4	7 3/4	4 1/2	1 3/4	1/2	4 3/16	1 1/8	9/16	4 13/16	11 7/16	12 11/16	2 13/16	6 7/8	3 1/2	4 3/8	4 5/8	4 1/4	4 1/16	3 9/16	4 3/4	3 3/8	6 3/16	11	—	—	—	—	—	—
SMU350000	3.500	5 3/8	9 3/8	5 1/2	1 3/4	1	4 7/8	1 1/4	9/16	5 1/2	13	14 1/4	4 3/8	10	4 5/8	5	5 3/16	4 3/4	4 5/8	4 1/8	5 1/4	4 3/16	7 3/8	14	7	14	—	—	—	—
SMU400000	4.000	6	10	5 7/8	1 3/4	1	5 3/4	1 1/2	11/16	6 1/2	14 3/4	16 1/4	4 3/8	10 1/4	4 13/16	5 1/4	6 1/16	5	5 7/8	5 3/16	6 1/2	4 7/8	7 5/8	14	7 1/4	14	—	—	—	—
SMU500000	5.000	6 7/8	12 1/4	7 3/8	1 3/4	1	6 3/8	1 3/4	13/16	7 3/16	15 1/4	16 7/8	5 1/8	11 7/8	5 9/16	5 3/4	7 3/16	6	6 1/4	5 3/4	7 5/8	5 5/16	8 5/16	14	8 5/8	14	9 3/8	18	—	—
SMU600000	6.000	7 3/4	13 1/8	7 1/8	1 5/8	1 1/8	7	1 1/2	13/16	7 13/16	16 1/2	18 1/8	5 5/8	12 7/8	6 1/16	6 5/16	7 3/4	7 1/8	7 1/2	6 3/4	8 15/16	6 1/4	9 1/16	14	9 3/8	14	10 1/8	18	—	—
SMU700000	7.000	10	16 23/32	8 7/8	1 7/8	5/8	8 1/2	2	15/16	9 11/16	19 5/8	22	7 3/8	16 5/8	8	8 3/8	10	9	8 3/4	7 5/8	10 3/16	7 5/16	—	—	11 1/8	16 1/2	11 11/16	18	11 5/8	22
SMU800000	8.000	10	16 23/32	9 7/8	1 5/8	7/8	9 7/8	2	15/16	11 1/16	22	24 3/8	7 3/8	16 5/8	8	8 3/8	11 1/4	10 1/8	8 3/4	7 5/8	10 3/16	8 1/16	—	—	12	16 1/2	12 9/16	18	12 1/2	22

Fig. 10–72 Problem 105: Right-angle gearmotor specifications. (Courtesy of Cone-Drive Gears.)

105 Two views of a right-angle gearmotor are shown in Fig. 10–72. These drawings represent various sizes of motors given in the table. The small drawing shows the position of mounting the gearmotors at a 20° angle with the horizontal surface. (A) Design a mounting bracket that will support the size of gearmotor assigned by your instructor. Make the necessary instrument views of the bracket to fully describe it. Select the scale and the size of paper best suited for your final drawings.

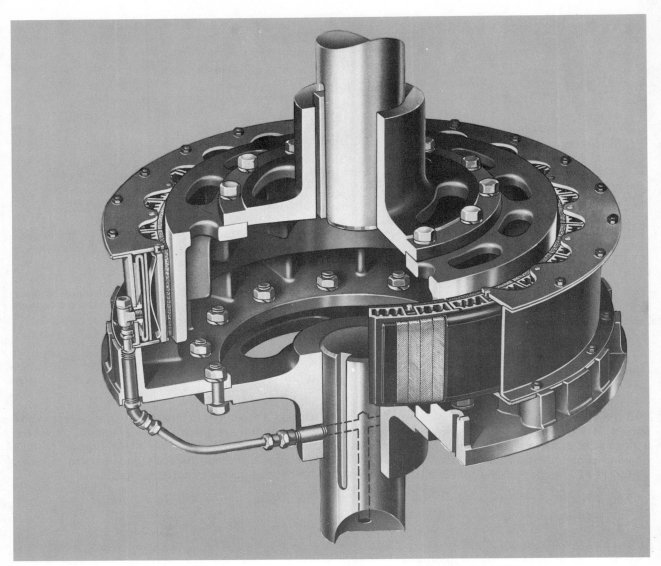

Photo courtesy of Fawick Corporation

11
SECTIONS AND
CONVENTIONS

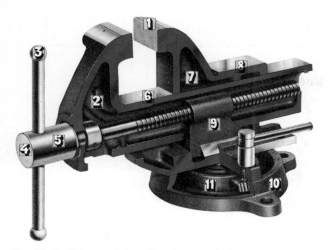

Fig. 11–1 This pictorial section gives a better understanding of the vise than would be possible without sections. (Courtesy of the Columbian Vise and Manufacturing Co.)

11–1 INTRODUCTION

On many occasions the draftsman will be required to represent objects that are difficult to explain in the customary orthographic views. Such objects may have interior features that cannot be shown except by the use of many hidden lines that make a drawing hard to understand. In illustrating such a part, a portion of the object may be thought of as removed in order to show inside features. This procedure is called *sectioning*. A pictorial of a section is shown in Fig. 11–1. Imaginary cutting planes were used to remove portions of the vise to give a better understanding of the interior details and of how the parts are assembled. The following articles will discuss how sectioning principles apply to orthographic views.

Previous chapters have established basic rules of orthographic projection that can be used to describe objects. Occasionally these rules are violated for the sake of clarity. Such modifications of rules for the purpose of making a drawing more readily understandable are called *conventional practices*. Various conventional practices will be discussed in this chapter to help you do a better job of making clear, understandable drawings.

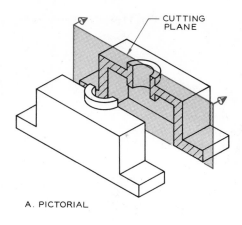

A. PICTORIAL

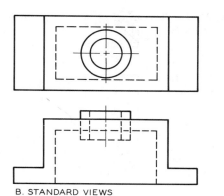

B. STANDARD VIEWS

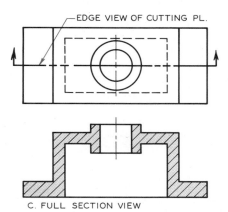

C. FULL SECTION VIEW

Fig. 11–2 A comparison of a regular view with a full section view of an object to show its internal as well as external features.

Fig. 11–3 Cutting-plane lines.

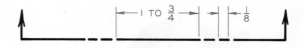

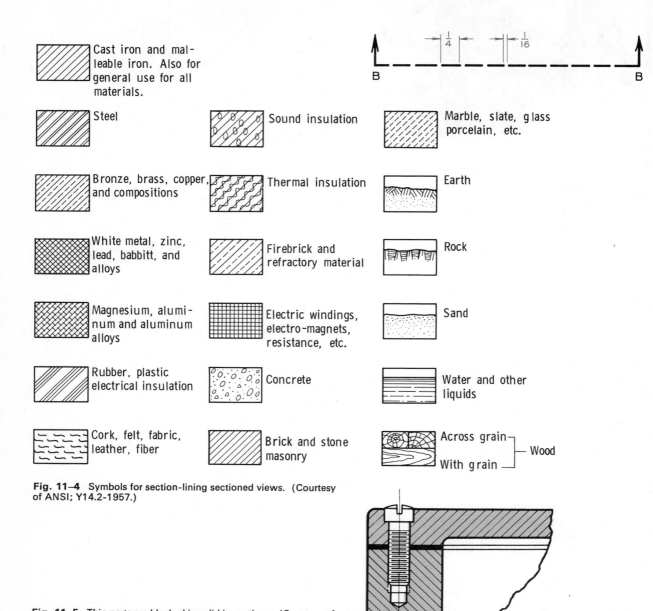

Cast iron and malleable iron. Also for general use for all materials.

Steel

Sound insulation

Marble, slate, glass porcelain, etc.

Bronze, brass, copper, and compositions

Thermal insulation

Earth

White metal, zinc, lead, babbitt, and alloys

Firebrick and refractory material

Rock

Magnesium, aluminum and aluminum alloys

Electric windings, electro-magnets, resistance, etc.

Sand

Rubber, plastic electrical insulation

Concrete

Water and other liquids

Cork, felt, fabric, leather, fiber

Brick and stone masonry

Across grain ⎤
⎬ Wood
With grain ⎦

Fig. 11–4 Symbols for section-lining sectioned views. (Courtesy of ANSI; Y14.2-1957.)

Fig. 11–5 Thin parts are blacked in solid in sections. (Courtesy of ANSI; Y14.2-1957.)

Sections and conventions   11–1

11–2 SECTIONS

A common type of sectional view is the *full section*. This is a view where the cutting plane is imagined to pass fully through the object and one-half of the object is removed. The primary purpose for this section is to reveal interior details that cannot be shown clearly in a regular view. Several regular views may be used in addition to a full section view.

A pictorial of a cutting plane passing fully through an object is shown in Fig. 11–2A. Without a section, the two views of the object would be drawn as in part B. Even though this is a rather simple object, you have some difficulty in understanding the object when referring to the top and front views. When the front half of the object is removed and the front view is drawn as a section (part C), you gain a better understanding of the object.

The section view is drawn in accordance with the same general principles of orthographic projection used in standard views. To indicate the position of the imaginary cut, a cutting plane is drawn in the top view (part C). The portion of the full section that has actually been cut by the imaginary plane is *cross-hatched* or *section-lined*. In this example one of the standard symbols—parallel, equally spaced section lines—is used. This symbol can be used for any material when material notes are used.

11–3 SYMBOLS AND TECHNIQUES

The symbol for a cutting plane can be either of the two types shown in Fig. 11–3. These lines are heavy lines equal in weight to a visible or object line. One contains two short dashes at intervals. The other is a series of heavy dashes. The arrows that are drawn perpendicular to the ends of the cutting plane indicate the direction of the line of sight for looking at the full section once half of the object has been removed. To understand this better, refer to the pictorial in Fig. 11–2A. Often, many sections will be made from the same view and perhaps placed elsewhere on the drawing sheet. This procedure may make it necessary to label each section in order to relate it to the view through which the section was taken. In this case, the cutting plane should be labeled at each end as B–B or C–C, for example (Fig. 11–3). The section view can also be labeled with these letters.

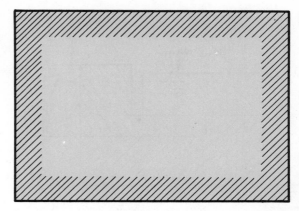

Fig. 11–6 Large sectioned parts are section-lined along their outlines. This is called an outline section.

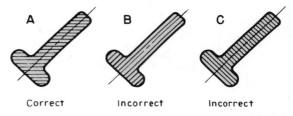

Fig. 11–7 Section lines should be drawn so that they are not parallel or perpendicular to the outlines of the part. (Courtesy of ANSI; Y14.2-1957.)

Cutting planes are not always shown in sections. They may be omitted if it is obvious where the sections were taken.

The standard symbols that are used to distinguish between different materials in sections are shown in Fig. 11–4. These symbols are drawn with thin lines with the aid of instruments and spaced by eye. These symbols can be used to identify the types of materials used, but to avoid misunderstandings it is good practice to use a material note in addition to the section symbols.

The cast iron symbol can be used to represent *any* material. When this symbol is used, it is *necessary* to use notes, since several different materials may be section-lined with the same symbol. The cast iron symbol is commonly drawn with a 2H-4H pencil, with the lines spaced approximately $\frac{1}{16}''$ apart. The

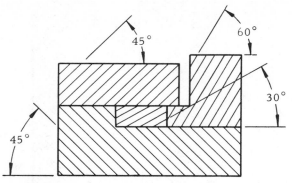

Fig. 11–8 Section lines of different parts in an assembly should be constructed at varying angles to distinguish the parts from one another. (Courtesy of ANSI; Y14.2-1957.)

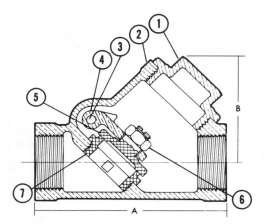

Fig. 11–9 Section lines are drawn in different directions in this check valve to distinguish the parts of the assembly. (Courtesy of Nibco Scott, Inc.)

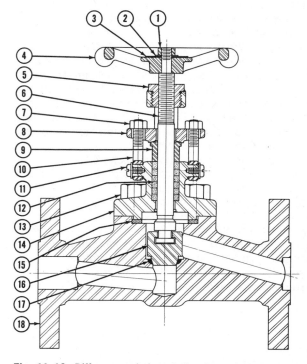

Fig. 11–10 Different symbols and directions of section lines are used to illustrate the assembly of this valve. (Courtesy of Jenkins Bros.)

angle for slanting these lines can be 45°, 60°, 30° or any convenient angle. For smaller parts the lines may be spaced closer together, and for larger parts farther apart.

Extremely thin parts, such as sheet metal parts, washers, or gaskets (Fig. 11–5), are sectioned by blacking in the area completely instead of using section lines. Large parts may be sectioned with an *outline section*, as shown in Fig. 11–6. Outline section-lining eliminates much of the time and effort that would be required to crosshatch the entire area.

Sectioned areas should be section-lined with line symbols that are neither parallel nor perpendicular to the outlines of the part. Lines parallel or perpendicular to the outlines might possibly be confused as serrations or other machined treatments of the surface. This danger is illustrated in Fig. 11–7.

11–4 SECTIONING ASSEMBLIES

When assemblies of several parts are sectioned to show the relationship of the parts, it is important that

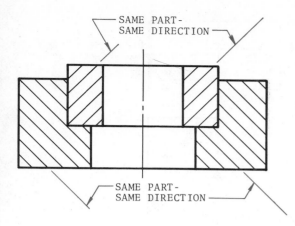

SAME PART-
SAME DIRECTION

SAME PART-
SAME DIRECTION

Fig. 11–11 Section lines must be in the same direction on various areas of the same part.

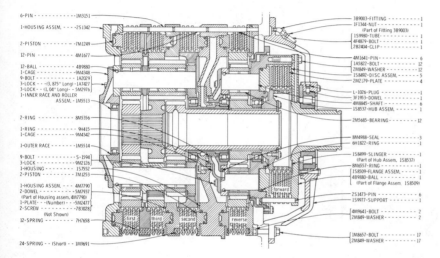

6-PIN - - - - - - - - - - - 1M3151
1-HOUSING ASSEM. - - -2S1342
2-PISTON - - - - - - - - 7M1249
12-PIN - - - - - - - - 4M1677
12-BALL - - - - - - - - - 4B9880
1-CAGE - - - - - - - - -9M4348
9-BOLT - - - - - - - - - 1A2029
3-LOCK - - -(3.875" Long)- 1A7427
3-LOCK - - (1.04" Long)- 5M2976
1-INNER RACE AND ROLLER
ASSEM. 1M5513

2-RING - - - - - - - - 8M5356

1-RING - - - - - - - - 9H415
1-CAGE - - - - - - - - 9M4342

1-OUTER RACE - - - - - - 1M5514

9-BOLT - - - - - - - - S-1594
3-LOCK - - - - - - - 9M2126
1-HOUSING - - - - - - 1S7552
2-PISTON - - - - - - 7M1253

1-HOUSING ASSEM. - - - 4M7790
2-DOWEL - - - - - - - 5M7937
(Part of Housing assem. 4M7790)
1-PLATE - - -(Number) - - 5M2477
2-SCREW - - - - - - -7B3028
(Not Shown)
12-SPRING - - - - - - - 7H7658

24-SPRING - - -(Short) - 1M9691

first   third   second   reverse
forward

3B9003-FITTING - - - - - - - -1
1F1344-NUT - - - - - - - - - - 1
(Part of Fitting 3B9003)
1S9980-TUBE- - - - - - - - - -1
4F4879-BOLT - - - - - - - - - 1
2B2404-CLIP - - - - - - - - - 1

4M1641-PIN - - - - - - - - 6
1A5822-BOLT - - - - - - - - 12
2M849-WASHER - - - - - - -12
1S8492-DISC ASSEM. - - - - -5
2M2179-PLATE - - - - - - - - 4

L-1026-PLUG - - - - - - - - - -1
3F1953-DOWEL - - - - - - - - -1
4M8845-SHAFT - - - - - - - - 1
1S8537-HUB ASSEM. - - - - - 1

2M5685-BEARING - - - - - - 12

8M4988-SEAL - - - - - - - - -3
6H1822-RING - - - - - - - - -1

1S8499-SLINGER - - - - - - - -1
(Part of Hub Assem. 1S8537)
8M6557-RING - - - - - - - - - 1
1S8509-FLANGE ASSEM. - - - - 1
4B9880-BALL - - - - - - - - - 1
(Part of Flange Assem 1S8509)

2S1473-PIN - - - - - - - - - 6
1S9977-SUPPORT - - - - - - - 1

4M9641-BOLT - - - - - - - - 2
2M849-WASHER - - - - - - - 2

1M8657-BOLT - - - - - - - 17
2M849-WASHER - - - - - - 17

Fig. 11–12 The parts of this complex assembly are defined by using section lines drawn in varying directions and with varying spacing. (Courtesy of the Caterpillar Tractor Company.)

the section lines be drawn at varying angles to distinguish the parts. In the assembly of four parts shown in Fig. 11–8 it is easy to separate the parts, since the direction of the section lines is different for each part. An industrial example of this principle can be seen in Fig. 11–9.

In the valve assembly shown in Fig. 11–10, the different parts are identified by section lines with varying angles and by the use of different section symbols. Note that for the sake of clarity each part

of the assembly is crosshatched at the same angle and with the same symbol throughout, even though the section of the part may be separated into several distinct areas. For example, see Fig. 11–11, where each of the two parts is divided into two areas.

A complex assembly is shown in Fig. 11–12. Note that the cast iron symbol is used on all parts. However, the angles of the section lines and the spacing of the lines make it possible to distinguish the parts even in such a complex assembly.

Fig. 11–13 A pictorial full section through an object.

Fig. 11–14 A comparison of a regular view with a full section of the same object.

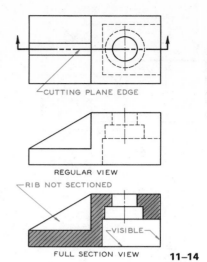

CUTTING PLANE EDGE

REGULAR VIEW

RIB NOT SECTIONED

VISIBLE

FULL SECTION VIEW

11–14

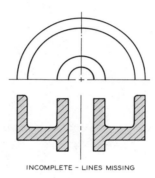

11–13

FIGURE 11–15

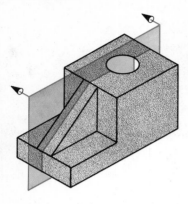

VISIBLE LINES

PICTORIAL

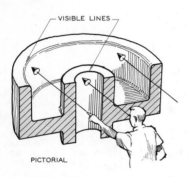

INCOMPLETE – LINES MISSING

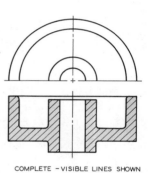

COMPLETE – VISIBLE LINES SHOWN

A. When a full section is taken through an object, you will see lines behind the sectioned area.

B. If only the sectioned area were shown, the view would be incomplete.

C. Visible lines behind the section must be shown also.

11–5 FULL SECTIONS

When the cutting plane passes fully through an object, the section is called a *full section*. When a full section is used, one-half of the object is imagined to be removed. A pictorial is used in Fig. 11–13 to illustrate a full section. The arrows show the direction of the line of sight that will be used to view the remaining half when the front portion of the object has been removed.

Compare the full section with the customary front view of the same object in Fig. 11–14. The portion cut by the cutting plane is crosshatched so that it will be understood that this is a section view.

Note that the thin rib is not crosshatched in the full section even though the cutting plane passes through it. Had it been section-lined like the other areas, a misleading impression of the object would have been given. Since the rib is very thin, and since it is not typical of the true section of the front view, the *conventional practice* is not to section-line it. In general, hidden lines are omitted in section views except when they clarify the drawing.

A common mistake in constructing section views is the omission of visible lines behind the cutting plane. In the lower right of the full section (Fig.

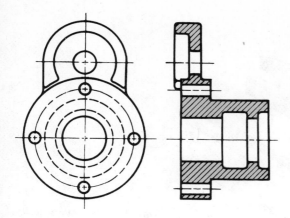

Fig. 11–16 A full section. (Courtesy of ANSI; Y14.2-1957.)

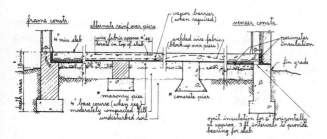

Fig. 11–17 The foundation section is typical of a section used in architectural drawings. (Courtesy of the Federal Housing Administration.)

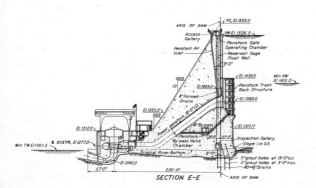

SECTION E–E

Fig. 11–18 Sections may be used to describe internal construction features of a dam. (Courtesy of the Tennessee Valley Authority.)

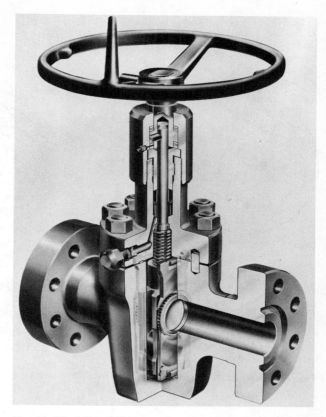

Fig. 11–19 A pictorial half section through a gate valve. (Courtesy of Mr. L. G. Whitfield and Cameron Iron Works.)

11–14) are two such lines that are labeled as visible. These lines will be seen behind the cutting plane even though the plane does not pass through them. Another example of visible lines of this type is shown in Fig. 11–15, where a cylindrical part is drawn as a full section. When you look at the sectioned object (part A), you see the portion that is cut by the imaginary section; this appears as shown in B. But this is not all that you see. In the complete view shown in C, the lines behind the cutting plane are shown. Note that hidden lines are omitted.

Another example of a full section is shown in Fig. 11–16. In this case, the cutting plane has been omitted in the front view, since it is obvious where the plane was passed to give the section view. This is another conventional practice which the draftsman may or may not use as he sees fit.

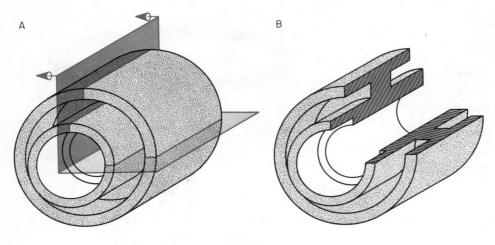

Fig. 11–20 A pictorial representation of a half section.

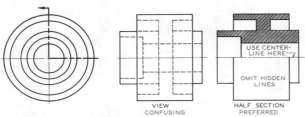

Fig. 11–21 A comparison of a regular view with a half section.

USE CENTER-
LINE HERE

OMIT HIDDEN
LINES

VIEW
CONFUSING

HALF SECTION
PREFERRED

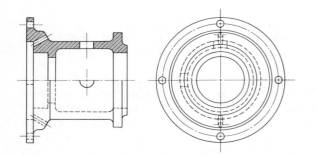

Fig. 11–22 A half section with hidden lines. Hidden lines should be omitted unless they are necessary to explain the part. (Courtesy of ANSI; Y14.2-1957.)

Most examples of sections shown in this chapter are sections of machine parts, but this is not the only type of drawing that requires sections. For instance, sections are used by architects to show details of construction. The foundation section shown in Fig. 11–17 describes the methods of con-

struction and the internal steel and bolts used in the concrete slab and footings. A full section can also be used to illustrate portions of a massive structure such as a dam (Fig. 11–18). A project of this type would be very difficult to describe without the use of sections.

11–6 HALF SECTIONS

When the cutting plane passes halfway through an object to remove a quarter of it, the resulting section is called a *half section*. A pictorial example of a half section is shown in Fig. 11–19. A half section shows both exterior and interior features in the same view.

Figure 11–20A illustrates a cutting plane that passes halfway through a pulley to remove one-quarter of the object. The three-quarters that remains is illustrated pictorially in Fig. 11–20B. The orthographic arrangement of the half section of this object is shown in Fig. 11–21, where the half section can be compared with a regular view. The standard view is more confusing and more difficult to read. The half section, in which the internal and external features are clearly seen in the same view, gives a better impression of the object because unnecessary hidden lines can be omitted. The cut portion of the half section is section-lined to show the cross section of the part. Note the use of a centerline rather than a solid line, since the removal of a quarter is imaginary and not an actual cut that would be represented by a solid line. The cutting-plane line could have been omitted in the circular view, since it is obvious where

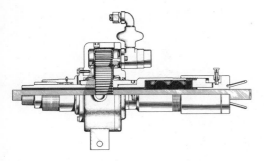

Fig. 11–23 A technical illustrator's drawing of a half section. (Courtesy of L. G. Whitfield.)

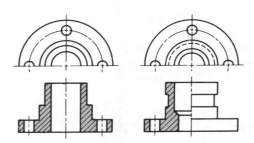

Fig. 11–24 Conventional use of half views in conjunction with sections to reduce space and drawing time. (Courtesy of ANSI; Y14.2-1957.)

FIGURE 11–25

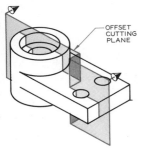

OFFSET CUTTING PLANE

A. An offset section may be necessary to show all typical features.

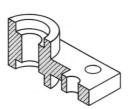

B. When the front portion is removed, the internal features can be seen.

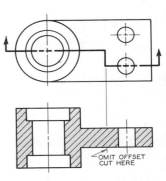

OMIT OFFSET CUT HERE

C. In an offset section, the offset cut is not shown; the section is shown as a smooth cut.

the plane was positioned in a symmetrical view of this type.

An example of a half section where the cutting plane is not shown is given in Fig. 11–22. Hidden lines are given in this example although they are not necessary. It is recommended that you do not use unnecessary hidden lines unless you feel they add to the clarity of the drawing. Figure 11–23 shows a half section drawn for a catalog illustration. This drawing contains no hidden lines, but it is very easy to read because the outside and inside details can be seen in the same view.

11–7 CONVENTIONAL HALF VIEWS

Space can be saved by drawing symmetrical views as half views for half or full sections. Examples are shown in Fig. 11–24, where the top views are half views. When the views are sections, the top views are arranged so that the removed halves are on the side of the section view. This is the opposite procedure to that used for half views in regular orthographic drawings that are not sectioned. A centerline rather than a solid object line is used along the imaginary cut in the top view. A solid object line would indicate that the top view was truly a semicircular shape.

11–8 OFFSET SECTIONS

An *offset section* is a type of full section in which the cutting plane is offset to pass through important features that would otherwise be missed by the usual full section. An example is shown in Fig. 11–25A,

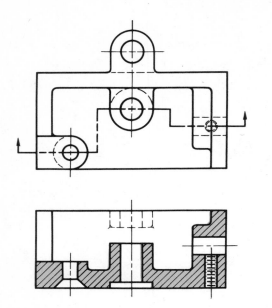

Fig. 11–26 An offset section. (Courtesy of ANSI; Y14.2-1957.)

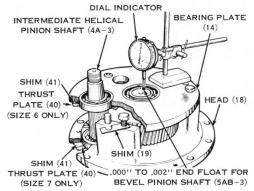

Fig. 11–27 A pictorial of a broken-out section in a gear assembly. (Courtesy of the Falk Corporation.)

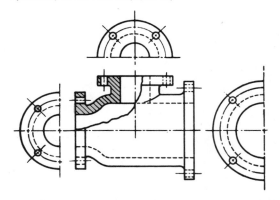

Fig. 11–28 A broken-out section. (Courtesy of ANSI; Y14.2-1957.)

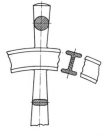

Fig. 11–29 An example of the use of revolved sections to describe the shape of an object. (Courtesy of ANSI; Y14.2–1957.)

where the cutting plane is offset in order to pass through both the large hole and the small hole. When the cut portion is removed and viewed in the direction of the line of sight, it appears as shown in part B. The conventional method of showing this offset section is shown in C. Note that the offset cut formed by the offset plane is not shown in the front view since this is an imaginary cut.

Another example of an offset section is shown in Fig. 11–26. The same general principles apply here. Note that the broken cuts formed by the offset cutting plane are not shown in the offset section. Instead, the section is shown as if it were cut by a smooth, continuous plane.

11–9 BROKEN-OUT SECTIONS

A *broken-out section* is a convenient way of showing interior parts; it clarifies a drawing without the need of an entire section view. A pictorial example is shown in Fig. 11–27, where a portion of the bearing plane has been broken out.

The method of showing a broken-out section can be seen in Fig. 11–28, where a portion of the

object is broken out to reveal details of the wall thickness of the part. This broken-out section reduces the need for additional hidden lines in the partial top view and the two side views, since the details can be shown in the front view.

FIGURE 11–30. A PICTORIAL OF A REVOLVED SECTION

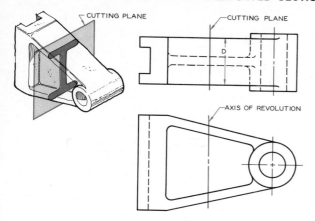

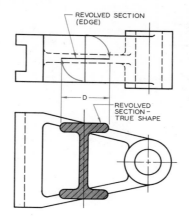

Step 1. An axis of revolution is shown in the front view. The cutting plane would appear in the top if drawn.

Step 2. The vertical section in the top view is revolved so that the section can be seen true size in the front view. Object lines do not pass through the revolved section.

11–10 REVOLVED SECTIONS

A *revolved section* can be used to describe the cross section of a part while eliminating the need for an entire additional view. Examples of revolved sections used to indicate cross sections of structural shapes are shown in Fig. 11–29. The dimensions of these revolved sections could not have been drawn unless their dimensions were known or an additional view were given from which measurements could be made.

Figure 11–29 illustrates two methods of constructing revolved sections. The circular section is revolved and drawn on top of the view where the section was taken. The section at the right of the figure is placed where the section was taken, but conventional break lines are used to separate the section from the view of the part.

An example of a revolved section is shown in Fig. 11–30 to illustrate the steps of construction. In Step 1, the top and front views of an object are shown. Because of the shape of the object, it would be hard to visualize the middle area in the given views in a side view, if one were drawn. By constructing a revolved section in this middle portion, you can clearly describe its shape. A cutting plane can be assumed to pass through the portion that is to be shown in a revolved section.

In Step 2, this section is revolved in the top view and projected to the front view where the section

can be drawn true size. This revolved section is drawn on top of the object, but the object lines are not drawn through the section. Note also that the top and bottom webs are perpendicular to the center web in the section; they are not parallel to the web in the front view. The crosshatched part of the front view in Step 2 represents the true shape of the cross section through this portion of the object. It is unnecessary to show the revolution in the top view because it is understood. The construction is shown here only to help in explaining the method of finding the revolved section.

Two methods of showing a revolved section are illustrated in Fig. 11–31. In part A a section is revolved to give a typical cross section through the ribs. The depth dimensions of the revolved section are taken from the top views, as indicated by the dimension lines. The revolved section is superimposed on the front view; object lines are not drawn through the section. The second method, shown in part B, is the same except that conventional breaks are used to separate the front view from the revolved section. Either of the methods shown in A and B can be used in most applications. The removed section shown in part C is a revolved section that has been displaced from its position of revolution. Removed sections will be discussed in Article 11–11.

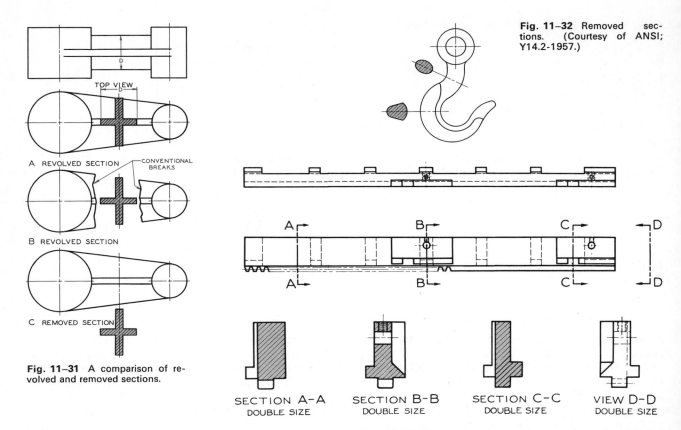

Fig. 11–32 Removed sections. (Courtesy of ANSI; Y14.2-1957.)

A REVOLVED SECTION

CONVENTIONAL BREAKS

B REVOLVED SECTION

C REMOVED SECTION

Fig. 11–31 A comparison of revolved and removed sections.

SECTION A–A
DOUBLE SIZE

SECTION B–B
DOUBLE SIZE

SECTION C–C
DOUBLE SIZE

VIEW D–D
DOUBLE SIZE

Fig. 11–33 Removed sections can be drawn larger than the view from which they were taken. (Courtesy of ANSI; Y14.2-1957.)

11–11 REMOVED SECTIONS

A *removed section* is a revolved section that has been displaced from the view in which it was revolved, as shown in part C of Fig. 11–31. A removed section may be necessary where space does not permit revolution on the given view or where removal would give a better description of the part. The removed sections shown in Fig. 11–32 give typical cross sections of a hook. It would be very difficult to describe the shape of this hook by means of regular orthographic views.

Removed sections may be drawn at a different scale from the given views, as shown in Fig. 11–33. The locations of the removed sections are noted by

means of cutting planes in the front view. The cutting plane lettered A–A produces section A–A, which may be near the front view or on a separate sheet of the working drawings. Section D–D is actually a right side view rather than a section. The scale of the removed sections is noted on each view when it is different from the scale on the original views.

A similar method for showing a removed view is illustrated in Fig. 11–34. This view cannot be shown except by hidden lines; therefore, an imaginary cutting plane is used to indicate the viewer's position and line of sight. The view from this position is removed and labeled as view A–A.

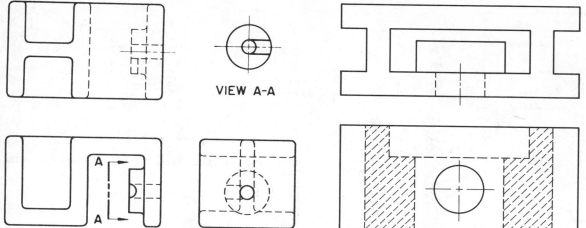

VIEW A-A

Fig. 11–34 A removed view. (Courtesy of ANSI; Y14.2-1957.)

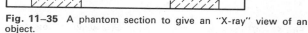

Fig. 11–35 A phantom section to give an "X-ray" view of an object.

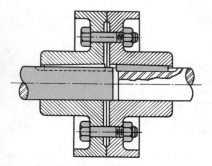

Fig. 11–36 Parts not section-lined in an assembly—shafts, keys, bolts, and nuts. (Courtesy of ANSI; Y14.2-1957.)

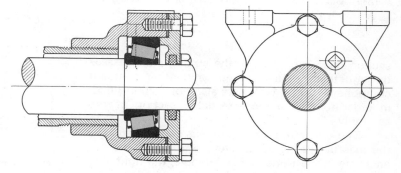

Fig. 11–37 Parts not section-lined in an assembly—shafts, bolts, and roller bearings. (Courtesy of the *Timken Engineering Journal*.)

11–12 PHANTOM SECTIONS

A *phantom section* or ghost section is used occasionally to depict special parts that cannot be shown as well by other methods. This type of section is used when exterior as well as interior features must be shown. The part shown in Fig. 11–35 is represented in a phantom section that gives both the outside and inside features.

Note that the section lines are drawn as dashed lines to give an "X-ray" view of the part. This method of sectioning is not often used, but there are times when this technique can be effectively applied.

11–13 PARTS NOT SECTIONED

Greater clarity can often be obtained in sections if some of the standard parts are not section-lined, even though the cutting plane passes through them. For example, see Fig. 11–36, where nuts, bolts, shafts, and keys are not section-lined. These parts have no internal features, and section-lining them would not show them any more clearly. Other parts that are usually not section-lined are ribs, spokes, webs, ball and roller bearings, rivets, pins, and similar parts.

The section in Fig. 11–37 gives examples of shafts, bolts, washers, and roller bearings that are not

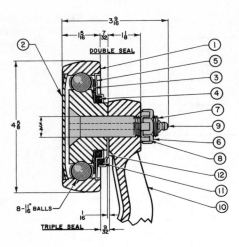

Fig. 11–38 Parts not section-lined in an assembly—nuts, bolts, and ball bearings. (Courtesy of Mechanical Handling Systems, Inc.)

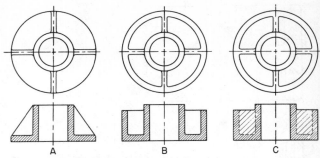

Fig. 11–39 Methods of sectioning ribs. (Courtesy of ANSI; Y14.2-1957.)

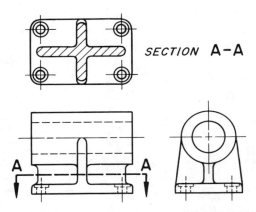

SECTION A-A

Fig. 11–40 Method of section-lining ribs when the cutting plane passes across the ribs. (Courtesy of General Motors Standards.)

section-lined even though the cutting plane passes through them. Ball bearings and other standard components (Fig. 11–38) are also not section-lined, in order to give a more readable section of the assembly.

When the cutting plane passes perpendicular to the axis of shafts, bolts, rivets, and webs, the cut areas are section-lined. For example, the right side view of the shaft in Fig. 11–37 shows a section-lined view of the shaft. The cutting plane passed perpendicular to the axis.

11–14 RIBS IN SECTION

Full sections through cylindrical parts are shown in Fig. 11–39, where the cutting plane passes through ribs that are used to add strength to the parts. The ribs in part A are not section-lined, since the cutting plane passes through the ribs flatwise and section-lining would give the misleading impression that the section was conical.

An alternative method of section-lining ribs and webs is shown in Fig. 11–39C. The rib is outlined with a dashed line where it joins the normally section-lined areas. Solid lines could have been used instead of dashed lines. Every other section line is extended

through the rib to indicate that it has been cut by the cutting plane, but that it is a rib rather than a solid cylinder. The rib in part B is not section-lined at all; this procedure is also correct. However, in this example, the alternative method shown in part C is preferable, since it prevents the rib from being overlooked as it could be in part B.

When the cutting plane passes perpendicular to the flatwise views of the ribs, the ribs are section-lined as shown in Fig. 11–40. This section view gives a true impression of the shape of the ribs. If the plane had passed through the ribs in a flatwise direction, the ribs would not have been section-lined, since this would not give a true impression.

FIGURE 11–41

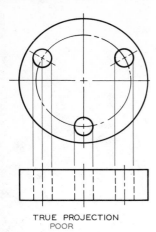

TRUE PROJECTION
POOR

A. A true projection of the equally spaced holes does not give a good impression of the object. One hole appears to go through the center of the plane.

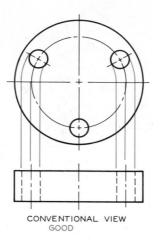

CONVENTIONAL VIEW
GOOD

B. A conventional view is used to show the true radial distance of the holes from the center by revolution. The center hole is omitted.

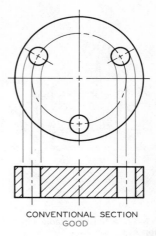

CONVENTIONAL SECTION
GOOD

C. Conventional revolutions are used in sections also. Conventional views are often more representative of circular parts than are true projections.

11–15 CONVENTIONAL REVOLUTIONS

To obtain clarity in engineering drawings, it is sometimes necessary to utilize *conventional practices* that may be violations of true projections. Conventional practices apply to both views and sections. An example of a conventional practice is shown in Fig. 11–41. The top view has three equally spaced holes that are the same distance from the center of the circular plate. In true projection (part A), the front view gives the impression that one hole passes through the center of the plate and that the holes are closer to the center of the plate than they really are. Although this is a true projection, it is not as good a view as the conventional view shown in part B, where the holes have been revolved to show their true distance from the center of the plate. The hole appearing on the vertical centerline is omitted to avoid giving the impression that it passes through the center of the plate.

The same procedure can be used in sections (part C). The part that has been cut is section-lined and the holes are revolved to give their true radial

distance from the center.

A similar example is the hoisting attachment shown in Fig. 11–42. This attachment has five equally spaced flanges that are welded to the center member. When this component is drawn in regular orthographic views as shown in Fig. 11–43A, the object does not appear to be symmetrical. In addition, the true shapes of the flanges are not shown, and they are hard to draw since they appear as ellipses when they are not shown in their true shape.

It is better to follow conventional practice and revolve the flanges as shown in Fig. 11–43B. Then you can draw a front view that is symmetrical and shows the true shape of the flanges. The same procedure has been applied to a section in part C. The flanges are not section-lined, since they are very thin members and a misleading representation would be given if they were crosshatched. The conventional view is easier to draw than a true projection; it also gives a better description of the part.

HOISTING

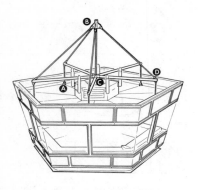

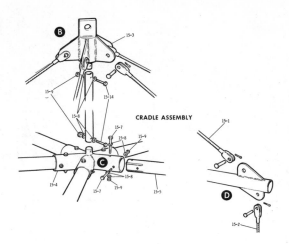

CRADLE ASSEMBLY

Fig. 11–42 A hoisting cradle assembly. (Courtesy of the Federal Aviation Agency.)

FIGURE 11–43

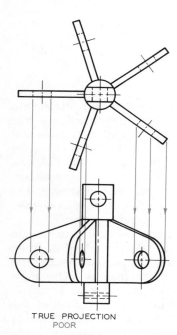

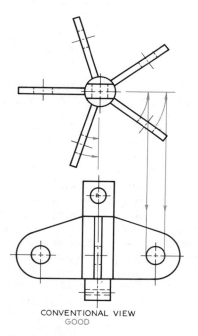

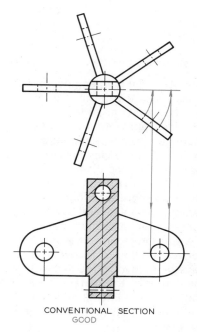

TRUE PROJECTION
POOR

CONVENTIONAL VIEW
GOOD

CONVENTIONAL SECTION
GOOD

A. A true projection gives a poor impression of the hoisting attachment; it does not appear to be symmetrical.

B. A conventional view is better; by revolving the flanges, it shows them true size and the part appears symmetrical.

C. The flanges are revolved in sections also. The flanges are not section-lined, since section-lining would give a mis-leading impression.

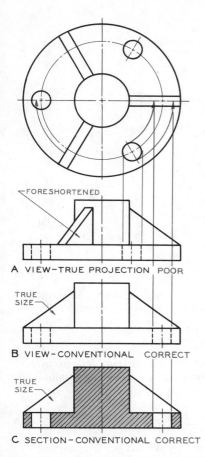

A VIEW—TRUE PROJECTION POOR

B VIEW—CONVENTIONAL CORRECT

C SECTION—CONVENTIONAL CORRECT

Fig. 11—44 The conventional method of revolving holes and ribs in views and sections.

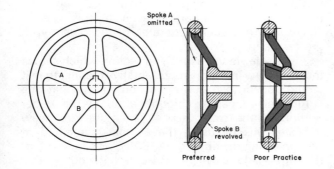

Fig. 11—45 The conventional method of representing spokes. (Courtesy of ANSI; Y14.2-1957.)

A combination of holes and ribs shown in one view is illustrated in Fig. 11—44. This figure involves the conventions discussed in both Figs. 11—41 and 11—43. The top view has three equally spaced ribs and holes. In the true projection of the front view (part A), one rib is foreshortened. A direct projection of the holes gives the impression that one of them is farther from the center than the others. Although this is a true projection, it is not as good as the view shown in part B, where the rib has been revolved to show its true size and one of the holes has been revolved to give its true radial distance from the center.

The same conventional practices have been applied to the section view in part C. The part cut by the cutting plane is section-lined except for the ribs, which in conventional practice are not sectioned.

Symmetrically spaced spokes are conventionally treated the same way as ribs, whether in a view or in a section. Figure 11—45 illustrates the preferred and poor-practice methods of depicting spokes in a section view. Like ribs, spokes are not section-lined. In addition, intermediate spokes are omitted to avoid confusion; two spokes are enough for a complete description of the hand wheel.

11—16 CONVENTIONAL BREAKS

The previous examples of revolved sections used *conventional breaks* to indicate the removal of a portion of the object. Several examples of conventional breaks are shown in Fig. 11—46. In parts A and B of the figure, the conventional breaks are used to represent cylindrical objects. From these breaks it is possible to see that these parts are cylindrical. The part in A is solid, while the part in B is tubular. Guidelines are used for construction of the "figure-8" breaks, which are drawn freehand. The tubular breaks are wider than are those for solid cylinders.

A cylindrical part has been sectioned in Fig. 11—46C. In this case the conventional breaks for rectangular parts are used. The break shown in D is used to represent metal, while the break in E represents wood.

Conventional breaks are used to shorten a long piece that has a uniform cross section; a portion of the object is broken out and removed. This procedure allows the part to be drawn in less space and at a

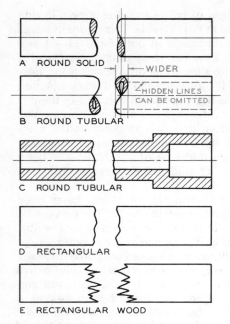

A ROUND SOLID

B ROUND TUBULAR

C ROUND TUBULAR

D RECTANGULAR

E RECTANGULAR WOOD

Fig. 11–46 Conventional breaks.

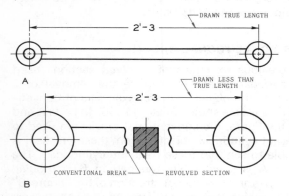

A

B

Fig. 11–47 Conventional breaks can be used to remove a portion of an object so that it can be drawn larger.

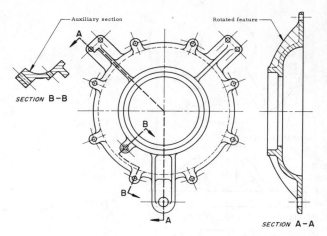

Fig. 11–48 Auxiliary sections used in combination with conventional revolutions to describe an object. (Courtesy of General Motors Standards.)

scale to show more detail. A revolved section is added to describe the part better. The actual length of the part is indicated on the drawing.

11–17 AUXILIARY SECTIONS

Auxiliary sections can be drawn to supplement the principal views used in orthographic projections, as shown in Fig. 11–48. An offset auxiliary plane B–B is passed through the top view. The auxiliary section is a direct auxiliary projection made in the conventional manner with a portion revolved. It is a partial view used to describe one area of the object with greater clarity.

The side view is a revolved section which shows the front view in a more representative manner than it would appear in a true projection. Note that one cutting plane passes through a rib in the upper portion of the front view. The right side view indicates this by using the alternative method of section-lining the rib (Fig. 11–39C). The lower rib of the right side view is not crosshatched in this manner. Either method is acceptable.

larger scale than would otherwise be possible. Compare the two drawings of a part in Fig. 11–47. The view in A shows the actual proportions of the part. Using conventional breaks and the same amount of space, you can draw the object at a larger

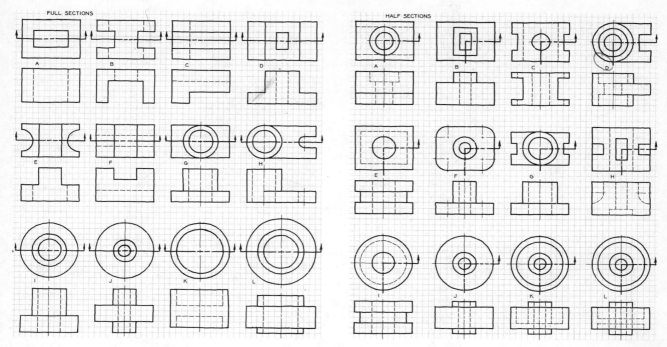

Fig. 11–49 Problems 1 through 12: Full sections.

Fig. 11–50 Problems 13 through 24: Half sections.

PROBLEMS

These problems are to be solved in accordance with Article 3–15 and the specifications of your instructor. Most problems are to be drawn on standard Size A paper (8½″ × 11″) using ink or pencil.

Many of the problems are laid out on a grid where each square represents ¼″. The drawings can be transferred to grid paper of a similar type, or else the problems can be drawn on blank paper (Fig. 3–32) with the endorsement, title strip, and border as described in Article 3–15. Refer to the text of this chapter to assist you in the solution of the problems.

General Problems

Full Sections

1–12 Refer to Fig. 11–49 for these problems. Use Size A paper. Using instruments, draw the two views of each part on a single sheet. Each square on the grid represents ¼″; some problems can be drawn twice this size, each square representing ½″. Convert the front views into full sections as indicated by the cutting planes. Some of the given views may not be complete. Study each view carefully to be sure that your solution is correct.

Half Sections

13–24 Refer to Fig. 11–50 for these problems. Use Size A paper. Using instruments, draw the two views of each part on a single sheet. Each square on the grid represents ¼″; some problems can be drawn twice this size, each square representing ½″. Convert the front views into half sections as indicated by the cutting planes. Some of the views may not be

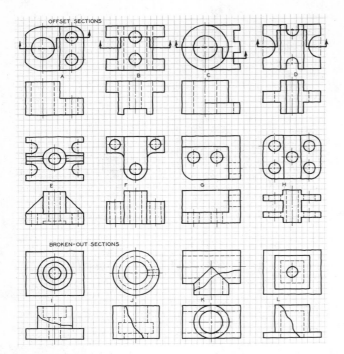

Fig. 11–51 Problems 25 through 36: Offset sections and broken-out sections.

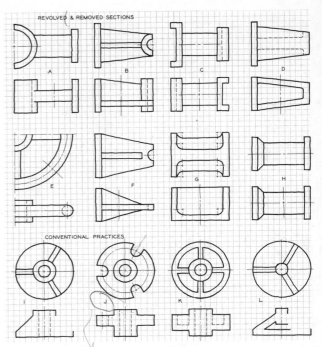

Fig. 11–52 Problems 37 through 60: Revolved and removed sections and conventional practices.

complete. Study each view carefully to be sure that your solution is correct.

Offset Sections

25–32 Refer to Fig. 11–51 for these problems. Use Size A paper. Using instruments, draw the two views of each part on a single sheet. Each square on the grid represents $\frac{1}{4}''$; some problems can be drawn twice this size, each square representing $\frac{1}{2}''$. Convert the front views into offset sections as indicated by the cutting planes. Some of the views may not be complete. Study each view carefully to be sure that your solution is correct. Note that in four of the problems the cutting planes are not drawn; these should be shown in your solutions.

Broken-out Sections

33–36 Refer to Fig. 11–51 for these problems. Use Size A paper. Using instruments, draw the two views

of each part on a single sheet. Each square on the grid represents $\frac{1}{4}''$; some problems can be drawn twice this size, each square representing $\frac{1}{2}''$. Convert the front views into broken-out sections as indicated by the break lines. Some of the views may not be complete. You are to supply all missing details that should be shown in a section of this type.

Revolved Sections

37–44 Refer to Fig. 11–52A through H. Using instruments, draw the two views of each part on Size A paper. Each square on the grid represents $\frac{1}{4}''$; some problems can be drawn twice this size, each square representing $\frac{1}{2}''$. Convert the views where the axes of revolution are shown into revolved sections. Conventional breaks can be used if the revolved section can be superimposed on the view as discussed in this chapter.

Removed Sections

45–52 Refer to Fig. 11–52A through H. Using instruments, draw the given views of each part on Size A paper. Each square on the grid represents $\frac{1}{4}$"; some problems can be drawn twice this size, each square representing $\frac{1}{2}$". Draw removed sections on the extensions of the axes of revolution shown in one of the views of each part.

Conventional Practices

53–56 Refer to Fig. 11–52 I through L. Using instruments, draw the given views of each part on Size A paper. Each square on the grid can represent either $\frac{1}{4}$" or $\frac{1}{2}$". Complete the front views, applying the conventional practices discussed in this chapter. The given views may not be complete as given.

57–60 Refer to Fig. 11–52 I through L. Using instruments, draw the given views of each part on Size A paper. Each square on the grid can represent either $\frac{1}{4}$" or $\frac{1}{2}$". Complete the front views as *full sections*, applying the conventional practices discussed in this chapter. The given views may not be complete as given.

Miscellaneous Problems

61 Using instruments, draw the cover plate shown in Fig. 11–53 on a sheet of Size A paper. Dimensions should be omitted from your final drawing. Convert the right side view to a full section.

62 Repeat Problem 61 but convert the right side view to a half section.

63 Using instruments, draw the gland shown in Fig. 11–54 on a sheet of Size A paper. Dimensions should be omitted from your final drawing. Convert the right side view to a full section.

64 Repeat Problem 63 but convert the right side view to a half section.

65 Using instruments, draw the link shown in Fig. 11–55 on a sheet of Size A paper. Dimensions should be omitted from your final drawing. Convert the top view to a full section.

66 Using instruments, draw the cap shown in Fig. 11–56 on a sheet of Size B paper. Dimensions should be omitted from your final drawing. Convert the right side view to a full section.

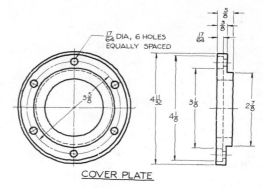

COVER PLATE

Fig. 11–53 Problems 61 and 62.

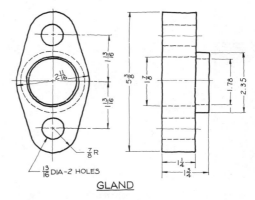

GLAND

Fig. 11–54 Problems 63 and 64.

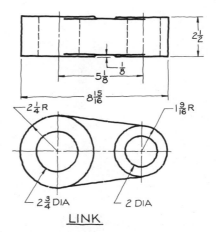

LINK

Fig. 11–55 Problem 65.

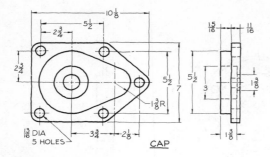

Fig. 11–56 Problems 66 and 67.

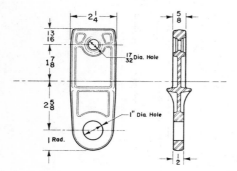

Fig. 11–57 Problem 68: Pendant attachment. (Courtesy of Mechanical Handling Systems, Inc.)

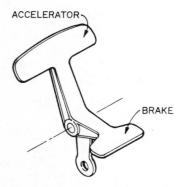

Fig. 11–58 Problem 69: Foot pedal. (Courtesy of Versal, Inc.)

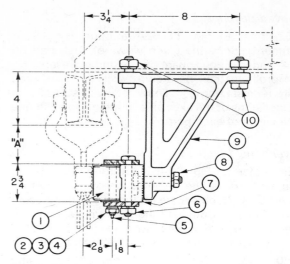

Fig. 11–59 Problem 70: Roller turn bracket. (Courtesy of Mechanical Handling Systems, Inc.)

67 Using the given views of the cap shown in Fig. 11–56 as a guide, draw a full section view as a top view by passing the cutting plane through the front view. Use instruments and omit dimensions. Use Size B paper.

Design Problems

68 The pendant attachment shown in Fig. 11–57 in a full section view is a part used in an overhead conveyor system for moving materials in a manufacturing plant. Using instruments, make an isometric pictorial of a full section of this pendant on Size A paper. This will enable you to understand the shape of the part better. Select the best scale for this drawing.

69 The pedal shown in Fig. 11–58 is used as an accelerator and brake on a Viking golf car. As the designer of this part, prepare the necessary views and sections to completely describe the part. Assume the dimensions. Use Size A paper and instruments.

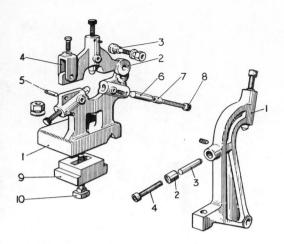

Fig. 11–60 Problem 71: Steadies. (Courtesy of Harrison and Sons Ltd.)

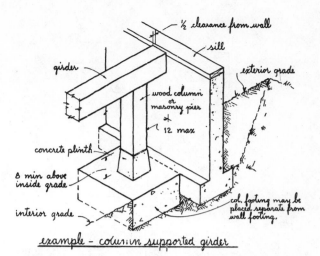

Fig. 11–61 Problem 72: Foundation detail. (Courtesy of Federal Housing Administration.)

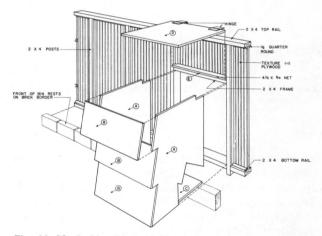

Fig. 11–62 Problem 73: Trash can bin. (Courtesy of the American Plywood Association.)

70 Part No. 9 in Fig. 11–59 is a roller bracket that is part of a roller device which guides a conveyor around a curve. Assume that you are the designer of this bracket. Supply the necessary views and sections to describe its design fully. You will have to assume some dimensions and supply others yourself. Use Size A paper and instruments.

71 The steadies shown in Fig. 11–60 are used in lathe work. Assume that these are preliminary sketches and that you are to make the necessary orthographic views and sections to explain each individual part. Assume all dimensions, with the base of part No. 1 being 4″ × 6″. Omit all threaded parts. Show threaded holes as drilled holes. Each part should be drawn independently of the other parts. Use sections as required. Use instruments and Size A paper. More than one sheet will probably be required.

72 The foundation detail shown in pictorial in Fig. 11–61 is a concrete wall foundation. Using instruments, prepare an orthographic section of this structure on Size A paper. Assume dimensions that are not given.

73 The trash can bin shown in pictorial in Fig. 11–62 has been designed to hold a standard size trash can.

The hole in the rear fence permits the sanitation men to remove and empty the can. Using Size B paper (11″ × 17″), make the necessary orthographic drawings and sections to clarify how this bin is to be constructed. Use as many sheets as necessary.

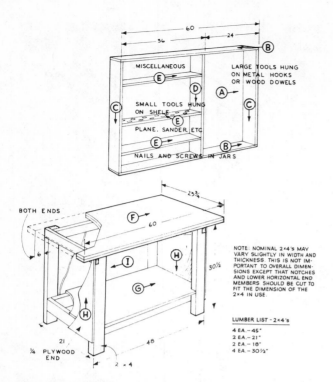

Fig. 11-63 Problem 74: Workbench and tool shelf. (Courtesy of the American Plywood Association.)

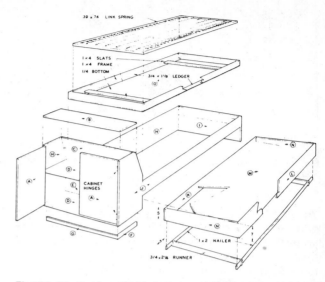

Fig. 11-64 Problem 75: A bed-train board for a model train. (Courtesy of the American Plywood Association.)

74 A workbench and tool shelf are shown in pictorial in Fig. 11-63. Several broken-out sections are used to explain the details of construction. Using Size B paper (11″ × 17″), make the necessary orthographic drawings and sections to clarify the details of construction. Use as many sheets as necessary. Use instruments.

75 The bed-train board shown in Fig. 11-64 is a bed with a pull-out board on which a model train layout can be installed. Using Size B paper (11″ × 17″), make the necessary orthographic drawings and sections to clarify the details of construction. Use $\frac{3}{4}″$ plywood as the building material. Use as many sheets as necessary.

12
FASTENERS

12–1 INTRODUCTION

Nuts, bolts, keys, and rivets are common fasteners used in the fabrication of engineering projects. The engineer and technician must have a fundamental knowledge of these fasteners in order to specify correctly the type to be used for a particular application.

This chapter deals primarily with the methods used to represent threaded fasteners, although keys and rivets will also be introduced. The draftsman must be familiar with these methods in order to prepare working drawings that involve the use of threaded fasteners. Emphasis is placed on the use of tables in the Appendix which specify the characteristics of standard threads. Threads are designed to be uniform so as to provide the greatest possible degree of interchangeability. This permits the replacement of nuts and bolts from stock sizes without the necessity of making a special nut or bolt as a replacement part.

Threaded fasteners made in different countries or by different manufacturers in the same country may use threads of different specifications that do not match. This problem has not been completely resolved; however, progress has been made toward standardizing threads in this country and abroad. A *Unified Screw Thread* has been adopted by the United States, Britain, and Canada (ABC Standards); this is a modification of both the American National thread and the British Whitworth thread.

12–2 THREAD TERMINOLOGY

Certain definitions must be presented before further discussion of threads is possible. Most of the following definitions are illustrated in Fig. 12–1.

External threads are threads on the outside of a cylinder such as a bolt (Figs. 12–1 and 12–2).

Internal threads are threads that are cut on the inside of a cylindrical hole, such as a nut (Figs. 12–1 and 12–2).

Major diameter is the largest diameter of an internal or external thread.

Minor diameter is the smallest diameter that can be measured on a screw thread.

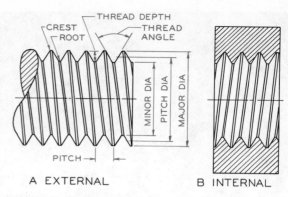

Fig. 12–1 Thread terminology.

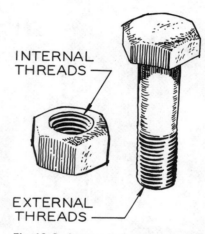

Fig. 12–2 A nut and a bolt represent internal and external threads, respectively.

Pitch diameter is the diameter of an imaginary cylinder passing through the threads at points at which the thread width is equal to the space between the threads.

Crest is the outermost edge of the screw thread.

Pitch is the distance between the crests of threads. Pitch is found mathematically by dividing one inch by the number of threads per inch of a particular thread.

Thread angle is the angle between threads cut by the cutting tool.

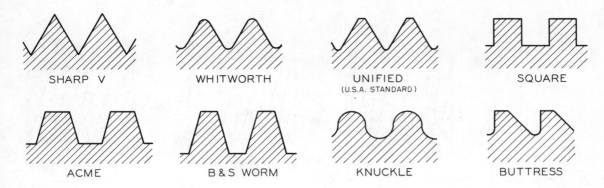

SHARP V   WHITWORTH   UNIFIED (U.S.A. STANDARD)   SQUARE

ACME   B & S WORM   KNUCKLE   BUTTRESS

Fig. 12–3 Standard thread forms.

Root is the bottom of the thread cut into the cylinder.

Thread form is the shape of the thread cut into a threaded part.

Thread series is a standard that specifies the number of threads per inch for a particular thread form.

Lead is the distance a screw thread advances in one full turn.

Thread class is the closeness of fit between two mating threaded parts such as a nut and bolt. Class 1 fit is a loose fit and Class 3 a tight fit.

Right-hand thread is a thread that will assemble when turned clockwise. A right-hand thread will slope downward to the right on an external thread when the axis of the threaded part is horizontal. The direction is opposite for an internal thread.

Left-hand thread is a thread that will assemble when turned counterclockwise. A left-hand thread slopes downward to the left on an external thread when the axis of the threaded part is horizontal. The direction is opposite for an internal thread.

12–3 THREAD FORM

Thread form is the shape of the thread that is cut into a part. Several types are shown in Fig. 12–3. The Unified form is widely used, since it is a combination of the American National and the British Whitworth. This thread is standard in several countries besides the United States, Britain, and Canada.

The American National thread form is indicated on drawings by the letter N. The Unified form is indicated by the letters UN. Tables in the Appendix give the specifications and dimensions for various thread forms for different sizes of threads.

The type of thread form selected by the designer depends on the application. The transmission of power is achieved by the use of the Acme, square, buttress, and worm threads. These are used in machinery and gearing. The Sharp V is used for set screws and in applications where friction in assembly is desired. The knuckle is a fast-assembly thread used for light assemblies such as light bulbs and bottle caps.

12–4 THREAD SERIES

Thread series is closely related to thread form. It specifies the number of threads per inch for various thread forms. For example, there are six series of threads listed under the American National form and the Unified National form. These six series and their symbols are: coarse (C), fine (F), extra-fine (EF), 8 thread (8), 12 thread (12), and 16 thread (16).

A Unified National form for a coarse-series thread is specified as UNC, which is a combination of form and series in a single note. Similarly, an American National form for a coarse thread is written as NC.

The *coarse* thread series (UNC or NC) is suitable for bolts, screws, nuts, and general use with

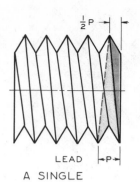
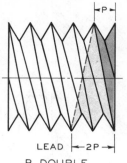
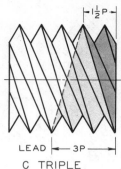

Fig. 12–4 Single and multiple threads.

A SINGLE   B DOUBLE   C TRIPLE

cast iron, soft metals, or plastics when rapid assembly is desired. The *fine* thread series (NF or UNF) is suitable for applications where a high degree of tightening is required. The *extra-fine* series (NEF or UNEF) is used to withstand high stresses. This series is suitable for sheet metal, thin nuts, ferrules, or couplings where the length of engagement is small.

The *8 thread* series (8 N or 8 UNC), *12 thread* series (12 N or 12 UN), and *16 thread* series (16 N or 16 UN) are threads with a uniform pitch for large diameters. The 8 N is used as a substitute for the coarse thread series on diameters larger than 1″ when a medium-pitch thread is required. The 12 N is used on diameters larger than $1\frac{1}{2}$″ with a thread of medium-fine pitch as a continuation of the fine thread series. The 16 N series is used on diameters larger than 2″ with threads of an extra-fine pitch as a continuation of the extra-fine series.

12–5 CLASS OF FIT

The class of fit is an indication of the tightness of fit between a nut and a bolt or any two mating threaded parts. The fit is determined by the tolerances and allowances of the threaded parts.

Classes of fit are indicated by the numbers 1, 2, or 3 followed, in the case of Unified National thread forms, by the letter A or B. The letter A represents an external thread, while the letter B represents an internal thread. These letters may be omitted when the American National form is used.

Classes 1A and 1B are used on parts which require assembly with a minimum of binding. Classes 2A and 2B are general-purpose fits for bolts, nuts, screws, and normal applications in the mechanical field; they are widely used in the mass production industries. Classes 3A and 3B are used in precision assemblies to withstand stress and vibration.

12–6 SINGLE AND MULTIPLE THREADS

A single thread (Fig. 12–4A) is a thread that will advance the distance of its pitch in one full revolution of 360°. In other words, a single thread is a thread whose pitch is equal to its lead. In a drawing of a single thread, the crest line will slope $\frac{1}{2}P$, since only 180° of the revolution is visible in a single view.

A double thread consists of two side-by-side threads that will advance the screw twice as far in one revolution as a single thread would. In a double thread the lead is equal to 2P; therefore, the threaded part will advance a distance of 2P in 360° of revolution (Fig. 12–4B). The crest of a double thread will slope a distance equal to P in a view in which 180° of revolution is visible.

A triple thread will advance a distance of 3P in 360° of revolution, and its crest line will slope $1\frac{1}{2}P$ in a view in which 180° of the cylinder is visible (Fig. 12–4C). The lead of a triple thread is 3P.

Multiple threads are used where rapid engagement and disengagement are required.

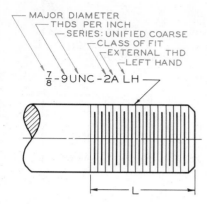

Fig. 12–5 The parts of a thread note.

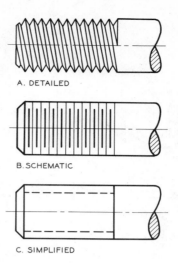

A. DETAILED

B. SCHEMATIC

C. SIMPLIFIED

Fig. 12–6 Three types of thread representations.

12–7 THREAD NOTES

A designer rarely spends time making an actual projection of a thread. Instead, he represents threads symbolically. Consequently, the most important part of a drawing of a threaded part is the thread note which gives the specifications.

A typical thread note is given in Fig. 12–5, which shows an external thread. The most important part of the specification, the major diameter, is given first. This is followed by the number or threads per inch, from which the pitch can easily be determined. Next is the form (UN) and the series (C) written together as UNC. The class of fit, 2A, completes the note if the thread is a single right-hand thread. The letter A represents external threads and B internal threads. However, if the thread is a left-hand or double thread, this information must be added to the note. The letters LH indicate a left-hand thread; right-hand threads do not have to be labeled, since threads are understood to be right-hand unless labeled LH. The word DOUBLE or TRIPLE is included after LH or immediately after the class of fit wherever applicable.

Thread notes must be placed on all drawings of threads, both internal and external. These notes are used in the manufacture of the threaded parts or their selection from the stock of standard fasteners.

12–8 THREAD REPRESENTATION

If threads were shown by true projections, they would have to be drawn as a series of helical curves. Since this procedure would require considerable construction time, the methods used to draw threads on a working drawing are approximations.

The three major types of thread representations are (1) detailed, (2) schematic, and (3) simplified (Fig. 12–6). The detailed drawing is the most realistic approximation of the true, helical thread, while the simplified drawing is the most symbolic.

12–9 THE HELIX

The helix is a curve formed by wrapping a line around a cylinder with a uniform angle of rise. This definition is illustrated in Fig. 12–7. All threads are based on the theory of the helix.

A helix can be constructed by drawing the top and front views of a cylinder (Fig. 12–7). Elements on the surface of the cylinder are found by dividing the circular view into equal divisions. The elements are lettered and projected from the circular view to the front view of the cylinder. The circumference of the cylinder is laid off to the right of the cylinder and each element labeled to correspond to the top view

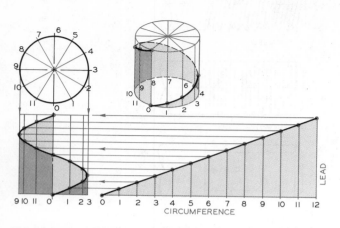

Fig. 12–7 Construction of a helix. Elements are drawn in the top and front views of the cylinder. The circumference and lead are laid out in the triangular view.

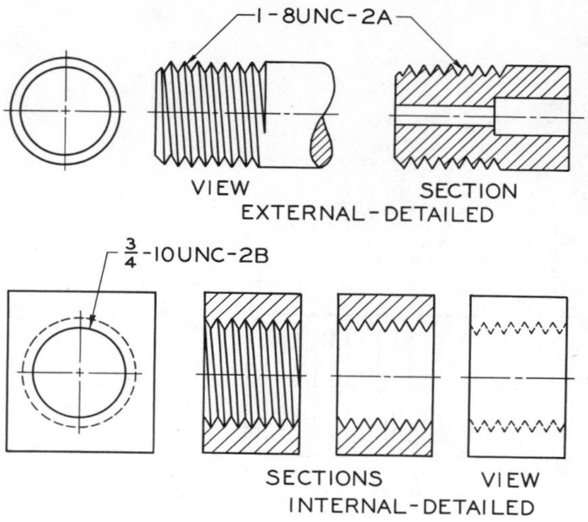

Fig. 12–8 Detailed thread representations.

of the cylinder. The *lead* (the vertical rise of the helix in one revolution) is used to form a right triangle. The hypotenuse of this triangle represents the line that is to be wrapped around the cylinder.

The elements of the cylinder shown in the right triangle are projected to the front view of the cylinder. The points at which these projection lines intersect projection lines from the same elements in the circular view are points on the helix. These points are connected with an irregular curve to give the completed helix.

A true drawing of a threaded bolt would show the threads drawn as a series of helixes. However, this process would require too much time and would be of no more value than the conventional methods that will be discussed in the following articles.

12–10 DETAILED UN AND N THREADS

Examples of *detailed representations* of internal and external threads are shown in Fig. 12–8. These detailed symbols can be used to represent the American National form, the Unified National form, or the Sharp V form.

Instead of helical curves, straight lines are used to indicate crest and root lines. In this type of drawing, internal threads in a section can be indicated in either of two ways. Thread notes are used in all cases.

The method of constructing a detailed representation of this type of thread is shown in Fig. 12–9. The pitch is found by dividing 1″ by the number of threads per inch. This can be done graphically as shown in Step 1. However, in most cases, this construction is unnecessary, since the pitch can be approximated by a measurement close to the true pitch by using your scale or dividers for spacing. The detailed representation is no more than a symbol used to represent a thread; the use of this symbol eliminates the need for a great deal of time-consuming construction that would be necessary to make a true projection.

When the threads are close, they should be drawn with a wider than actual spacing to make the drawing easier. Note in Step 3 of Fig. 12–9 that a 45° chamfer is used to bevel the threaded end for ease of assembly of the threaded parts. The chamfer originates at the minor diameter and is drawn at an angle of 45°.

FIGURE 12–9. CONSTRUCTION OF DETAILED THREADS

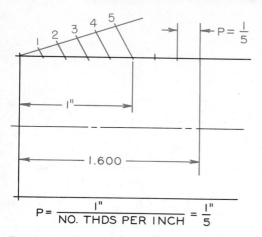

$$P = \frac{1''}{\text{NO. THDS PER INCH}} = \frac{1''}{5}$$

Required: Construct a detailed representation of a thread specified by the note 1¾–5UNC–2A.

Step 1. The major diameter is constructed. The pitch is determined by dividing 1″ by the number of threads per inch (found in the table in Appendix 5). The pitch is laid off with dividers for the full length of the thread.

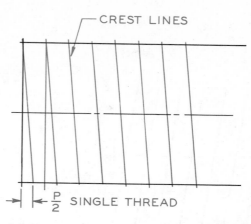

Step 2. Since this is to be a right-hand thread, the crest lines slope downward to the right. The amount of slope is ½P, since the thread is a single thread. The crest lines are drawn parallel as shown. In the final drawing these lines will be drawn with a medium-weight pencil (H-F).

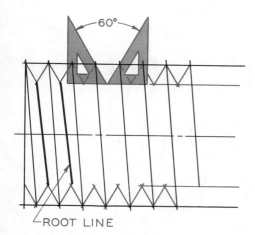

Step 3. Angles of 60° are drawn between the crest lines to establish the root lines. These are lines that are parallel to each other, but are not parallel to crest lines. They can be drawn as finished lines in this step, with the same weight as the crest lines.

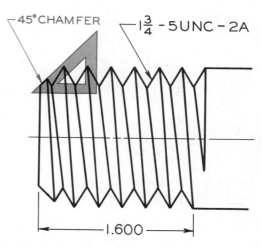

Step 4. A 45° chamfer is constructed at the end of the thread, starting from the minor diameter. All lines are strengthened to an acceptable degree. The thread note is added to give the specifications of the thread.

FIGURE 12–10. DRAWING THE SQUARE THREAD

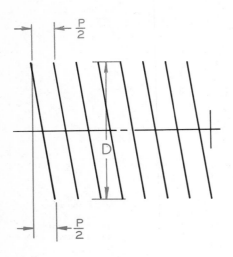

Step 1. Lay out the major diameter. Space the crest lines $\frac{1}{2}P$ apart. Slope them downward to the right for right-hand threads.

Step 2. Connect every other pair of crest lines. Find the minor diameter by measuring $\frac{1}{2}P$ inward from the major diameter.

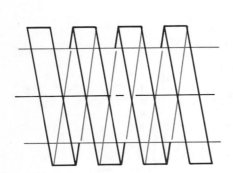

Step 3. Connect the opposite crest lines with light construction lines. This will establish the profile of the thread form.

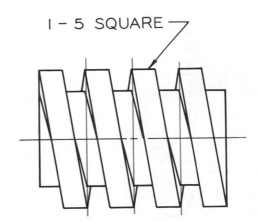

Step 4. Connect the inside crest lines with light construction lines to locate the points on the minor diameter where the thread wraps around the minor diameter. Supply the thread note.

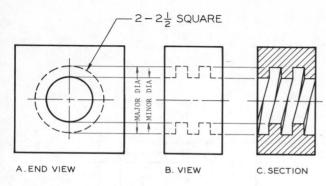

A. END VIEW   B. VIEW   C. SECTION

Fig. 12–11 Internal square threads.

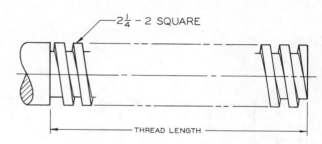

Fig. 12–12 Conventional method of showing square threads without drawing each thread.

12–11 DETAILED SQUARE THREADS

The method of drawing a detailed representation of a square thread is shown in four steps in Fig. 12–10. This method gives an approximation of the true projection of a square thread.

Step 1. The major diameter is laid off. The number of threads per inch is taken from the table in Appendix 4 for this size of thread. The pitch is found by dividing $1''$ by the number of threads per inch. Distances of $P/2$ are marked off with dividers. For right-hand single threads the slope is equal to $P/2$, and the lines slope downward to the right.

Step 2. The minor diameter is found by measuring a distance of $P/2$ from the major diameter. The tops of the threads are drawn in.

Step 3. The tops of the threads are connected with light diagonal construction lines. These lines represent the threads on the back side of the cylinder, mostly invisible in this view. Visible lines are drawn to represent the visible parts of the threads on the back side, between the major diameter and the minor diameter.

Step 4. The inside of each thread is connected with the inside of the opposite thread by a light construction line. This line gives the points on the minor diameter that are to be used for drawing visible root lines. After the root lines are drawn, the thread note is added to complete the drawing.

Square internal threads are drawn in the same manner, as shown in Fig. 12–11. Note that the

threads in the section view are drawn in a slightly different way. The thread note for an internal thread is placed in the circular view whenever possible, with a leader pointing toward the center.

When a square thread is rather long, it need not be drawn continuously, but can be represented conventionally using the symbol shown in Fig. 12–12. This method will save drafting time.

12–12 DETAILED ACME THREADS

The four steps in making a detailed drawing of an Acme thread are shown in Fig. 12–13.

Step 1. Lay off the length and the major diameter of the thread with light construction lines. The pitch can be found by dividing the number of threads per inch (from the table in Appendix 4) into $1''$. If there are 4 threads per inch, then $P = \frac{1}{4}''$. Using light construction lines, mark off a series of divisions $\frac{1}{2}P$ apart.

Step 2. Locate the minor diameter by measuring a distance $\frac{1}{2}P$ from each side of the major diameter. Locate a line between the major and minor diameters that has a depth of $\frac{1}{4}P$.

Step 3. Construct the sides of the threads by drawing lines at an angle of $15°$ with the vertical through the points marked off on the middle line, the pitch diameter. The total angle between the crests is $30°$. For right-hand threads, connect the crests with parallel lines that slope $\frac{1}{2}P$ downward to the right.

FIGURE 12–13. DRAWING THE ACME THREAD

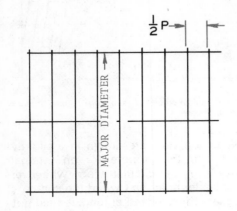

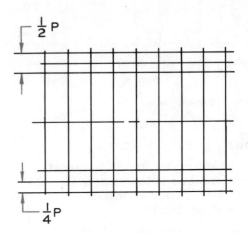

Step 1. Lay out the major diameter and divide the shaft into equal divisions $\frac{1}{2}P$ apart.

Step 2. Locate the minor diameter a distance of $\frac{1}{2}P$ inside the major diameter. Locate the pitch diameter between the major and minor diameters.

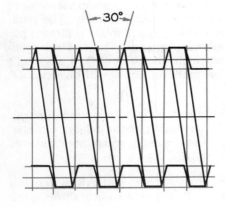

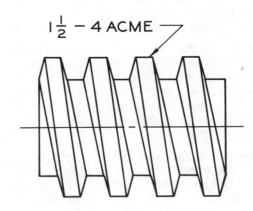

Step 3. Draw lines through the points at which the vertical lines intersect the pitch diameter to make an angle of 30° (15° on each side). Draw the crests and the thread profile.

Step 4. Darken the lines and add the thread note to complete the drawing of the Acme thread.

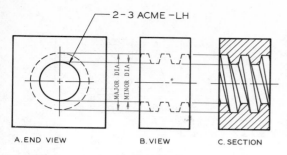

A. END VIEW   B. VIEW   C. SECTION

Fig. 12–14 Internal Acme threads.

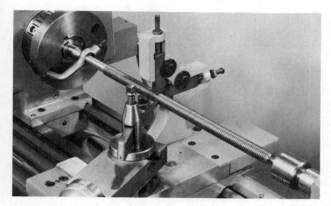

Fig. 12–15 Cutting an Acme thread on a lathe. (Courtesy of the Clausing Corporation.)

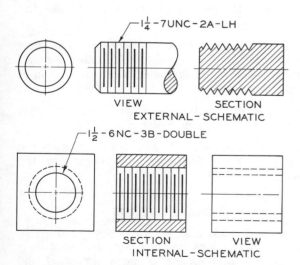

VIEW   SECTION
EXTERNAL – SCHEMATIC

SECTION   VIEW
INTERNAL – SCHEMATIC

Fig. 12–16 Typical schematic thread representations.

Step 4. Construct the root lines to complete the drawing. Add a thread note to complete the specifications.

Internal Acme threads are shown in Fig. 12–14. Note that in the section view, left-hand internal threads are sloped so that they appear the same as right-hand external threads.

Figure 12–15 shows a shaft that is being threaded on a lathe. These are Acme threads that are being cut as the tool travels the length of the shaft.

12–13 SCHEMATIC THREADS

Examples of schematic thread symbols for internal and external threads are shown in Fig. 12–16. Threads are represented here by parallel lines that do not slope as do the lines in detailed thread drawings. These schematic symbols are easy to construct and yet give an approximation of threads. Consequently, they are the most frequently used method of representing threads.

The method of constructing schematic thread symbols is illustrated in Fig. 12–17 in four steps.

Step 1. The major diameter of the thread is drawn with light construction lines. The pitch is laid off by graphical construction or by estimation, since accuracy is not important. Thin lines are drawn as crest lines across the diameter.

Step 2. The minor diameter of the thread is found by constructing a 60° angle between the crest lines. The minor diameter is drawn with light construction lines.

Step 3. Heavy root lines are drawn across the minor diameter.

Step 4. A 45° chamfer is drawn from the last full thread to the minor diameter. The lines are strengthened and a thread note is added to complete the drawing.

12–14 SIMPLIFIED THREADS

Figure 12–18 illustrates the use of simplified representations with notes to specify thread details. Of the three types of thread representation covered here, this is the easiest to draw. Hidden lines are used to represent the minor diameter. These can be con-

FIGURE 12–17. DRAWING SCHEMATIC THREADS

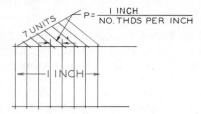

Step 1. Lay out the major diameter and divide the shaft into equal divisions a distance *P* apart. These division lines will be the crest lines; they should be drawn as thin lines.

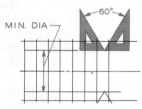

Step 2. Find the minor diameter by drawing a 60° angle between two crest lines.

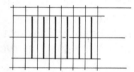

Step 3. Draw heavy root lines between the crest lines.

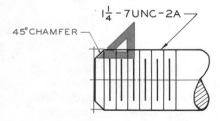

Step 4. Chamfer the end of the thread and give a thread note.

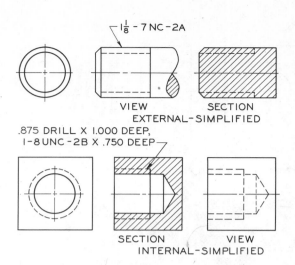

Fig. 12–18 Simplified thread representations.

structed or drawn by eye to approximate the minor diameter.

The steps involved in constructing a simplified thread drawing are shown in Fig. 12–19.

Step 1. The major diameter is laid off with dark visible lines. The pitch is determined to establish the distance between the crest lines.

Step 2. A 60° angle is drawn between these crest lines on each side of the shaft to locate the minor diameter. The minor diameter is drawn with light construction lines.

Step 3. A 45° chamfer is drawn from the minor diameter to the major diameter.

Step 4. Dashed lines are drawn to represent the minor diameter. A thread note completes the drawing.

12–15 DRAWING SMALL THREADS

Very small threads may be impossible to draw to their true dimensions without crest and root lines that touch. This is true of both simplified and schematic thread drawings.

FIGURE 12–19. DRAWING SIMPLIFIED THREADS

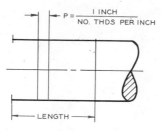

$$P = \frac{1\ INCH}{NO.\ THDS\ PER\ INCH}$$

LENGTH

Step 1. Lay out the major diameter. Find the pitch (P) and lay out two lines a distance P apart.

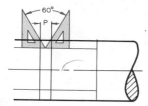

60°

P

Step 2. Find the minor diameter by constructing a 60° angle between the two lines.

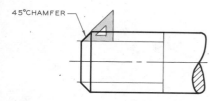

45°CHAMFER

Step 3. Draw a 45° chamfer from the minor diameter to the major diameter.

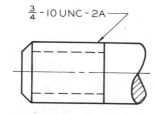

$\frac{3}{4}$ – 10 UNC – 2A

Step 4. Show the minor diameter as a dashed line. Add a thread note.

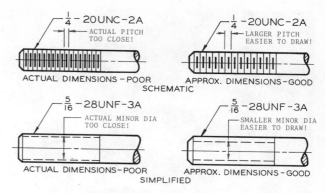

$\frac{1}{4}$ – 20UNC – 2A
ACTUAL PITCH TOO CLOSE!
ACTUAL DIMENSIONS – POOR

$\frac{1}{4}$ – 20UNC – 2A
LARGER PITCH EASIER TO DRAW!
APPROX. DIMENSIONS – GOOD

SCHEMATIC

$\frac{5}{16}$ – 28UNF – 3A
ACTUAL MINOR DIA TOO CLOSE!
ACTUAL DIMENSIONS – POOR

$\frac{5}{16}$ – 28UNF – 3A
SMALLER MINOR DIA EASIER TO DRAW!
APPROX. DIMENSIONS – GOOD

SIMPLIFIED

Fig. 12–20 Simplified and schematic threads should be drawn using approximate dimensions if the actual dimensions result in a drawing with lines drawn too close together.

Instead of using exact measurements to draw small threads, minor diameters can be drawn smaller by eye in order to separate the root and crest lines, as illustrated in Fig. 12–20. This procedure makes the drawing more readable and easier to draw. Accuracy is unnecessary, since the drawing is only a symbolic representation of a thread. The draftsman should develop his ability to represent threads symbolically by eye, thereby saving drafting time.

For both internal and external threads, a thread note is added to the symbolic drawing to give the necessary specifications and to complete the description of the threaded part.

12–16 NUTS AND BOLTS

Nuts and bolts come in many forms and sizes for different applications (Fig. 12–21). Drawings of the more common types of threaded fasteners are shown in Fig. 12–22. A *bolt* is a threaded cylinder with a head and a nut for holding two parts together (Fig. 12–22A). A *stud* does not have a head, but is screwed into one part with a nut attached to the other end (Fig. 12–22B). A *cap screw* is similar to a bolt, but it does not have a nut; instead it is screwed into a member with internal threads for greater strength (Fig. 12–22C). A *machine screw* is similar to a cap screw, but it is smaller. A *set screw* is used to adjust one member with respect to another, usually to prevent a rotational movement.

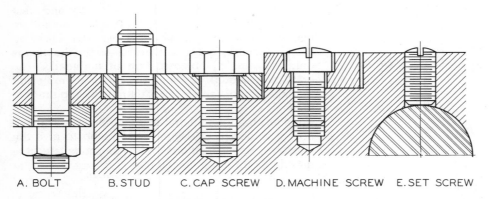

A. BOLT   B. STUD   C. CAP SCREW   D. MACHINE SCREW   E. SET SCREW

Fig. 12–22 Types of threaded bolts and screws.

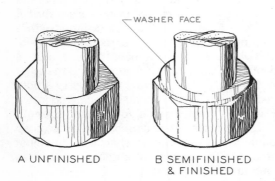

WASHER FACE

A UNFINISHED   B SEMIFINISHED & FINISHED

Fig. 12–23 Three types of finish for a bolt head.

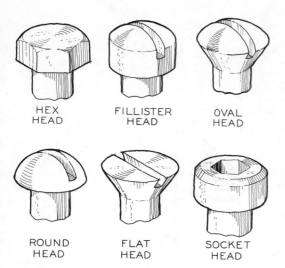

HEX HEAD   FILLISTER HEAD   OVAL HEAD

ROUND HEAD   FLAT HEAD   SOCKET HEAD

Fig. 12–24 Common types of bolt and screw heads.

Fig. 12–26 Examples of the variety of nuts that are available for special applications. (Courtesy of Russell, Burdsall & Ward Bolt and Nut Company.)

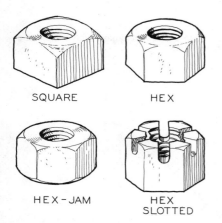

SQUARE   HEX

HEX–JAM   HEX SLOTTED

Fig. 12–25 Common types of nuts.

The types of heads used on standard bolts and nuts are illustrated in Fig. 12–23. These heads are used on all three series of bolts: *regular*, *light*, and *heavy*. The thickness of the head is the primary difference among the three series. Heavy-series bolts have the thickest heads and are used at points where bearing loads are heaviest. Bolts and nuts are classified as *finished*, *semifinished*, and *unfinished*. Figure 12–23A shows an unfinished head; that is,

none of the surfaces of the head are machined. The semifinished head has a washer face that is $\frac{1}{64}''$ thick to provide a circular boss on the bearing surface of the bolt head or the nut. The finished bolt looks like the semifinished one (Fig. 12–23B), but it has been machined to conform to prescribed tolerances.

Other standard forms of bolt and screw heads are shown in Fig. 12–24. These heads are used primarily on cap screws and machine screws. Many tables and standards are available for use in selecting the proper head for an application. Standard types of nuts are illustrated in Fig. 12–25. These can be machined to give a washer face for the finished and semifinished series. A hexagon jam nut does not have a washer face, but it is chamfered on both sides.

A photograph of several types of nuts is shown in Fig. 12–26. Many more specialized heads and nuts are available for less common applications.

12–17 DRAWING THE SQUARE BOLT HEAD

Detailed tables are available in the Appendix and in published standards for various types of threaded parts. In most cases it is sufficient to draw nuts and bolts using only general proportions. This method will be described here.

FIGURE 12–27. DRAWING THE SQUARE HEAD

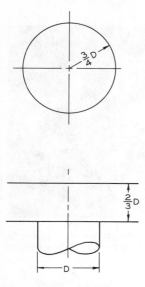

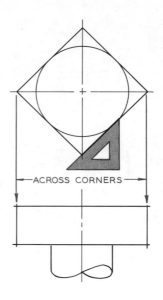

Step 1. Draw the diameter of the bolt. Use this to establish the head diameter and thickness.

Step 2. Draw the top view of the square head with a 45° triangle to give an across-corners view.

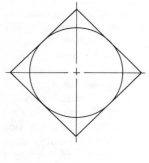

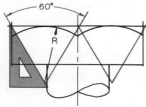

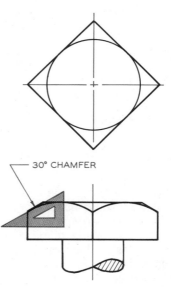

Step 3. Show the chamfer in the front view by using a 30°-60° triangle to find the centers for the radii.

Step 4. Draw a 30° chamfer that is tangent to the arcs in the front view. Strengthen the lines.

FIGURE 12–28. DRAWING THE HEXAGON HEAD

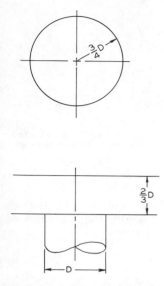

Step 1. Draw the diameter of the bolt. Use this to establish the head diameter and thickness.

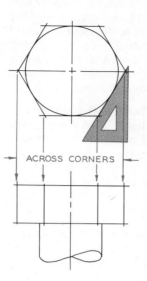

Step 2. Construct a hexagon with a 30°-60° triangle to give an across-corners view.

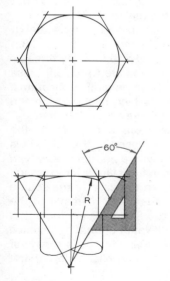

Step 3. Find arcs in the front view to show the chamfer of the head.

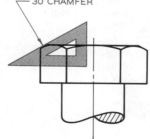

Step 4. Show a 30° chamfer tangent to the arcs in the front view. Strengthen the lines.

The first step in drawing a bolt head or a nut is to determine whether it is to be *across corners* or *across flats*. In other words, are the outlines at either side of the view going to represent corners, or are they going to be edge views of flat surfaces of the part? The head in Fig. 12–27 is drawn across corners. Nuts and bolts should be drawn across corners whenever possible; this type of drawing gives a better representation than drawing across flats.

Step 1. The diameter of the bolt is used as the basis for most of the construction involved in drawing the bolt head. The thickness of a regular bolt head is equal to two-thirds the diameter of the bolt. The distance from one flat surface on the head to the opposite flat surface is equal to $1\frac{1}{2}$ times the diameter. Therefore, a circle with a radius of $\frac{3}{4}D$ is drawn in the top view.

Step 2. Since the head is to be drawn across corners, the top view of the square head is drawn with a 45° triangle. This will give a view across corners in the front view.

Step 3. To show a 30° chamfer of the head, use a 60° triangle to locate the centers for radius R. Use these centers to draw two arcs in the front view.

Step 4. Use a 30° triangle to draw the chamfer at the two corners. Strengthen the lines to complete the drawing. Square heads are unfinished and have no washer face.

12–18 DRAWING THE HEXAGON BOLT HEAD

As previously mentioned, it is desirable that nuts and bolts be drawn across corners since this gives a better impression of the parts. An example of constructing the head of a bolt is shown in Fig. 12–28.

Step 1. The diameter of the bolt is D. The thickness of the head is drawn equal to $\frac{2}{3}D$. The top view of the head is drawn as a circle with a radius of $\frac{3}{4}D$.

Step 2. A hexagon is drawn tangent to the circle with the aid of a 60° triangle. The corner edges are projected to the front view.

Step 3. The radii for drawing the arcs formed by chamfering the head in the manufacturing process are located with a 30°-60° triangle.

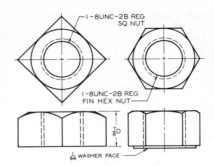

Fig. 12–29 Drawings of hexagon and square nuts are constructed in the same manner as drawings of bolt heads. Standard notes are added to give nut specifications.

Step 4. A 30° chamfer is drawn at each corner with a 30° triangle. The lines are strengthened to complete the drawing.

12–19 DRAWING NUTS

The construction of a drawing of a square nut or a hexagon nut across corners is exactly the same as the construction of a drawing of a bolt head across corners. The only variation is the thickness of the nut. The regular nut thickness is $\frac{7}{8}D$, and for the heavy nut the thickness is equal to the diameter (D).

Examples of square and hexagon nuts drawn across corners are shown in Fig. 12–29. Hidden lines are shown in the front view to indicate threads. Since it is understood that nuts are threaded, these hidden lines may be omitted in general applications.

Note that a $\frac{1}{64}''$ washer face is shown on the hexagon nut. This is usually drawn thicker than $\frac{1}{64}''$ so that the face will be more noticeable in the drawing. Thread notes are placed in the top views rather than the front views where possible; however, these notes may be placed in front views if necessary. These are standard notes. In the case of the square nut, the note tells us that the major diameter of the thread is 1″, that the nut has 8 threads per inch, that the thread is of the Unified National form and coarse series, with a fit of 2, and that the nut is a regular square nut. The hexagon nut is similar except that it is a finished hexagon nut.

The leader from the note is directed toward the center of the circular view, but the arrow stops at the first visible circle it makes contact with.

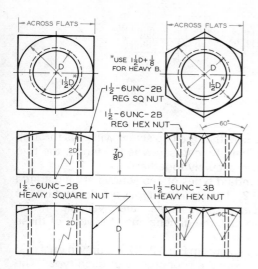

Fig. 12–30 Examples of hexagon and square nuts drawn across flats. Notes are added to give nut specifications.

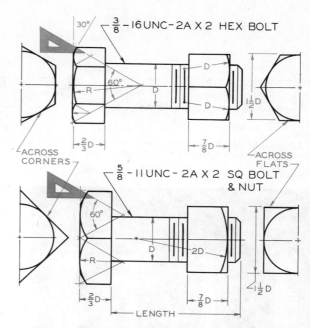

Fig. 12–31 Construction of nuts and bolts in assembly.

Nuts can be drawn across flats in situations where doing so improves the drawing. Examples of nuts drawn across flats are shown in Fig. 12–30.

For regular nuts, the distance across flats is $1\frac{1}{2} \times D$ (D is the major diameter of the thread). For heavy nuts this distance is increased by $\frac{1}{8}''$. The top views are drawn in the same manner as in across-corners drawings except that they are positioned to give different front views.

In the case of the square nut (Fig. 12–30), the front view is a simple rectangle, with only the arc formed by the chamfer giving a hint that the object is a nut. This is one of the disadvantages of drawing nuts across flats. The arc is drawn with a radius of $2D$, with the center located on the centerline of the nut. The heavy nut has a thickness equal to the major diameter of the threads.

The hexagon nut drawn across flats looks more like a nut in the front view than does the square nut. Still, the hexagon nut drawn across corners is a better representation. The method of drawing a nut across flats is shown in Fig. 12–30. The centers for the arcs used to show the chamfer are found with a

30°-60° triangle. Notes are added with leaders to complete the representation of the nuts. A washer face should be added to a nut if it is finished or semi-finished, except in the case of the square nut. Square nuts are always unfinished.

12–20 DRAWING NUTS AND BOLTS IN COMBINATION

It is often necessary to draw a nut and bolt assembled. The same rules followed in drawing nuts and bolts separately apply. Examples are shown in Fig. 12–31.

The construction illustrated here is the same as that covered earlier. The diameter of the bolt is used as the basis for other dimensions. The note is added to give the specifications of the nut and bolt. In the figure, the bolt heads are drawn across corners and the nuts across flats. The end views have been included to show how the front views were found by projection. These may not be necessary in a finished drawing if only one view of the nut is needed. Again the bolt diameter is used as the basis for this construction.

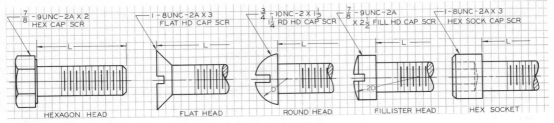

Fig. 12–32 Standard types of cap screws. The proportions shown here can be used for drawing cap screws of all sizes.

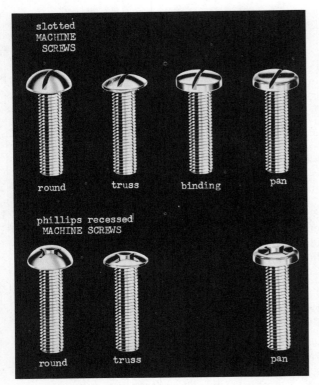

Fig. 12–33 Examples of the different types of machine screws. (Courtesy of the H. M. Harper Company.)

12–21 CAP SCREWS

Cap screws are used to hold two parts together without the use of a nut. One of these two parts has a threaded cylindrical hole and thus serves the same function as the nut. The other part is drilled with an oversize hole so that the cap screw will pass through it freely. When the cap screw is tightened, the two parts are held securely together.

The standard types of cap screws are illustrated in Fig. 12–32. The standard types are defined by the type of head used. Tables are available in the Appendix to give the dimensions of several of these types of cap screw.

The cap screws in Fig. 12–32 are drawn on a grid in order to show the proportions of each type. The proportions shown here can be used for drawing cap screws of all sizes. These types of cap screws range in diameter from No. 0 (0.060″) to 1½″. Standard thread notes are given on each type to show the correct form for specifying cap screws.

12–22 MACHINE SCREWS

Machine screws are smaller than most cap screws, usually less than 1″ in diameter. The machine screw is used to attach parts together; it is screwed either into another part or into a nut. Machine screws are threaded their full length when they are 2″ long or shorter. Several types of slotted and Phillips recessed machine screws are shown in Fig. 12–33.

Drawings of common machine screws are given in Fig. 12–34. Many other types are available in addition to these types. The dimensions of round-head machine screws are given in the Appendix. Typical notes are shown with these basic types of machine screws.

The four types of machine screws in Fig. 12–34 are drawn on a grid to give the proportions of the head in relation to the major diameter of the screw. The proportions shown here can be used for drawing these screws regardless of their size or scale.

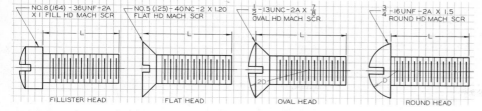

Fig. 12-34 Drawings of the standard types of machine screws. The proportions shown here can be used for drawing machine screws of all sizes.

Machine screws range in size from No. 0 (0.060" in diameter) to a diameter of $\frac{3}{4}$".

When slotted-head screws are drawn, it is conventional practice to show the slots in the circular view positioned at a 45° angle in the circular view as illustrated in Fig. 12-35. Even though the slot is turned at this angle in the top view, the front view of the slot is drawn to show the width and depth of the slot, as in Fig. 12-35A and B. By inspection, you can see that this gives a better representation of the screw head than does the example in Fig. 12-35C. This practice applies to all types of slotted fasteners.

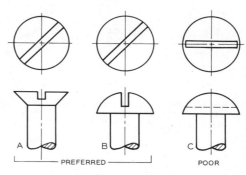

Fig. 12-35 Slotted-head screws should be drawn with the slot at 45° in the top view and with the notch shown in the front view.

12-23 SET SCREWS

Parts such as wheels or pulleys are commonly attached to shafts. To attach these parts to a shaft, set screws or keys are used. Examples of various types of set screws are shown in Fig. 12-36.

Table 12-1 shows the dimensions of the various features of the set screws shown in Fig. 12-36. This table is useful in selecting the appropriate standard size of set screw for the application at hand. Drawings of set screws need not employ these dimensions precisely; like the other fasteners discussed in this chapter, set screws can be drawn as approximations.

Note that the points and the heads of these set screws are of different types. Set screws are available in any desired combination of point and head. The shaft against which the set screw is tightened may have a flat surface machined to give a good bearing surface for the set screw point. In this case a dog point or a flat point would be most effective to press against the flat surface. The cup point gives good friction when applied to a round shaft where there is no flat surface.

Study the types of notes and abbreviations used to specify the set screws. As with all threaded fasteners, the use of such notes is essential.

12-24 WOOD SCREWS

A wood screw is a pointed screw having a sharp thread of coarse pitch for insertion in wood. The three most common types of wood screws are shown in Fig. 12-37. These are drawn on a grid to show the proportions of the various heads in relation to the major diameter of the screw. The same proportions can be used for all sizes of wood screw in practical applications. Many of the detailed dimensions for wood screws are given in tables published by the American National Standards Institute.

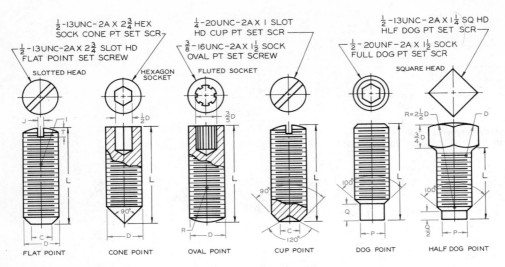

Fig. 12–36 Types of set screws. Set screws are available with various combinations of heads and points. Notes give their specifications. Dimensions are given in Table 12–1.

Table 12–1
Dimensions for the set screws shown in Fig. 12–36 (all dimensions given in inches).

D		I	J	T	R	C		P		Q	q
Nominal size		Radius of headless crown	Width of slot	Depth of slot	Oval point radius	Diameter of cup and flat points		Diameter of dog point		Length of dog point	
						Max	Min	Max	Min	Full	Half
5	0.125	0.125	0.023	0.031	0.094	0.067	0.057	0.083	0.078	0.060	0.030
6	0.138	0.138	0.025	0.035	0.109	0.074	0.064	0.092	0.087	0.070	0.035
8	0.164	0.164	0.029	0.041	0.125	0.087	0.076	0.109	0.103	0.080	0.040
10	0.190	0.190	0.032	0.048	0.141	0.102	0.088	0.127	0.120	0.090	0.045
12	0.216	0.216	0.036	0.054	0.156	0.115	0.101	0.144	0.137	0.110	0.055
$\frac{1}{4}$	0.250	0.250	0.045	0.063	0.188	0.132	0.118	0.156	0.149	0.125	0.063
$\frac{5}{16}$	0.3125	0.313	0.051	0.078	0.234	0.172	0.156	0.203	0.195	0.156	0.078
$\frac{3}{8}$	0.375	0.375	0.064	0.094	0.281	0.212	0.194	0.250	0.241	0.188	0.094
$\frac{7}{16}$	0.4375	0.438	0.072	0.109	0.328	0.252	0.232	0.297	0.287	0.219	0.109
$\frac{1}{2}$	0.500	0.500	0.081	0.125	0.375	0.291	0.270	0.344	0.344	0.250	0.125
$\frac{9}{16}$	0.5625	0.563	0.091	0.141	0.422	0.332	0.309	0.391	0.379	0.281	0.140
$\frac{5}{8}$	0.625	0.625	0.102	0.156	0.469	0.371	0.347	0.469	0.456	0.313	0.156
$\frac{3}{4}$	0.750	0.750	0.129	0.188	0.563	0.450	0.425	0.563	0.549	0.375	0.188

Courtesy of ANSI; B18.6.2–1956.

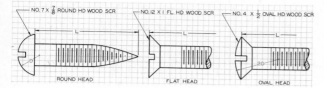

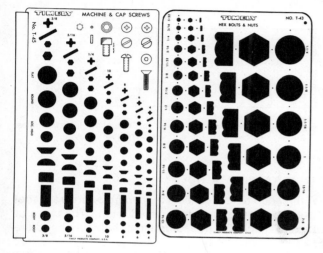

Fig. 12–37 Drawings of the standard types of wood screws. The proportions shown here can be used for drawing wood screws of all sizes.

Fig. 12–38 Examples of templates that can be used for drawing threaded fasteners. (Courtesy of Timely Products Company.)

Sizes of wood screws are specified by single numbers such as 0, 6, or 16. From 0 to 10 each digit represents a different size. Beginning at 10 only even-numbered sizes are standard, i.e., 10, 12, 14, 16, 18, 20, 22, and 24. The following formula can be used to relate these numbered sizes to the actual diameter of the screws:

Actual Dia. = 0.060 + Screw Number × 0.013.

For example, the actual diameter of a No. 5 screw is

$$0.060 + 5(0.013) = 0.125.$$

Standard notes are given to specify the wood screws illustrated in Fig. 12–37. These should be added in all cases to explain the symbolic drawing of the wood screw.

12–25 USE OF TEMPLATES

Templates are available for drawing threads, nuts, and threaded fasteners. They are available for a range of sizes that is satisfactory for most applications, since thread representations are approximations at best.

Two typical templates are shown in Fig. 12–38. The black areas represent the holes cut into the thin plastic templates. The template is laid on the drawing and the threaded features are drawn using the

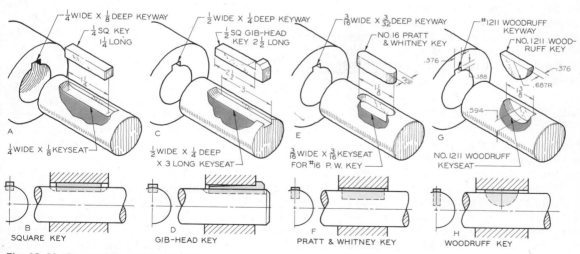

Fig. 12–39 Standard keys used for holding parts on a shaft.

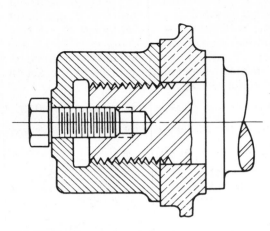

Fig. 12–40 Three types of thread representations used on the same drawing for clarity.

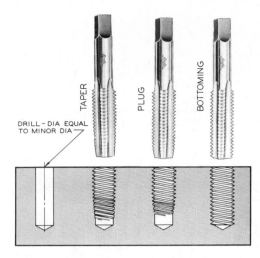

Fig. 12–41 Three types of taps for threading internal holes. (Courtesy of Greenfield Tap and Die Corporation.)

template as a guide. Templates are also available for drawing nuts and bolts in pictorial. These are used primarily by the technical illustrator.

12–26 KEYS

Keys are used to attach parts to shafts in order to transmit power to pulleys, gears, or cranks. Several types of keys are shown pictorially and orthographically in Fig. 12–39. The four types illustrated here are the most commonly used keys. To specify a key, notes must be given for the keyway, the key, and the keyseat, as shown in Fig. 12–39A, C, E, and G. The notes given in Fig. 12–39 are typical of the notes used to give key specifications.

12–27 THREAD REPRESENTATIONS IN COMBINATION

It is good practice to use the same type of thread representation—simplified, schematic, or detailed— throughout a single drawing. However, there are cases where using these representations in combination adds clarity to the drawing. Such a case is shown in Fig. 12–40. In this example, all three representations are used—simplified, schematic, and detailed. This is permissible for the sake of clarity.

12–28 TAPPING A HOLE

A threaded hole is called a *tapped hole*, since the tool used to cut the threads is called a tap. The types of taps available for threading small holes by hand are shown in Fig. 12–41.

The taper, plug, and bottoming hand taps are identical in size, length, and measurements, their only difference being the chamfered portion of their ends. The taper tap has a long chamfer (8 to 10 threads), the plug tap has a chamfer of 3 to 5 threads, and the bottoming tap has a short chamfer of only 1 to $1\frac{1}{2}$ threads.

When tapping by hand in open or "through" holes, the taper should be used for coarse threads, since it ensures straighter starting. The taper tap is also recommended for the harder metals. The plug tap can be used in soft metals or for fine-pitch threads. When it is desirable to tap a hole to the very bottom, all three taps—taper, plug, and bottoming—should be used in this order.

Notes are added to specify the depth of the drilled hole and the depth of the threads. For example, a note reading $\frac{7}{8}$ DRILL, 3 DEEP, 1-8UNC-2A, 2 DEEP means that the hole will be drilled deeper than it is threaded and the last usable thread will be 2" deep in the hole. Note that the drill point has an angle of 120°.

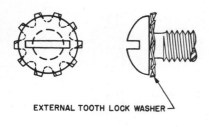

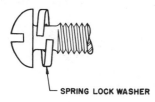

EXTERNAL TOOTH LOCK WASHER

SPRING LOCK WASHER

Fig. 12–42 Two types of lock washers for preventing a bolt from unscrewing.

Fig. 12–43 Types of lock washers. (Courtesy of the H. M. Harper Company.)

cotter pin   jam nut   castle nut

Fig. 12–44 Other types of locking devices. (Courtesy of the H. M. Harper Company.)

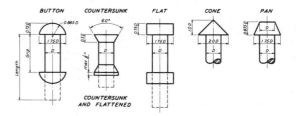

Fig. 12–45 Rivet forms. (Courtesy of the Tennessee Valley Authority.)

12–29 LOCK WASHERS

A lock washer is a device that is used to prevent a nut or a cap screw from loosening as a result of vibration or movement. These washers may take many forms, but two of the most common types are shown in Fig. 12–42.

The external-tooth lock washer has a series of teeth around the circumference of the washer. These teeth are angled to resist unscrewing after tightening. The spring lock washer is the more common type. This is simply a washer that has a cut and has been sprung so that it will resist unscrewing once tightened. Photographs of lock washers are shown in Fig. 12–43.

Other locking devices of this type are cotter pins and specially designed nuts such as the castle nut and the jam nut (Fig. 12–44). Some locking devices have inserts of plastic that fuse the threads together when tightened. Many manufacturers specialize in making locking nuts and fasteners that resist heavy vibrations without unscrewing.

12–30 RIVETS

Rivets are a type of fastener used to join thin materials in a permanent joint. Rivets are designed to fit into holes that are slightly larger than the diameter of the rivet. The rivet is inserted in the hole and the headless end is formed into the specified shape by applying extreme pressure to the projecting end. This forming operation is done when the rivets are either hot or cold, depending on the application.

Typical shapes and proportions of rivets are shown in Fig. 12–45. These rivets vary in diameter from $\frac{1}{16}''$ to $1\frac{3}{4}''$. Rivets are used extensively in pressure-vessel fabrication and in heavy structures such as bridges and buildings. They are also used in construction with sheet metal.

A simple lap joint is illustrated in Fig. 12–46 where two button-head rivets are applied. The rivets are shown with circles to represent their heads. The diameter of the rivet passing through the hole is not shown as a hidden circle. A more detailed set of riveting symbols is used by industries specializing in fabrication that uses this type of fastening.

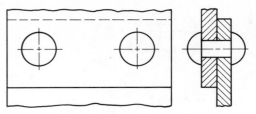

Fig. 12–46 Representation of a lap joint fastened with two rivets.

PROBLEMS

These problems are to be solved in accordance with Article 3–15 and the specifications given by your instructor. Most problems are to be drawn on standard Size A Paper ($8\frac{1}{2}'' \times 11''$) using ink or pencil as assigned. Many of the problems are laid out on a grid where each grid represents $\frac{1}{4}''$. The drawings can be transferred to grid paper of a similar type, of else the problems can be drawn on blank paper with the endorsement, title strip, and border shown in Article 3–15. Refer to the text of this chapter to assist you in the solution of the problems.

General Problems

1 Refer to Fig. 12–47 to lay out the top and front views of a cylinder. Construct a helix that will make two complete revolutions around this cylinder. Show the visibility of the helix as it wraps around the cylinder. Show all construction.

2 The layout in Fig. 12–48 is to be used for constructing a detailed representation of an Acme thread with a major diameter of 3″. The thread note specifications are 3–1$\frac{1}{2}$ ACME. Show both external and internal thread representations. Show the thread note.

3 Repeat Problem 2, but draw internal and external detailed representations of a square thread that is 3″ in diameter. The note specifications are 3–1$\frac{1}{2}$ SQUARE. Apply notes to both parts.

4 Repeat Problem 2, but draw internal and external detailed thread representations of an American National thread form. The major diameter of each part is 3″. The note specifications are 3–4NC–2. Apply notes to both parts.

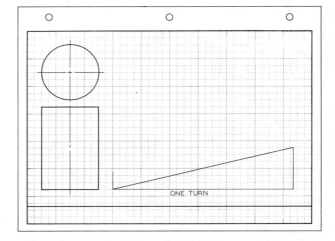

Fig. 12–47 Problem 1: Construction of a helix.

5 Notes are given in Fig. 12–49 to specify the depth of the hole that is to be drilled and the threads that are to be tapped in the hole. Following these notes, draw detailed representations of the threads as views according to the specifications.

6 Repeat Problem 5, but use schematic representations.

7 Repeat Problem 5, but use simplified thread representations.

8 Figure 12–50 shows a layout of two external threaded parts and their end views. Also shown is a piece into which the external threads will be screwed.

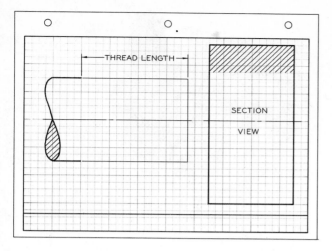

Fig. 12–48 Problems 2, 3, and 4: Construction of thread symbols.

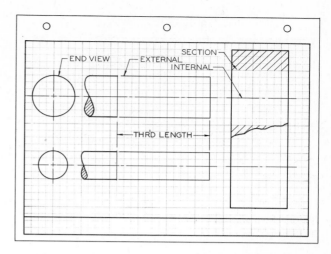

Fig. 12–50 Problems 8, 9, and 10: Internal and external threads.

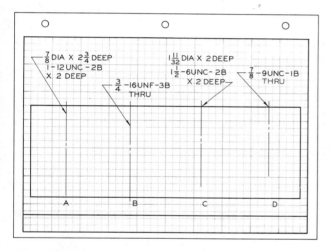

Fig. 12–49 Problems 5, 6, and 7: Internal threads.

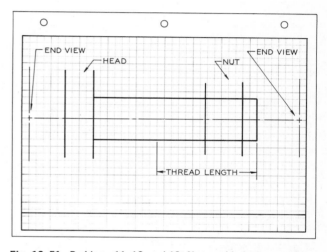

Fig. 12–51 Problems 11, 12, and 13: Nuts and bolts in assembly.

Complete all three views of each of the parts. Use detailed threads and apply notes to the internal and external threads. Use the table in Appendix 5 for thread specifications.

9 Repeat Problem 8, but use schematic thread representations.

10 Repeat Problem 8, but use simplified thread representations.

11 Referring to Fig. 12–51, complete the drawing with instruments as a semifinished hexagon bolt and nut. The bolt head is to be drawn across corners. The nut is a heavy nut drawn across corners. Use

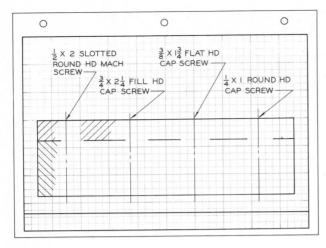

Fig. 12–52 Problems 14, 15, and 16: Cap screws and machine screws.

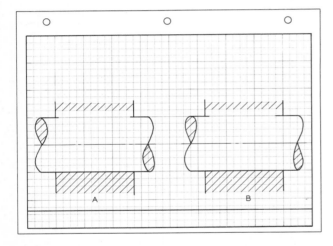

Fig. 12–53 Problems 17 and 18: Keys.

Fig. 12–54 Problems 19 and 20: A design involving threaded parts. (Courtesy of Koh-I-Noor Corporation.)

detailed thread representations. Show notes to specify the parts of the assembly. Thread specifications are $1\frac{1}{2}$–6UNC–3.

12 Referring to Fig. 12–51, complete the drawing with instruments as an unfinished square-head bolt and nut. The bolt head is drawn across corners. The regular nut is to be drawn across corners. Use

schematic thread representations. Show notes to specify the parts. Use the table in Appendix 5 for thread specifications.

13 Referring to Fig. 12–51, complete the drawing with instruments as a finished hexagon nut and bolt. The regular bolt and nut are to be drawn across flats. Use simplified thread representations. Show notes to specify the parts. Use the table in Appendix 5 for specifications.

14 The notes in Fig. 12–52 apply to machine and cap screws that are to be drawn in the section view of the two parts. The holes in which the screws are to be drawn should be considered as through holes. Complete the drawings and show the notes as given.

Show the remaining section lines. Use detailed thread symbols.

15 Repeat Problem 14, but use schematic thread symbols.

16 Repeat Problem 14, but use simplified thread symbols.

17 Two parts are shown assembled on a cylindrical shaft in Fig. 12–53. These parts are to be held in position by a key. Draw each view of the assembly using a square key in A and a gib-head key in B. Show the necessary notes to specify the key, keyway, and keyseat.

18 Repeat Problem 17, but use a No. 16 Pratt & Whitney key in A and a No. 1211 Woodruff key in B.

Show the necessary notes to specify the key, the keyway, and the keyseat.

Design Problems

19 The pencil pointer shown in Fig. 12–54 has a shaft of $\frac{1}{4}''$ that fits into a bracket designed to clamp onto a desk top. A set screw holds the shaft in position. Make a drawing of the bracket, estimating its dimensions. Show the details and the method of using the set screw to hold the shaft. Give the specifications for the set screw.

20 Referring to Fig. 12–54, make the necessary drawings to illustrate the threaded screw that is used to clamp the bracket to the table. Give the necessary specifications in a note.

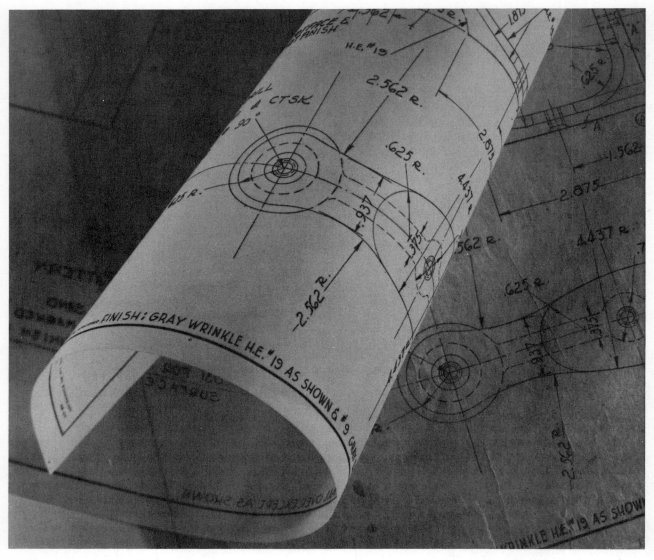

Photo courtesy of Eastman Kodak Company

13
DIMENSIONING

Fig. 13–1 This model SL 3388 snowmobile is an example of a machine that could not have been built unless each individual part had been precisely dimensioned. (Courtesy of Yamaha International Corporation.)

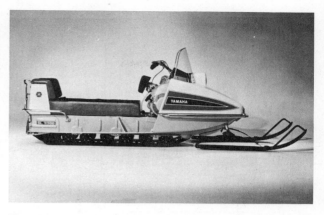

Fig. 13–2 The model SL 3388 is designed with an 18″ wide track to propel it over the snow. (Courtesy of Yamaha International Corporation.)

13–1 INTRODUCTION

The last step of the design process is implementation. In this step, a working drawing is prepared from which the product will be manufactured. Dimensions must be placed on the drawing to specify the sizes of the various components and features of the design. The shape and form of a single part can be shown in an orthographic drawing or pictorial, but the craftsman who has to make the part from the drawing is interested primarily in the part's dimensions, details, and the location of its various features. In fact, the drawing is actually a schematic representation of a part that is defined by the dimensions placed on it rather than by the accuracy of the drawing itself.

A drawing may be drawn slightly out of scale or may have other inaccuracies, but it will still be a usable drawing if the dimensions are correct. With this in mind, you should never expect a technician or craftsman to measure a drawing to determine a dimension. Of course, it is best if a drawing is drawn to scale so that the dimensions shown will correspond to actual measurements.

A new vehicle, the snowmobile, has come into widespread use during recent years. It is easy to imagine the importance of dimensioning each individual part of this machine (Fig. 13–1) so that the parts can be assembled and can function properly. Construction and manufacture of such a machine

would be impossible without clearly dimensioned drawings and specifications. Note that this snowmobile has an 18″ wide track to propel it over the snow (Fig. 13–2).

This chapter will cover the fundamentals of dimensioning and the application of dimensions to a working drawing. The accepted methods of dimensioning according to the latest approved standards will be discussed to introduce the current methods used by industry.

There are more variations of the rules for dimensioning than of the rules for any other aspect of mechanical drawing. This is so because there are many possible combinations of situations in which dimensions must be applied. Rules are not intended to be barriers to the draftsman, but should serve only as guidelines. In some cases it will be necessary to violate rules in order to dimension an object satisfactorily. You must learn to use your judgment to decide when a rule ought to be violated. However, you should not break rules unnecessarily, because they are based on the experience of many draftsmen over many years.

13–2 TERMINOLOGY OF DIMENSIONING

This chapter will introduce the basic terminology of dimensioning, using words that have special meaning in this context. A review of these words here will make it easier to understand the remainder

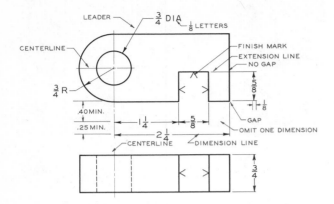

Fig. 13–3 A typical dimensioned drawing with various terms defined.

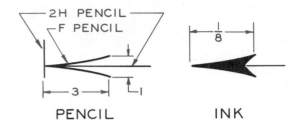

Fig. 13–4 Proportions of arrowheads in pencil and ink.

of the chapter. Refer to Fig. 13–3 for illustrations of most of these terms.

Dimension lines are lines which have numerals placed near their midpoints to give the length of the line. An arrowhead is placed at each end of the dimension line. Dimension lines are drawn as thin lines with a hard pencil (2H–4H).

Extension lines are lines that extend from a view of an object in order that a measurement may be dimensioned outside the area of the object. The arrowheads of dimension lines are positioned against these extension lines. Note that extension lines do not touch the view from which they are projected, but there is a gap between the object and the extension lines.

Centerlines are thin lines used to locate the centers of cylindrical parts, such as cylindrical holes. Refer to Fig. 13–3 to see how centerlines are applied to circular and rectangular views of cylinders.

Leaders are lines drawn from a note to indicate the feature to which the note applies. An example is the $\frac{3}{4}$ DIA note in Fig. 13–3. Leaders are thin lines of the same weight as dimension and extension lines.

Arrowheads are used at the ends of dimension lines and leaders to indicate the endpoints of these

lines. The proper drawing of an arrowhead is important in the preparation of an attractive, readable drawing. The length of an arrowhead is the same as the height of the numerals and letters used on the drawing. In most cases, this is $\frac{1}{8}''$. Methods of drawing arrowheads are shown in Fig. 13–4. The arrowhead at its widest point is one-third as wide as it is long; it is drawn with two strokes of an F or HB pencil. If ink is used, these strokes will tend to fill in and darken the arrowhead.

Dimension numerals are a very important part of the dimensioning of a drawing, since these numbers specify the dimensions of the parts. If the specifications are poorly lettered and difficult to interpret, the drawing is ineffective. Numerals should be made in accordance with the lettering practices discussed in Chapter 3.

General rules of dimensioning can be observed in Fig. 13–3. Notes are given in this figure to show the placement and spacing of the dimension lines. These dimensioning rules will be discussed in detail in the following articles.

13–3 UNITS OF MEASUREMENT

The latest standards recommend that dimensioning units be decimals of an inch. The reason for this is that decimals are easier to multiply, divide, add, and

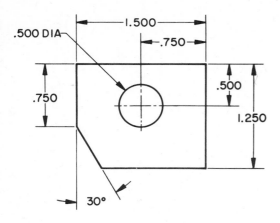

Fig. 13–5 An example of decimal dimensions used on a drawing. (Courtesy of ANSI; Y14.5–1966.)

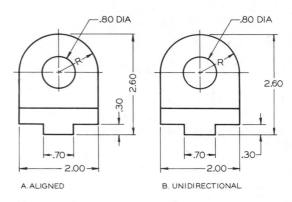

Fig. 13–6 A comparison of aligned and unidirectional dimensions on a drawing.

subtract than are fractions. However, common fractions may be used if desired.

An example of decimal dimensions is shown in Fig. 13–5. For values of less than one, zeros are not used before the decimal point. All decimal fractions should have the same number of decimal places to the right of the decimal point, even if the last digits are zeros. It is important to draw decimal points dense and dark to make sure that they are readable and clearly noticeable.

All dimensions are given in inches unless the dimensions exceed six feet. Since it is understood that all dimensions under six feet are in inches, the inch marks are omitted. When dimensions exceed six feet, the foot marks are given, but the inch marks are still omitted. Example: 12′-5. Some industries use inches for all measurements, even for dimensions greater than six feet.

13–4 ALIGNED AND UNIDIRECTIONAL NUMERALS

There are two methods of positioning dimension numerals on a dimension line: *aligned* and *unidirectional*.

The unidirectional system has gained wider acceptance since it is easier to apply numerals to a drawing that reads from the bottom of the page regardless of the direction of the dimension line (Fig. 13–6B). Guidelines are easier to draw in this system than the aligned system.

As its name implies, the aligned system aligns numerals in the same direction as the dimension lines (Fig. 13–6A). The numerals must always be read from the bottom or the right side of the page. Since the numerals do not all read in the same direction, the construction of guidelines may be somewhat time-consuming.

13–5 PLACEMENT OF DIMENSIONS

The following examples illustrate typical rules of good practice in dimensioning and contrast them with poor practices.

The single views in Fig. 13–7 show overall dimensions and two intermediate dimensions. In general, one dimension is not given, since the overall dimension determines this omitted dimension. It is good practice to place all the dimensions on the same side of the drawing for ease in reading. The intermediate dimensions should be placed in a single line rather than offset as shown in the "not recommended" portion of the figure.

Note that one intermediate dimension is omitted in Fig. 13–8A, since this dimension can be found by subtracting from the overall dimension. It is permissible to show the missing dimension if the abbreviation REF is placed after this dimension. This indicates that it is a *reference* dimension, that is, the least important dimension. Giving the reference

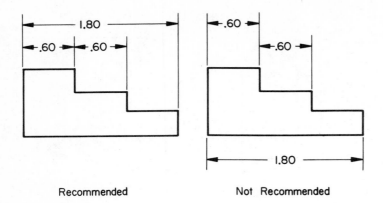

Recommended   Not Recommended

Fig. 13–7 Grouping dimension lines on a drawing. (Courtesy of ANSI; Y14.5–1966.)

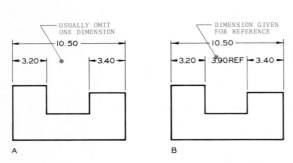

A   B

Fig. 13–8 One intermediate dimension is omitted; if all dimensions are given, one should be noted REF to show that it is for reference only.

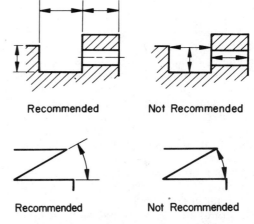

Recommended   Not Recommended

Recommended   Not Recommended

Fig. 13–9 Placement of dimension lines: good and poor practice. (Courtesy of ANSI; Y14.5–1966.)

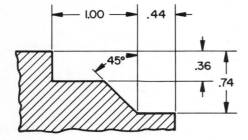

Fig. 13–10 Extension lines may cross each other or object lines. (Courtesy of ANSI; Y14.5–1966.)

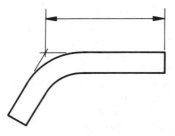

Fig. 13–11 Extension lines are used to locate a theoretical point outside a curved surface. (Courtesy of ANSI; Y14.5–1966.)

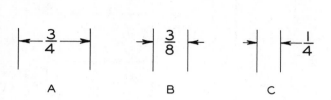 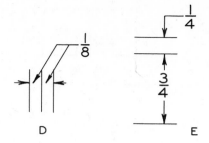

Fig. 13–12 Placement of dimensions in limited spaces.

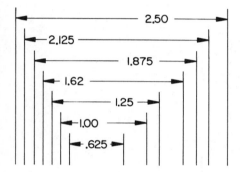

Fig. 13–13 Staggering dimension numerals to save space. (Courtesy of ANSI; Y14.5–1966.)

dimension reduces the possibility of errors resulting from faulty arithmetic.

If at all possible, dimension lines should be placed outside of the object. A dimension line should not be used as an extension line, as is done in Fig. 13–9. Also, in dimensioning angles, extension lines should be used to avoid placing the dimension lines inside the angular feature (Fig. 13–9).

Extension lines are drawn from the view being dimensioned, with a gap between the view and the extension line. Extension lines may cross other extension lines or even object lines (Fig. 13–10); when this occurs, there are no gaps at the points of crossing.

Extension lines are also used to locate a theoretical point outside a curved surface (Fig. 13–11). This point is dimensioned and used to describe the shape of the object.

13–6 DIMENSIONING IN LIMITED SPACES

Many parts have very small features that do not allow much room for the placement of numerals or arrowheads. A series of examples of dimensioning in limited spaces is shown in Fig. 13–12. Regardless of the smallness of the space, the numerals should not be drawn smaller than the numerals used elsewhere in the drawing.

Often, rows of dimension lines are placed close together. In such a case (Fig. 13–13), it is good practice to stagger the numerals for the sake of readability.

13–7 DIMENSIONING PRISMS

The most basic element is the prism, which when reduced to its simplest form is no more than a block. Variations of the prism are dimensioned in Fig. 13–14 to illustrate general rules of dimensioning. These rules apply to both freehand sketches and instrument drawings.

1. Dimensions should extend from the most descriptive view (Fig. 13–14A).

2. Dimensions which apply to two views should be placed between these two views (Fig. 13–14A).

3. The first row of dimension lines should be placed a minimum of .40" ($\frac{3}{8}$") from the object. Succes-

FIGURE 13–14. DIMENSIONING PRISMS

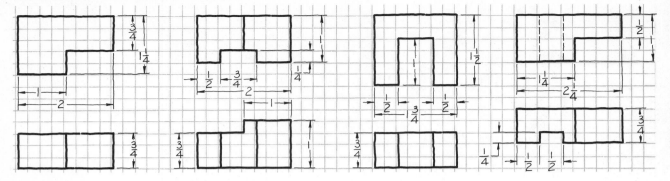

A. Dimensions should extend from the most descriptive view and be placed between the views to which they apply.

B. One intermediate dimension is not given. Extension lines may cross object lines.

C. It is permissible to dimension a notch inside the object if this improves clarity.

D. Whenever possible, dimensions should be placed on visible lines and not hidden lines.

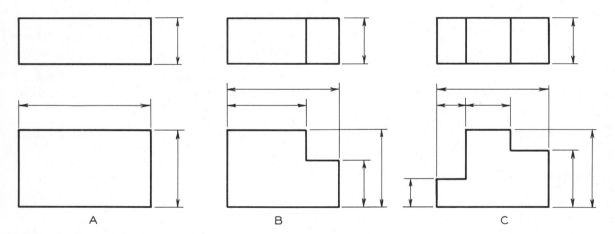

Fig. 13–15 Placement of dimensions on simple prisms.

sive rows of dimensions are placed at least .25″ (¼″) from one another (Fig. 13–14A).

4. Extension lines may cross, but dimension lines should not cross another line unless absolutely necessary.

5. In order to dimension each measurement in its most descriptive view, you may have to place dimensions in more than one view (Fig. 13–14B).

6. In the case of notches, it may be more effective from the point of view of clarity to place the dimension line inside the notch (Fig. 13–14C).

7. Whenever possible, dimensions should be applied to visible lines rather than hidden lines (Fig. 13–14D).

8. Dimensions should not be repeated nor should unnecessary information be given.

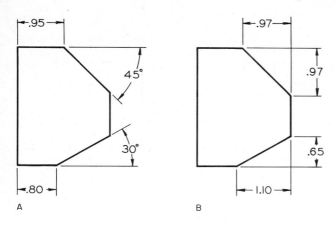

A

B

Fig. 13–16 Two acceptable methods of dimensioning angles: (A) angular measurements and (B) coordinates.

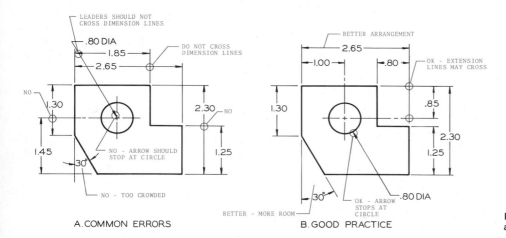

A. COMMON ERRORS

B. GOOD PRACTICE

Fig. 13–17 A comparison of errors and good practice in dimensioning.

Examples of dimensioned prisms drawn with instruments are shown in Fig. 13–15. Numerals have been omitted, since the purpose of this figure is to illustrate the placement of the dimension lines.

13–8 DIMENSIONING ANGLES

Angles can be dimensioned by means of either angular measurements (degrees) or coordinates to locate the ends of the angular lines or planes. In

Fig. 13–16A a part is dimensioned by means of angular measurements. When this method is used, it is necessary to locate the vertex of the angle with a dimension.

Coordinates are used in Fig. 13–16B to locate the two ends of each sloping plane. This method is more accurate than the use of angular measurements.

These two methods of dimensioning angles should not be mixed in the dimensioning of any single angle. Either one or the other method should

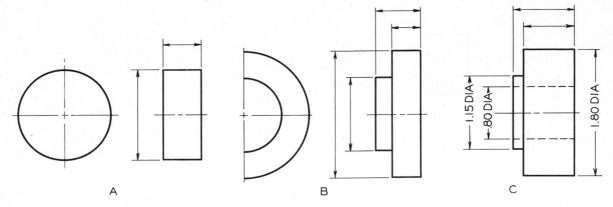

Fig. 13–18 Placement of dimensions on simple cylindrical shapes.

be used exclusively, so that there will be no conflicts in measurement.

13–9 COMMON ERRORS OF DIMENSIONING

Figure 13–17A illustrates a few of the most common mistakes in dimensioning and the placement of dimensions. Whenever possible, dimension lines should not cross another line of any type. In addition, always try to avoid crowding notes and numerals. Figure 13–17B illustrates a better application of dimensions to the object.

You should become aware of the mistakes shown in this figure in order to avoid them. It is the responsibility of checkers in industry to catch errors of this type so that they can be corrected before drawings are released.

13–10 DIMENSIONING CYLINDERS

Most drawings contain cylinders, represented either as solids or as cylindrical holes. The simplest form of a cylinder is shown in Fig. 13–18A. The cylinder shown here is dimensioned entirely in its rectangular view; note that the diameter is given, not the radius, since it is easier to measure a diameter than a radius. Note also that the dimensions are placed between the views for easy association with the two views.

Diameters are also placed between the views

when an object consists of more than one cylindrical part (Fig. 13–18B). It is understood that cylinders such as these are concentric unless there is a note stating otherwise. The smallest diameter is dimensioned first and placed nearest the rectangular view; the larger diameters are placed outward from this view. This arrangement prevents the extension lines from crossing dimension lines.

A cylindrical part may be dimensioned with only one view if the abbreviation DIA is placed after the dimensions of the diameters in the given rectangular view (Fig. 13–18C). This procedure reduces drawing time by eliminating the need to draw the circular view.

13–11 MEASURING CYLINDRICAL PARTS

Cylindrical parts are dimensioned with diameters rather than radii because diameters are easier to measure. An internal cylindrical hole is measured with an *internal caliper* (Fig. 13–19). This diameter is transferred to a *rule* to obtain the diameter of the hole (Fig. 13–20). This kind of measurement is adequate for most general applications.

The *micrometer caliper* can be used for a higher degree of accuracy. The diameter can be measured from a gage on the measuring instrument (Fig. 13–21).

The diameter of an external cylinder can be measured with an *outside caliper* (Fig. 13–22).

Fig. 13–19 A cylindrical hole is measured with an internal caliper.

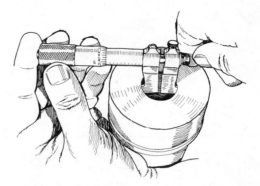

Fig. 13–21 A micrometer caliper is an instrument for measuring internal cylindrical diameters with more accuracy than is possible with the caliper shown in Fig. 13–20.

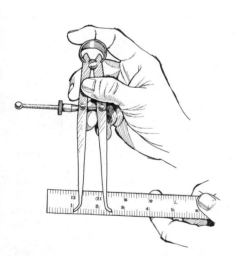

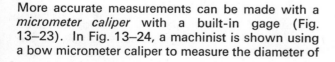

Fig. 13–20 The internal caliper is used to transfer the diameter of an internal hole to a rule.

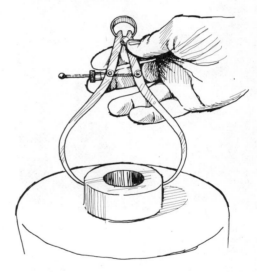

Fig. 13–22 An outside caliper is used to measure the diameter of a cylinder and transfer it to a rule.

More accurate measurements can be made with a *micrometer caliper* with a built-in gage (Fig. 13–23). In Fig. 13–24, a machinist is shown using a bow micrometer caliper to measure the diameter of a cylindrical part that is being machined on a lathe. It is obvious that the diameter of a cylindrical part is much more convenient and accurate as a dimension than is the radius.

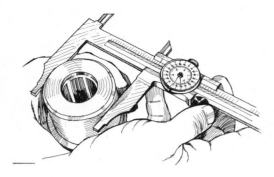

Fig. 13–23 An outside micrometer caliper with a built-in gauge can be used to measure the diameter of a cylinder with more accuracy than is possible with the caliper shown in Fig. 13–22.

Fig. 13–24 A large micrometer caliper is being used here to measure the diameter of a cylindrical feature. (Courtesy of Brown and Sharpe Manufacturing Company.)

13–12 CYLINDRICAL HOLES

Cylindrical holes may be dimensioned by one of the methods shown in Fig. 13–25. The particular method used depends on the type of drawing and the space available. The diameter is indicated in all cases where a full circle is used. In the preferred method of dimensioning a cylindrical hole, a leader is drawn

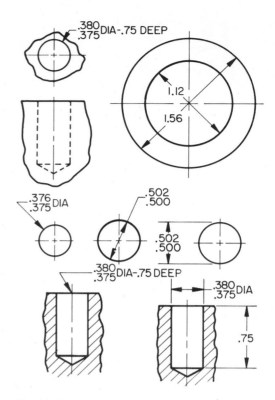

Fig. 13–25 Acceptable methods of dimensioning cylinders. (Courtesy of ANSI; Y14.5–1966.)

from the circular view, and the dimension is followed by the abbreviation DIA to indicate that it is the diameter. Sometimes the note specifies the shop operation such as DRILL or BORE, but current standards suggest that the diameter (DIA) be indicated rather than the machine operation.

An example of a part containing cylindrical shapes is dimensioned in Fig. 13–26. Note that the cylindrical features are dimensioned by two methods. Two of these features are dimensioned in the rectangular view and two are dimensioned in the circular view.

13–13 DIMENSIONING CONES

Methods of dimensioning cones and truncated cones (cones that have portions removed) are shown in Fig. 13–27. In A and B the height and diameter of the cones are dimensioned in the

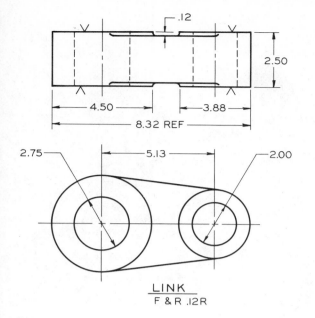

Fig. 13–26 An example of a dimensioned part composed of cylindrical shapes.

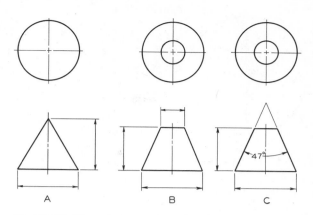

Fig. 13–27 Dimensioning conical shapes.

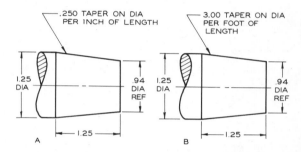

Fig. 13–28 Two acceptable methods of dimensioning tapers.

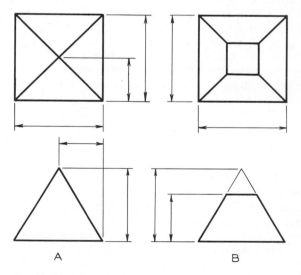

Fig. 13–29 Dimensioning pyramids.

triangular view and trapezoidal view. The diameter of the base is placed at the lower side of the front view, since this requires shorter extension lines and gives a more direct association with the view.

Another method of dimensioning cones is shown in Fig. 13–27C. Here the base and the angular measurements of the cone are given. Either of the two methods of dimensioning a cone given in Fig. 13–27 is acceptable.

Tapers can be either conical surfaces or flat planes. Examples of tapered concial features are dimensioned in Fig. 13–28. The taper can be indicated in units of taper per inch or per foot. Both of the examples in Fig. 13–28 illustrate good practice.

13–14 DIMENSIONING PYRAMIDS

The pyramid in Fig. 13–29A is dimensioned in both the top and front views. The top view gives the measurements of the base and locates the apex of the pyramid. The height and the other location

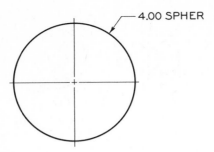

Fig. 13–30 Dimensioning spheres.

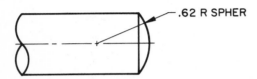

Fig. 13–31 Dimensioning a spherical radius. (Courtesy of ANSI; Y14.5–1966.)

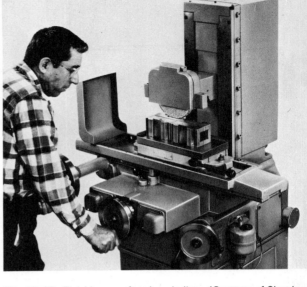

Fig. 13–32 Finishing a surface by grinding. (Courtesy of Clausing Corporation.)

dimension for the apex are given in the front view. If the dimensions locating the apex were not given, it would be assumed that the pyramid was a right pyramid with its altitude perpendicular to the base at its midpoint.

The pyramid in Fig. 13–29B, with its upper portion removed, is dimensioned with extension lines to establish the theoretical shape of the pyramid before truncation. Note that the apex is not located in this case.

13–15 DIMENSIONING SPHERES

The sphere is the simplest geometric element to dimension, since it appears as a circle in any view. Consequently, only one view is necessary, with a note placed outside the view as shown in Fig. 13–30. When an object has a feature that is a partial sphere, a radius and an abbreviation are used as shown in Fig. 13–31.

13–16 FINISHED SURFACES

Many machine parts are formed as castings in a mold which gives their exterior surfaces a rough finish. Parts formed by forging or stamping also have uneven surfaces. If the surfaces of such parts are designed to come into contact with surfaces of other parts, these rough surfaces must be machined by grinding, shaping, lapping, or some other process. A part is shown being finished by grinding in Fig. 13–32. Finishing provides a smooth, uniform surface that permits accurate measurements. The casting must be made oversize to allow the removal of excess material during machining.

To indicate that a surface is to be finished, *finish marks* are drawn on the edge view of that surface (Fig. 13–33).   Finish marks should be repeated in every view where the surface appears as an edge, even if it is a hidden line.

The symbol used to indicate the surface to be finished should be drawn with a 30°-60° triangle $\frac{1}{8}''$ in height, as shown in Fig. 13–33.   This symbol

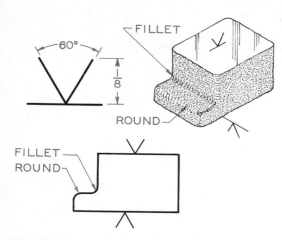

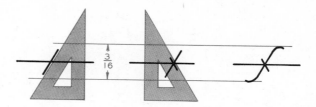

Fig. 13-34 An alternative method of drawing a finish mark.

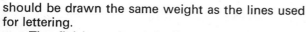

Fig. 13-33 Finish marks and fillets and rounds.

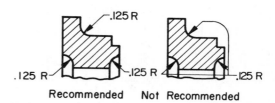

Recommended   Not Recommended

Fig. 13-35 Dimensioning fillets and rounds: good and poor practice. (Courtesy of ANSI; Y14.5–1966.)

should be drawn the same weight as the lines used for lettering.

The finish mark originally was drawn as the letter *f*, as shown in Fig. 13–34. This symbol is still acceptable, but it is used less than the simple V finish mark.

Finish marks are sometimes used on pictorial drawings that are dimensioned and labeled, as shown in Fig. 13–33. In this case the symbols are drawn pictorially to appear perpendicular to the finished surface. Invisible surfaces, such as the bottom plane of an object, can be identified by the use of an extension line with a finish mark applied (Fig. 13–33). When an object is finished on all surfaces, the note F.A.O. can be placed on the drawing to eliminate the need for finish marks; F.A.O. means "finished all over."

13–17 FILLETS AND ROUNDS

Fillets and rounds are rounded corners convention-ally used on castings. A *fillet* is an internal rounding at the intersection between two planes. A *round* is an external rounding at the intersection of two planes (Fig. 13–33). It is common practice to use the same radius for all fillets and rounds on a given drawing.

When fillets and rounds are of equal radii, a note can be added to the drawing to eliminate the need for repetitive dimensioning. The note can read as follows: ALL FILLETS AND ROUNDS .125R. If most but not all of the fillets and rounds are of equal radii, the following type of note can be used: ALL FILLETS AND ROUNDS .25R UNLESS OTHER-WISE SPECIFIED. In this case, only the fillets and rounds of different radii are dimensioned, and it is understood that those not dimensioned are $\frac{1}{4}''$ in radius.

A method of dimensioning fillets is illustrated in Fig. 13–35. It is preferable to place the dimensions so that the leaders are close to the fillets and rounds rather than to use long, confusing leaders. Since these features are dimensioned with radii, the letter R follows the numeral. If possible, the leaders should extend through the actual center of the fillet or round.

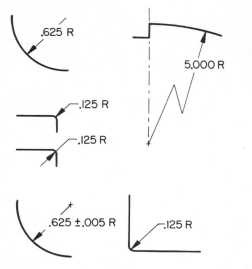

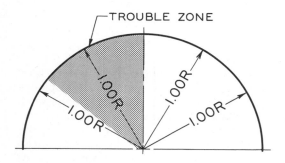

Fig. 13–36 Methods of dimensioning arcs. (Courtesy of ANSI; Y14.5–1966.)

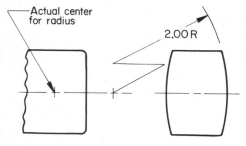

Fig. 13–37 Placement of radial dimensions when using the aligned numeral system.

Fig. 13–38 Dimensioning a large radius. (Courtesy of ANSI; 14.5–1966.)

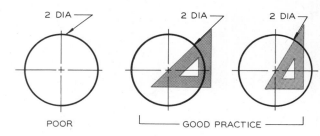

Fig. 13–39 Placement of leaders on holes.

Fig. 13–40 Placement of notes with leaders. Leaders should begin with a horizontal segment at the left of the first word or the right of the last word.

13–18 DIMENSIONING ARCS

When cylindrical or circular parts are less than a full circle, they are dimensioned with a radial dimension line extending from the center to the arc, as illustrated in Fig. 13–36. Where space permits, the numeral should be placed between the center and the arc, and the letter R should be placed to the right of the numeral. When space does not allow this, the numeral can be placed in one of the other positions shown in the figure. However, in all cases, the arrowhead touches the arc being dimensioned either from the inside or from the outside.

When aligned dimensions are used to dimension arcs, the numbers should be placed so as to avoid the "trouble zone" shown in Fig. 13–37. In this figure it is necessary to read one of the dimensions from the left of the page. The correct procedure is to place all lettering so that it can be read from either the bottom or the right side of the page. Also, dimensions should not lie on the vertical and horizontal centerlines.

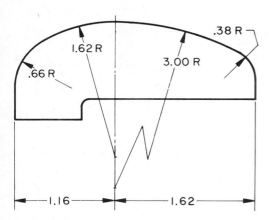

Fig. 13-41 Dimensioning a shape composed of arcs. (Courtesy of ANSI; Y14.5-1966.)

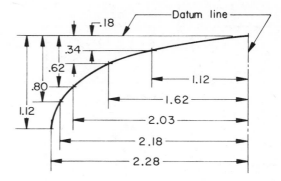

Fig. 13-42 Dimensioning an irregular curve from datum lines. (Courtesy of ANSI; Y14.5-1966.)

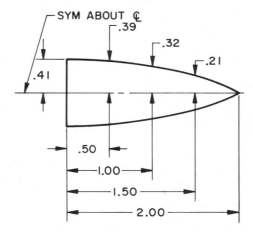

Fig. 13-43 Dimensioning a symmetrical curve about its centerline and a datum line. (Courtesy of ANSI; Y14.5-1966.)

When the radius of an arc is very long, the dimensioned drawing may show a radius that is less than the true radius. To indicate that the radius is not a true measurement, the radius is drawn with a "zigzag" as shown in Figs. 13-36 and 13-38. The portion of the radius nearest the arc should be drawn toward the arc's true center; the other portion of the false radius can be drawn in another direction to reduce the length. The center of the arc should lie on the centerline or the extension line on which the true center lies. The dimension given must be the actual radius, since this will be the dimension used in making the part.

13-19 LEADERS

Leaders are used to relate notes and dimensions on a drawing to the feature which they describe. Leaders were used in Fig. 13-36 to give the radii of the small fillets. In previous examples leaders were used to dimension spheres and to give the diameters of cylindrical holes.

A leader should be drawn as shown in Fig. 13-39. A standard triangle can be used for constructing the leader so that it will pass through the center if extended, but the arrow stops at the arc or circle to which the leader applies.

The notes that are attached to leaders should be positioned so that the leader begins at either the first word or the last word of the note (Fig. 13-40). It is poor practice to have the leader extend from a word in the middle of the note. Leaders will be used extensively in the remainder of this chapter.

13-20 DIMENSIONING CURVED SURFACES

An irregular shape composed of a number of arcs of varying sizes (Fig. 13-41) can be dimensioned by using a series of radii. The basic centerline is located

FIGURE 13–44. LOCATION DIMENSIONS

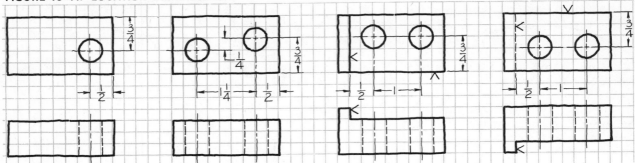

A. Cylindrical holes should be located in the circular view from two surfaces of the object.

B. When more than one hole is to be located, the other holes should be located in relation to the first from center to center.

C. A more accurate location is possible if holes are located from finished surfaces.

D. Holes should be located in the circular view and from finished surfaces, even if the finished surfaces are hidden.

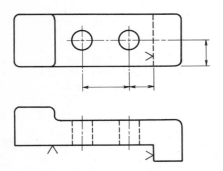

Fig. 13–45 Location of cylindrical holes from a finished surface.

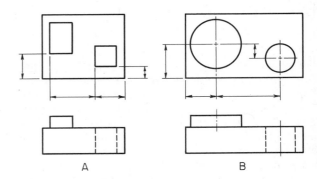

Fig. 13–46 Location of prisms and cylinders.

for the construction of the first curves. Note that the 3.00R arc is dimensioned with a false radius to conserve space. The other dimensions are located with the aid of the principles of tangency construction discussed in Chapter 5.

When the curve to be dimensioned is irregular rather than composed of arcs (Fig. 13–42), the coordinate method can be used to locate a series of points along the curve from two datum lines. The draftsman must use his judgment to determine the proper spacing for the points. In general, a gradual curve requires fewer points than a curve whose curvature is sharp or highly irregular. A special case

of an irregular curve is the symmetrical curve shown in Fig. 13–43. In this example, points are located by coordinates along only one side of the centerline; this procedure eliminates repetitive dimensions. Note that dimension lines are used as extension lines in violation of a previously established rule. This is done because it is the easiest method of dimensioning the curve.

13–21 LOCATION DIMENSIONS

Location dimensions are different from size dimensions in that, instead of establishing size, they indicate the positions of various geometric features. The geometric element most often located is the cylindrical hole. A hole, and likewise any cylindrical shape such as a boss, must be located with respect to the surface on which it lies.

Figure 13–44 illustrates the basic rules of locating cylindrical holes. The size dimensions of the holes and the prisms are omitted for clarity.

The cylindrical hole in A is located in the circular view by means of two dimensions. These dimensions locate the center of the hole. Any two surfaces of the prism can be used from which to draw extension lines for indicating the dimensions.

The two holes in B are located with respect to each other from center to center. The hole at the right is located with respect to the surfaces of the prism, and the other hole is located from the center of the first hole.

The two holes in C are located in the same way as in B except that they are located with respect to two finished surfaces. Since the surfaces are to be machined to a uniform surface, this procedure will give more accurate locations. Location dimensions should be related to finished surfaces wherever possible.

In part D, two holes are located with respect to a hidden line. This is a violation of a previous rule, but in this case it is good practice since the hidden surface is finished. The holes are located from center to center in the circular view.

An instrument drawing of a similar object is shown in Fig. 13–45. The holes are located in accordance with the previously discussed rules.

Prisms are located with respect to each other as shown in Fig. 13–46A. It is necessary to locate only a single corner of a prism with respect to another. It will be understood that the sides are parallel to those of the other prism. If the sides are not parallel, additional dimensions are needed to locate specific corners.

Location dimensions are placed on whatever view permits both dimensions to be shown, the top view in this example. For maximum accuracy, the prisms are located with respect to each other or from the same plane on the object. Cylindrical elements are located in Fig. 13–46B in accordance with the principles just discussed.

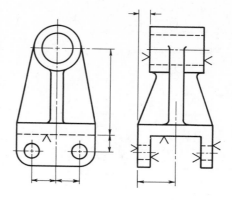

Fig. 13–47 Examples of location dimensions used to locate geometric elements.

Another example of location dimensions is shown in Fig. 13–47. Since it is best to locate a cylinder in its circular view, its center is located in relation to the finished surface, which is hidden in the front view. In addition, the two smaller holes are located in this view from the centerline of the larger hole.

13–22 LOCATION OF HOLES

When the location of holes must be very accurate, the dimensions should originate from a common reference plane on the part to eliminate the accumulation of errors in measurement as successive holes are located. Two examples of coordinate dimensions of this type are shown in Fig. 13–48A and B. When dimensions are located in this manner, the accumulation of errors will be minimal, especially if the reference surfaces are finished surfaces.

When several holes in a series are to be equally spaced, as in Fig. 13–48C, a note specifying that they are equally spaced can be used to locate the holes. The first and last holes of the series are determined by the usual location dimensions.

Holes may be located on circular plates as shown in Fig. 13–49. For the most accurate location of these holes, coordinate dimensions should be used as shown in A. These coordinates are measured

A

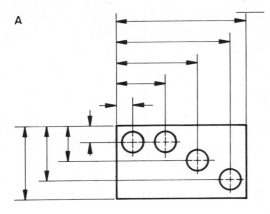

A

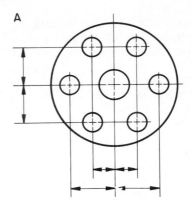

B

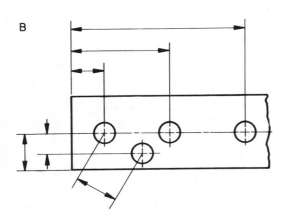

B

.245-.255 DIA
8 HOLES
EQUALLY SPACED

2.40

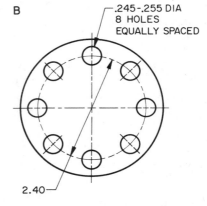

Fig. 13–49 Two methods of locating holes in a circular plate. (Courtesy of ANSI; Y14.5–1966.)

C

.250$^{+.005}_{-.000}$ DIA
5 HOLES
EQ SP

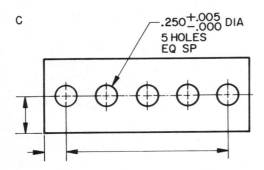

Fig. 13–48 Three methods of locating holes. (Courtesy of ANSI; Y14.5–1966.)

from the vertical and horizontal centerlines of the plate. A second, less accurate method of locating equally spaced holes is illustrated in Fig. 13–49B. Here a diameter of the circle passing through the centers of the holes is located in the circular view. A note indicates the size of the holes and specifies that they are equally spaced.

A similar method of locating holes is the polar system illustrated in Fig. 13–50. A polar point is selected from which several dimensions are measured. The radial distance from this point must be given together with the angular measurements (in degrees) between the holes. This method could be used on the circular plates shown in Fig. 13–49.

Dimensioning   **13–22**

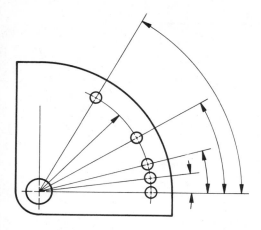

Fig. 13–50 Location of holes by polar dimensions. (Courtesy of ANSI; Y14.5–1966.)

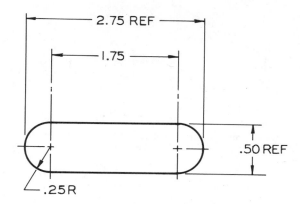

Fig. 13–52 An alternative method of dimensioning an object with rounded ends.

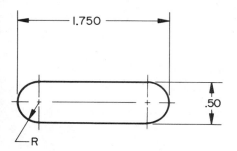

Fig. 13–51 Dimensioning an object with rounded ends. (Courtesy of ANSI; Y14.5–1966.)

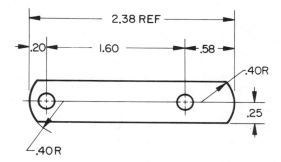

Fig. 13–53 Dimensioning an object with a partially rounded end. (Courtesy of ANSI; Y14.5–1966.)

13–23 DIMENSIONING OBJECTS WITH ROUNDED ENDS

Objects with rounded ends are dimensioned from rounded end to rounded end. This is a recommended practice to ensure that the overall length of the piece is given directly without calculations. An example is shown in Fig. 13–51. The dimension across the flat surfaces is given and a leader is used to show that the ends are arcs. The radius is not dimensioned but is noted with the letter R. The radius can be found by halving the dimension across the flat surfaces.

The same object may be dimensioned as shown in Fig. 13–52 by giving a measurement from center to center of the rounded ends. The overall dimension is given as a reference dimension to eliminate the need for the shop personnel to calculate the length. In this case the dimension of the radius at the rounded ends is given.

A part with partially rounded ends is dimensioned as shown in Fig. 13–53. The radii and their centers are given, since this information could not be known unless supplied. In this example it is probably more important to locate the holes with respect to each other with a high degree of accuracy than to dimension the distance between the rounded ends, since the holes will probably be aligned with another pair of holes to receive bolts or pins. Note

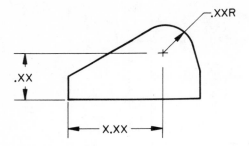

Fig. 13–54 Locating centers of arcs for objects with rounded features. (Courtesy of ANSI; Y14.5–1966.)

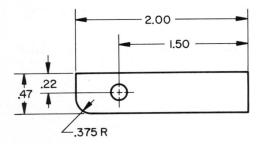

Fig. 13–55 Dimensioning objects with rounded corners. (Courtesy of ANSI; Y14.5–1966.)

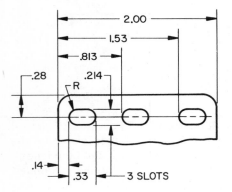

Fig. 13–56 Dimensioning slotted holes. (Courtesy of ANSI; Y14.5–1966.)

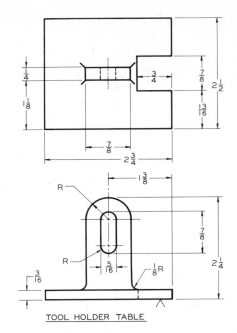

TOOL HOLDER TABLE

Fig. 13–57 An example of a part dimensioned in accordance with the principles discussed here.

that the overall dimension is labeled as a reference dimension (REF); this means that it can serve as a check on the addition of the other dimensions, but is itself of secondary importance.

When an object contains a rounded end that is less than a full semicircle (Fig. 13–54), location

dimensions must be used to locate the center of the arc. Location measurements are the first dimensions that are laid out in the construction of a drawing or pattern. The arc is dimensioned and then used for constructing the contour of the object. To complete the drawing, lines are drawn from other established points tangent to the arc. In drawing parts with rounded corners, the outside surfaces of the objects should be located first; then arcs can be drawn tangent to these edges. The arcs in Fig. 13–55 are dimensioned with a radius.

Slots with rounded ends are dimensioned in Fig. 13–56. Note that the same general principles discussed in this article apply to these shapes even though they are holes rather than solid objects. The rounded ends are located with a radius that is indicated but not dimensioned. The longitudinal centerlines of the slots are located from nearby surfaces. Since it is noted that three slots are desired, it is not necessary to dimension each separately; only one need be dimensioned. For greater accuracy the slots are located from the same reference surface.

Dimensioning 13–23

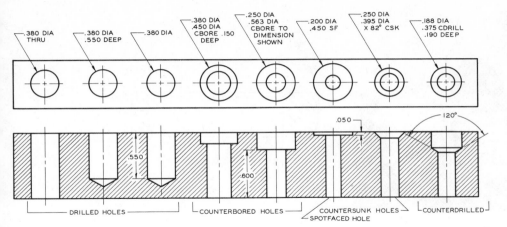

.380 DIA THRU

.380 DIA .550 DEEP

.380 DIA

.380 DIA .450 DIA CBORE .150 DEEP

.250 DIA .563 DIA CBORE TO DIMENSION SHOWN

.200 DIA .450 SF

.250 DIA .395 DIA X 82° CSK

.188 DIA .375 CDRILL .190 DEEP

.050

120°

.550

.600

DRILLED HOLES   COUNTERBORED HOLES   COUNTERSUNK HOLES   COUNTERDRILLED
SPOTFACED HOLE

Fig. 13–58 Various types of machined holes and the proper notes to specify them.

The dimensioned drawing of a tool holder table in Fig. 13–57 shows examples of arcs and slots. Note that the principles discussed in this article have been applied in every case. To prevent the crossing of dimension lines, it is often necessary to place dimensions in a view that is not as descriptive of the features as might be desired.

13–24 MACHINED HOLES

Machined holes are holes that are made or refined by a machine. The most common method of making small holes is by drilling. Machined holes are specified by notes attached to leaders. The notes are positioned horizontally on the drawing regardless of the direction of the leader. Note that the leader begins with a short horizontal segment at the note (Fig. 13–58).

It is preferable to give the diameter of the hole with the abbreviation DIA, with no reference to the method of making the hole. Previously, drafting standards recommended that machining operations be given in the note: for example, $\frac{3}{4}''$ DRILL.

Holes can be dimensioned to give their depth, or their depth can be given in a note as in Fig. 13–58. Notes can be given in the rectangular views of holes, but the circular view is preferable.

Drilled holes can be drawn through a part (in which case they are called through holes) or drilled to a specified depth. The specified depth of a drilled hole

Fig. 13–59 A cylindrical boss being spotfaced to provide a smooth bearing surface for a bolt. (Courtesy of Clausing Corporation.)

is the usable depth of the hole, not the depth to the point made by the drill. The drill point angle is 120°.

Counterbored holes are holes that have been enlarged by boring a hole with the same center as a smaller hole (Fig. 13–58). A note can be given to indicate the diameter of the counterbore and its depth. An alternative method is to use a dimension in combination with a note.

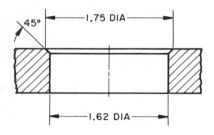

Fig. 13–60 Boring a large hole on a lathe with a boring bar. (Courtesy of Clausing Corporation.)

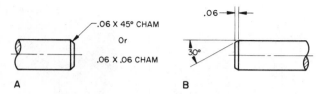

Fig. 13–61 Methods of dimensioning chamfers. (Courtesy of ANSI; Y14.5–1966.)

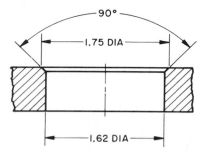

Fig. 13–62 Dimensioning internal chamfers. (Courtesy of ANSI; Y14.5–1966.)

Spotfacing is a machining process whereby the surface around the top of a hole is finished to provide a level seat for a washer or fastener head. The note in Fig. 13–58 gives the diameter of the through hole first, then the diameter of the spotface. The depth of the spotface can be shown with a dimension or in a note. The depth of the spotface is seldom a critical dimension.

A spotfacing tool is shown in Fig. 13–59. Here it has been used to finish a boss (a raised cylindrical surface). This finished surface ensures that the part resting against it will be properly aligned.

Countersinking is the process of forming a conical enlargement at the top of a hole to receive a screw with a head of this shape (Fig. 13–58). The diameter of the countersunk hole (the maximum diameter at the surface) and the angle of the countersink are given in the note.

Counterdrilled holes are holes that have been enlarged by drilling a hole with the same center as a smaller hole, as shown in Fig. 13–58. The diameter of the counterdrill and its depth are given in the note. This recessed hole provides a concealed hole for a fastener to be inserted below the surface of the part.

Boring is a machine operation that is usually performed on a lathe with a boring bar (Fig. 13–60). Bored holes are larger than drilled holes.

Reamed holes are holes that have been "finished" or slightly enlarged after being drilled or bored. This is done with a ream, which is similar to a drill bit.

13–25 CHAMFERS

Chamfers are beveled edges that are used on cylindrical parts such as shafts and threaded fasteners. They facilitate the assembly of these parts

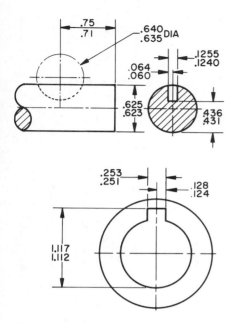

with other components and eliminate rough corners and edges.

When a chamfer is at a 45° angle, a note can be used as shown in Fig. 13–61A. The word CHAMFER may be added or omitted as desired. When the chamfer is at an angle other than 45°, the angle and the length are given as in Fig. 13–61B.

Notes of this type can also be used for internal chamfers at the openings of holes. If the design of a part requires that the chamfer diameter be controlled, the chamfer should be dimensioned as in Fig. 13–62.

13–26 KEYSEATS

A *keyseat* is a slot cut into a shaft for the purpose of aligning the shaft with a part mounted on it. This part may be a pulley or a collar. The proper method of dimensioning a key, keyway, and keyseat is shown in Fig. 13–63; this method was discussed in Chapter

12. Tolerances are shown in this example and will be discussed in more detail later in this chapter.

A milling machine is shown in Fig. 13–64 being used to cut a slot. This machine can also be used to cut keyseats in shafts.

13–27 KNURLING

Knurling is the operation of cutting diamond-shaped or other parallel patterns on cylindrical surfaces for

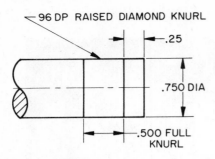

Fig. 13–66 Dimensioning a knurled cylinder. (Courtesy of ANSI; Y14.5–1966.)

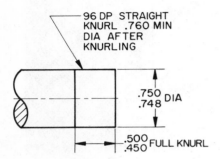

Fig. 13–67 Dimensioning a knurled surface for a press fit. (Courtesy of ANSI; Y14.5–1966.)

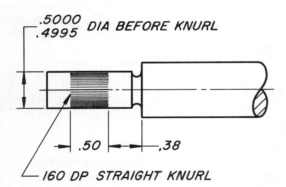

Fig. 13–68 Dimensioning a straight knurl. (Courtesy of General Motors Corporation.)

gripping or for decoration, or for a press fit between two parts that will be permanently assembled as though welded. An example of a knurled part is shown in Fig. 13–65.

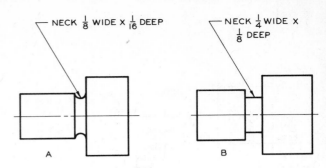

Fig. 13–69 Methods of noting undercuts.

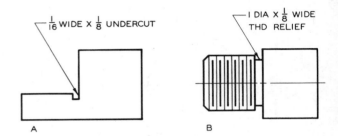

Fig. 13–70 Methods of noting undercuts and thread reliefs.

Knurls are specified in terms of type, diametral pitch (DP), and diameter before and after knurling. The diameter can be omitted when control is not required, as in the case of a knurl used for gripping. A note is used to dimension a knurled surface in Fig. 13–66. The knurled surface need not be drawn; a note is sufficient.

When the knurled part is to be press-fitted with another part, the diameter before and after knurling must be given, as shown in Fig. 13–67. An example of a straight knurl is shown in Fig. 13–68.

13–28 NECKS AND UNDERCUTS

A *neck* is a recess cut into a cylindrical part. This recess is commonly used at the point where the cylinder changes size from one diameter to another (Fig. 13–69). The neck ensures that a pulley or a part that is assembled on the shaft can fit flush against the shoulder of the larger cylinder without binding.

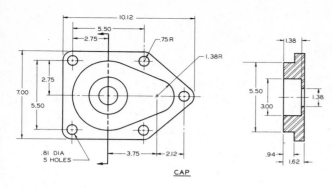

Fig. 13–71 A dimensioned section.

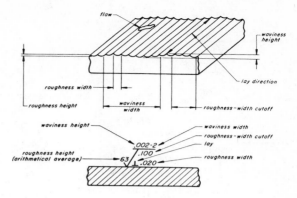

Fig. 13–72 Surface texture definitions. (Courtesy of ANSI; B46.1–1962.)

A neck is often used at the end of a series of threads or at the base of a fastener head that must fit flush against a bearing surface (Fig. 13–70B). As shown in Fig. 13–69, necks can be semicircular or can have square corners.

Undercuts are somewhat similar to necks and serve much the same purpose. An undercut at the intersection between two perpendicular planes of a part is shown in Fig. 13–70A. This ensures that a mating part designed to fit into this corner will fit flush against both surfaces. The undercut provides a space for fragments of metal or other obstacles to fall out of the way so as not to interfere with the functioning of the mating parts. In Fig. 13–70B, a *thread relief* is used, since it is difficult to cut threads to the very end of a cylinder that joins a larger cylinder.

13–29 DIMENSIONED SECTIONS

Sections are dimensioned in the same manner as regular views. Sections add clarity to a drawing that might otherwise be difficult to interpret.

A dimensioned section is shown in Fig. 13–71. The dimensioning principles discussed in this chapter have been applied to the cap shown in this figure.

13–30 SURFACE TEXTURE

Many parts which must operate within close tolerances require a special surface finish; this finish needs to be more accurately specified than by the

"V" customarily used to show a finished surface. Since there are many types of finish, a single symbol is not sufficient. Therefore, in instances where the type of finish is important, the symbol is accompanied by notes that specify the degree of finish required.

Notes and symbols must be understood before they can be used on drawings. For help in understanding the various types of surface texture, refer to Fig. 13–72. The terms used in this figure are defined below.

Surface texture is the term used to indicate repetitive or random deviations from a perfectly smooth surface. These deviations, which form the pattern of the surface, include roughness, waviness, lay, and flaws.

Roughness is the term applied to the finer irregularities in surface texture caused by variations in the manufacturing and production processes.

Roughness height is the average deviation from the mean plane of the surface. Roughness is measured in micro-inches or millionths of an inch, 0.000001″ (abbreviated as μin.).

Roughness-width cutoff (measured in inches) is the largest spacing of repetitive surface irregularities to be included in the measurement of average roughness height.

Waviness (measured in inches) is a widely spaced component of surface texture, the spacing exceeding the roughness-width cutoff. Waviness may result

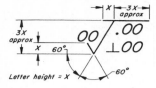

Fig. 13–73 The surface texture symbol. (Courtesy of ANSI; B46.1–1962.)

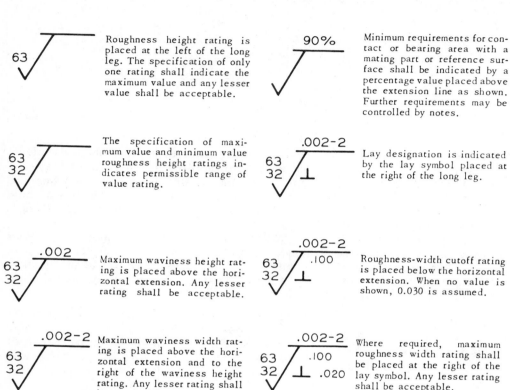

63 / — Roughness height rating is placed at the left of the long leg. The specification of only one rating shall indicate the maximum value and any lesser value shall be acceptable.

90% — Minimum requirements for contact or bearing area with a mating part or reference surface shall be indicated by a percentage value placed above the extension line as shown. Further requirements may be controlled by notes.

63 32 / — The specification of maximum value and minimum value roughness height ratings indicates permissible range of value rating.

.002-2 63 32 ⊥ — Lay designation is indicated by the lay symbol placed at the right of the long leg.

.002 63 32 — Maximum waviness height rating is placed above the horizontal extension. Any lesser rating shall be acceptable.

.002-2 .100 63 32 ⊥ — Roughness-width cutoff rating is placed below the horizontal extension. When no value is shown, 0.030 is assumed.

.002-2 63 32 — Maximum waviness width rating is placed above the horizontal extension and to the right of the waviness height rating. Any lesser rating shall be acceptable.

.002-2 .100 63 32 ⊥ .020 — Where required, maximum roughness width rating shall be placed at the right of the lay symbol. Any lesser rating shall be acceptable.

Fig. 13–74 Surface texture notes and their meaning. (Courtesy of ANSI; B46.1–1962.)

from variations in machine operations, vibration, chatter, or warping. Roughness may be considered as superimposed on a wavy surface.

Waviness height (measured in inches) is the peak-to-peak distance between waves.

Waviness width (measured in inches) is the spacing of successive wave peaks or successive wave valleys.

Lay is the direction of the predominant surface pattern, ordinarily determined by the production method used.

Flaws are irregularities or defects that occur infrequently or at widely varying intervals on a surface. These include cracks, blow holes, checks, ridges, scratches, etc. Unless otherwise specified, the effect of flaws is included in the roughness height measurement.

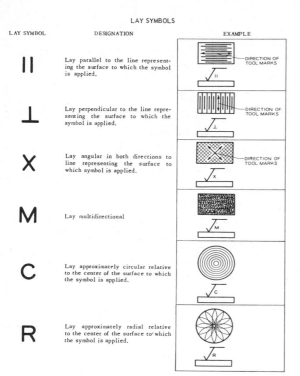

Fig. 13–75 Lay notations used with surface texture symbols. (Courtesy of ANSI; B46.1–1962.)

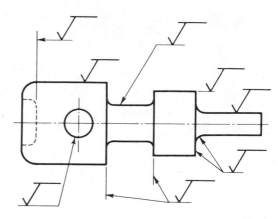

Fig. 13–76 The application of texture symbols on a drawing. (Courtesy of ANSI; B46.1–1963.)

Contact area is the surface area that will make contact with a mating surface.

13–31 SURFACE TEXTURE SYMBOLS

Features of surface texture are specified on a drawing by the symbol shown in Fig. 13–73. The lettering on the symbol should be of the same size as all other lettering on the drawing. The top extension line can extend as far to the right as required. In some cases, the surface texture must be specified with a high degree of accuracy; in other cases, general instructions are sufficient.

Figure 13–74 shows how roughness, waviness, and lay are specified by inserting the ratings in the appropriate portions of the symbol. Only the specifications that are necessary for a given surface should be included in the surface symbol; in this way

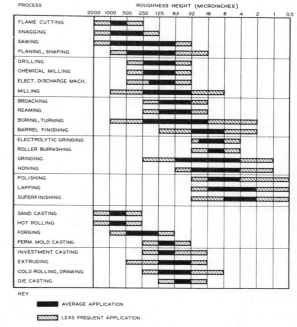

Fig. 13–77 Surface roughness produced by common production methods. (Courtesy of ANSI; B46.1–1962.)

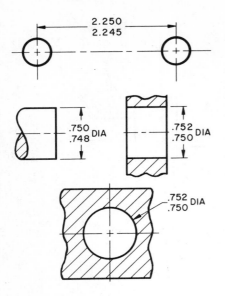

Fig. 13–78 Tolerances applied to dimensions. (Courtesy of ANSI; Y14.5–1966.)

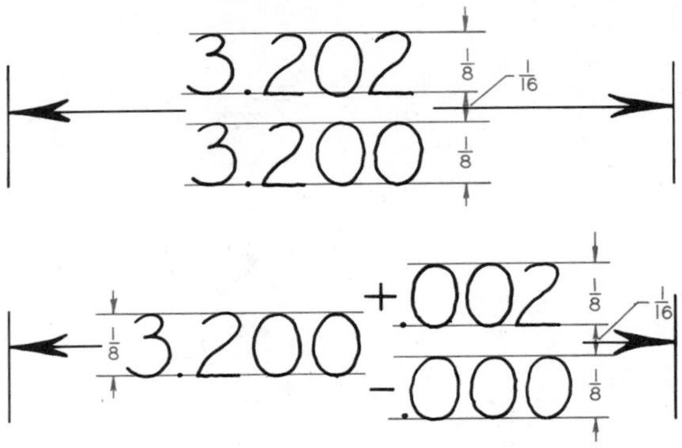

Fig. 13–79 Methods of lettering to indicate tolerance.

unessential finishing procedures and increased production costs resulting from them can be avoided.

Lay symbols and their combination with surface symbols are illustrated in Fig. 13–75. The notes shown here describe the direction of lay when necessary. An example of a drawing of a part with surface symbols applied is shown in Fig. 13–76.

Various production methods result in roughness heights that are peculiar to the process used. The designer specifying a surface texture must know these characteristics and the machines available to him. Figure 13–77 gives the roughness in micro-inches resulting from the more common production methods. This table can be used as a guide in selecting the proper machining operations.

13–32 TOLERANCES

Engineering components made today require more accurate dimensions than did those made in the past. The reason for this is that many parts are made by different companies in different geographical locations. Parts made by any one company must be interchangeable with those made by other companies. If they are not, the parts must be modified to

fit into the assembly—a very expensive process. Interchangeability of parts is also an important factor when replacement is necessary.

The technique of ensuring that manufactured parts are the proper size is called *tolerancing*. In tolerancing, each dimension is allowed a certain degree of variation within a specified zone, the range of permissible variation depending on the function of the part. It is not only very expensive, but almost impossible to produce parts whose measurements are accurate to thousandths or ten-thousandths of an inch. Therefore, the manufacturer is given an allowable variation that will reduce costs while still controlling the size or position of the parts.

13–33 TOLERANCE NOTES

All dimensions of a part are toleranced to some degree either by the judgment of the manufacturer or by a note on the drawing. The usual practice is to supply a general tolerance note on a drawing or in specifications. Dimensions that are not critical because they do not involve mating parts may be toleranced by a general note such as TOLER-ANCE $\pm \frac{1}{64}$.

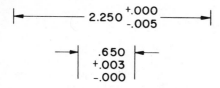

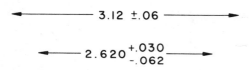

Fig. 13–80 Unilateral tolerances. (Courtesy of ANSI; Y14.5–1966.)

3.12 ±.06

2.620 +.030 / −.062

Fig. 13–81 Bilateral tolerances. (Courtesy of ANSI; Y14.5–1966.)

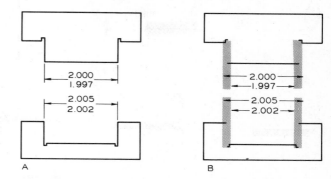

Fig. 13–82 Tolerances between two mating parts. Both parts have a tolerance of .003″ and an allowance of .002″.

Other tolerances, for dimensions which involve mating parts, can be indicated more accurately by such a note as "TOLERANCE ± .001."

13–34 TOLERANCE DIMENSIONS

Several of the acceptable methods of specifying tolerances are shown in Fig. 13–78. Two numerals are used; the upper number gives the largest acceptable measurement and the lower number gives the smallest. These numbers are the *limits* of size permitted in the manufacture of the part. Tolerances may be specified in a note with the two dimensions on one line; in this case, the smaller dimension precedes the larger one.

The positioning and spacing of the numerals used to indicate the limits of tolerance are shown in Fig. 13–79. Both of the methods illustrated here give the same information and both are acceptable.

In "plus-and-minus" tolerancing the tolerance is given from a single dimension. When the plus and minus dimensions allow variation in only one direction (see Fig. 13–80), the tolerancing is described as *unilateral*. Tolerancing that permits

variation in either direction from the basic dimension is called *bilateral* tolerancing (Fig. 13–81).

In both unilateral and bilateral tolerancing the plus dimension is placed above the minus dimension, in agreement with the rule that the larger dimension should be placed over the smaller one.

13–35 MATING PARTS

Mating parts are parts that fit together with a reasonably high degree of accuracy. Two mating parts are shown in Fig. 13–82A where a piece is to fit into a rectangular notch. The upper piece is dimensioned with two measurements that indicate the upper and lower limits on the size. The tolerance dimensions for the notch are slightly larger than those for the block that fits into it. Note that undercuts are specified to allow dirt or obstructions to fall out of the way when the parts are assembled.

The variation in size permitted in each part is shown in Fig. 13–82B. In all possible variations of size in the two parts, the notch will be larger than the block that fits into it. This form of tolerancing ensures that the parts will assemble and function as desired. However, you can see that a few thou-

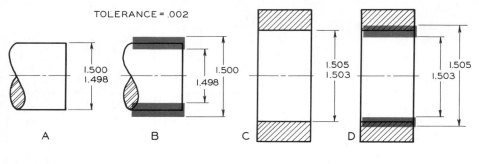

TOLERANCE = .002

Fig. 13–83 Tolerances on holes and shafts. Each has a tolerance of .002″.

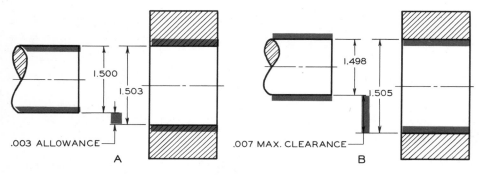

.003 ALLOWANCE

A

.007 MAX. CLEARANCE

B

Fig. 13–84 Allowance and clearance between mating parts.

sandths of an inch of variation could cause the notch to be too small for the block to fit into it. Clearly, tolerances are important in this type of situation.

An example of mating cylindrical parts is shown in Fig. 13–83. Part B of the figure illustrates the meaning of the tolerance dimensions given in part A; that is, it shows that the size of the shaft can vary in diameter from 1.500″ (its maximum size) to 1.498″ (its minimum size). The difference between these limits (on a single part) is called the tolerance. In this case, the tolerance is .002. The dimensions of the hole in part C are given the limits of 1.505 and 1.503, for a tolerance of .002 (the difference between the limits) as illustrated in part D.

13–36 TERMINOLOGY OF TOLERANCING

The meaning of most of the terms of tolerancing can be illustrated by Figs. 13–83 and 13–84. When the shaft and the hole shown in Fig. 13–83 are assem-

bled, the extreme conditions—the tightest and the loosest fit—are those shown in Fig. 13–84.

Allowance specifies the tightest permissible fit between mating parts. In Fig. 13–84, the allowance between the shaft and the hole is +.003 (+ indicates that the parts will clear and − indicates that they will not clear but will interfere).

Nominal size is an approximate size. The nominal size of the shaft and the hole in Figs. 13–83 and 13–84 is $1\frac{1}{2}''$.

Basic size is the exact, theoretical size from which limits are derived by the application of tolerances and allowances. In Fig. 13–83, the basic size is the decimal equivalent of the nominal size or 1.500″.

Actual size is the measured size of a finished part.

Limits of tolerance are the extreme measurements permitted by the tolerance, or the maximum and

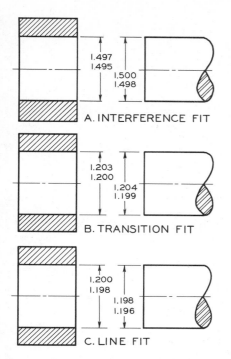

Fig. 13–85 Types of fits between mating parts.

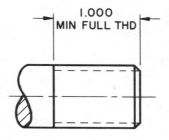

Fig. 13–86 Single tolerance dimensions. (Courtesy of ANSI; Y14.5–1966.)

minimum sizes of a part. The limits of tolerance on the shaft in Fig. 13–83 are 1.500 and 1.498.

Tolerance is the difference between the limits prescribed for a single part. The tolerance of the shaft in Fig. 13–83 is .002.

Fit is the range of tightness between two parts which may result from a specific combination of allowances and tolerances in the design of mating parts. The four major types of fit are *clearance*, *transition*, *interference*, and *line*.

Clearance fit is a fit which will proved an air space between the parts under the tightest conditions. The fit between the shaft and the hole in Fig. 13–84 is a clearance fit.

Interference fit is a fit in which the part that is to fit into another part is slightly larger than this other part. The shaft in Fig. 13–85A is larger than the hole; the

result is a *force fit* or a *press fit* that is almost the same as a weld between the two parts.

Transition fit is a fit between two parts that can result in either interference or clearance. The shaft in Fig. 13–85B can be either smaller or larger than the hole and still be within the prescribed tolerances.

Line fit is a fit that can result in either a clearance between two parts or contact of their surfaces. The shaft and the hole in Fig. 13–85C can have either contact or clearance depending on which limits are approached.

Selective assembly is a method of selecting and assembling parts by trial and error. Using this method, one can assemble parts made with larger tolerances than would be necessary if each individual part had to fit into a particular mating part. Because of the larger tolerances, manufacturing costs are considerably reduced. Parts can be toleranced with dimensions that will result in transition fits (either interference or clearance). The manufactured parts will be selected manually so that they will assemble to give the proper fit. Selective assembly represents a compromise between a high degree of manufacturing accuracy and ease of assembly or interchangeability of parts.

Single limits are dimensions that are specified in terms of only a minimum or a maximum (MIN or MAX), rather than both. An example is shown in Fig. 13–86. Depths of holes, threads, corner radii, and chamfers are dimensioned with single limits.

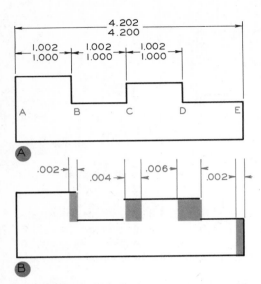

Fig. 13–87 Accumulation of tolerances resulting from chain dimensions.

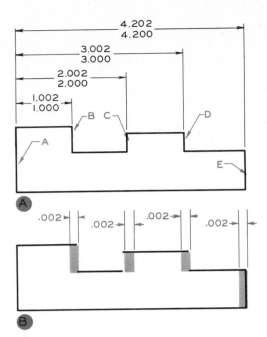

Fig. 13–88 Location of surfaces from a datum plane to reduce the accumulation of tolerances.

13–37 BASIC HOLE SYSTEM

The *basic hole system* is a widely used system of dimensioning holes and shafts to give the required allowance between the two assembled parts. In the basic hole system, the smallest hole is taken as the basic diameter from which the limits of tolerance and allowance are applied.

The hole is used because many of the standard drills, reamers, and machine tools are designed to give standard sizes of holes. Therefore, it is advantageous to use this diameter as the basic dimension.

If the lower limit on the diameter of a hole is 1.500″, the allowance (.003, for example) can be subtracted from this diameter to give the largest diameter of the shaft (1.497″). The lower limit for the shaft can then be found by subtracting the tolerance from 1.497″. In the basic hole system, it is assumed that varying the size of the shaft is easier than varying the hole.

13–38 BASIC SHAFT SYSTEM

Some industries use the *basic shaft system* of applying tolerances to dimensions, since many shafts come in standard sizes. In this case the largest diameter of the shaft is used as the basic dimension from which the tolerances and allowances are applied.

For example, if the largest permissible shaft is 1.500″, the allowance can be added to this dimension to yield the smallest possible diameter of the hole into which the shaft must fit. Therefore, if the parts are to have an allowance of .004″, the smallest hole would have a diameter of 1.504″.

13–39 CHAIN DIMENSIONS

When parts are dimensioned to locate surfaces or geometric features by a chain of dimensions as shown in Fig. 13–87A, variations may occur that exceed the tolerances specified. As successive measurements are made, each new measurement being based on the preceding one, the tolerances accumulate. The final tolerance may equal the sum of the tolerances on the intermediate dimensions. For example, the tolerance between A and B is .002; between A and C, .004; between A and D, .006 (see Fig. 13–87B). This accumulation of tolerances could be reduced if the dimensions were made from a *datum plane* or reference surface. A datum plane is usually a plane on the object, but it could be a plane on the machine used to make the part.

An example of tolerancing from a datum plane is shown in Fig. 13–88. Note that the tolerance between two intermediate points is equal to the tolerance on a dimension measured from the datum plane. In the example this is .004, which is the maximum tolerance that should be specified when datum plane or baseline dimensions are used. The designer must understand the function of each part in order to specify tolerances that will ensure the required conditions. In all cases, it is desirable to allow as much tolerance as possible to reduce costs and to simplify production methods.

PROBLEMS

These problems are to be solved in accordance with Article 3–15 and the specifications of your instructor. Most problems are to be drawn on Size A paper (8½″ × 11″) using ink or pencil and instruments.

Many of the problems are laid out on a grid where each square represents ¼″. The drawings can be transferred to grid paper of a similar type, or else the problems can be drawn on blank paper (Fig. 13–32) with the endorsement, title strip, and border described in Article 3–15. Refer to the text of this chapter to assist you in the solution of the problems.

General Problems

1–16 Refer to Figs. 13–89 through 13–104. Use Size A paper. Using instruments, draw the orthographic views of the parts to be dimensioned on detail paper or tracing paper. Complete the views if lines are missing. Dimension each part using the principles discussed in this chapter. Each square on the grid represents ¼″ (.25″). Concentrate on placement of dimensions and neatness in lettering and construction.

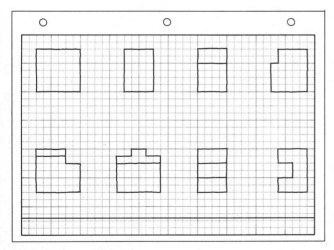

Fig. 13–89 Problem 1: Prisms.

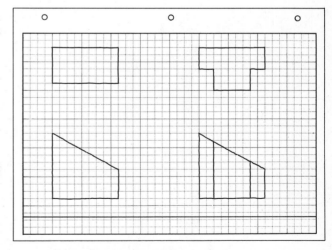

Fig. 13–90 Problem 2: Dimensioning angles.

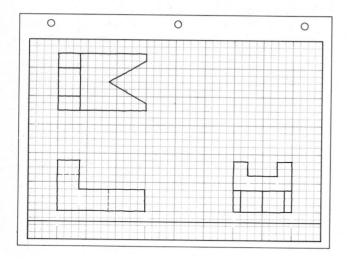

Fig. 13–91 Problem 3.

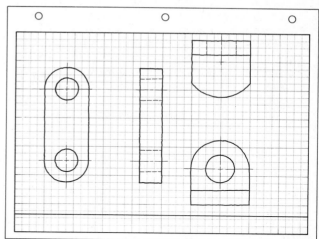

Fig. 13–93 Problem 5: Objects with rounded ends.

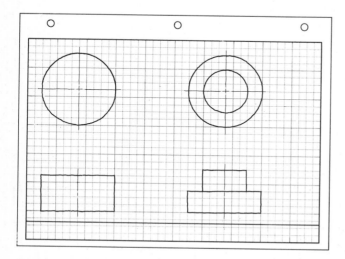

Fig. 13–92 Problem 4: Cylinders.

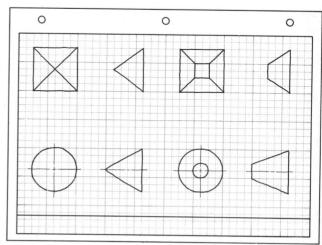

Fig. 13–94 Problem 6: Pyramids and cones.

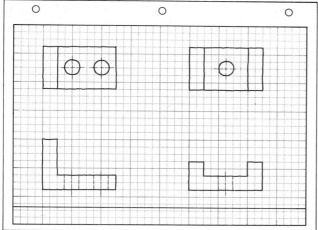

Fig. 13–95   Problem 7: Prisms.

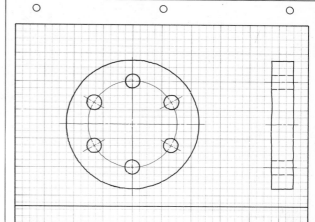

Fig. 13–97   Problem 9: End plate.

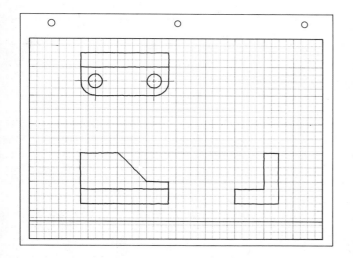

Fig. 13–96   Problem 8: Guide block.

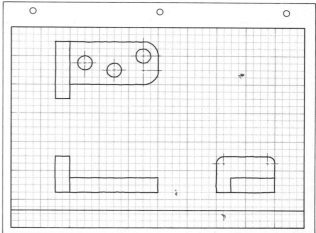

Fig. 13–98   Problem 10: Thrust block.

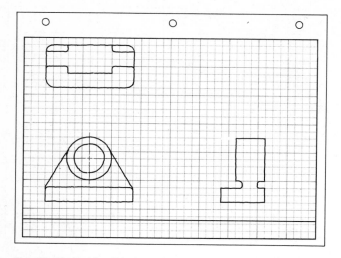

Fig. 13–99 Problem 11: Journal support.

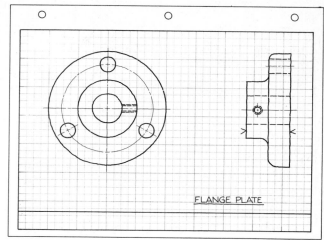

FLANGE PLATE

Fig. 13–101 Problem 13: Flange plate.

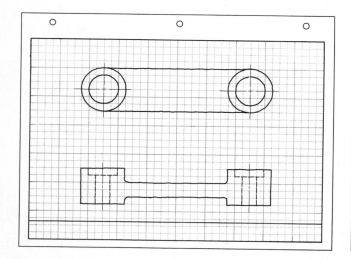

Fig. 13–100 Problem 12: Crank arm.

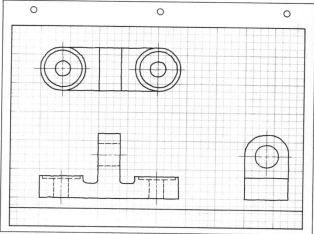

Fig. 13–102 Problem 14: Shaft guide.

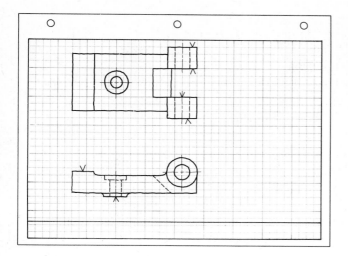

Fig. 13–103   Problem 15: Hinge plate.

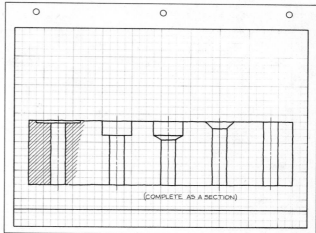

(COMPLETE AS A SECTION)

Fig. 13–105   Problem 17: Machined holes.

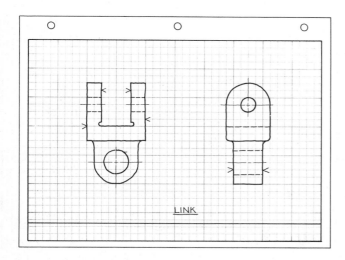

LINK

Fig. 13–104   Problem 16: Link.

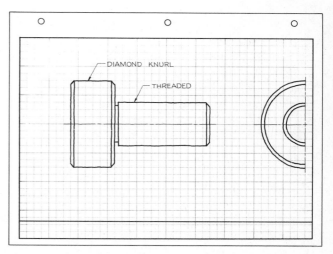

DIAMOND KNURL

THREADED

Fig. 13–106   Problem 18: Thumb screw.

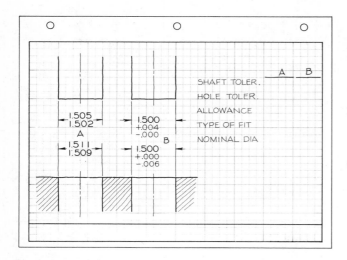

Fig. 13–107 Problem 19: Tolerances.

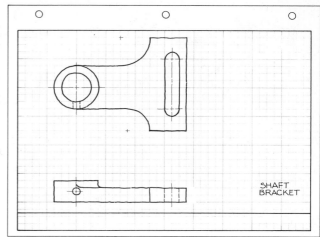

Fig. 13–109 Problem 21: Shaft bracket.

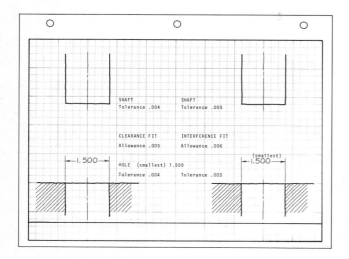

Fig. 13–108 Problem 20: Tolerances.

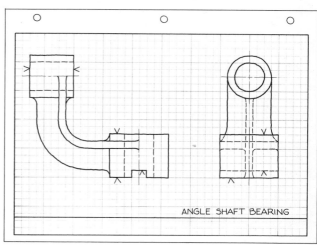

Fig. 13–110 Problem 22: Angle shaft bearing.

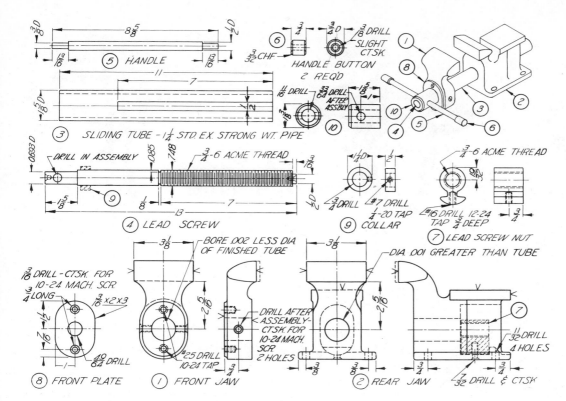

Fig. 13-111 Problem 23: A partially completed working drawing of a machinist's bench vise. (Courtesy of C. F. Struck Corporation.)

17 Refer to Fig. 13–105 and Article 13–24. Dimension these holes with the appropriate notes and dimensions.

18 Dimension the knurled screw shown in Fig. 13–106. Draw a 96-DP raised diamond knurl on the head and give a note. Dimension the chamfered head and the neck. Measure the major diameter of the threaded body and give a thread note using specifications from the UNC tables in the Appendix. Use simplified thread representations.

19 Refer to Fig. 13–107. Shafts and holes are shown in A and B. Repeat this drawing and complete the table at the right to give the information requested. This information can be found from the dimensions given.

20 Shafts and holes are shown in Fig. 13–108. The smallest hole is given (1.500″) in both drawings. Apply tolerances and allowances to this given dimension to find the other dimensions.

21 and **22** Refer to Figs. 13–109 and 13–110. Using instruments, draw the views of the objects, supplying any missing lines. Dimension the views you have drawn.

Design Problems

23 A partially dimensioned working drawing of a machinist's bench vise is shown in Fig. 13–111. These parts are available from the C. F. Struck Corporation, Cedarburg, Wisconsin as unfinished castings for shop projects. Consequently, only the

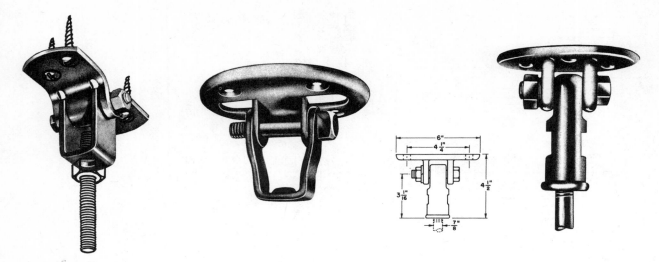

Fig. 13–112 Problem 24: Swinging hanger flanges for supporting overhead steam pipes. (Courtesy of Midland-Ross Corporation.)

dimensions that must be machined are shown. Using Size B paper (Article 3–15) and instruments, draw the parts assigned by your instructor. Dimension these views to show *all* dimensions and notes necessary to supply the information needed to make each part. Several parts may fit on a single sheet. You will have to use your judgment to arrive at the dimensions of the parts that are not given. Do not crowd your drawing.

24 Three swinging hanger flanges are shown in Fig. 13–112. These are to be attached to a ceiling from which steam pipes will be hung. Prepare dimensioned orthographic views of the individual parts of these assemblies. You must estimate the dimensions not given. A small dimensioned sketch is shown to give the approximate dimensions for the major features of the flanges. Use instruments and Size B paper. More than one part can be shown on a sheet. Select the best scale.

Additional Problems

25–34 Refer to Figs. 10–53 through 10–62. Draw the necessary orthographic views of these objects on paper of a size chosen by you or assigned by your instructor. Dimension and add notes to these views.

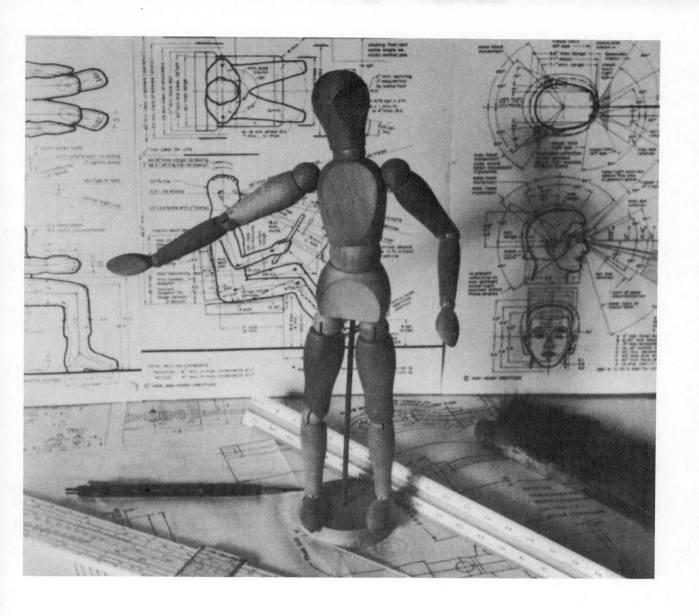

14
WORKING DRAWINGS

Fig. 14–1 The construction of Hoover Dam would have been impossible without hundreds of working drawings to explain its every detail. (Courtesy of the Bureau of Reclamation, Department of the Interior.)

Fig. 14–2 The top view and a sectional view of Hoover Dam. (Courtesy of the Bureau of Reclamation, Department of the Interior.)

14–1 INTRODUCTION

Working drawings must be prepared before a design can be implemented as described in the discussion of the design process in Chapter 6. Engineers, designers, technicians, and draftsmen cooperatively prepare detailed *working drawings* or *engineering drawings* after they have progressed through the previous steps of the design process—identification, preliminary ideas, refinement, analysis, and decision. Every product, project, or process that you know today was presented in the form of a working drawing before it was constructed.

The Hoover Dam, one of the most famous engineering projects, is 726 feet high and has a capacity of 32,471,000 acre-feet in Lake Mead on the Colorado River in Nevada and Arizona. This dam could be built only after thousands of detail drawings had been prepared to give the dimensions and specifications of every detail of the project (Fig. 14–1). An example of such a drawing is the top view and sectional view of the dam in Fig. 14–2. This is a general drawing with much less detail than was needed in most of the drawings used for the project.

Working drawings give the necessary information to the craftsmen and technicians so that the project can be constructed as the designer envisioned

Fig. 14–3 With the help of working drawings, you can build a one-man helicopter. (Courtesy of RotorWay Aircraft, Incorporated.)

it. For example, the one-passenger *Scorpion* helicopter shown in flight in Fig. 14–3 was built to plans prepared by RotorWay Aircraft Incorporated.* With the aid of these detailed plans and specifications,

---

*RotorWay Aircraft Incorporated, 14805 S. Interstate 10, Tempe, Arizona 85281.

this aircraft can be built as a shop project. This would be impossible unless every detail of the design was presented as a working drawing to describe clearly the ideas of the designer. The *Scorpion* has a rotor diameter of 19.2 feet and a gross weight of 750 pounds (Fig. 14–4).

The drawings used to implement a design are prepared by engineers, technicians, and draftsmen. Much of this work is routine and can be performed by draftsmen with the minimum of supervision. Other, more complicated drawings are prepared or supervised by technicians trained in a specialty. In almost all cases, the engineer must direct the preparation of working drawings and specify the critical dimensions and tolerances. Much of the engineer's work may be in the form of freehand sketches and notes which communicate his thoughts to his drafting staff. The final drawings will be closely reviewed by his staff, but the engineer is responsible for their correctness.

Fig. 14–4 The *Scorpion* helicopter has many details of construction that would be impossible to describe without the language of working drawings. (Courtesy of RotorWay Aircraft, Incorporated.)

14–2 THE WORKING DRAWING

A working drawing is often called a *detail drawing* because it describes the features and dimensions of

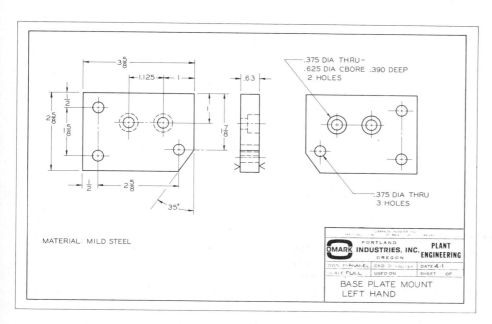

Fig. 14–5 A working drawing of a simple part. (Courtesy of Omark Industries, Inc.)

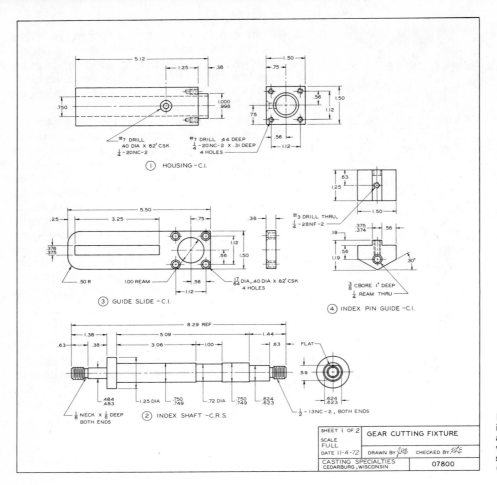

Fig. 14–6 A detail drawing showing a number of parts of the same assembly. Abbreviations: W.I., wrought iron; C.R.S., cold rolled steel; C.I., cast iron. (Courtesy of C. F. Struck Corporation.)

the details of the various parts of a design. Working drawings are usually drawn in accordance with the principles of orthographic projection, sectioning, revolution, and dimensioning as discussed in previous chapters. All the techniques and principles of graphics must be used in the working drawing because the purpose of a working drawing is to describe the parts of a design with as much clarity as possible. If this is not accomplished, it will be difficult to produce the parts in the shop to the desired specifications.

A detail drawing of a base plate mount is shown in Fig. 14–5. Three orthographic views describe the part, and dimensions are added to give its measurements. Notes specify the material and the sizes of the holes. If you built this part in the shop from a piece of wood, the end product would be the same, except for the material, as a part made from the same drawing by anyone else.

If a drawing is incomplete or if it can be misinterpreted, the working drawing does not serve its purpose. One of the best ways to check a drawing for its completeness is to make a scale drawing of the part by reading the detail drawing. The same

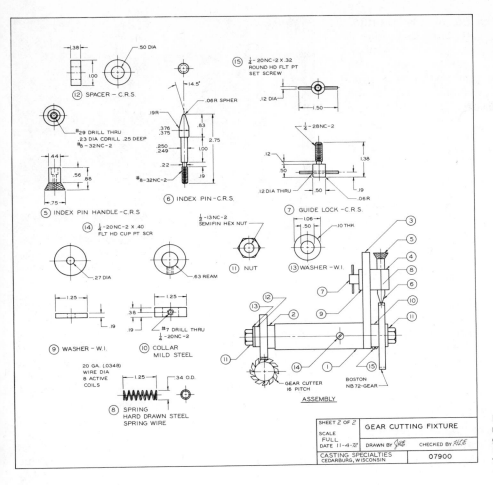

SHEET 2 OF 2

SCALE
FULL
DATE 11-4-72 DRAWN BY JHE   CHECKED BY ALE

GEAR CUTTING FIXTURE

CASTING SPECIALTIES
CEDARBURG, WISCONSIN   07900

Fig. 14–7 A detail drawing of a number of parts and an orthographic assembly of the parts. (Courtesy of C. F. Struck Corporation.)

information must be known to draw a part as to make it. Missing or incorrect dimensions can be found quickly by this method.

Note that the drawing in Fig. 14–5 has a border and title block. The line border represents the edge of the sheet on which the drawing was made. The title block gives information about the drawing.

Most working drawings are drawn on tracing paper with a printed border and title block. The sheets are usually standard sizes to provide uniformity in format. Tracing paper is used because it permits rough pencil layouts to be traced by placing transparent tracing paper over the layout. In addition, it is necessary to use tracing paper in order to make a diazo print (a blue-line print).

14–3 DETAILS OF SEVERAL PARTS

When an assembly consists cf a number of components, several of them can be drawn on the same sheet. Examples of detail drawings with several parts on a single sheet are given in Figs. 14–6 and 14–7. These drawings are parts of a gear cutting fixture.

Each part is drawn with the necessary ortho-graphic views, dimensions, and notes to explain it fully. The name of the part, the identifying number, and the material are given near the views. No attempt is made to align the parts with one another to indicate their order of assembly. Instead, the parts are located to make the best use of the available space.

Each sheet is numbered in the title block with respect to the total number of sheets in the set of drawings. For example, Fig. 14–6 is numbered as sheet 1 of 2 sheets. This enables anyone referring to the set of drawings to know whether it is complete.

An orthographic *assembly drawing* is given in Fig. 14–7 to show how the parts fit together. The identifying number of each part is attached to the assembly with a leader. These numbers can be cross-checked with the details of each part for specific information. If the shop makes each of the parts from these detail drawings, they will assemble correctly as shown in the assembly drawing. You could not describe the design of a simple assembly like this without using the principles of graphics as applied in these two drawings. (Assembly drawings are discussed further in Article 14–9.)

Fig. 14–8 Draftsmen make changes in navigational charts to give the latest information. (Courtesy of the Department of the Army.)

14–4 THE ROLE OF THE DRAFTSMAN

The draftsman is involved with the total process of developing plans and specifications for a product. While the craftsman in the shop may work on one part of the product, he may never know how his contribution will fit in with the work of other crafts-men and technicians working on the same project at other locations.

The draftsman may specialize in one area of drafting but, in general, he sees more of the total project and the relationship of the various compo-nents than does the craftsman. The draftsman makes preliminary drawings from the engineer's rough sketches. These are checked, modified, and re-drawn for additional study by the designer. Finally, after all details are agreed upon, the finished detail drawings are prepared.

The engineer is always responsible for the correctness and accuracy of the drawings even though he does not make them himself. Conse-quently, he must rely upon the draftsman for assistance. This experience of assisting in the development of design projects qualifies many draftsmen to handle assignments of responsibility, since they are in a position to understand the overall aspects of a project. They often become project supervisors, estimators, or construction inspectors because of their experience as draftsmen.

Most companies have drafting standards that outline the formats, rules, and practices used by that company. All draftsmen in the company must be-come familiar with these standards so that there will be uniformity among the work done by different draftsmen. Some projects and contracts require that specific drawing techniques be used in order for the drawings to be acceptable. Such standards also regulate sizes of sheets, title blocks, types of lettering, and terminology of notes.

Most draftsmen are required to add the neces-sary information to a drawing so that it will conform to the company's standards. The draftsman may need to refer to tables in the standards or to previous drawings for some of this information. However, the draftsman is usually not an engineer and cannot be expected to furnish all the information on a drawing. The engineer must supply information

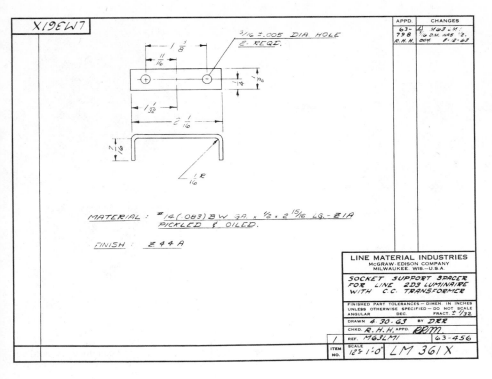

such as grades of metal, tolerances, surface treatments of metals, and similar information based on the analysis of the design.

Draftsmen are used in many capacities. They may add information to a chart (Fig. 14—8), prepare layout drawings, revise drawings, or prepare detail drawings. Draftsmen are essential to an engineering project whether it is a small manufactured device or a large superstructure.

14—5 TYPES OF DETAIL DRAWINGS

Some companies prepare working drawings with only one part to a sheet regardless of how small the part may be. This procedure makes it possible to assign various parts to the shop without using bulky drawings that contain more parts and information than some of the workmen may need. In addition, more copies may be needed of the drawings of some parts than of others, and it is more convenient to obtain the required numbers of copies if there is only one part per sheet.

An example of a drawing of only one part is given in Fig. 14—9. The drawing is given a number, LM361X, in the title block to identify it for filing purposes. A table is printed on the sheet to keep a record of the revisions that occur during the checking process.

The Yamaha 360 motorcycle shown in Fig. 14—10 represents the end product of an extensive design process. Each part is the result of experience, testing, and refining. Products of this type are constantly undergoing the process of improvement and evolution. Many of the parts of a motorcycle like this may be used on varying sizes of motorcycles; the only difference in these is their dimensions. When this is the case, *tabulated drawings* can be made, as shown in Fig. 14—11. The part is drawn and referenced with letters that correspond to a table of dimensions placed on the drawing. The sizes can be

Fig. 14–10 Many standard parts are used on a product such as this Yamaha 360 motorcycle. These parts may be detailed with the aid of a table of dimensions when the only variation in the parts is size. (Courtesy of Yamaha Incorporated.)

Fig. 14–12 An unfinished forging and the same part after machining. A drawing is needed to give the specifications of the forging and the details of the machining operations required to complete the part. (Courtesy of Lycoming Division of Avco.)

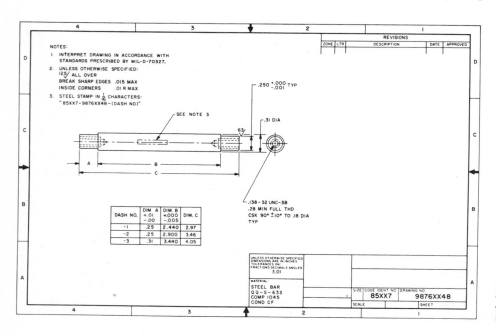

NOTES:
1. INTERPRET DRAWING IN ACCORDANCE WITH STANDARDS PRESCRIBED BY MIL-D-70327.
2. UNLESS OTHERWISE SPECIFIED:
   125/ ALL OVER
   BREAK SHARP EDGES .015 MAX
   INSIDE CORNERS .01 R MAX
3. STEEL STAMP IN 1/16 CHARACTERS:
   "85XX7-9876XX48-(DASH NO.)"

SEE NOTE 3

.250 +.000 -.001 TYP

.31 DIA

63/

A   B   C

.138-32 UNC-3B
.28 MIN FULL THD
CSK 90° ±10° TO .18 DIA
TYP

DASH NO.	DIM. A +.01 -.00	DIM. B +.000 -.005	DIM. C
-1	.25	2.440	2.97
-2	.25	2.900	3.46
-3	.31	3.440	4.05

UNLESS OTHERWISE SPECIFIED DIMENSIONS ARE IN INCHES
TOLERANCES ON:
FRACTIONS DECIMALS ANGLES
±.01

MATERIAL:
STEEL BAR
QQ-S-633
COMP 1045
COND CF

SIZE	CODE IDENT NO	DRAWING NO
85XX7		9876XX48

SCALE   SHEET

REVISIONS

ZONE	LTR	DESCRIPTION	DATE	APPROVED

Fig. 14–11 A tabulated drawing with a table of values for parts that vary in size. (Courtesy of the Department of Defense.)

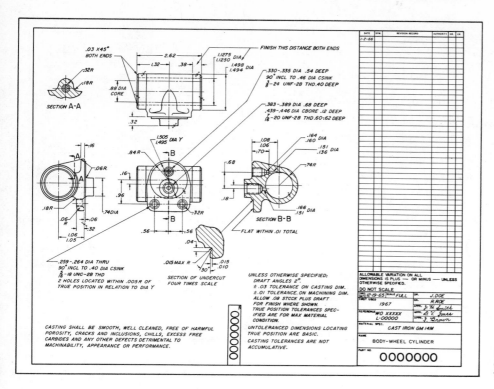

Fig. 14–13 A machining drawing of a body-wheel cylinder. (Courtesy of General Motors.)

selected from the table to correspond to the letters on the drawing. This procedure makes it possible for one drawing to serve several parts.

The two parts shown in Fig. 14–12 illustrate the difference between a forged part and a machined part. The unfinished forging at the top was produced by a die-casting process whereby a piece of material is formed in a mold by the application of force. The forged piece is then machined to its finished form as shown in the lower portion of the figure.

The drawings that give the dimensions and details for making the forging are called *forging drawings*. The drawing that specifies the machining operations is called a *machining drawing*. These drawings are often combined into one drawing, with the understanding that the forgings must be made with additional material in order to allow the removal of the excess by machining to meet the final specifications of the design.

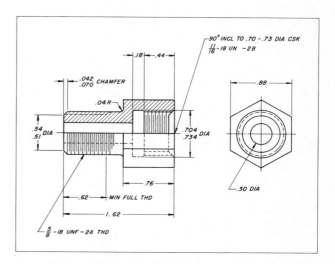

Fig. 14–14 A detail drawing that indicates machining specifications. (Courtesy of General Motors.)

14–5   **Types of detail drawings**

FLAT SIZES				ROLL SIZES				
SIZE DES LTR	X WIDTH	Y LENGTH	Z MARGIN	SIZE DES LTR	X WIDTH	Y MIN LENGTH	Y MAX LENGTH	Z MARGIN
A(HORIZ)	8.50	11	.25 & .38*	G	11	42	144	.38
A(VERT)	11	8.50	.25 & .38*	H	28	48	144	.50
B	11	17	.38	J	34	48	144	.50
C	17	22	.50	K	40	48	144	.50
D	22	34	.50					
E	34	44	.50					
F	28	40	.50					

*HORIZONTAL MARGINS .38-INCH; VERTICAL MARGIN .25-INCH

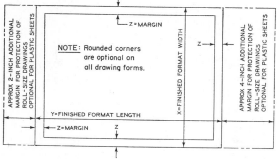

Fig. 14–15 Standard sizes of working drawings. (Courtesy of the Department of Defense.)

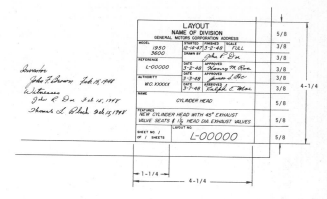

Fig. 14–16 A typical title block used on working drawings in industry. (Courtesy of General Motors.)

Fig. 14–17 A title strip and parts list satisfactory for most student assignments.

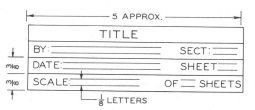

The machining drawing in Fig. 14–13 uses orthographic views and sections to describe the features of a body-wheel cylinder. Notes and finish marks are used with tolerance dimensions to give the final measurements of the part. The detail drawing in Fig. 14–14 gives the specifications for a threaded component. Thread notes and machining operations are noted. You should refer to Chapter 12 to review the methods of specifying threads.

14–6 LAYOUT OF A WORKING DRAWING

The standard sizes of working drawings are shown in Fig. 14–15. These sizes correspond to those discussed in Article 3–15. A diagram is shown here to indicate the layout of the sheet and the position of the borders for each size.

Most commercial drafting offices have title blocks and borders printed on the drawing sheets. This reduces the amount of valuable drafting time that has to be spent on this part of the drawing.

The title block can take many forms. All companies use title blocks and they usually contain the same information, but most are different in layout. A title block used by the General Motors Corporation is shown in Fig. 14–16. All title blocks include the name of the person making the drawing, the checker's name, the date, the name of the drawing, the scale, the sheet number, and the name of the company. Many companies give a layout number to each drawing sheet; this number may also be the number of the part drawn.

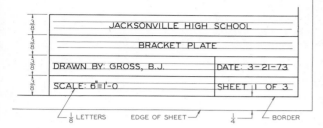

Fig. 14–18 A title block layout for class assignments.

Fig. 14–19 An engineering department is required to check working drawings before they are released for production. (Courtesy of The Austin Company.)

When a design that is presented on a working drawing is unique enough to be considered for a patent as a new invention, additional information should be given near the title block. The inventor should sign and date his work and have it witnessed by at least two people to establish ownership of the ideas (Fig. 14–16). Even though the idea must be patented in the name of the inventor, the rights to the design may by previous agreement be the property of the company for which he works.

Student drawings prepared as class assignments are usually more simple than those used by large industries. An example of a title block and a parts list is shown in Fig. 14–17. The title block should be placed against the border in the lower right corner of the drawing. The parts list should be above the title block and in contact with it.

An alternative title block that can be used for class assignments is shown in Fig. 14–18. The spacing between the lines should not be changed, but the width of the block can vary to provide adequate space for all titles and names. Each title block on a set of drawings should be the same size. Each sheet should also be the same size so that the set can be bound with staples and the pages will turn like those of a book for easy reference.

14–7 CHECKING A DRAWING

All drawings must be checked before they are released for production, since a slight mistake could prove very expensive when many parts are made. The people who check drawings have special qualifications that enable them to suggest revisions and modifications that will result in a better product at less cost (Fig. 14–19). The checker may be a chief draftsman who is experienced in this type of work, or the engineer or designer who originated the project. In larger companies the drawings are reviewed by the various shops involved to determine whether the most efficient methods of production are specified for each particular part.

The checker never checks an original drawing, but instead he checks a diazo print (a blue-line print). He marks the print with a colored pencil, making notes and corrections that he feels are desirable. The print is returned to the draftsman for revision of the original drawing and another print is made for approval.

In Fig. 14–20 a detail drawing of a special bushing is shown. In this drawing the various modifications made by checkers are labeled with letters which are circled and placed near the revisions. The changes are listed and dated in the revision record by the draftsman. Note that the change numbers are placed in a row along the lower border approximately below the revisions. This procedure serves as a check on the various revisions to prevent one from being overlooked.

Note that several draftsmen and checkers were involved in the approval and preparation of the drawing. Tolerances and general information are

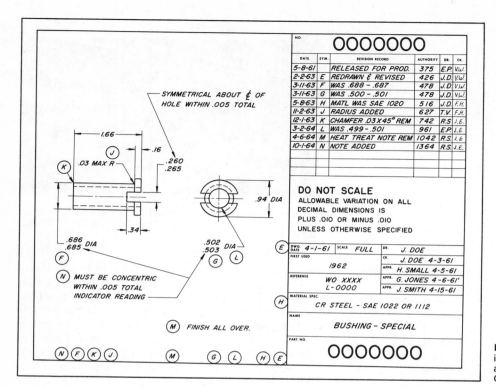

Fig. 14–20 A detail drawing showing various revisions that were made and listed in the table. (Courtesy of General Motors.)

printed in the title block to ensure uniformity in the production of similar parts.

The checker is responsible for the soundness of the design and its functional characteristics. He is also responsible for the completeness of the drawing, the quality of the drawing, its readability, lettering, drafting techniques, and clarity. A poorly drawn view must be redrawn to meet company requirements so that it will reproduce well and be clearly understood by those using it. Quality of lettering is very important. Since working drawings should not be scaled, the craftsmen in the shop must rely on lettered notes and dimensions for their information. The best method for the student to check his drawing is to make a scale drawing of the part from his working drawings when they are complete. It is often easier for someone to find another's mistakes than his own. It is good exercise to exchange drawings with a classmate and check each other's drawing.

14–8 DRAFTSMAN'S LOG

The draftsman will find that many changes and revisions must be made before a final drawing is approved. He should keep a record called a *log* to show all changes and modifications and decisions that were made during the project. Changes, dates, and the people involved should be recorded for reference as the project progresses and as a review of the finished project.

An example of a draftsman's log is shown in Fig. 14–21. The description of the project and its objectives are given first. Each change and the reason for it are tabulated under "Progress, Decisions and Authority." The people responsible for the changes are mentioned by name.

These notes serve to refresh the memory of anyone who wishes to review the project. Calculations are often made during the process of preparing a drawing. If they are lost or if they are poorly done, it

DRAFTSMAN'S DESIGN LOG

Sheet No. /
of / Sheet

Detailed Description: Layout and details of new transmission low speed gear and mainshaft combination. Low speed gear to have I.D. of splines accurately ground with respect to gear teeth, and mainshaft to have three ground lands for mounting low speed gear on these surfaces.

Job no. 9344-97
Job name Trans. Mainshaft First and Reverse Gear
Models 1950
Engineer Poe
Job started 3-25-48
Job finished 4-7-48
Layout numbers L-35042

Job Objective: To eliminate selective fit on mating parts.

References: L-33827

Progress, Decisions and Authority:
3-30-48 - Messrs. Roe and Poe decided to change from a 22 tooth basic spline with 3 unevenly spaced lands to both a 24 tooth basic spline with 6 evenly spaced lands and a 24 tooth basic spline with 8 evenly spaced lands.
Engineers also requested study of a longer hub for 1st reverse gear to reduce runout.
4-6-48 After preliminary investigation Messrs. Roe and Poe decided to cancel the 8 lands construction and the elongated hub.
4-7-48 Mr. Poe decided to have an additional layout made of a 22 tooth basic spline with alternating teeth and lands.

Calculations and sketches
to be dated and attached.

R. Doe
Signature

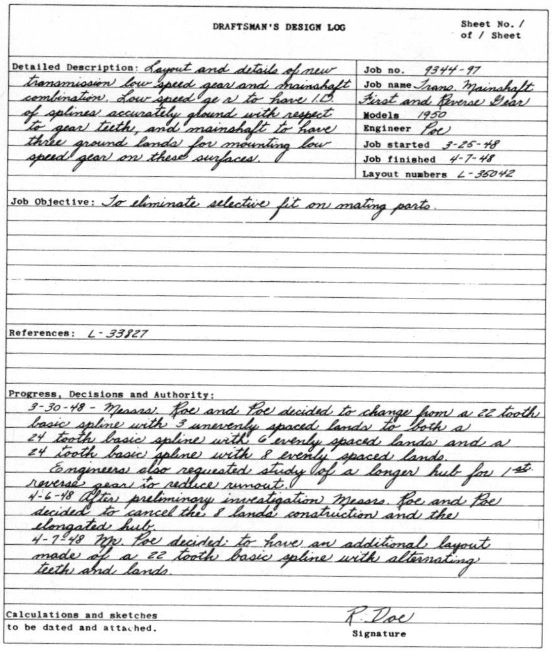

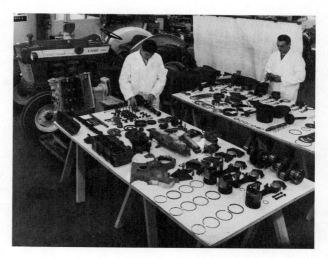

Fig. 14–21 A draftsman's log should be kept as a record of the project to explain the actions taken that might otherwise be forgotten. (Courtesy of General Motors.)

Fig. 14–22 An assembly drawing is used to explain how the parts of a product such as this Ford tractor are assembled. (Courtesy of Ford Motor Company.)

may be necessary to make them again. Consequently, they should be made a permanent part of the log and attached to the log. This will reduce lost time and repetition of effort. All notes should be complete enough to be understood by anyone who may read the log.

14–9 ASSEMBLY DRAWINGS

Most designs are composed of a number of parts that fit together in a particular manner to perform the desired function. Most parts are made independently and perhaps in separate geographical locations by different people. When the parts are completed and ready for assembly, a drawing is needed to explain how they should be put together. For example, the parts of the tractor engine and transmission shown in Fig. 14–22 fit together in the order specified by an assembly drawing.

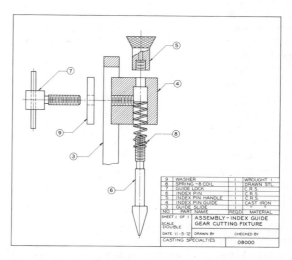

Fig. 14–23 A partially exploded orthographic assembly drawing of the index guide that was shown in the detail drawings in Figs. 14–6 and 14–7.

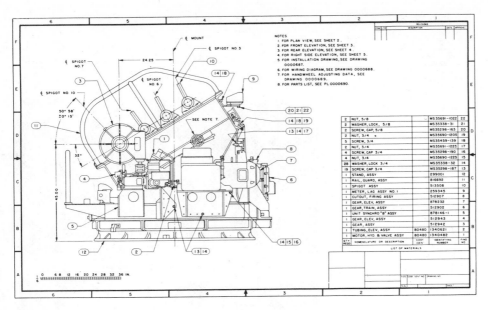

NOTES
1. FOR PLAN VIEW, SEE SHEET 2.
2. FOR FRONT ELEVATION, SEE SHEET 3.
3. FOR REAR ELEVATION, SEE SHEET 4.
4. FOR RIGHT SIDE ELEVATION, SEE SHEET 5.
5. FOR INSTALLATION DRAWING, SEE DRAWING 0000687.
6. FOR WIRING DIAGRAM, SEE DRAWING 0000688.
7. FOR HANDWHEEL ADJUSTING DATA, SEE DRAWING 0000689.
8. FOR PARTS LIST, SEE PL 0000690.

QTY REQD	NOMENCLATURE OR DESCRIPTION	CODE IDENT	IDENTIFYING NUMBER	FIND NO
2	NUT, 5/8		MS35691-1022	22
2	WASHER, LOCK, 5/8		MS35338-31	21
2	SCREW, CAP, 5/8		MS35298-163	20
2	NUT, 3/4		MS35690-1205	19
5	SCREW, 3/4		MS35459-139	18
2	NUT, 3/4		MS35691-1225	17
4	SCREW, CAP 3/4		MS35298-190	16
4	NUT, 3/4		MS35690-1225	15
28	WASHER, LOCK 3/4		MS35338-32	14
19	SCREW, CAP 3/4		MS35298-187	13
1	STAND, ASSY		299001	12
1	RAIL, GUARD, ASSY		816692	11
1	SPIGOT ASSY		513508	10
1	METER, LAG ASSY NO.1		259345	9
1	CUTOUT, FIRING ASSY		512907	8
1	GEAR, ELEV, ASSY		878232	7
1	GEAR, TRAIN, ASSY		512902	6
1	UNIT SYNCHRO "B" ASSY		878146-1	5
1	GEAR, ELEV, ASSY		512943	4
1	GEAR, ASSY		512942	3
1	TUBING, ELEV, ASSY	80480	1340621	2
1	MOTOR, HYD. & VALVE ASSY	80480	1340482	1

LIST OF MATERIALS

Fig. 14–24 An outline assembly drawing shows the general relationship of the parts of an assembly. (Courtesy of the Department of Defense.)

An assembly drawing can be either an orthographic or a pictorial drawing. In addition, it may show the parts actually assembled or it may show them in an exploded assembly, whichever gives the greater clarity.

A subassembly of the index guide of the gear cutting fixture shown in Figs. 14–6 and 14–7 is presented in Fig. 14–23. Several of the parts are exploded apart for clarity, and the index pin and spring are partially exploded. Only the part numbers are given to identify each of the parts, since they have been fully dimensioned and described in the working drawing. A parts list is provided as a cross reference for listing the parts of the assembly. Sections are used to clarify details of the assembly.

This drawing makes it possible for the shop to assemble the parts in the desired arrangement. Dimensions are unnecessary on an assembly drawing of this type.

An *outline assembly* is shown in Fig. 14–24. This represents the assembly of various components, several of which have their own assembly of parts. Only a few essential dimensions are given to locate important components in relation to others. Each component of the assembly is listed by number in the list of materials. The materials list also gives the identifying number of each part required to complete the assembly.

A more detailed assembly drawing is shown in Fig. 14–25. This drawing describes how a vertical instrument panel will be supported. In addition to showing the method of assembly, this drawing gives the complete dimensions of the support.

14–10 PICTORIAL ASSEMBLIES

The Evinrude Skeeter, a snowmobile (Fig. 14–26), is a product that has only recently come into existence. Consequently, its assembly requires more explanation than does that of older, more traditional vehicles. A technical illustrator has prepared a cutaway section (Fig. 14–27) to show the relationship of various interior components. This makes it easier for the nontechnical person to understand the design.

A more typical pictorial assembly is shown in Fig. 14–28. All of the parts of the lathe assembly are exploded apart in this pictorial. Each component is positioned so as to make it clear how the parts fit

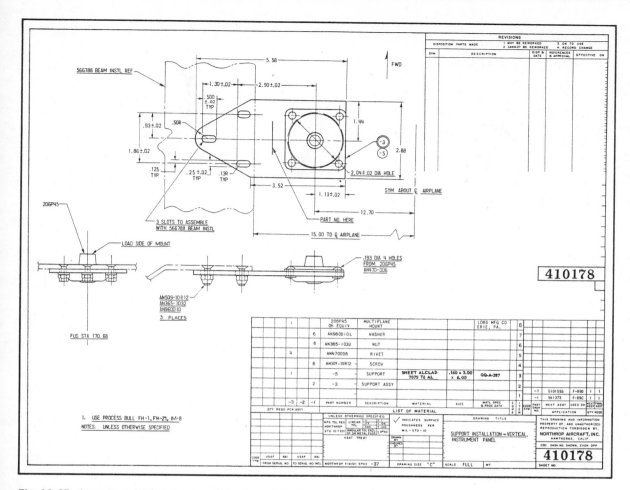

Fig. 14–25 An assembly-detail drawing. (Courtesy of Northrop Corporation.)

Fig. 14–26 This Evinrude Skeeter would be difficult to assemble without an assembly drawing. (Courtesy of Evinrude Corporation.)

Fig. 14–27 Details of assembly are more clearly shown pictorially in complicated products such as this snowmobile. (Courtesy of Evinrude Corporation.)

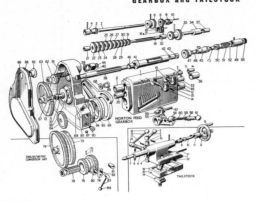

Fig. 14–28 A pictorial exploded assembly of the parts of the gear-box and tailstock of a lathe. (Courtesy of T. S. Harrison & Sons Limited.)

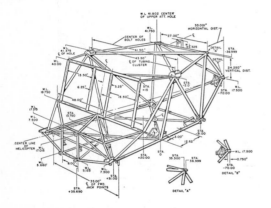

Fig. 14–29 A dimensioned pictorial assembly drawing of a helicopter frame. (Courtesy of Bell Helicopter Corporation.)

together. The parts are numbered to correspond to a parts list (not shown).

Since pictorials are more easily understood by the nontechnical person than are orthographic views, many drawings are dimensioned in their pictorial views for greater clarity. Such an example is the frame of a helicopter in Fig 14–29. This illustration shows the details and dimensions of the assembly more clearly than would any other type of drawing.

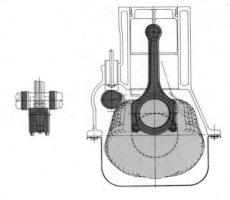

Fig. 14–30 A layout drawing is used to analyze the clearances between the connecting rod and crankcase walls. (Courtesy of General Motors.)

14–11 LAYOUT DRAWINGS

A *layout drawing* is a preliminary drawing which shows a part or several parts and their relationship to one another. A layout may be one of the first steps of developing a new design. It can be useful in determining how several parts should be assembled and what their clearances should be. It is also useful in the study of the geometric relationships between moving parts.

The layout drawing in Fig. 14–30 was used to analyze the clearance between the connecting rod path and the crankcase walls and the camshaft. The clearance between the connecting rod path and the crankcase walls must necessarily be greater, since the connecting rod forging and the rough crankcase walls are involved. Allowances must be given on both sides for the connecting rod as shown at the left.

14–12 PIPING LAYOUTS

A piping drawing gives the layout of a piping system, specifying the lengths of pipe and the standard components of the system. A piping layout may be represented in an orthographic drawing or in a pictorial. The example in Fig. 14–31 is a *single-line* isometric drawing. Single lines and symbols are used to represent the pipe. These symbols are explained in Appendix 3 both as single-line and double-line symbols.

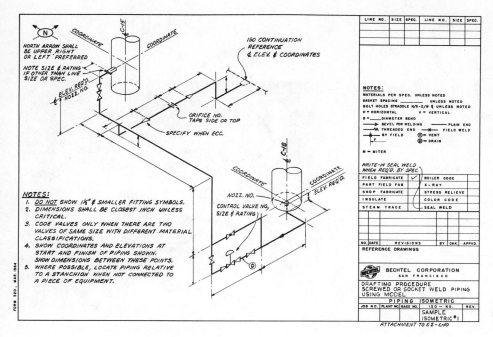

Fig. 14–31 A piping layout using single-line symbols. (Courtesy of the Bechtel Corporation.)

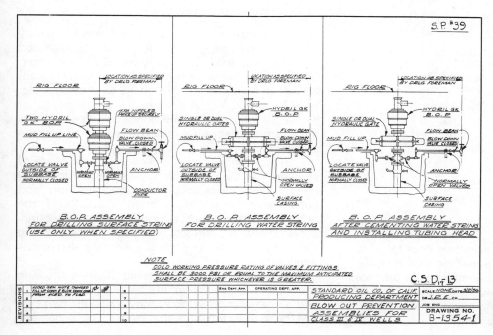

Fig. 14–32 A double-line piping drawing. (Courtesy of Standard Oil Corporation of California.)

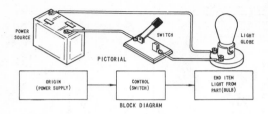

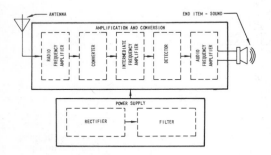

Fig. 14–33 A comparison of a block diagram of an electrical circuit with a pictorial drawing of the circuit. (Courtesy of the Boeing Company.)

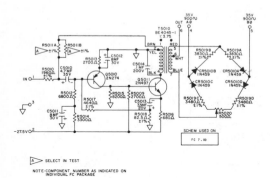

Fig. 14–34 A block diagram combines parts of an electronic system into functional blocks. (Courtesy of the Boeing Company.)

Fig. 14–36 An electronic schematic drawing is necessary to check out a faulty circuit. (Courtesy of the U.S. Air Force.)

Fig. 14–35 A schematic diagram of an electronic circuit. (Courtesy of the Boeing Company.)

A *double-line* drawing uses two lines to represent the pipe; it is thus more realistic than a single-line drawing. Both are equally effective in practice; however, the single-line drawing has the advantage of being easier to prepare. An example of a double-line drawing is shown in Fig. 14–32.

14–13 ELECTRONIC DRAWINGS

Electrical and electronic drawings are more closely related to schematics than to actual dimensioned working drawings as discussed in this chapter. Components can be represented in a block diagram instead of being drawn pictorially, as shown in Fig. 14–33. A simple block diagram is composed of blocks that are labeled and connected in sequence; the end block represents the desired function of the system.

Block diagrams can be used to combine parts of an electrical or electronic system into functional units beginning with the power supply, the input, and ending with the output function (Fig. 14–34); the output of a radio, for example, would be sound. Block diagrams cannot be used for assembling electronic circuits. For this a *schematic drawing* is required.

Figure 14–35 is a schematic diagram showing the various parts of a circuit. Each symbol is drawn and a note is supplied to specify a specific part that will be connected into the circuit. A schematic

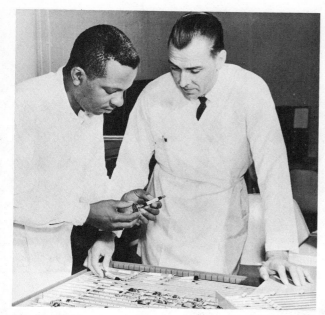

Fig. 14–37 The external threads of a part are being checked with a ring gauge to ensure that the part conforms to the specifications of the drawing. (Courtesy of the DoAll Corporation.)

The next few articles discuss the more general processes and machines used in the metal shop. This complex topic will be touched on only briefly.

14–15 CASTINGS

A *casting* is a part that is formed by pouring molten metal into a mold to produce the desired shape. When the metal has set, the part is removed and is then machined to bring it to the required dimensions. Since material must be removed in the machining process, a casting is designed to be slightly oversize to allow for this removal.

The common types of castings are (1) sand mold castings, (2) plaster mold castings, (3) permanent mold castings, (4) centrifugal castings, and (5) die castings.

Sand castings are castings in which the molten metal is poured into a mold formed of a special sand that holds the proper cavity while the molten metal is being poured into it. The cavity is formed by ramming the sand around a *pattern* made of wood. The pattern is gently removed prior to pouring. This is the oldest and most often used method of casting for general purposes. The sand is broken loose when the metal has set to leave the finished casting. The pattern can be used with fresh sand to form another mold.

Plaster mold castings work on the same principle as sand mold castings except that a plaster mold is used to give a smoother finish and finer detail to the casting. A new mold is required after each casting, since the mold is damaged in the casting process.

Permanent mold castings employ a metal mold that can be used again and again. The life of a metal mold is longer if nonferrous alloys (those with little or no iron) are used in the castings. Nonferrous alloys have relatively low melting temperatures; consequently, they do not damage the metal mold by subjecting it to high temperatures. The molds are usually made of cast iron and result in a highly accurate and smooth casting.

Centrifugal castings are used for cylindrical parts. The molten metal is poured into a rapidly rotating

drawing is also used to check out an electronic system when there is a malfunction (Fig. 14–36). There is no relationship between the sizes of the symbols or the lengths of the lines and actual physical dimensions. The schematic drawing simply specifies the sequence in which the parts are connected to complete the circuit.

Templates and guides are available to assist the draftsman in preparing schematic drawings. The table in Appendix 2 gives the relative sizes of the symbols used in schematic drawings.

14–14 SHOP PROCESSES

Parts made of metal often have to be made to very accurate dimensions so that they will function properly. All measurements of the finished parts are checked to ensure that they meet the specifications (Fig. 14–37). It is possible to obtain a finished part whose measurements are accurate within a thousandth of an inch only with the help of skilled craftsmen and advanced equipment.

Fig. 14–38 A partially formed part in a forging die. (Courtesy of the Drop Forging Association.)

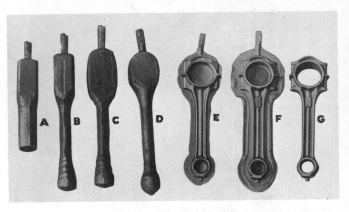

Fig. 14–39 The successive steps of forging a billet into the finished connecting rod. (Courtesy of the Drop Forging Association.)

Fig. 14–40 A partially machined forging for a landing gear (weight 12,366 lb). (Courtesy of Cameron Iron Works.)

mold where the metal is forced to the outside by centrifugal action. Since the molten metal is forced away from the center, these molds usually have hollow centers.

Die casting is the process of forming parts by forcing molten metal into metal molds called *dies*. Die castings are very accurate in size and shape. Very thin sections are possible by this method when other casting processes fail. The most common materials used in die casting are zinc, aluminum, magnesium, and copper.

14–16 FORGINGS

Forging is the process of forming a part by hammering or forcing heated metal (not molten) into a die (Fig. 14–38). The raw metal that is placed in the die is called a *billet*.

The various steps in the process of forging a connecting rod can be seen in Fig. 14–39. The billet is hammered into a series of dies, each a little different, until the final shape is attained (A through F). The forging must be trimmed to remove the excess metal called *flashing* around the edges (G). The forging is now ready for the final machining.

The installed connecting rod can be seen in the layout drawing in Fig. 14–30. It connects the crankshaft with the piston in an automobile engine. A partially machined forging of the main landing gear of an aircraft is shown in Fig. 14–40; this forging weighs 12,366 lb.

14–17 STAMPINGS

Stampings are parts that are formed by pressing sheet metal into the desired shape while the metal is unheated. This technique is widely used for making parts in the automobile industry.

The stamping process can also be used to cut a piece of metal to shape or to punch a hole in a sheet of metal. The majority of stampings are made from flat steel; this material gives strength and is at the same time economical.

14–18 MACHINING EQUIPMENT

Much of the draftsman's work is concerned with the drawing and representation of parts that must be made of metal and will be processed through the machine shop. Consequently, the draftsman should have a general understanding of the shop processes and machining operations that are available to him. The shop personnel can assist the draftsman and the designer by suggesting economical and efficient methods of construction that are well adapted to the available machining processes.

Fig. 14–41 A 17″ geared head lathe for production work. (Courtesy of Clausing Corporation.)

The machine shop finishes a rough casting or forging. All machine shop processes involve the removal of metal from a part in the process of finishing a surface, drilling a hole, or similar operations. Consequently, most parts are made oversize to allow for this removal of a portion of the surface.

The basic machines will be discussed briefly in the following articles. The operation of these machines requires a skilled craftsman with many years of experience, or else a completely automated machining system that is operated by a computer.

The machines discussed here are (1) the lathe, (2) the shaper, (3) the drill press, and (4) the milling machine.

14–19 THE LATHE

The lathe is a machine that is used to remove material from a part being revolved about its axis. This process of removing material from the outside of a piece is called *turning*. A production lathe is shown in Fig. 14–41. The major application of the lathe is the making of cylindrical and conical parts.

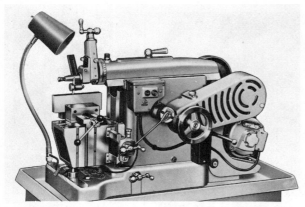

Fig. 14–42 A shaper is used to finish a piece of stock held in a vise. (Courtesy of Southbend Lathe Company.)

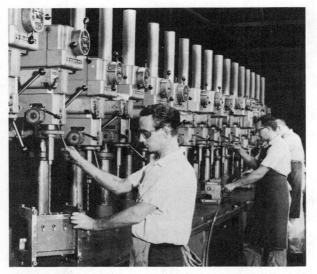

Fig. 14–43 A production shop where a series of drill presses are used for the various operations of machining a part. (Courtesy of Clausing Corporation.)

The lathe has many uses. It is used for boring, drilling, and reaming holes. Threads can be formed by a lathe as described in Chapter 12. Attachments and adjustments are available to permit highly accurate cuts and measurements. For example, threads are formed by feeding the cutting tool parallel to the axis of the cylinder; this ensures that

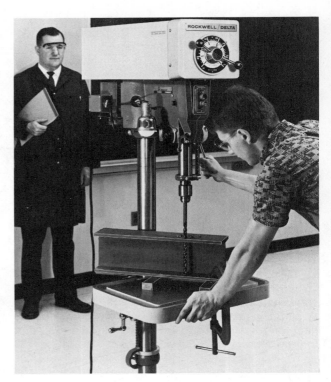

Fig. 14–44 A drill press being used by a student. (Courtesy of Rockwell Manufacturing Company.)

the part is threaded at a constant rate and that a perfect helix is formed.

The ends of cylinders can be finished while held in a lathe; this process is called *facing*. *Knurling* is another operation that is performed on this machine; knurling was described in Chapter 12. The lathe is probably the most essential machine in the machine shop.

14–20 THE SHAPER

The shaper is used to cut slots in a piece or to finish a flat surface by removing small cuts of material with a large number of strokes. A shaper is shown in Fig. 14–42; here the cutting tool is finishing a surface on a block that is held stationary in a vise. After each stroke the block is moved slightly in preparation for the next stroke of the shaper's

Fig. 14–45 The center of a hole is being located within a ten-thousandth of an inch for drilling on this large drill press. (Courtesy of the Department of the Interior.)

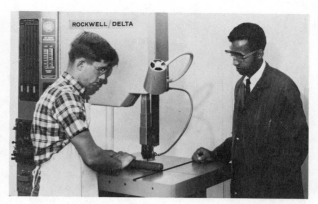

Fig. 14–47 A 20″ two-speed band saw being used to cut a cylindrical bar. (Courtesy of Rockwell Manufacturing Company.)

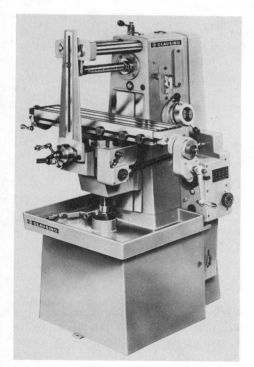

Fig. 14–46 A horizontal-spindle milling machine. (Courtesy of Clausing Corporation.)

cutting tool. Finally, the whole surface is finished to the desired measurements.

The cutting tool can be turned at various angles to cut slots with beveled sides or to finished inclined surfaces. Slots for keyways are cut by this machine.

14–21 THE DRILL PRESS

The drill press is used to drill or to bore holes in a part. Other operations such as reaming, spotfacing, countersinking, and counterboring are also performed on a drill press. In the production shop shown in Fig. 14–43 a series of drill presses is available to perform a number of different operations. A drill press that is used for student applications is shown in Fig. 14–44.

The drill press is designed with a vertical drill chuck in which can be held a variety of tools for different operations. A view of a chuck is shown in Fig. 14–45. Here the center of a hole is being located by a machinist. The work, the part being drilled, is held firmly in position during drilling by a fixture, a vise or a clamp. This is necessary for accuracy and to prevent the work from turning with the drill.

14–22 THE MILLING MACHINE

The milling machine is a machine with a horizontal or a vertical spindle to which are attached cylindrical

Fig. 14–48 Using a light pen, a sensitized cathode-ray tube (CRT), and the full power of a large-scale computer, a designer can draw a design in seconds. (Courtesy of IBM.)

Fig. 14–49 Computers can be programmed to analyze human factors in various positions of the body. (Courtesy of the Boeing Company.)

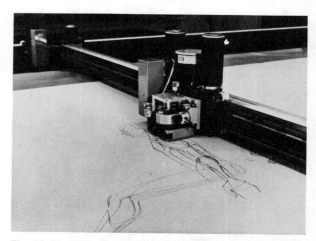

Fig. 14–50 With the aid of a computer, an automatic drafting machine draws the human figure in a given position. (Courtesy of the Boeing Company.)

cutters with many teeth. A milling machine with a horizontal spindle but with no cutters attached is shown in Fig. 14–46. The horizontal surface under the spindle is the table on which the work is clamped prior to milling.

The table passes back and forth under the revolving cutters to finish the surface of a plane, cut a slot or gear teeth, or other similar operations. The cutters come in various shapes and sizes to give a wide variety of operations and applications.

Milling machines also perform operations such as cutting dovetail slots, T-slots, and corner rounds. They can be used to finish flat surfaces in much the same manner as the shaper. However, in the case of the milling machine the work moves under the cutter, whereas in the shaper the cutter moves across the work.

Other machines are used in the machine shop for miscellaneous operations. An example is the metal-cutting band saw shown in Fig. 14–47.

14–23 COMPUTER GRAPHICS

The computer is being used to solve more and more of the engineer's problems, leaving him more time for creative work that requires imagination. At first, computers were used only to solve numerical problems, but now many graphical applications have been developed.

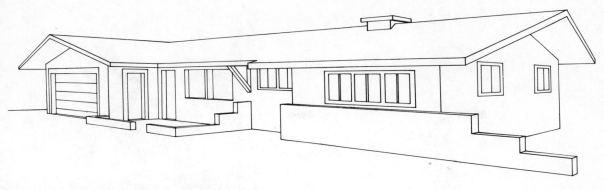

Fig. 14–51 A perspective drawn by a computer. (Courtesy of Electronic Associates, Inc.)

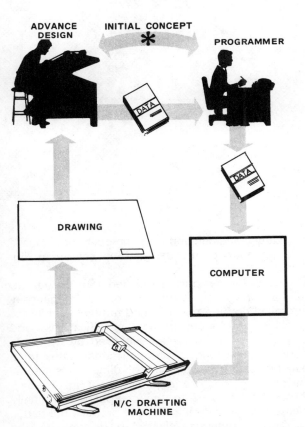

ADVANCE DESIGN

INITIAL CONCEPT

PROGRAMMER

DRAWING

COMPUTER

N/C DRAFTING MACHINE

Fig. 14–52 A schematic showing the relation between the computer and the designer working in conjunction with a numerical control system. (Courtesy of General Dynamics Corporation.)

Some advanced computer graphical systems allow the designer to draw a pictorial of his design and even revolve it for various views of the object (Fig. 14–48). By using a light pen and a cathode-ray tube (CRT), he can modify the shape and form of his design.

A unique application of computer graphics is the study of the body movements of a pilot operating an aircraft (Fig. 14–49). This method of analysis is used by the Boeing Company. Commands given to the computer result in a graphical plot of the man in any desired position (Fig. 14–50). A number of positions can be photographed in sequence on movie film to give an animated film. When this film is projected, the result is a motion picture that shows the man walking, sitting, and making typical movements.

Another example of computer graphics is the construction of perspectives and pictorials. The perspective shown in Fig. 14–51 was plotted from data fed to the computer in the form of numbers.

The relation between the computer and the designer can be seen in the schematic in Fig. 14–52. In developing a new idea, the designer works in conjunction with a programmer who provides him with computer techniques to assist with the formulation of the design. The designer furnishes the data and specifications to the programmer, who in turn supplies the data in computer language to the computer. The data are processed and fed to an automatic drafting machine that plots the drawing.

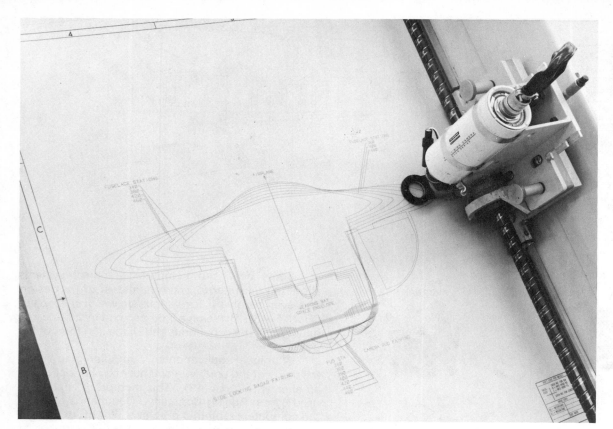

Fig. 14–53 A series of sections through the fuselage of an aircraft drawn by a computer with an automated drafting machine. (Courtesy of General Dynamics Corporation.)

The designer checks this drawing for correctness and then analyzes the initial design and modifies it if necessary.

An example of a series of sections through the fuselage of an aircraft is shown in Fig. 14–53. It is faster to prepare a drawing by hand than by computer if only a few drawings are needed. The advantage of a computer is its ability to modify or change a drawing when slight variations are required. Repetitive drawings, each slightly different, can be produced effectively and rapidly by computer graphics.

14–24 NUMERICALLY CONTROLLED MACHINING

Many manufacturing operations are equipped with machines that are run by a computer rather than by individual craftsmen and machine operators. This is a continuation of the design loop shown in Fig. 14–52.

When the designer is satisfied with his design, he has drawings produced on a numerically controlled drafting machine and returned to him for checking and adding notes, specifications, and dimensions. The drawings are used by the tool-programming group to program cutter paths for a machine part in terms of tool dimensions, feeds, speeds, and machine requirements (Fig. 14–54). These data are fed to the computer and finally released to the machine that will produce the part.

The computer has released the designer and the engineer from many repetitive chores which in the past reduced their creative productivity. They can now function much more effectively, since they can

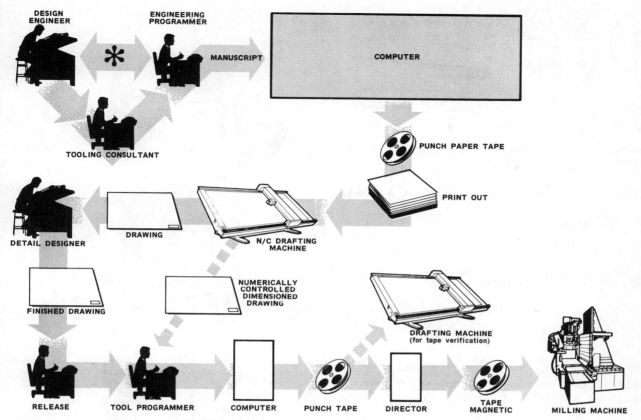

Fig. 14–54 The total system of a numerically controlled machining operation, from the designer to the milling machine. (Courtesy of General Dynamics Corporation.)

use the computer as an aid for the recall of stored knowledge and drawings, for solving problems, and for performing logic operations. However, the output of data and graphical information from the computer will be only as accurate as the data fed into it; consequently, the user must evaluate this output for its correctness. Although the computer has many valuable applications, it cannot think. Therefore, the engineer or designer must use his own reasoning ability to review computer output, since he will be responsible for its correctness.

14–25 SHORTCUTS FOR WORKING DRAWINGS

Modern methods of reproduction and new products have reduced the time required to prepare a finished working drawing. For example, many standard details can be cut out from existing drawings and pasted into position for reproduction. This procedure eliminates the need for repetitive drafting work.

Manufacturers of transparent overlay film have assisted the draftsman in improving his working drawings and illustrations, and also in saving him time. The use of symbols printed on transparent film has become widespread in the preparation of electronic circuit drawings. Some of the typical electronic symbols that are available are shown in Fig. 14–55. These are printed on thin acetate sheets with adhesive surfaces that adhere to the drawing surface when burnished down. The acetate sheet can be cut with a sharp blade to leave the symbol intact. This process is illustrated in Fig. 14–56.

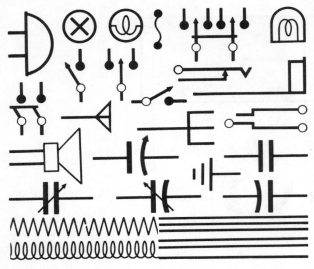

Fig. 14–55 Samples of electronic symbols that are available on overlay film. (Courtesy of Artype® Incorporated.)

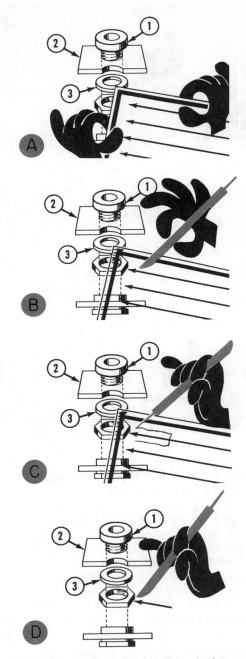

Fig. 14–56 The steps of applying leaders and numbers to an assembly drawing. (Courtesy of Artype® Incorporated.)

The application of press-on symbols to a circuit diagram is shown in the photographs of Fig. 14–57. The layout of the circuit is drawn on a grid, then overlaid with plastic drafting film. The printed symbols are applied to the sheet of plastic film. The completed circuit can be reduced photographically from the drawing and etched in copper on a plastic board (Fig. 14–58). Various electrical components are connected to this circuit so that it will function in the same way as a wired circuit.

Frequently used symbols, trademarks, and title blocks can be prepared on transfer film to the specifications of the drafting office. An example of such a symbol is the NASA emblem shown in Fig. 14–59. Some types of overlay symbols separate from the transparent backing film when burnished to the drawing surface. These symbols give the appearance of being printed directly on the surface.

A wide variety of patterns and symbols are available that can be applied to a drawing in much less time than it would take the draftsman or illustrator to draw them. Shortcuts should be used wherever possible to save valuable drafting time.

FIGURE 14–57. APPLYING PRESS-ON SYMBOLS TO A CIRCUIT DIAGRAM

Step 1. Determine the configuration of components and engineering requirements.

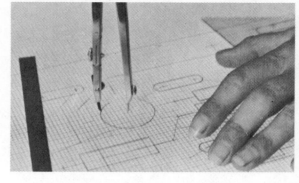

Step 2. Draw a scale layout of the circuit.

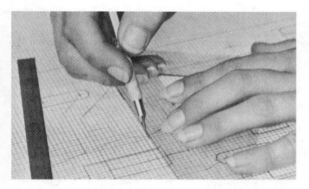

Step 3. Complete the drawing and overlay it with a sheet of drafting film.

Step 4. Transfer the electronic symbols to the master drawing to complete the circuit. (Photos courtesy of Bishop Graphics, Incorporated.)

14–26 MODELS

Some engineering designs are so complex that it is difficult to interpret the drawings. In these cases, models may be built to supplement the drawings and, in some cases, to provide the specifications for the completed project (Fig. 14–60).

Contours that show the variations in the surface of the ground are easily understood when presented in the form of a model (Fig. 14–61). Pictorial drawings can also give an impression of how a finished project will appear (Fig. 14–62), but there is no substitute for a three-dimensional model for a complete understanding of a design.

Models are valuable in analyzing the operational effectiveness of a design. The model of the Grand Coulee Dam in Fig. 14–63 can be used to evaluate the design when water is applied to it to simulate the completed dam.

Student models (Fig. 14–64) can be used to present the result of a design project. Models can be made of inexpensive materials to show an idea that would be hard to communicate by other methods.

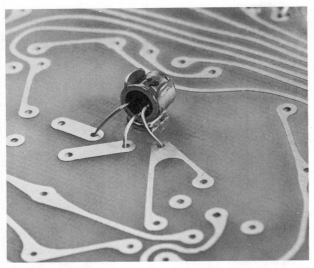

Fig. 14–58 The completed circuit is shown etched in copper on a plastic board. (Courtesy of Bishop Graphics, Incorporated.)

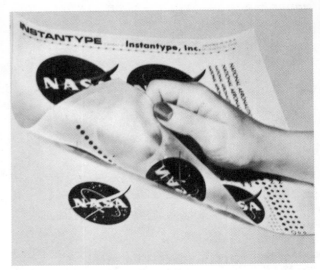

Fig. 14–59 Frequently used symbols can be specially made for drafting room applications. (Courtesy of Instantype® Incorporated.)

Fig. 14–60 Models are used to supplement working drawings of complex projects. (Courtesy of E. I. du Pont de Nemours & Co., Inc.)

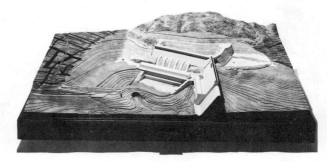

Fig. 14–61 A model of the Grand Coulee power plant showing the contours of the ground. (Courtesy of U.S. Department of the Interior.)

14–27 REPRODUCTION OF WORKING DRAWINGS

A drawing made by a draftsman is of little use in its original form. It would be impractical for the original to be handled by checkers and, even more so, by workmen in the field or in the shop. The drawing would quickly be damaged or soiled and no copy

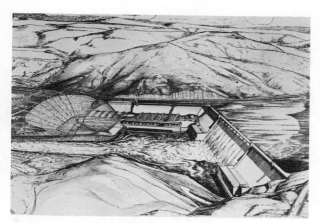

Fig. 14–62 A pictorial illustration of the Grand Coulee power plant. (Courtesy of U.S. Department of the Interior.)

Fig. 14–64 A student model of a design project can be constructed of inexpensive materials.

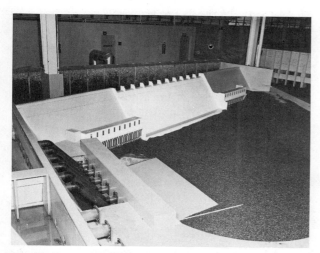

Fig. 14–63 A scale model of the Grand Coulee power plant that can be tested using real water. (Courtesy of U.S. Department of the Interior.)

would be available as a permanent record of the job. Consequently, reproduction of drawings is necessary so that copies can be available for use by the various people concerned. A checker can mark corrections on a work copy without damaging the original drawing. The draftsman in turn can make the corrections on the original from the work copy.

Copies of the original drawing must be made for the people who will bid on a job or for the workman who will build according to the specifications of the drawing. Several methods of reproduction are used for making the copies that have traditionally been called "blueprints." This term comes from the original reproduction process which gives a blue background with white lines. The term blueprint is still used, although incorrectly, to describe almost all reproduced working drawings regardless of the process. However, you should become familiar with the various processes so that you can refer to them properly.

The processes discussed here are (1) diazo printing, (2) blueprinting, (3) microfilming, and (4) xerography. These are the most often used processes of reproducing engineering drawings.

14–28 DIAZO PRINTING

The diazo print is more correctly called a "white-print" or a "blue-line print" than a blueprint since it has a white background and blue lines. Other colors of lines are available depending on the type of paper used. The white background makes notes and corrections drawn on the drawing more clearly visible than does the blue background of the blueprint.

Both blueprinting and diazo printing require that the original drawing be made on semitransparent tracing paper, cloth, or film that will allow light to pass through the drawing. The paper on which the copy is made, the diazo paper, is chemically treated so that it has a yellow tint on one side. This paper must be stored away from heat and light to prevent spoilage.

The tracing-paper drawing is placed face up on the yellow side of the diazo paper and is run through the diazo-process machine, which exposes the drawing to a built-in light. The light passes through the tracing paper and burns out the yellow chemical on the paper except where the drawing lines have shielded the paper from the light. After exposure to light, the diazo paper is a duplicate of the original drawing except that the lines are light yellow and are not permanent. The diazo paper is then passed through the developing unit of the diazo machine where the yellow lines are developed into permanent blue lines by exposure to ammonia fumes. Diazo printing is a completely dry process.

A typical diazo printer-developer, sometimes called a whiteprinter, is shown in Fig. 14–65. This machine will take sheets up to 42" wide.

The speed at which the drawing passes under the light determines the darkness of the copy. A slow speed burns out more of the yellow and produces a clear white background; however, some of the lighter lines of the drawing may be lost. Most diazo copies are made at a somewhat slower speed to give a light tint of blue in the background and stronger lines in the copy. Ink drawings give the best reproductions since the lines are uniform in quality.

It is important to remember that the quality of the diazo print is determined by the quality of the original drawing. A print will not be clear and readable unless the lines of the drawing are dark and dense. Light will pass through gray lines and the result will be a fuzzy print that will not be satisfactory.

14–29 BLUEPRINTING

Blueprints are made with paper that is chemically treated on one side. As in the diazo process, the tracing-paper drawing is placed in contact with the chemically treated side of the paper and exposed to

Fig. 14–65 The Bruning 450 whiteprinter for making diazo prints of drawings up to 42" wide. (Courtesy of the Bruning Company.)

light. The exposed blueprint paper is washed in clear water for a few seconds and is coated with a solution of potassium dichromate. The print is washed again and dried. The wet sheets can be hung on a line to dry or dried by special equipment made for this purpose.

This process is still used but to a lesser degree than in the past. Being a wet process, more time is required for it than for the diazo process.

14–30 MICROFILMING

Microfilming is a photographic process that converts large drawings into film copies—either aperture cards or roll film. Drawings must be photographed on either 16 mm or 35 mm film. A camera and copy table are shown in Fig. 14–66.

The roll film or aperture cards can be placed in a microfilm enlarger-printer (Fig. 14–67) where the individual drawings can be viewed on a built-in screen. The selected drawings can then be printed from the film to give standard size drawings. The range of enlargement varies with the equipment used.

Fig. 14–66 The Micro-Master® 35 mm camera and copy table for microfilming engineering drawings. (Courtesy of Keuffel & Esser Company.)

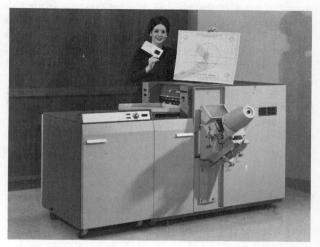

Fig. 14–67 The Bruning 1200 microfilm enlarger-printer that makes drawings up to 18″ × 24″ from aperture cards and roll film. (Courtesy of the Bruning Company.)

Microfilm copies are usually smaller than the original drawings; this saves paper and makes the drawings more manageable and easier to use.

Microfilming makes it possible to eliminate large, bulky files of drawings, since hundreds of drawings can be stored in miniature size on a small amount of film. The aperture cards shown in Fig. 14–67 are data processing cards that can be catalogued and recalled by a computer to make them accessible with a minimum of effort. The main advantage of microfilming is the saving in time and space.

14–31 XEROGRAPHIC REPRODUCTION

Xerography is an electrostatic process of duplicating drawings on ordinary, unsensitized paper. This process was developed originally for office duplication uses, but has recently been used for the reproduction of engineering drawings.

An advantage of the xerographic process is the possibility of making copies of drawings at a reduced size (Fig. 14–68). The new Xerox 840 reduces

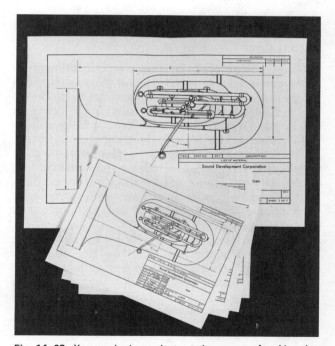

Fig. 14–68 Xerography is an electrostatic process of making dry copies on ordinary, unsensitized paper. Copies can be reduced to more convenient sizes. (Courtesy of Xerox Corporation.)

drawings as large as 24″ × 36″ directly from the original to paper sizes ranging from 8″ × 10″ to 14″ × 18″ (Fig. 14–69). This machine can make 40 copies per minute.

A sorter and folder can handle up to 50 sets of drawings and specifications automatically. Thirty sets of 15 drawings each (450 documents in all) can be reproduced, folded, and sorted in less than 30 minutes' Other processes of this type will be developed in the future to save time and effort.

Fig. 14–69 The Xerox 840 reduces drawings as large as 24″ × 36″ to sizes as small as 8″ × 10″. Forty prints per minute can be made by this machine, which uses the xerographic reproduction process. (Courtesy of Xerox Corporation.)

PROBLEMS

These problems are to be solved with instruments in accordance with Article 3–15 and the specifications of your instructor. Some problems are to be drawn on Size A sheets (8½″ × 11″) using ink or pencil as assigned. Other problems will need to be drawn on larger sheets, Size B or C, depending on the scale.

Each problem is to be a complete, detailed working drawing that includes all dimensions and notes necessary to release the drawings for production. The drawings are to be drawn with instruments, and should display the best line technique and lettering possible.

Each drawing sheet should be laid out with a title strip and border (see Figs. 14–15 through 14–18). A parts list is required where more than one part is involved. Tracing paper or film is suggested as the drawing surface so that diazo prints can be made from the finished drawings.

General Problems

These problems have only one solution since all dimensions are given; however, there are a number of ways of laying out and dimensioning any problem. You must use all the principles discussed previously in preparing these working drawings. Refer to previous chapters where necessary to refresh your understanding of these principles.

1 Refer to Fig. 14–70. Make a detail drawing of the brace on a Size A sheet. Show all notes and dimensions necessary to describe the part.

2 Refer to Fig. 14–71. Make a detail drawing of the part on a Size A sheet. Show all notes and dimensions necessary to describe the part.

3 Refer to Fig. 14–72. Make a detail drawing of the locking plate on a Size A sheet.

4 Refer to Fig. 14–73. Make a detail drawing of the air compressor base on a Size A sheet.

5 Refer to Fig. 14–74. Make a detail drawing of the support on a Size A sheet.

6 Refer to Fig. 14–75. Make a detail drawing of the clevis on a Size B sheet.

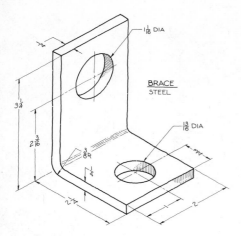

Fig. 14–70 Problem 1.

BRACE
STEEL

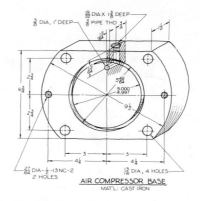

Fig. 14–73 Problem 4.

AIR COMPRESSOR BASE
MAT'L: CAST IRON

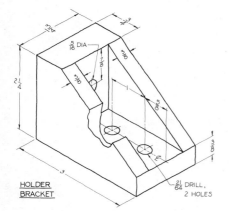

HOLDER
BRACKET

Fig. 14–71 Problem 2.

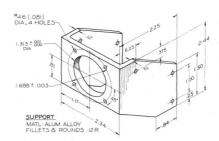

SUPPORT
MATL: ALUM ALLOY
FILLETS & ROUNDS .12 R

Fig. 14–74 Problem 5.

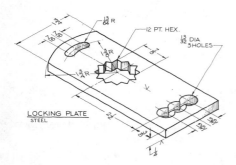

LOCKING PLATE
STEEL

Fig. 14–72 Problem 3.

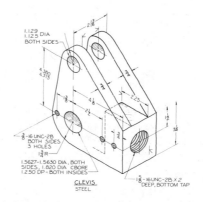

CLEVIS
STEEL

Fig. 14–75 Problem 6.

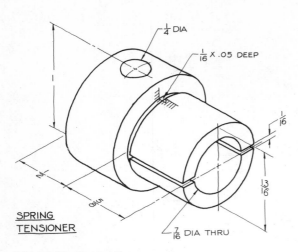

SPRING
TENSIONER

Fig. 14–76 Problem 7.

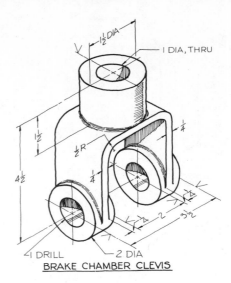

BRAKE CHAMBER CLEVIS

Fig. 14–78 Problem 9.

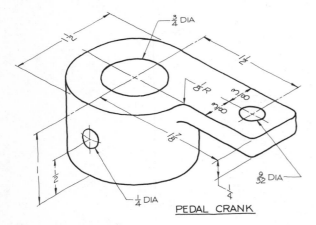

PEDAL CRANK

Fig. 14–77 Problem 8.

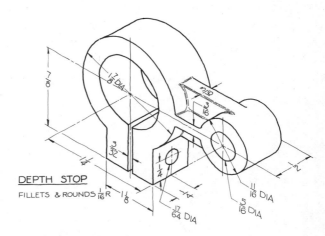

DEPTH STOP

FILLETS & ROUNDS $\frac{1}{16}$R

Fig. 14–79 Problem 10.

7   Refer to Fig. 14–76.   Make a detail drawing of the spring tensioner on a Size B sheet.

8   Refer to Fig. 14–77.   Make a detail drawing of the pedal crank on a Size B sheet.

9   Refer to Fig. 14–78.   Make a detail drawing of the brake chamber clevis on a Size B sheet.

10   Refer to Fig. 14–79.   Make a detail drawing of the depth stop on a Size B sheet.

11   Refer to Fig. 14–80.   Make a detail drawing of the saw-horse on a Size B sheet.

12   Refer to Fig. 14–81.   Make a detail drawing of the slider on a Size B sheet.

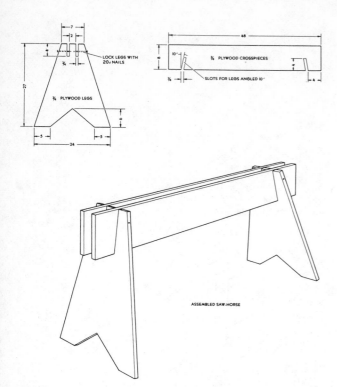

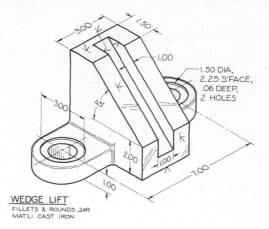

WEDGE LIFT
FILLETS & ROUNDS .24R
MAT'L: CAST IRON

Fig. 14–82 Problem 13.

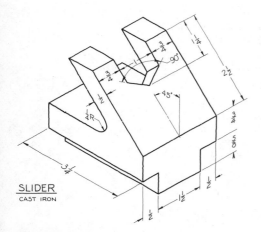

ASSEMBLED SAW-HORSE

Fig. 14–80 Problem 11.

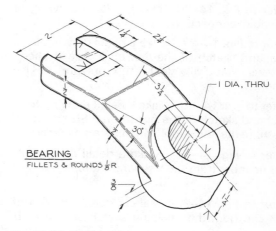

BEARING
FILLETS & ROUNDS $\frac{1}{8}$R

Fig. 14–83 Problem 14.

SLIDER
CAST IRON

Fig. 14–81 Problem 12.

13 Refer to Fig. 14–82. Make a detail drawing of the wedge lift on a Size B sheet.

14 Refer to Fig. 14–83. Make a detail drawing of the bearing on a Size B sheet.

15 Refer to Fig. 14–84. Make a detail drawing of the column base on a Size B sheet.

16 Refer to Fig. 14–85. Make a detail drawing of the support arm on a Size A sheet.

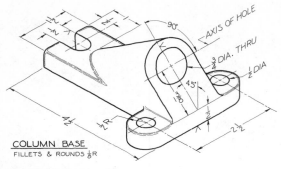

COLUMN BASE
FILLETS & ROUNDS ⅛R

Fig. 14–84 Problem 15.

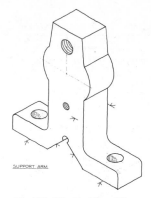

SUPPORT ARM

Fig. 14–85 Problem 16.

17 Refer to Fig. 14–86. Make a detail drawing of the solenoid connection on a Size A sheet.

18 Refer to Fig. 14–87. Make a detail drawing from the freehand sketch of the link on a Size B sheet. Add views that will clarify the drawing. Use instruments.

19 Refer to Fig. 14–88. Make a detail drawing from the freehand sketch of the piston on a Size A sheet. Use instruments and supply the missing dimensions.

20 Refer to Fig. 14–89. Make a detail drawing of the end member from the freehand sketch on a Size B sheet.

21 Refer to Fig. 14–90. Make a detail drawing of the link cap from the freehand sketch on a Size B sheet.

22 Refer to Fig. 14–91. Make a detail drawing of the foot pedal from the freehand sketch on a Size C sheet.

23 Refer to Figs. 14–6 and 14–7. Make working drawings of the parts of the gear cutting fixture on Size B sheets. Additional views or drafting techniques (such as sections) can be used to draw the details of each part if desired. Show a parts list on one of the sheets. Use as many sheets as necessary to show the parts.

24 Refer to Figs. 14–6, 14–7, and 14–23. Make an assembly drawing of all the parts of the gear cutting fixture on a Size C sheet. The assembly drawing

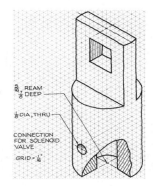

Fig. 14–86 Problem 17.

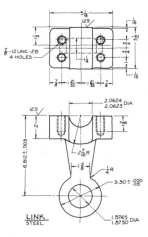

LINK
STEEL

Fig. 14–87 Problem 18.

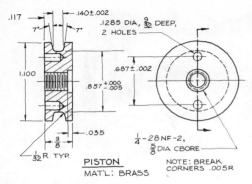

Fig. 14–88   Problem 19.

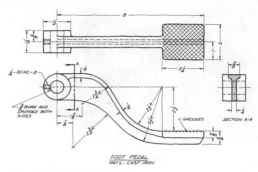

Fig. 14–91   Problem 22.

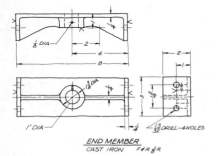

Fig. 14–89   Problem 20.

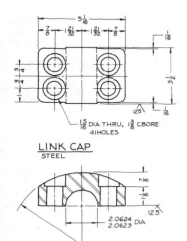

Fig. 14–90   Problem 21.

should be orthographic; it may show either an exploded assembly or an actual assembly.

25 Refer to Figs. 14–6 and 14–7. Draw a pictorial assembly of the parts of the gear cutting fixture on a Size C sheet.

26 Refer to Fig. 14–92. Make detail drawings of the parts of the pipe support on Size B sheets. Give a parts list.

27 Refer to Fig. 14–92. Make an assembly drawing, either orthographic or pictorial, of the pipe support.

28 Refer to Fig. 14–93. Make a detail drawing of the parts of the pipe support. Give a parts list.

29 Refer to Fig. 14–93. Make an assembly drawing, either orthographic or pictorial, of the pipe support.

30 Refer to Fig. 14–94. Make detail drawings of the parts of the valve assembly. Give a parts list.

31 Refer to Fig. 14–94. Make an assembly drawing, either orthographic or pictorial, of the valve assembly on a Size B sheet.

32 Refer to Fig. 14–95. Make a detail drawing of the guide on a Size B sheet.

33 Refer to Fig. 14–96. Make detail drawings of the parts of the C-clamp. Give a parts list and supply any missing dimensions.

34 Refer to Fig. 14–96. Make an assembly drawing, either orthographic or pictorial, of the C-clamp on a Size B sheet.

35 Refer to Fig. 14–97. Make a detail drawing of the traverse guide on a Size B sheet.

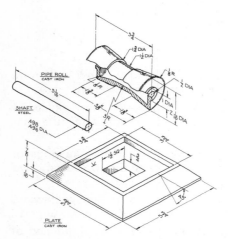

Fig. 14–92 Problems 26 and 27. (Courtesy of the Grinnel Company.)

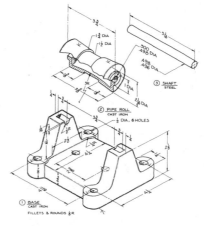

Fig. 14–93 Problems 28 and 29. (Courtesy of the Grinnel Company.)

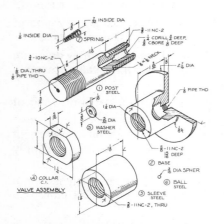

Fig. 14–94 Problems 30 and 31. (Courtesy of Allis-Chalmers Manufacturing Company.)

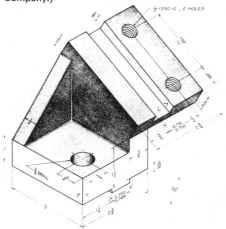

Fig. 14–95 Problem 32.

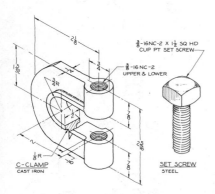

Fig. 14–96 Problems 33 and 34. (Courtesy of the Grinnel Company.)

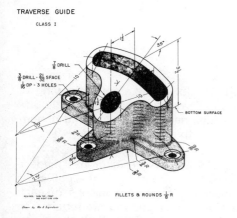

Fig. 14–97 Problem 35.

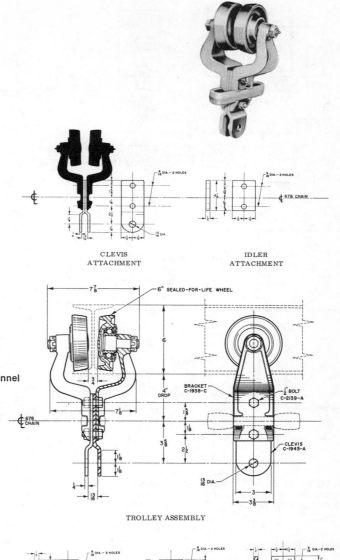

CLEVIS ATTACHMENT

IDLER ATTACHMENT

TROLLEY ASSEMBLY

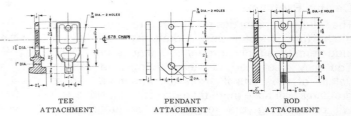

TEE ATTACHMENT

PENDANT ATTACHMENT

ROD ATTACHMENT

Fig. 14–98 Problem 36. (Courtesy of Mechanical Handling Systems Incorporated.)

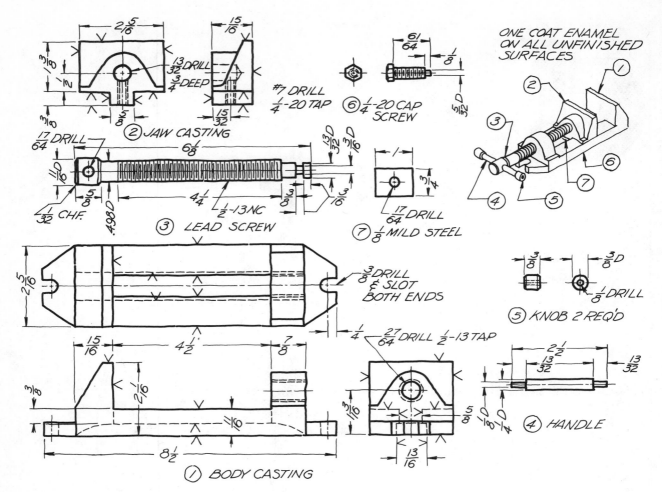

Fig. 14-99 Problems 37, 38, and 39. (Courtesy of C. F. Struck Corporation. Ready-made castings of this project and others are available from this company in Cedarburg, Wisconsin 53012.)

Design Problems

The following problems require you to perform more of the function of a design draftsman, using your judgment to supply information that is not given. You may also need to make changes in various details of the parts if errors are apparent. These problems will have more than one answer, since you will be applying your imagination and judgment to their solution. More analysis will be required than in the previous problems.

36 Refer to Fig. 14-98. Make a detail drawing of the parts assigned. Draw each part on a single Size A or B sheet. Additional views, notes, and dimensions may be needed to explain the parts.

37 Refer to Fig. 14-99. A designer has made a freehand layout of the various parts of a drill press vise and has given the major dimensions of each part. As the design draftsman, you are required to make a complete detail drawing of all the parts, adding any views or notes that would make the drawing easier to understand. Other dimensions must be added also. Show a parts list.

Machining Operations

The following machining operations are given to describe the steps that will be performed by the machine shop in finishing the rough casting of the parts of this assembly.

BODY CASTING (No. 1)

1. Grind bottom, sides, jaw surface, and sliding surface.
2. Machine bottom in four-jaw chuck on lathe or by shaper.
3. Machine one side as in operation 2 above.
4. Machine surface of jaw and sliding surface with milling machine, milling machine attachment on lathe with end mill, or by shaper.
5. Machine section for Part No. 7. Same setup as in operation 4.
6. Machine opening for sliding jaw. Same setup as in operation 4.
7. Lay out, drill, and slot both ends for bolting.
8. Lay out and center-punch location for lead screw.
9. Drill and tap for lead screw.

JAW CASTING (No. 2)

1. Grind both surfaces, sides, and bottom.
2. Machine surfaces in four-jaw chuck on lathe or by shaper.
3. Machine bottom section to fit opening in body casting. Use same setup as in operation 4 for the body casting, or file by hand.
4. Lay out, center-punch, and drill for end of lead screw as shown in drawing.
5. Lay out, center-punch, drill, and tap for cap screw as shown in drawing.

LEAD SCREW (No. 3)

1. Select and machine stock in preparation for threading.
2. Prepare lathe for threading. Check lead screw with threads in body casting. Machine for perfect thread fit.

HANDLE (No. 4)

1. Select and machine stock as shown on drawing.

Fig. 14–100   Problem 40. (Courtesy of Omark Industries.)

KNOBS (No. 5)

1. Select and machine stock as shown on drawing.

ASSEMBLING INSTRUCTIONS

1. Place one knob on handle and upset. Place in three-jaw chuck, face end, machine surface of knob, and chamfer.
2. Place handle in position of lead screw and place other knob on other end of handle and upset end. Repeat operation 1 above.
3. Assemble jaw casting to body casting with Parts Nos. 3, 6, 7, and 8.
4. Draw up jaw casting to jaw of body casting in four-jaw chuck on lathe, by milling machine, or by shaper.

38 Refer to Fig. 14–99. Prepare an orthographic assembly drawing of the drill press vise on a Size B sheet. Give a parts list.

39 Refer to Fig. 14–99. Make a pictorial assembly drawing of the drill press vise on a Size B sheet. Give a parts list.

40 Refer to Fig. 14–100. Two photographic views of the same cast iron base are shown. The overall height of the part is $7\frac{3}{4}''$ and the base is to be held in position by four $\frac{3}{16}''$ bolts. Make a detail drawing of the base on a Size B sheet.

41 Refer to Fig. 14–101. The rotary pump has a $\frac{3}{8}''$ outside diameter flexible hose through which fluid is pumped by a rotational motion. Prepare a detail drawing of the parts of this pump by applying the

CONSTRUCTION OF THE PUMP

COMPONENT PARTS OF MODEL 500 RANDOLPH PUMP
THE MODEL 610 PUMP HAS SIMILAR CONSTRUCTION

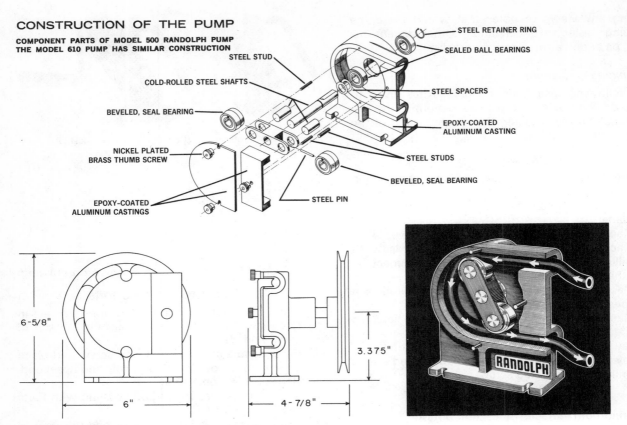

Fig. 14–101 Problems 41 and 42. (Courtesy of the Randolph Company.)

general dimensions given and estimating the others. Show a parts list. Use Size B sheets.

42 Refer to Fig. 14–101. Prepare an assembly drawing, either orthographic or pictorial, of the pump on a Size B sheet. Give a parts list.

43 Refer to Figs. 14–102 and 14–103. A testing device is shown that was designed to test the quality of bonds in metal-to-metal constructions. This device applies a "peeling" action to determine the resistance of test samples. Prepare a detail drawing to describe each part of this apparatus, including the upper and lower clevises shown in the photograph and the cylindrical base pieces.

44 Refer to Figs. 14–102 and 14–103. Prepare an assembly drawing, either orthographic or pictorial, of the parts of the testing apparatus.

45 Refer to Figs. 14–104 and 14–105. A designer has made a preliminary detail drawing of a machinist's bench vise as a freehand layout on grid paper. The drawing is made generally to scale with each grid equal to $\frac{1}{4}$". The more important dimensions have been given, but many will have to be supplied by the draftsman. Some of the parts need additional views or sections to explain them more clearly to the craftsman in the shop.

Prepare a complete working drawing of the parts of the bench vise on Size C sheets. Give all

Fig. 14–102 Problems 43 and 44. (Courtesy of U.S. Department of Agriculture, Forest Service.)

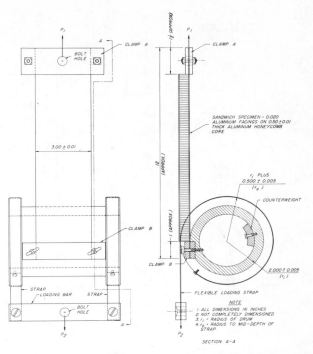

Fig. 14–103 Problems 43 and 44. (Courtesy of U.S. Department of Agriculture, Forest Service.)

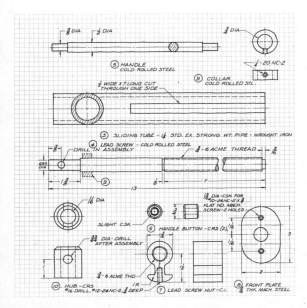

Fig. 14–104 Problems 45 and 46. (Courtesy of C. F. Struck Corporation.)

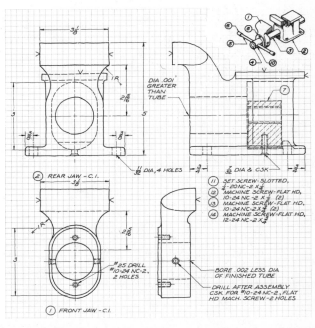

Fig. 14–105 Problems 45 and 46. (Courtesy of C. F. Struck Corporation.)

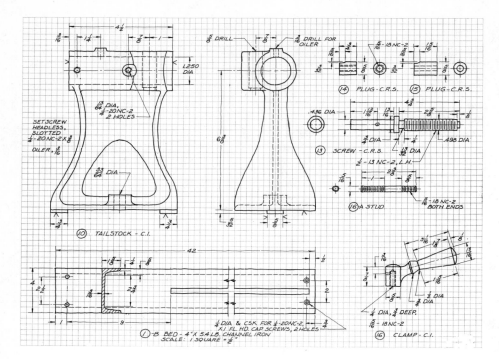

Fig. 14–106 Problems 47 and 48. (Courtesy of C. F. Struck Corporation.)

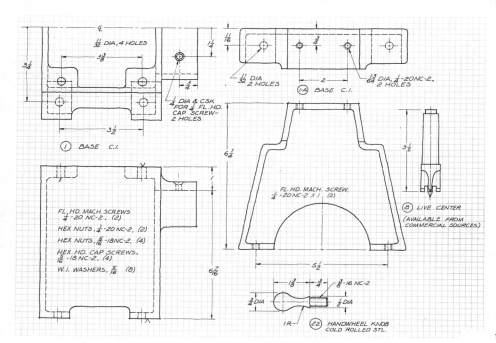

Fig. 14–107 Problems 47 and 48. (Courtesy of C. F. Struck Corporation.)

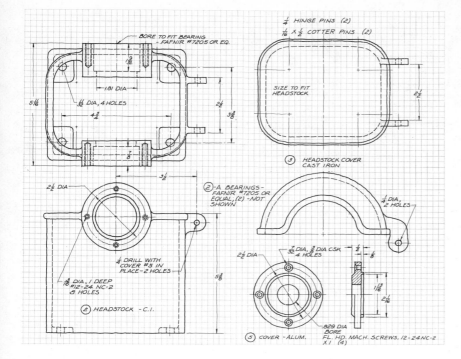

Fig. 14–108 Problems 47 and 48. (Courtesy of C. F. Struck Corporation.)

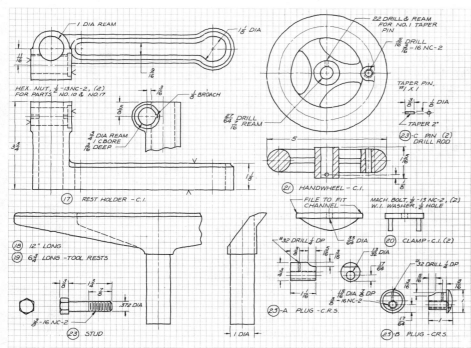

Fig. 14–109 Problems 47 and 48. (Courtesy of C. F. Struck Corporation.)

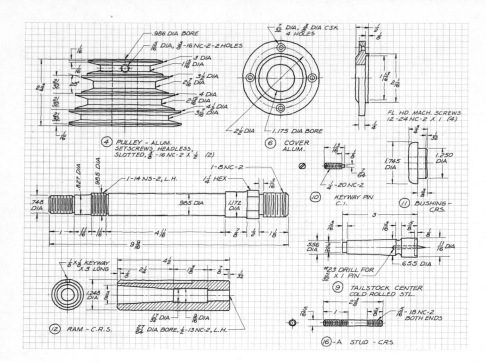

Fig. 14–110   Problems 47 and 48. (Courtesy of C. F. Struck Corporation.)

dimensions and views that are necessary to explain the design. Give a parts list. Estimate the dimensions that are not given. Study the assembly of the parts to make sure that mating parts are properly dimensioned to fit.

46 Refer to Figs. 14–104 and 14–105. Prepare an assembly drawing, either orthographic or pictorial, of the bench vise. Give a parts list.

47 Refer to Figs. 14–106 through 14–111. A designer has made a partial freehand detail drawing of the parts of a wood lathe. Each grid on the layout represents $\frac{1}{4}''$. As a design draftsman, you are required to make a complete working drawing of these parts on Size C sheets for the approval of the engineer. It will be necessary to study each view in order to decide on additional views and methods of drawing that will make the completed drawing easier to understand. Many dimensions must be determined by your judgment and your analysis of the parts and their relation to one another.

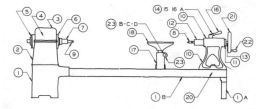

Fig. 14–111   Problems 47 and 48.   (Courtesy of C. F. Struck Corporation.)

The assembly drawing (Fig. 14–111) will assist you in understanding how the parts fit together. Give a parts list.

48 Refer to Figs. 14–106 through 14–111. Prepare assembly drawings of (A) the headstock assembly, (B) the tailstock assembly, and (C) the tool rest assembly in Size C sheets. Give a parts list for each assembly. These assembly drawings may be either orthographic or pictorial.

Photo courtesy of A. H. Nilson Company

15
CAMS, GEARS, AND
SPRINGS

Fig. 15–1 Examples of two cylindrical cams and a plate cam. (Courtesy of Ferguson Machine Company.)

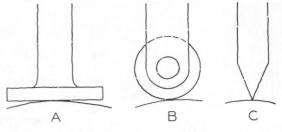

Fig. 15–2 Three basic types of cam follower: flat surface, roller, and knife-edge.

15–1 INTRODUCTION

Cams, gears, and springs are standard parts that regulate the motion of a mechanism. Each is a complicated engineering problem in itself, and companies have been established that specialize in the design and supply of a particular type of these components. Only a brief introduction to each type of component will be given here. The major emphasis will be on how the draftsman prepares drawings to communicate the specifications of the engineer.

Extensive tables are available from which standard dimensions can be taken for cams, gears, and springs. These are available from the American National Standards Institute and other associations.

15–2 CAMS

A cam is a device that causes a special type of motion of another part (usually called a follower) when the cam is revolved. Examples of three types of cams are shown in Fig. 15–1. As you can see, if any of these cams is revolved about its axis, a follower will have to move up and down in order to remain in contact with the surface of the cam.

The two cams at the left of Fig. 15–1 are *cylindrical cams*, the other is a *grooved plate cam*. A third type is a *plate cam* with a follower that remains in contact with the outside of the cam rather than in a groove. These three are the most common types of cams, though others are available for special applications.

These cams give an up-and-down motion to a follower through the effect of the inclined plane. The slope of the cam's surface causes the desired change in movement of its follower. The analysis of the motion of the follower and the design of cams can be done graphically.

15–3 CAM FOLLOWERS

There are three basic types of cam follower: (a) the flat surface, (b) the roller, and (c) the knife edge (see Fig. 15–2). The flat-surface and the knife-edge followers are used with slow-moving cams where only a small force is applied. The roller is the most often used follower since it can withstand higher speeds and transmit greater forces.

15–4 TYPES OF CAM MOTION

The three basic types of motion produced by cams are (a) uniform motion, (b) harmonic motion, and (c) uniform acceleration. Combinations of the three types can be produced on the same cam. Motion that does not fit into any of these three categories can be specified to fit the need at hand.

Displacement diagrams are used to represent the travel of the follower relative to the rotation of the cam. A displacement diagram is no more than a graph that shows the travel (displacement) of the follower that is caused to move by the cam.

Uniform motion is shown in the displacement diagram in Fig. 15–3A. This graph represents the motion of the follower as the cam rotates through 360°. Note that the uniform-motion curve has sharp

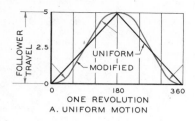

A. UNIFORM MOTION

ONE REVOLUTION

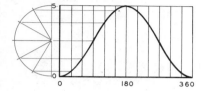

B. HARMONIC MOTION

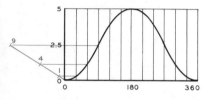

C. UNIFORM ACCELERATION

Fig. 15–3 Methods of plotting the three basic motions of cams: uniform, harmonic, and uniform acceleration.

corners, indicating sharp changes of speed at two points that will cause the follower to bounce. Therefore, the motion of the follower is usually modified with arcs that smooth this bump. The radius of the modifying arc can vary up to one-half the total follower travel, depending on the speed of operation. Usually a radius of about one-third to one-fourth of the total travel is best.

Harmonic motion is plotted in part B of Fig. 15–3 as a smooth, continuous motion projected from various positions on the circumference of a circle. At moderate speeds, this type of motion is satisfactory. Note how the curve was plotted using a semicircle to establish points in the displacement diagram.

Uniform acceleration, plotted in part C, is commonly used for high-speed operation. The variation of the displacement is based on the square of the intervals on the axis from 0° to 360°. For instance, from point 0, $1^2 = 1$, $2^2 = 4$, $3^2 = 9$, and so on. This motion is repeated in reverse order for the remaining half of the movement of the follower. Note that a line is drawn from point 0 and is divided into the required number of divisions. Points on this line are then projected to the vertical axis of the displacement diagram. This principle of geometric construction was discussed in Chapter 5.

Points between the major divisions can be found by squaring fractional divisions; for example, $(2.5)^2 = 6.25$. The uniform acceleration of the follower is designed so that the follower as it falls will remain in contact with the cam for a smooth operation.

15–5 CONSTRUCTION OF A PLATE CAM—HARMONIC MOTION

The steps of constructing a plate cam with harmonic motion are shown in Fig. 15–4. The draftsman must know certain information before he can design a cam. He must know the desired motion of the follower, the total rise of the follower, the size of the follower and type, the position of the follower, the diameter of the base circle, and the direction of rotation. When this information is available, he proceeds as follows.

Step 1. The displacement diagram is laid out. The vertical axis represents the rise of the follower from its lowest point. The horizontal axis is divided into equal divisions representing degrees of rotation of the cam (each division usually represents 15° or 30°). A semicircle with a diameter equal to the rise of the follower is constructed and divided into the same number of equal units as are drawn between 0° and 180° on the horizontal axis of the displacement diagram. The points on the semicircle are projected to their respective lines drawn vertically through the divisions of the horizontal axis. These points are connected with an irregular curve.

Step 2. The same semicircle is used to find points on the curve from 180° to 360° starting from the top of the semicircle (point 6) and proceeding down-

FIGURE 15-4. CONSTRUCTION OF A PLATE CAM WITH HARMONIC MOTION

Step 1. Construct a semicircle whose diameter is equal to the rise of the follower. Divide the semicircle into the same number of divisions as there are between 0° and 180° on the horizontal axis of the displacement diagram. Plot half of the displacement curve in the displacement diagram.

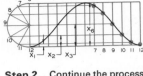

Step 2. Continue the process of plotting points by projecting from the semicircle, starting from the top of the semicircle and proceeding to the bottom. Complete the curve.

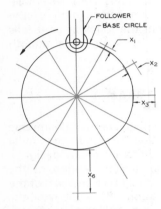

Step 3. Construct the base circle and draw the follower. Divide the base circle into the same number of sectors as there are divisions on the displacement diagram. Transfer distances from the displacement diagram to the respective radial lines of the base circle, measuring outward from the base circle.

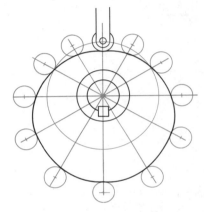

Step 4. Draw circles to represent the positions of the roller as the cam revolves in a counterclockwise direction. Draw the cam profile tangent to all the rollers to complete the drawing.

ward to point 12. The points are projected to their respective lines and are connected with a smooth irregular curve. The right side and left side of the displacement diagram are symmetrical.

Step 3. The base circle is drawn from given specifications and the follower is drawn with its center on the base circle. The circle is divided into the same number of sectors as shown on the displacement diagram. There are twelve in this example, since the circle is divided into 30° sectors. The displacement of the cam follower is taken from the displacement diagram, and since the motion of the cam is counter-

clockwise, the displacement is plotted to the right of the follower. For example, the distances X_1, X_2, and X_3 are measured from the base circle outward. Points are located in this manner all the way around the base circle.

Step 4. Construction circles representing the roller follower are drawn with the points plotted in Step 3 as centers. The profile of the cam is drawn with an irregular curve to be tangent to each of the roller constructions. Additional intervals can be found to construct a more accurate profile. The cam hub and keyway are drawn to given specifications.

FIGURE 15-5. CONSTRUCTION OF A PLATE CAM WITH UNIFORM ACCELERATION

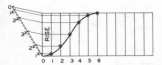

Step 1. Construct a displacement diagram to represent the rise of the follower. Divide the horizontal axis into angular increments of 30°. Draw a construction line through point 0; locate the 1^2, 2^2, and 3^2 divisions and project them to the vertical axis to represent half of the rise. The other half of the rise is found by laying off distances along the construction line with descending values.

Step 2. Use the same construction to find the right half of the symmetrical curve.

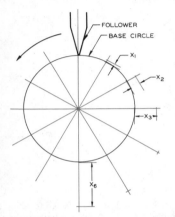

Step 3. Construct the base circle and draw the knife-edge follower. Divide the circle into the same number of sectors as there are divisions in the displacement diagram. Transfer distances from the displacement diagram to the respective radial lines of the base circle, measuring outward from the base circle.

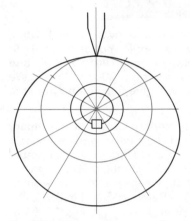

Step 4. Connect the points found in Step 3 with a smooth curve to complete the cam profile. Show also the cam hub and keyway.

15-6 CONSTRUCTION OF A PLATE CAM—UNIFORM ACCELERATION

This construction is the same as the previous example except for the displacement diagram and the knife-edge follower. The steps involved in constructing a plate cam with uniform acceleration are shown in Fig. 15-5.

Step 1. The displacement diagram is drawn with each division on the horizontal axis representing 30° and with the vertical axis equal to the rise of the follower. The rate of travel of the follower changes constantly, producing acceleration and deceleration. The changes in rise are based on the square of each division. Note that these divisions are laid off on the construction line and are projected back to the vertical axis. The follower accelerates from 0° to 90° and decelerates from 90° to 180°. This half of the curve is plotted as an irregular curve.

Step 2. The same construction is used to find the displacement curve from 180° to 360° to complete the symmetrical curve.

Step 3. The base circle is drawn to represent the lowest position of the knife-edge follower. The circle is divided into 30° sectors—the same number of divisions as in the displacement diagram. Since the rotation of the cam is counterclockwise, the displacement is plotted outward from the base circle to the right of the follower in a clockwise direction.

Step 4. The profile of the cam is drawn with an irregular curve through the plotted points. The cam hub and keyway are added to complete the drawing.

15–7 CONSTRUCTION OF A PLATE CAM—COMBINATION MOTION

In this example a knife-edge follower is used with a plate cam to produce harmonic motion from 0° to 180°, uniform acceleration from 180° to 300°, and dwell (no follower motion) from 300° to 360°. We are to draw a cam that will give this motion from the given base circle.

Step 1. The harmonic portion of the displacement diagram is constructed by drawing a semicircle whose circumference is divided into the same number of equal parts as there are horizontal divisions on the displacement diagram between 0° and 180°—six in this case (Fig. 15–6). Refer to Fig. 15–3B. The uniform acceleration (four divisions in Fig. 15–6) of the follower is found by dividing the number of horizontal divisions by 2; that is, $4 \div 2 = 2$. Then 1^2 would give a travel of 1 during the first 30°, and 2^2 would give a travel of 4 from the peak, or a fall of 3 units between 210° and 240°. The units are laid off as shown in Fig. 15–6C. From 300° to 360°, where a dwell condition exists, the follower does not move; consequently, this portion of the curve is a horizontal line.

Step 2. Radial lines are drawn from the center of the base circle to correspond to the intervals used on the horizontal scale of the displacement diagram. The displacement is measured outward along the radial lines from the base circle with dividers. Distance X is shown as an example.

Step 3. The points on the radial lines are connected with a smooth curve to form the cam profile that will produce the specified motion. The hub and keyway are drawn to complete the construction.

FIGURE 15–6. CONSTRUCTION OF A PLATE CAM WITH COMBINATION MOTIONS

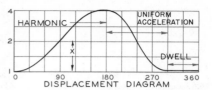

Step 1. The cam is to rise 4″ in 180° with harmonic motion, fall 4″ in 120° with uniform acceleration, and dwell for 60°. These motions are plotted on the displacement diagram.

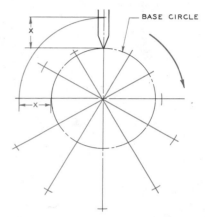

Step 2. Construct the base circle and draw the knife-edge follower. Transfer distances from the displacement diagram to the respective radial lines of the base circle, measuring outward from the base circle.

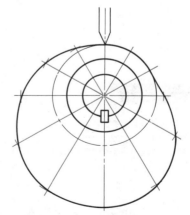

Step 3. Draw a smooth curve through the points found in Step 2 to complete the profile of the cam. Show also the cam hub and keyway.

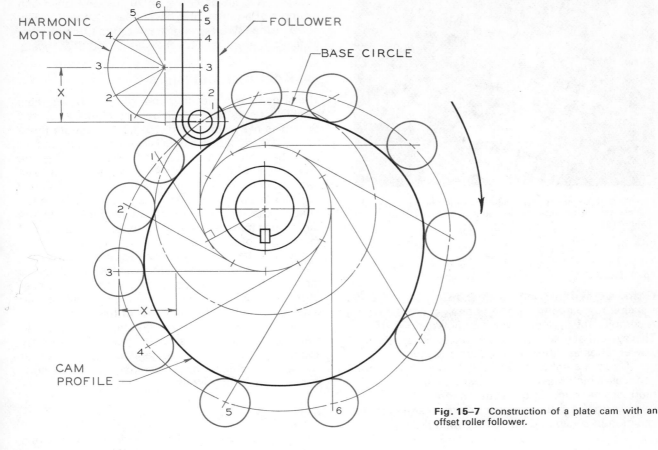

HARMONIC MOTION

FOLLOWER

BASE CIRCLE

X

CAM PROFILE

Fig. 15–7 Construction of a plate cam with an offset roller follower.

15–8 CONSTRUCTION OF A PLATE CAM WITH AN OFFSET ROLLER FOLLOWER

A cam with an offset follower is required to produce harmonic motion through 360° (Fig. 15–7). Since there are no combinations of motion, this motion can be plotted directly from the follower without the use of a displacement diagram. A semicircle is drawn with its diameter equal to the total motion desired in the follower. As before, the base circle passes through the center of the roller follower. The vertical centerline of the follower is extended downward, and a circle is drawn with its center at the center of

the base circle and tangent to the extension of the follower centerline. This circle is divided at 30° intervals to establish points of tangency for the follower as it revolves through 360°.

The tangent lines are constructed perpendicular to the 30° interval lines extended from the center of the circle to the points on the circumference (only one of these lines is shown in the figure). Distances are transferred from the harmonic-motion diagram to each successive tangent line. Distance X is measured as an example of the procedure. The circular roller is drawn in all positions and the profile of the cam is drawn tangent to all views of the roller.

Fig. 15–8 A system of gears and linkages in the main drive of a multiple spindle bar machine. (Courtesy of the National Acme Company.)

15–9 GEARS

Gears are toothed wheels that mesh together to transmit force and motion from one gear to the next. A complicated system of gears is shown in Fig. 15–8. This system of gears can give a variety of speeds and power ratios as different gears are engaged.

Gears are linked together by teeth cut into the surfaces which make contact with each other. The ratio of the number of teeth on one gear to the number on the matching gear determines the rate of variation in speed and power between the two.

15–10 TYPES OF GEARS

The more common types of gears are shown in Fig. 15–9. These are (a) the spur gear (straight and helical), (b) the rack, and (c) the bevel gear.

The *spur gear* is a circular gear with teeth cut around the circumference. Two spur gears can transmit power from a shaft to a parallel shaft. When the two meshing gears are unequal in size, the smaller gear is called the *pinion* and the larger one is called the *gear*.

The *rack* is a series of teeth in a straight line on which a spur gear can travel. The axes of the two are perpendicular but do not intersect.

The *bevel gear* is a gear mounted on an axis whose centerline intersects the centerline of the axis

of another gear at some angle, usually 90°. An example of a pinion and bevel gear is shown in Fig. 15–9. When two bevel gears with the same number of teeth intersect at 90°, they are called *miter* gears.

15–11 GEAR RELATIONSHIPS

The sizes of two meshing spur gears or bevel gears establish ratios that are important to the engineer. Examples are given in Fig. 15–10 to illustrate these ratios. If the radius of a gear is twice that of its pinion, then the gear's diameter and circumference are twice those of the pinion. Also, the gear must have twice as many teeth as the pinion. The pinion, in this case, must make two turns to a single turn of the gear. This means that the number of revolutions of the pinion per minute is equal to twice the number of revolutions of the gear.

When the diameter of the gear is four times the diameter of the pinion, there must be four times as many teeth on the gear as on the pinion. The number of revolutions of the pinion per minute will be four times the number of revolutions of the gear.

These ratios and formulas can be applied to many combinations of sizes of gears. The primary application of a gear is to regulate the speeds of various components of a machine so that they conform to certain predetermined ratios.

15–12 GEAR TERMINOLOGY

A number of terms are used to describe the parts of a gear and the features of gear teeth (Fig. 15–11). Each of the features has different dimensions with each size of gear. These dimensions can be found in tables of values or calculated from formulas.

Pitch diameter is the diameter that would establish the same ratio of speeds between two components if friction wheels without teeth were used to link them in place of two meshing gears.

Outside diameter is the diameter of a gear measured from the outside of the gear teeth.

Root diameter is the diameter of a gear measured from the bottom of the gear teeth.

Addendum is the height of the gear tooth above the pitch diameter.

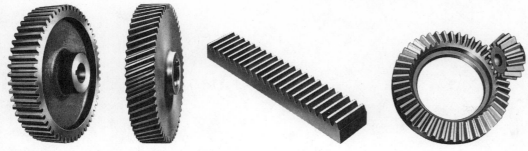

Fig. 15-9 Left to right: a straight spur gear, a helical spur gear, a rack, and bevel gears. (Courtesy of Philadelphia Gear Corporation.)

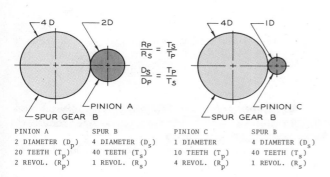

$$\frac{R_P}{R_S} = \frac{T_S}{T_P}$$

$$\frac{D_S}{D_P} = \frac{T_P}{T_S}$$

PINION A	SPUR B
2 DIAMETER (D_p)	4 DIAMETER (D_s)
20 TEETH (T_p)	40 TEETH (T_s)
2 REVOL. (R_p)	1 REVOL. (R_s)

PINION C	SPUR B
1 DIAMETER	4 DIAMETER (D_s)
10 TEETH (T_p)	40 TEETH (T_s)
4 REVOL. (R_p)	1 REVOL. (R_s)

Fig. 15-10 The difference in size between gears and pinions affects the speed and power ratios.

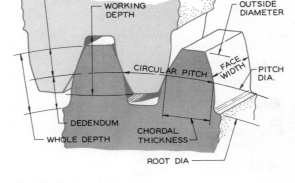

Fig. 15-11 Gear terminology.

Dedendum is the height of the gear tooth below the pitch diameter.

Whole depth is the total depth of a gear tooth: the addendum plus the dedendum.

Working depth is the depth to which a tooth fits into the meshing gear.

Circular pitch is the circular measurement from one point on a tooth to the corresponding point on the next tooth along the pitch diameter.

Chordal thickness is the straight-line distance across a tooth at the pitch diameter.

Circular thickness is the circular distance across a tooth along the pitch diameter.

Face width is the distance across a gear tooth measured perpendicular to the axis of a gear.

Diametral pitch is the ratio between the number of teeth on a gear and its pitch diameter. For example, a gear with 20 teeth and a 4″ pitch diameter will have a diametral pitch of 5, which means 5 teeth per inch of pitch diameter.

Formulas for some of the more important gear measurements are as follows:

$$N = \text{number of teeth,}$$

$$PD = \text{pitch diameter} = \frac{N}{DP},$$

$$DP = \text{diametral pitch} = \frac{N}{PD},$$

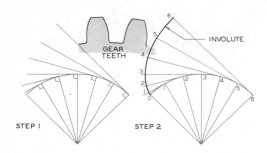

Fig. 15–12 Construction of an involute that represents the geometric shape of gear teeth.

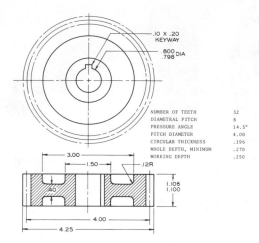

NUMBER OF TEETH	32
DIAMETRAL PITCH	8
PRESSURE ANGLE	14.5°
PITCH DIAMETER	4.00
CIRCULAR THICKNESS	.196
WHOLE DEPTH, MINIMUM	.270
WORKING DEPTH	.250

Fig. 15–13 A typical detail drawing of a spur gear with a table of values to give the gear specifications.

$$RD = \text{root diameter} = PD - 2D,$$

$$OD = \text{outside diameter} = \frac{N + 2}{DP},$$

$$A = \text{addendum} = \frac{1}{DP},$$

$$D = \text{dedendum} = \frac{1.157}{DP},$$

$$CP = \text{circular pitch} = \frac{\pi \times DP}{N},$$

$$WD = \text{whole depth} = A + D,$$

$$CT = \text{circular thickness} = \frac{CP}{2}.$$

15–13 TOOTH FORMS

The most common gear tooth is an involute tooth with a $14\frac{1}{2}°$ pressure angle. The $14\frac{1}{2}°$ pressure angle is the angle of contact between two gears when the tangents of both gears pass through the point of contact. Gears with $20°$ and $25°$ pressure angles are also used. The gear teeth with larger pressure angles are wider at the base and thus are stronger than the standard $14\frac{1}{2}°$ teeth.

The standard gear face is an involute that keeps the meshing gears in contact as the gear teeth are revolved past one another.

The method of constructing an involute is shown in Fig. 15–12.

Step 1. An arc, called the base arc, is drawn and divided into equal divisions with radial lines from the center of the arc. Tangents are drawn perpendicular to these radial lines at the points where they intersect the base arc.

Step 2. The chordal distance from point 1 to point 0 is used as a radius with point 1 as the center. This distance is revolved to find point 1 on the involute. Then the distance from point 2 to the newly found point 1 is revolved to the line tangent to the arc through point 2, to give point 2 on the involute. This procedure is followed until the complete involute curve is found.

The involute curve thus found is an approximation of the path followed by the end of a string that is kept taut as it is unwound from the base arc. Instead of an arc, a full circle could be used as the base to find a full involute that would look like a spiral when completed.

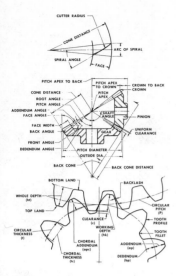

Fig. 15–14 Terminology of bevel gearing. (Courtesy of Philadelphia Gear Corporation.)

It is unnecessary to use this procedure to draw gear teeth, since most detail drawings employ approximations of gear teeth. Gear teeth are, in fact, seldom shown on drawings; instead, conventional methods of specifying them are used with appropriate notes and tables.

15–14 DRAWING A SPUR GEAR

The detail drawing of the spur gear in Fig. 15–13 shows the conventional method of drawing this type of gear. The circular view is often omitted since the sectional view is adequate for most applications. When the circular view is shown, circular centerlines are drawn to represent the root diameter, pitch diameter, and outside diameter of the gear teeth.

Note that a table of values is given to describe the gear. These values can be computed using the formulas given in Article 15–12. Other information must be taken from standard gear tables. Some industries require much more information in gear specifications. Individual teeth should not be drawn unless required for a special application.

15–15 DRAWING BEVEL GEARS

Bevel gears are gears with axes that intersect at angles. This angle is usually 90°, but other angles are sometimes used. The smaller of the two bevel gears is called the pinion.

The terminology of bevel gearing is shown in Fig. 15–14. Many of these terms are common to all types of gears.

The method of constructing two bevel gears whose axes intersect at 90° is illustrated in Fig. 15–15.

Step 1. The pitch diameters of the two gears are measured along two perpendicular intersecting lines. Intersecting centerlines are then drawn with their construction lines to represent the axes of the two gears. Points are connected to form two adjacent isosceles triangles having the pitch diameters as their bases.

Step 2. Perpendiculars to the sides of the two triangles are drawn through the corner points. The addendum and dedendum are located on these lines on either side of each of the corner points. Radial lines are drawn from these addendum and dedendum points to the point of intersection of the axes of two gears.

Step 3. The gears are drawn to standard dimensions taken from bevel-gear tables.

Step 4. Each gear is drawn separately in a working drawing and dimensioned. A table of specifications is also given. The circular views may be omitted since the sectional views are sufficient to explain the details of each gear.

15–16 WORM GEARS

A worm gear is illustrated in Fig. 15–16. The threaded shaft is called the *worm* and the circular gear is sometimes called the *spider*. The worm is revolved in a continuous motion which causes the spider to revolve about its axis.

Typical drawings of worms and gears are shown in Fig. 15–17 with tables of values for various sizes. Letters are used to specify certain dimensions that must be taken from the tables.

FIGURE 15–15. CONSTRUCTION OF BEVEL GEARS

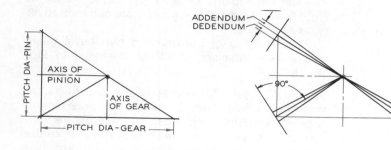

Step 1. Lay out the pitch diameters and axes of the two bevel gears.

Step 2. Draw construction lines to establish the limits of the teeth by using the addendum and dedendum as shown.

Step 3. Draw the pinion and the gear using specified dimensions or dimensions taken from gear tables.

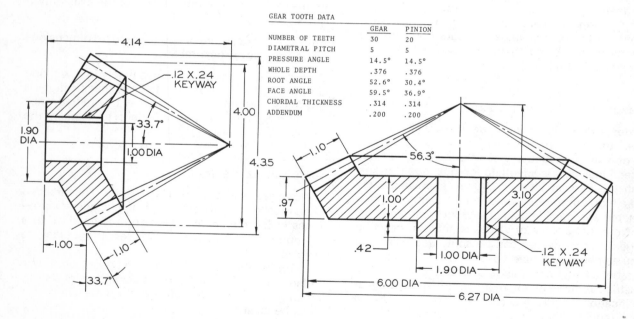

GEAR TOOTH DATA

	GEAR	PINION
NUMBER OF TEETH	30	20
DIAMETRAL PITCH	5	5
PRESSURE ANGLE	14.5°	14.5°
WHOLE DEPTH	.376	.376
ROOT ANGLE	52.6°	30.4°
FACE ANGLE	59.5°	36.9°
CHORDAL THICKNESS	.314	.314
ADDENDUM	.200	.200

Step 4. Complete the detail drawings of both gears. The table of gear tooth data applies to both the pinion and the gear.

Fig. 15–16 A worm gear. (Courtesy of Ex-Cell-O Corporation.)

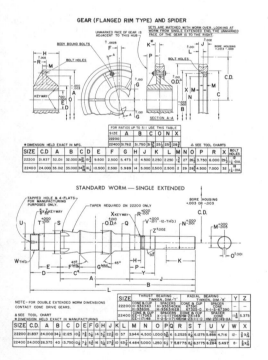

Fig. 15–17 Working drawings of a worm gear and a spider with tables of dimensions. (Courtesy of Ex-Cell-O Corporation.)

Fig. 15–18 A post office sorter that makes use of both gearing and chain drives. (Courtesy of American Sprocket Chain Manufacturers Association.)

15–17 CHAIN DRIVES

A combination of gears is often used with chain-driven gears called *sprockets* (Fig. 15–18). Chains make it possible for the gears to be separated by several feet rather than in actual contact with each other. The installation of chain drives does not require such close tolerances as do the standard gear installations. Chains have the advantage over belt drives that there is no power loss due to slippage.

A conventional drawing of a sprocket is shown in Fig. 15–19. The same general techniques are used for sprockets as are used for representing gears.

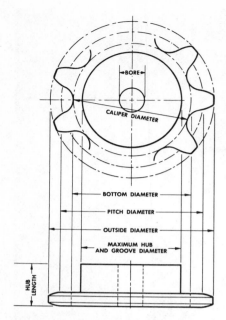

Fig. 15–19 A conventional drawing of a sprocket. (Courtesy of American Sprocket Chain Manufacturers Association.)

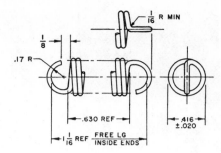

WIRE DIA   .042

DIRECTION OF HELIX   OPTIONAL

TOTAL COILS   14 REF

RELATIVE POSITION OF ENDS   180° ± 20°

EXTENDED LG INSIDE ENDS
WITHOUT PERMANENT SET   2.45 IN. (MAX)

INITIAL TENSION   1.0 LB ± .10 LB

LOAD   4 LB ± .4 LB AT 1.56 IN.
EXTENDED LG INSIDE ENDS

LOAD   6.3 LB ± .63 LB AT 1.95 IN.
EXTENDED LG INSIDE ENDS

Fig. 15–21 A conventional detail drawing of an extension spring. (Courtesy of the Department of Defense.)

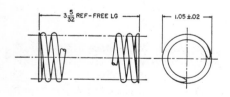

WIRE DIA   .120

DIRECTION OF HELIX   OPTIONAL

TOTAL COILS $12\frac{1}{2}$ REF

LOAD AT COMPRESSED LG OF 2.05 IN.
= 39 LB ± 3.9 LB

LOAD AT COMPRESSED LG OF 1.69 IN.
= 51.5 LB ± 5.2 LB

Fig. 15–20 A detail drawing of a compression spring. (Courtesy of the Department of Defense.)

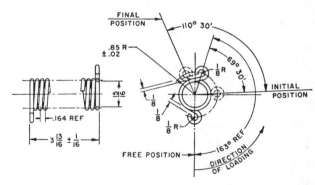

WIRE DIA   .148

DIRECTION OF HELIX   LEFT HAND

TOTAL COILS   20.55 REF

TORQUE   15 LB IN. ± 1.5 LB IN. AT INITIAL POSITION

TORQUE   33 LB IN. ± 3.3 LB IN. AT FINAL POSITION

MAXIMUM DEFLECTION WITHOUT SET BEYOND FINAL POSITION   56°

SPRING RATE   .16 LB IN. / DEG REF

Fig. 15–22 A conventional detail drawing of a helical torsion spring. (Courtesy of the Department of Defense.)

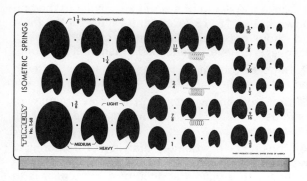

Fig. 15–23 A template for drawing springs in isometric pictorials. (Courtesy of Timely Products Company.)

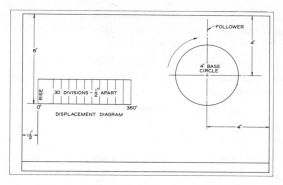

Fig. 15–24 Problem layout for the cam problems on Size B sheets.

15–18 DRAWING SPRINGS

Many types of springs are available for different applications. Some of these types are (a) compression, (b) extension, (c) torsion, (d) flat, (e) constant force, and (f) garter. The three types to be discussed here are compression, extension, and torsion.

A typical working drawing of a *compression spring* is shown in Fig. 15–20. Only the ends of the spring are drawn and conventional lines are used to indicate the undrawn portion of the spring. Only the diameter and the free length of the spring are given on the drawing itself. The remaining specifications are given in tabular form below the drawing.

A working drawing of an *extension spring* (Fig. 15–21) is very similar to that of a compression spring. In a drawing of a helical *torsion spring* (Fig. 15–22), angular dimensions must be shown to specify the initial and final positions of the spring as torsion is applied to it. All types of springs require a table of specifications to describe the details of the spring.

It is difficult to illustrate springs in pictorial drawings using the conventional methods of isometric drawing. However, templates are available for a variety of sizes and types of springs (Fig. 15–23). These can be used for rapid representation of springs in isometric drawings to save construction time.

PROBLEMS

These problems are to be solved in accordance with Article 3–15 and the specifications of your instructor. Standard Size A or B sheets are to be used with either ink or pencil. Use the endorsement, title strip, and border in Fig. 3–32.

Cams

The following cam problems are to be solved on Size B sheets (11″ × 17″) with the following standard dimensions: base circle, 4″; roller follower, .75″ diameter; shaft, .75″ diameter; hub, 1.25″ diameter. The direction of rotation is clockwise. The follower is positioned vertically over the center of

the base circle except in Problems 9 and 10. Lay out the problems and displacement diagrams as shown in Fig. 15–24.

1 Make a drawing of a plate cam with a knife-edge follower for uniform motion and a rise of $1\frac{1}{4}″$.

2 Make a displacement diagram and a drawing of the cam that will give a modified uniform motion to a knife-edge follower with a rise of 1.5″. Use an arc of one-quarter of the rise to modify the uniform motion in the displacement diagram.

3 Make a displacement diagram and a drawing of the cam that will give a harmonic motion to a roller follower with a rise of $1\frac{3}{8}″$.

4 Make a displacement diagram and a drawing of the cam that will give harmonic motion to a knife-edge follower with a rise of .75".

5 Make a displacement diagram and a drawing of the cam that will give uniform acceleration to a knife-edge follower with a rise of 1.5".

6 Make a displacement diagram and a drawing of the cam that will give uniform acceleration to a roller follower with a rise of 1.25".

7 Make a displacement diagram and a drawing of the cam that will give the following motion to a knife-edge follower: dwell for 90°; rise 1" with harmonic motion in 100°; fall 1" with a modified uniform motion in 100°; and dwell for 70°.

8 Make a displacement diagram and a drawing of the cam that will give the following motion to a roller follower: rise 1.25" with uniform acceleration in 120°; dwell for 120°; and fall 1.25" with a harmonic motion in 120°.

9 Repeat Problem 1, but offset the follower .75" to the right of the vertical centerline.

10 Repeat Problem 3, but offset the follower .75" to the left of the vertical centerline.

Gears

Use Size A (8½" × 11") sheets for the following gear problems.

11 Make a drawing of a spur gear similar to the one shown in Fig. 15–13. Compute values for the table and show necessary dimensions on the drawing. The gear is to have 25 teeth and a diametral pitch of 5.

12 Repeat Problem 11 for a gear that has 36 teeth and a diametral pitch of 8.

13 Construct an involute using a 60° arc drawn with a radius of 4". Use 10° intervals and show all construction.

14 Construct an assembly drawing of a spur gear and pinion that are assembled. The pinion is to have 10 teeth and a diametral pitch of 4. The gear is to have 15 teeth and a diametral pitch of 4.

15 Make a layout on a Size B sheet (11" × 17") showing a pinion and a bevel gear assembled at 90° to give a miter fit. On the same sheet show a separate detail drawing of each gear.

16 Make detail drawings of the gears shown in Fig. 15–15 using the dimensions given. Complete the table of values.

Springs

17 Make a detail drawing of the extension spring shown in Fig. 15–21 on a Size A sheet. Show all notes and specifications.

18 Make a detail drawing of the compression spring shown in Fig. 15–20 on a Size A sheet. Show all notes and specifications.

Photo courtesy of AT & T Long Lines

16
GRAPHS AND DATA
ANALYSIS

Fig. 16-1 Technical data are presented graphically in oral reports and in oral presentations.

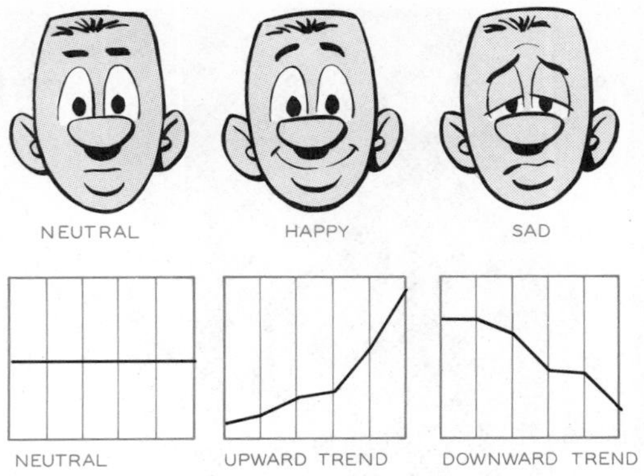

NEUTRAL   HAPPY   SAD

NEUTRAL   UPWARD TREND   DOWNWARD TREND

Fig. 16-2 Reading a graph is similar to reading an expression on a face.

16-1 INTRODUCTION

The engineer, designer, and technician must work with data pertaining to various types of projects and design assignments. This data must be presented and analyzed before they can be used effectively. Examples of data include a count of the automobiles passing a certain corner on a busy street, or the number of gallons of water that a dam will hold at a particular level. Information of this type is often difficult to grasp as a series of numbers; therefore, graphs are used to present data in a manner that makes them easier to interpret.

Data presented in the form of a graph may be a part of a technical report that describes the activities of a design group and its recommendations. These same data may also be presented to a group of associates who are involved with the project. In this case, the graphs are prepared as visual aids—flip charts, photographic slides, or overhead transparencies. The presentation of data by a flip chart is illustrated in Fig. 16-1.

16-2 INTERPRETATION OF GRAPHICAL DATA

You have undoubtedly practiced interpreting graphical data even though you may not know it. A person's facial features give a picture that we call an expression. This combination of lines often tells us more about a person's true feelings than do the things he says. When we "read" a person's face, we are actually interpreting a graph.

A comparison of three faces and graphs is given in Fig. 16-2. Look at the two "neutral" examples; the face has a blank expression, and the black line on the graph is a straight line with no variation. Data that have no variation are like a face with no expression—there is not enough activity to make the graph interesting. Now compare the happy face with the "upward trend" graph. The feeling is positive in both cases; both the face and the graph tend to lift your spirits when you look at them.

The third face has a sad expression and the black line on the graph shows a downward trend that makes you think of depression. Note that the combination of lines in each of these three faces is more complex than the lines in most graphs. However, because of your constant practice in interpreting facial expressions, you are probably very good at it. You should develop your ability to analyze data shown in graphs with the same degree of assurance.

16-3 TYPES OF GRAPHS

A number of types of graphs are available for different applications. The major types will be presented in this chapter. You should become aware of the importance of graphs in the communication and analysis of data so that you can evaluate the

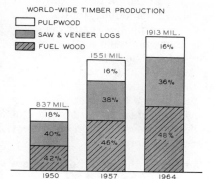

Fig. 16–3 An example of a bar graph in which each bar represents 100% of the total even though the bars represent different amounts.

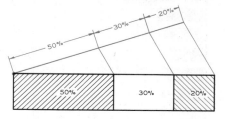

Fig. 16–4 A method of constructing a bar so that the parts will add up to 100%.

various graphs that appear in the magazines and newspapers you see every day.

The following types of graphs will be discussed:

1. Bar graphs.
2. Line graphs—broken line.
3. Line graphs—smooth curve.
4. Circle graphs.
5. Map charts.
6. Flow charts.
7. Organization charts.

Examples will be given to familiarize you with the various ways in which these graphs can be used.

16–4 BAR GRAPHS

Bar graphs are used often on television and in publications directed toward the general public, since they can be understood by most people regardless of their educational background. The bar graph in Fig. 16–3 shows the timber production by type during three periods. This particular type of bar graph uses bars stacked on top of one another so that the relationship of the three types of production can be compared for each period. The total length of each bar represents 100% of the production for that period. The differences in the lengths of the bars show the differences in total production in millions during the three years.

The method of constructing each bar so that it will be equal to 100% is shown in Fig. 16–4. The total length of the bar is laid off and the percentage represented by each segment is determined—50%, 30%, and 20% in this example. A convenient scale on the civil engineers' scale is selected. The civil engineer's scale is most convenient for determining percentages because its divisions represent multiples of 10; that is, it is a decimal scale. A diagonal is drawn from one end of the bar at any convenient angle. The length of this diagonal should be such that it can easily be divided into the required segments. Points are marked on this diagonal to represent the percentages. The end point on the diagonal, which represents 100%, is projected back to the end of the bar. The other points on the bar are found by projecting from the diagonal parallel to the line joining the end points of the bar and the diagonal. This procedure divides the bar in the desired proportions. The bar can be drawn to any convenient width.

The geometric construction used here was introduced in Article 5–4. It will work with any line regardless of its length.

16–5 CONSTRUCTION OF A BAR GRAPH

The most common type of bar graph is shown in Fig. 16–5, where the employment activities of

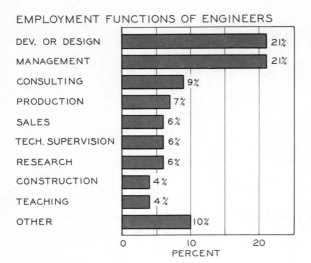

EMPLOYMENT FUNCTIONS OF ENGINEERS

DEV. OR DESIGN	21%
MANAGEMENT	21%
CONSULTING	9%
PRODUCTION	7%
SALES	6%
TECH. SUPERVISION	6%
RESEARCH	6%
CONSTRUCTION	4%
TEACHING	4%
OTHER	10%

0   10   20
PERCENT

Fig. 16–5 A horizontal bar graph. (Courtesy of the U.S. Department of Labor.)

engineers are compared. It is customary to arrange the bars in ascending or descending order of length so that the overall trend can be seen at a glance. Of course, if the data are related to time intervals such as months or years, the bars should be placed in the order of the times that they represent. The graph in Fig. 16–5 has horizontal bars, but vertical bars can also be used. Note that all bars begin at the zero point. A more accurate comparison between the bars can be made at a glance when the bars begin at zero rather than at some greater value.

The data given in the table in Fig. 16–6 are to be plotted in the form of a bar graph for easier interpretation. This bar graph will give a readily understood picture of the data.

Step 1. Lay out the *X*- and *Y*-axes. The *X*-axis is the horizontal axis and the *Y*-axis is the vertical axis. Scales are selected for both axes that will permit the data to fit conveniently on the graph. The maximum value on the vertical axis is $1.20, a value which is somewhat greater than the largest amount to be represented, $1.03. Only the even values are marked on the axes; this makes construction and interpretation easier.

Step 2. The vertical bars are laid off on the graph. It is preferable, for the sake of readability, for the width of the bars to be different from the space between them. In this case the space between the bars is less than the width of the bars. The actual value represented by each bar is labeled at the top of the bar. Horizontal lines are drawn through the major intervals on the vertical axis; these lines are not drawn through the bars. Only the more important horizontal reference lines should be drawn; if too many are drawn, the graph becomes confusing.

Step 3. The lines are strengthened, the axes are labeled, the bars are crosshatched, and the graph is titled. The title can be placed inside the graph in a box, as in Fig. 16–6, or it can be placed outside the graph.

16–6 ELEMENTS OF A LINE GRAPH

A line graph consists of a line plotted on a rectangular grid to show the relationship between two values which are represented by the vertical and horizontal axes (Fig. 16–7). The line (either broken or smooth) that shows the relationship is called a curve. It is customary to use the term curve regardless of the actual shape of the line.

The vertical axis is sometimes called the *ordinate*, and the horizontal axis the *abscissa*. The grid on which the curve is to be plotted should be selected to give the best relationship. Graph papers with printed grids are available from commercial sources. Of course, you can construct your own grid; you can then draw only the grid lines that are important to the graph. As noted earlier, graphs are more readable if only the important grid lines are drawn.

The axes of the graph should be labeled to describe the units that are used on each. Labeling along the vertical axis should be readable from the right side of the page and not from the left side.

Data points should be plotted with circles or other symbols to show the actual points that were used to form the curve. A template can be used for these data-point symbols. A reasonably large number of data points is needed to construct a meaningful graph. A graph with only a few data points is not conclusive, since these few points are

FIGURE 16–6. CONSTRUCTION OF A BAR GRAPH

DIVIDENDS PAID BY
THE AJAX COMPANY

YEAR	AMOUNT
A	$.44
B	.63
C	1.03

Given: These data are to be plotted as a bar graph.

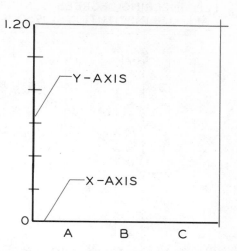

Step 1. Lay off the vertical and horizontal axes so that the data will fit on the grid. Make the bars begin at zero.

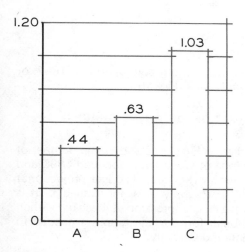

Step 2. Construct and label the bars. The width of the bars should be different from the space between the bars. Horizontal grid lines should not pass through the bars.

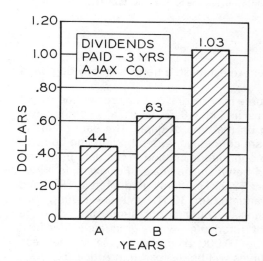

Step 3. Strengthen lines, title the graph, label the axes, and crosshatch the bars.

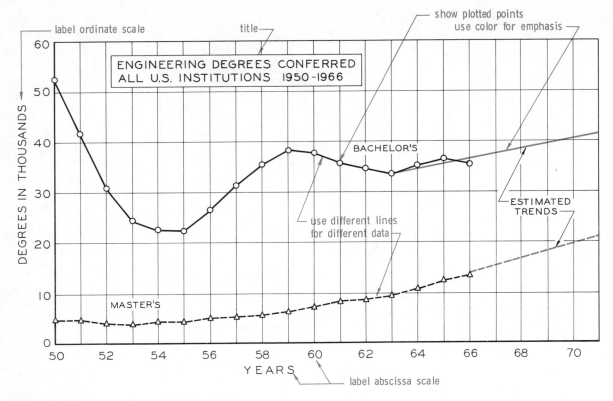

ENGINEERING DEGREES CONFERRED
ALL U.S. INSTITUTIONS 1950-1966

DEGREES IN THOUSANDS

BACHELOR'S

use different lines
for different data

ESTIMATED
TRENDS

MASTER'S

YEARS

label abscissa scale

Fig. 16–7 The layout and the basic elements of a typical line graph.

not sufficient to establish a trend with any degree of accuracy.

The curve may be drawn as a broken line (point to point) as in Fig. 16–7, or as a smooth curve, depending on the type of data. The data points in Fig. 16–7 are connected with a broken line because there is no continuous change in the data from year to year and between the years. For example, when you say that 52,000 students graduated in 1950 and 42,000 graduated in 1951, you are stating two separate facts. You are not suggesting that the number of students who graduated declined gradually by 10,000 over the course of the year. Smooth curves will be discussed in Article 16–8.

Every graph should have a title to explain the type, the dates, and the source of the data. The title

may be placed inside the graph, as in Fig. 16–7, or outside the graph, as in Fig. 16–5.

16–7 CONSTRUCTION OF A LINE GRAPH— BROKEN LINE

The table of data in Fig. 16–8 shows the number of billions of gallons of water used between 1890 and 1980 (the figures for 1980 are, of course, projections) compared with the supply of water available. It is difficult to form a clear impression of these data when they are in tabular form; a line graph is needed to present the data more clearly.

Step 1. The vertical and horizontal axes are laid off and scales are selected so that the data will fit conveniently on the graph.

FIGURE 16–8. CONSTRUCTION OF A BROKEN-LINE GRAPH

BILLIONS OF
GALLONS - DAILY

	SUPPLY	DEMAND
1890	85	40
1900	85	41
1910	110	68
1920	137	85
1930	155	109
1940	240	130
1950	260	195
1960	310	315
1970	380	410
1980	455	550

(Dept. of HEW)

Given: A record of water supply and water demand since 1890 has been obtained to determine the future relationships that may occur. These data are to be plotted as a line graph.

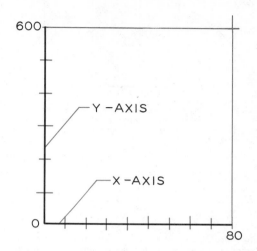

Step 1. The vertical and horizontal axes are laid off to provide adequate space for the years and the largest values.

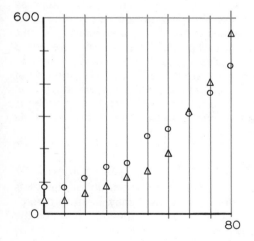

Step 2. The points are plotted directly over the respective years. Different symbols are used for each curve.

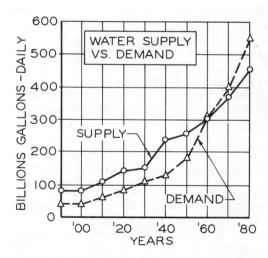

Step 3. The data points are connected with straight lines, the axes are labeled, the graph is titled, and the lines are strengthened.

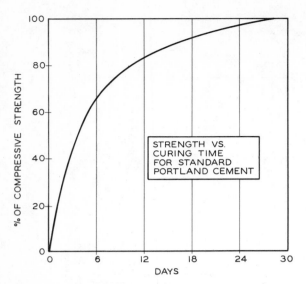

Fig. 16–9 When the process that is graphed involves gradual, continuous changes of relationships, the curve should be drawn as a smooth line.

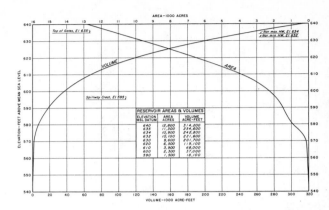

Fig. 16–10 A combination graph with two different horizontal scales and two curves that represent different units. This is a smooth curve, since these changes are gradual and continuous. (Courtesy of the Tennessee Valley Authority.)

Step 2. The data points are plotted at each ten-year interval. Different symbols are used for each curve: triangles for one and circles for the other.

Step 3. The points are connected with a broken line. A broken line is used because we do not know how the supply and demand changed within each ten-year period. The axes are labeled, the curves are labeled, and the graph is titled. Note that the curves are drawn with different types of lines—a solid line for the supply curve, a dashed line for the demand curve—to make it easy to distinguish one from the other.

16–8 LINE GRAPHS—SMOOTH CURVES

Some data are represented by a smooth (continuous) curve rather than a broken-line curve. An example is shown in Fig. 16–9, where the percent of compressive strength is plotted against the number of days of curing time for portland cement. You know that the variation of compressive strength with curing time is a gradual, continuous process; there is no way for the compressive strength to attain 100% without first

attaining every percent between zero and 100%. Therefore, a smooth, continuous curve is used to represent the change.

Another example of a smooth-line curve is the comparison of reservoir water volume and water area in Fig. 16–10. As the elevation of the reservoir rises, the volume increases and the area increases, but this increase is a gradual process that is best represented by a smooth curve. This graph is a combination graph with two different horizontal axes; the one at the top represents units of 1000 acres, and the one at the bottom is in units of 1000 acre-feet of volume. Each of the two curves must be read in terms of its particular scale.

16–9 THE BEST CURVE

Some data are obtained from laboratory or field tests and experiments. These data may have imperfections and flaws that come from the way in which the experiment was conducted or from the instruments that were used to obtain the measurements. When the data are plotted, the resulting curves may form a very irregular curve that does not give a true impression of the data.

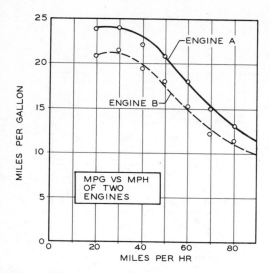

Fig. 16–11 These curves are "best curves," which approximate the data without necessarily passing through each data point.

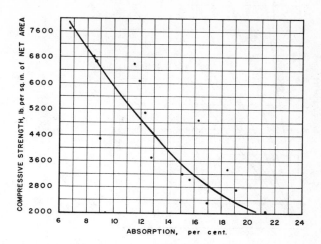

Fig. 16–12 An example of an approximate curve that represents scattered data points. (Courtesy of the Structural Clay Products Institute.)

In these cases, a curve called the *best curve* is fitted to the data to approximate their general trend. For example, the data points plotted in Fig. 16–11 are experimental data obtained from field tests of two engines which were to be compared in terms of their miles-per-gallon efficiency. To obtain a smooth curve, it was necessary to draw the curve through some of the points and near others. It is understood that errors in measurements or other irregularities probably caused the data to vary from the smooth line.

The compressive strength of structural clay tile is related to the absorption characteristics of this material in Fig. 16–12. The more moisture absorbed by a material, the more porous it is and the less compressive strength it has. The curve of this graph does not pass through the points, but represents the average trend shown by the somewhat scattered data. This curve is the average that would be obtained if many repetitive tests were made.

16–10 ANALYSIS OF DATA

Graphs are useful in determining specific values for dimensions and characteristics that have been found

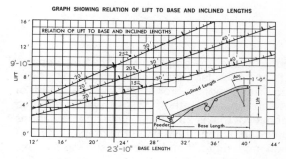

Fig. 16–13 This graph can be used to analyze physical relationships of conveyors. These relationships are in turn used to determine dimensions for conveyor systems. (Courtesy of Logan Conveyors.)

to exhibit a certain relationship. If the relationship is expressed in the form of a curve on a graph, once one of the dimensions or characteristics is known or given, the other can easily be found. The same graph can be used over and over many times. Engineers use graphs to select the best characteristics of machines, power, sizes, volumes, and similar specifications.

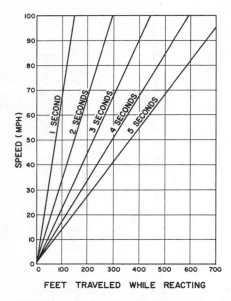

FEET TRAVELED WHILE REACTING

Fig. 16–14 A graph that can be used to determine a third value when two variables are known. Taking this information from a graph is easier than computing each answer separately. (Courtesy of the Texas Transportation Researcher.)

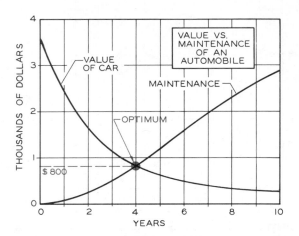

Fig. 16–15 An analysis of the depreciation of an automobile and the accumulation of maintenance costs to determine the best time to purchase a new car.

For example, the graph in Fig. 16–13 compares the lifts and base lengths of conveyors at 15°, 20°, and 25° inclinations. For a 25° incline, a lift of 9'-10" and a base length of 23'-10" will be required for a conveyor that is 25 ft long. Other combinations of values can be found easily on the graph. It would be much more difficult and time-consuming to make each computation separately as a mathematical problem than it is to use the graph.

Another graph (Fig. 16–14) gives the number of feet that an automobile travels in various numbers of seconds (1, 2, 3, 4, and 5) in relation to the speed of the automobile. This graph enables you to evaluate the time it takes you to react to an emergency situation at your normal driving speed in terms of the distance your car will travel while you are in the process of reacting. For example, if you have a reaction time of four seconds—that is, if four seconds elapse between the moment you become aware of the emergency and the moment you actually apply

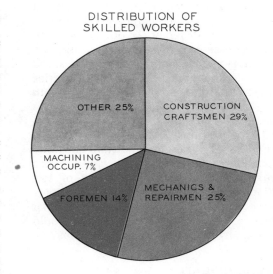

Fig. 16–16 A circle graph shows the relationship of the parts to the whole. (Courtesy of the U.S. Department of Labor.)

FIGURE 16–17. CONSTRUCTION OF A CIRCLE GRAPH

```
WEEKLY ALLOWANCE
EXPENDITURES

LUNCHES          $ 5   50% =  180°

ENTERTAINMENT      2   20% =   72°

SCHOOL SUPPLIES 2      20% =   72°

MISCELLANEOUS      1   10% =   36°
                 ——   ————   ————
          TOTAL $10  100%     360
```

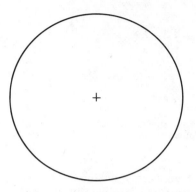

Step 1. Compute the percentage of each part in relation to the whole, and determine the number of degrees of a 360° circle this percentage will represent.

Step 2. Draw a circle of the desired size.

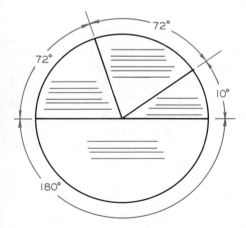

Step 3. Divide the circle into the proper sectors using the values found in Step 1. Narrow sectors should be positioned horizontally for ease of lettering.

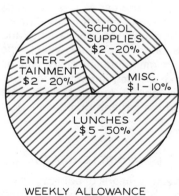

WEEKLY ALLOWANCE
EXPENDITURES

Step 4. The sectors are labeled and crosshatched. A title is added to complete the graph.

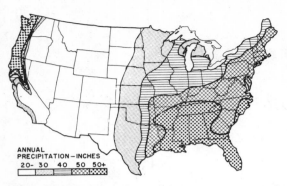

Fig. 16–18 A map chart that shows the characteristics of various geographical areas. (Courtesy of the Structural Clay Products Institute.)

ANNUAL PRECIPITATION—INCHES
20- 30 40 50 50+

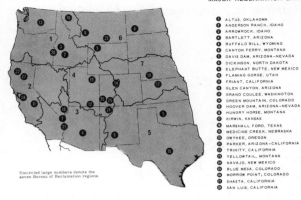

MAJOR RECLAMATION DAMS

1 ALTUS, OKLAHOMA
2 ANDERSON RANCH, IDAHO
3 ARROWROCK, IDAHO
4 BARTLETT, ARIZONA
5 BUFFALO BILL, WYOMING
6 CANYON FERRY, MONTANA
7 DAVIS DAM, ARIZONA–NEVADA
8 DICKINSON, NORTH DAKOTA
9 ELEPHANT BUTTE, NEW MEXICO
10 FLAMING GORGE, UTAH
11 FRIANT, CALIFORNIA
12 GLEN CANYON, ARIZONA
13 GRAND COULEE, WASHINGTON
14 GREEN MOUNTAIN, COLORADO
15 HOOVER DAM, ARIZONA–NEVADA
16 HUNGRY HORSE, MONTANA
17 KIRWIN, KANSAS
18 MARSHALL FORD, TEXAS
19 MEDICINE CREEK, NEBRASKA
20 OWYHEE, OREGON
21 PARKER, ARIZONA–CALIFORNIA
22 TRINITY, CALIFORNIA
23 YELLOWTAIL, MONTANA
24 NAVAJO, NEW MEXICO
25 BLUE MESA, COLORADO
26 MORROW POINT, COLORADO
27 SHASTA, CALIFORNIA
28 SAN LUIS, CALIFORNIA

Uncircled large numbers denote the seven Bureau of Reclamation regions.

Fig. 16–19 A map chart that locates the various reclamation dams in the western portion of the United States. (Courtesy of the Bureau of Reclamation.)

your brakes—and if you are traveling at 50 mph, then your car will travel 300 ft while you are in the process of reacting. Problems such as these are easy to solve with the aid of graphs. The solution would be more complicated if each problem of this type had to be solved separately. The information given in Fig. 16–14 could, of course, be presented in the form of a table of numbers. However, the graph is much easier to use and to understand.

Figure 16–15 is an example of the use of data analysis to determine the optimum time to trade an automobile. The value of the car is plotted over a ten-year period of time. This curve represents the estimated trade-in value of the car as it depreciates each year. The other curve is an approximation of the accumulation of the cost of maintaining and repairing the automobile. After four years, the accumulated repair and maintenance costs will be greater than the value of the car, indicating that this may be the best time, or the *optimum* time (see Article 6–1), to trade in the car and purchase a new one.

16–11 CONSTRUCTION OF A CIRCLE GRAPH

Circle graphs are an effective means of comparing the relationship of parts to a whole. Any group of values that add up to a total of 100% can be compared easily in a circle graph. Figure 16–16 is a comparison of the distribution of skilled workers in each of several categories as related to the total group.

The table of information in Fig. 16–17 shows how a student spends his weekly allowance during an average week. His budget of $10 represents 100% of the money available. A circle graph to present this information is constructed as follows.

Step 1. Express each expense as a percentage of the $10 total. For example, entertainment is $2 or 20% ($2 × 100 ÷ $10 = 20%) of the total; therefore, entertainment should occupy 72° (360° × .20 = 72°) of the circle. The other sectors of the circle are found in the same manner.

Step 2. A circle of the desired size is drawn to provide the basic outline of the circle graph.

Step 3. The sectors found in Step 1 are laid off on the circle and radial lines are drawn. It is best to position the narrow sectors near the horizontal position so that lettering will be easier.

Step 4. Each sector is labeled with the actual amount and the percentage. The areas are cross-hatched to give a better visual impression of the sectors and the graph is titled.

16–12 MAP CHARTS

Data that are related to geographical areas are often shown on a map that charts the various characteristics of those areas. The annual rainfall in inches is shown by area across the nation in Fig. 16–18. This is by far the most direct way of communicating such

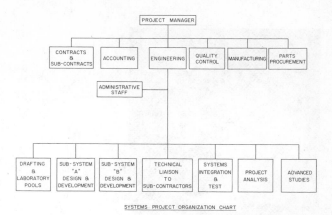

SYSTEMS PROJECT ORGANIZATION CHART

Fig. 16–21 Organization charts show the lines of authority and responsibility in an organization. (Courtesy of Fairchild Camera and Instrument Company.)

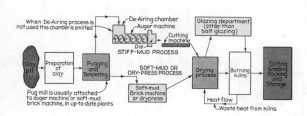

STIFF-MUD PROCESS

SOFT-MUD OR DRY-PRESS PROCESS

Fig. 16–20 A flow chart is a schematic that describes the steps of a process. (Courtesy of the Structural Clay Products Institute.)

information. You can tell at a glance where the rainfall is greatest and where it is least.

A similar type of chart is shown in Fig. 16–19 that shows where the major reclamation dams are located. The numbers on the map are keyed to the list at the right.

16–13 FLOW CHARTS

A flow chart is a combination of pictures, diagrams, and notes which describes the sequence of operations required to arrive at a particular result. The series of steps involved in manufacturing structural clay tile is shown in Fig. 16–20.

This type of graph is very similar to an electronic schematic, discussed in Chapter 14. A brief description of each operation can be placed in each block. Notice that the auger is shown pictorially in the "stiff-mud process' block in Fig. 16–20.

16–14 ORGANIZATION CHARTS

Organization charts are similar to flow charts in that they show the flow of authority and responsibility within an organization (Fig. 16–21). Each connecting line in an organization chart shows part of the chain of command or the supervisory control of each group. Note that there is no line of authority between the administrative staff and any other group. This means that the administrative staff provides a service to the entire organization, but does not supervise any of the groups below.

Organization charts also show the route that groups at the lower level should take when they are in need of assistance from upper levels. In most organizations this route is carefully specified so that employees always seek help from people who are in the line of responsibility.

16–15 GRAPHS FOR VISUAL AIDS

Graphs may be used in technical reports or they may be used as visual aids in person-to-person presentations to a group of associates. If they are to be used as flip charts (Fig. 16–1), they are drawn to a large size, with colors or bold lines to make them clearly visible to the group to which they are to be presented.

Other methods of presenting visual aids are the overhead projector and the slide projector. For overhead projection, a transparency is made that is the same size as the original drawing. The size of the transparency is about $7\frac{1}{2}'' \times 10''$. Drawings for overhead projection should therefore be drawn to this size. The transparencies are made on machines by a process similar to the blueprinting process.

To make a slide for use on a slide projector, a drawing must first be photographed. Photography allows you to shoot graphs of various sizes from postage-stamp size to full-wall size (Fig. 16–22). However, the shape of the graph or illustration that is photographed must be the same as the shape of the film used in the camera. Some film gives square pictures, but the most commonly used film is 35 mm

Fig. 16–22 A copy stand and camera are used to photograph a drawing to be used with a slide projector.

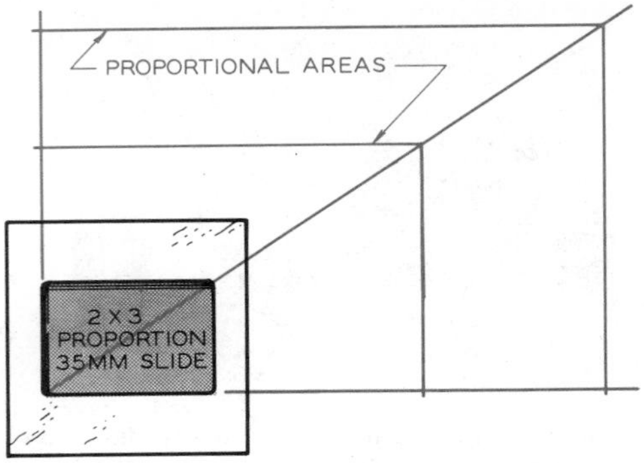

Fig. 16–23 The method of constructing rectangular areas whose sides will have the same proportions as those of a 35 mm slide.

slide film whose vertical and horizontal dimensions have a ratio of 2 to 3.

The method of drawing a graph or an illustration that will be proportional to a 35 mm slide is shown in Fig. 16–23. A diagonal is drawn across the slide opening. Then the bottom of the slide opening is extended to the right and the left side is extended upward. Now if any point on either of these extension lines is projected to the diagonal and then to the other extension line, a rectangle will be formed whose sides are proportional to the sides of the slide opening. Graphs that are to be photographed should be sized in this manner so that they will be properly proportioned.

16–16 HOW TO LIE WITH GRAPHS

Graphs are an effective way of presenting data visually so that they can be easily understood. But graphs can also be used to distort data to the extent that the person using the graphs is actually lying. You should become familiar with graphs and their uses in order to have a better understanding of the information that is being presented.

The three bar graphs shown in Fig. 16–24 present the same data concerning the mileage obtained from two types of fuel. A different impres-

sion is obtained from each graph unless you analyze the construction of each very closely.

The upper graph gives the impression, when you compare the lengths of the bars, that Fuel B is almost five times better than Fuel A. But note that the bars do not begin at zero but at about 13. This is one way of misrepresenting data.

The center graph begins at zero. Thus a comparison of the lengths of the bars gives a true picture of the difference between the two fuels. It can be seen that Fuel B is about 35% better than Fuel A.

The lower graph deemphasizes the difference between the two fuels. By using a much larger range than is needed—no car gets over 90 miles to the gallon, as the graph seems to imply—it makes both fuels look ineffective. The bars are lost on this graph, and even though they are drawn accurately the difference in their lengths appears much less than in the other two graphs.

The width of the bars and the colors used can also give misleading impressions in bar graphs. Beware of bar graphs in which the bars run off the top of the graph; these never give a true graphical picture of the data.

In Fig. 16–25 identical data are plotted on two graphs with different values on the vertical axes. Graph A shows little variation in the data. Graph B

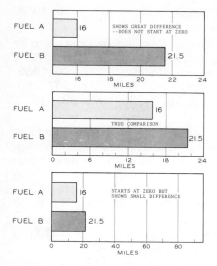

Fig. 16–24 All three graphs show the same data, but a different visual impression is given by each.

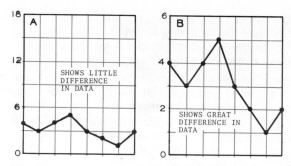

Fig. 16–25 The data in both graphs are the same, but the variation of the data in Graph B appears to be greater than in Graph A.

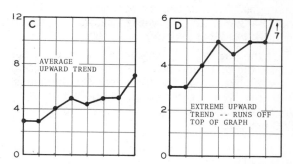

Fig. 16–26 The upward trend of Graph D appears to be greater than that in Graph C, although the data represented by each curve are identical.

gives a more dramatic effect because the different vertical scale emphasizes the differences in the data. The differences appear to be greater than in Graph A. Other scales could have been used to emphasize or deemphasize the data to an even greater extent.

The two graphs in Fig. 16–26 give a different appearance when seen at a glance, even though the same data are plotted on them. In Graph D there appears to be a greater upward trend than in Graph C because of the different scale on the vertical axis. Note that the curve of Graph D runs off the top of the graph, thus giving the impression that the rise was too great to be contained on any graph.

Many other tricks can be used to lie with graphs. These misuses of graphs are often unintentional, but the result is always a misleading impression. Become familiar with the characteristics of a good graph so that you can make effective use of graphs without either misleading or being misled.

PROBLEMS

These problems are to be solved in accordance with Article 3–15 and the specifications of your instructor. Most problems are to be drawn on standard Size A paper ($8\frac{1}{2}'' \times 11''$) using ink or pencil.

The graphs can be drawn on printed grid paper or on blank sheets. Use the standard endorsement, title strip, and border as described in Article 3–15. Refer to the text of this chapter to assist you in the solution of the problems.

Bar Graphs

1 Construct a single-bar graph to show the following family expenses for one month: rent, $150; food, $250; clothing, $75; other, $100.

2 Construct a single-bar graph that shows the relationship of the ages of your classmates: for example, the number who are 16, the number who are 17, and so on.

3 Construct a single-bar graph that shows how your typical 24-hour day is spent. The following categories may be used: time in class, sports, meals, sleeping, chores, and other.

4 Plot the following information as a bar graph. The number of employees at the Brown Manufacturing Company has increased during a four-year period as follows: 1971, 25 employees; 1972, 29 employees; 1973, 37 employees; 1974, 38 employees.

5 Plot the unemployment status of high school dropouts and high school graduates not in college as a bar graph. The vertical scale should be labeled in percentages. The four bars are as follows: less than 5 weeks, 54.3%; 5 to 14 weeks, 32.4%; 15 to 26 weeks; 11.4%; 27 weeks or more, 1.9%.

6 Plot the pay rates of college graduates as a bar graph for the following fields: engineering, $10,000 per year; physics, $9,500 per year; mathematics, $8,700 per year; accounting, $8,500 per year; business administration, $8,900 per year; chemistry, $7,800 per year.

Line Graphs

7 Construct a line graph that will show lifetime earnings in thousands of dollars as related to each year of schooling that a person receives. The horizontal axis shows the years of schooling and the vertical axis shows thousands of dollars. The earnings are as follows: 0 years, 190 thousands; 8 years, 240 thousands; 9 years, 260 thousands; 10 years, 280 thousands; 12 years, 345 thousands; 14 years, 395 thousands; 16 years, 500 thousands; 17 years, 540 thousands; 18 years, 590 thousands.

8 Construct a line graph that compares the high and the low starting salaries of college graduates in the following fields of study: engineering, $6,600 to $12,000; physics, $7,300 to $11,600; mathematics, $4,000 to $10,800; accounting, $5,200 to $10,500; business administration, $4,800 to $10,000; chemistry, $5,000 to $10,000.

9 Construct a line graph to show the average monthly starting salary from 1959 to 1969 of technicians graduating after two years of study at the Southern Technical Institute: 1959, $375; 1960, $385; 1961, $370; 1962. $400; 1963, $420; 1964,

$400; 1965, $490; 1966, $580; 1967, $580; 1968, $625; 1969, $660.

10 The sales of Anderson Department Store are to be plotted as a line graph. Sales from 1962 to 1972 in thousands of dollars are as follows: 1962, 200; 1963, 275; 1964, 311; 1965, 295; 1966, 281; 1967, 350; 1968, 360; 1969, 371; 1970, 350; 1971, 382; 1972, 379.

11 The speeds of an automobile are measured at various intervals as the car is accelerated from a stop. Plot these data as a line graph with distance in feet along the horizontal axis and miles per hour along the vertical axis: 0 ft, 0 mph; 50 ft, 2 mph; 100 ft, 5 mph; 150 ft. 11 mph; 200 ft, 18 mph; 250 ft, 29 mph.

12 Plot the weight variation of a person during a two-year period as a line graph: beginning, 150 lb; fourth month, 152 lb; eighth month, 160 lb; twelfth month, 163 lb; sixteenth month, 171 lb; twentieth month, 174 lb; twenty-fourth month, 176 lb.

13 Plot the following temperatures during a day as a line graph: 8:00 A.M., 40°F; 10:00 A.M., 59°F; 12:00 noon, 71°F; 2:00 P.M., 75°F; 4:00 P.M., 68°F; 6:00 P.M., 61°F.

14 Parts cost less per part when larger numbers are produced because the equipment and manpower are used more efficiently. Plot the following costs for parts versus the number of parts produced as a line graph. The vertical axis will represent cost in dollars, and the horizontal axis the numbers produced. Draw the best curve through these points: 20 parts, $1.10 each; 50 parts, $.72 each; 100 parts, $.46 each; 150 parts, $.45 each; 200 parts, $.29 each; 250 parts, $.30 each; 300 parts, $.28 each.

15 A tank is being filled with fuel through a hose from a pump. Instruments are used to measure the volume of the tank at 10-minute intervals to determine the accumulation of the fuel in gallons. Plot these data as a line graph, and draw the best curve since there may be errors in the instruments and variations in the pump: 0 min, 0 gal; 10 min, 98 gal; 20 min, 401 gal; 50 min, 440 gal; 60 min, 500 gal.

Circle Graphs

16 Construct a circle graph using the data given in Problem 5.

17 Construct a circle graph of the following percentages of the employment status of the 1969 graduates of two-year technician programs: employed, 63%; continuing full-time study, 23%; considering job offers, 6%; military, 6%; other, 2%.

18 Construct a circle graph of the following percentages of the employment status of the 1969 graduates of four-year degree programs: employed, 72%; continuing full-time study, 7%; considering job offers, 8%; military, 12%; other, 1%.

19 Construct a circle graph that shows the relationship between the types of degrees held by engineers in aeronautical engineering: bachelor's degree, 65%; master's degree, 29%; Ph.D. degrees, 6%.

20 Construct a circle graph of the data given in Problem 1.

Photo courtesy of Bureau of Reclamation, U.S. Department of the Interior

17

INTERSECTIONS AND DEVELOPMENTS

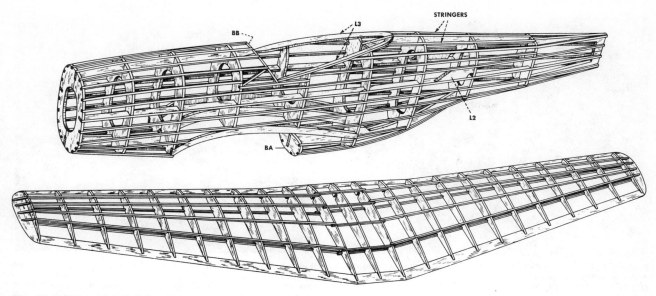

Fig. 17–1 This model of a P-51 Mustang fighter plane is composed of many irregular shapes that intersect and form surfaces that must be developed. (Courtesy of Paul K. Guillow Inc.)

17–1 INTRODUCTION

Most products, structures, and vehicles are composed of geometric shapes that must be formed in such a way that they intersect each other properly when assembled. Drawings made for the purpose of determining the lines formed by joining members are called *intersections*. This chapter will present the basic intersections of standard geometric elements. These intersections can be easily applied to more complex constructions.

An example of a design project requiring the use of intersections is shown in Fig. 17–1. The fuselage and wing structure of this P-51 Mustang fighter plane model were designed so that each member intersects the other members to produce the desired fit. Note that the wing section will fit into the space provided in the lower portion of the plane's body.

The framework of the fuselage and wing shown in Fig. 17–1 must be covered with thin sheet metal to provide a smooth outer surface. In order for the covering to fit properly over the frame, the engineer must develop flat layouts to be used in cutting the covering material. Flat layouts for materials such

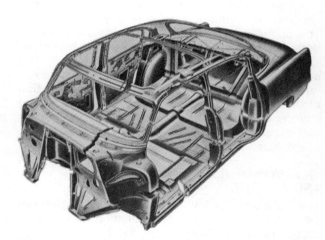

Fig. 17–2 Layouts of flat patterns of sheet metal that are formed to various geometric shapes are called developments. (Courtesy of General Motors Corporation.)

as sheet metal which are to be formed into three-dimensional shapes are called *developments*. Another, similar application of developments is the automobile body shown in Fig. 17–2.

Fig. 17–3 A snowmobile's body, made of sheet metal, is designed with the aid of the principles of intersections and developments. (Courtesy of Innovar Incorporated.)

Fig. 17–4 The petroleum and chemical industries make extensive use of sheet metal shapes that must be designed in accordance with the principles of intersections and developments. (Courtesy of Arco.)

You can find many applications of intersections and developments in your everyday surroundings. The SnowCoupe® (Fig. 17–3) is a vehicle whose body is composed of many intersecting geometric shapes requiring the use of developments. The petroleum and chemical industries must apply intersections and developments to the construction of their processing systems (Fig. 17–4). Shipping cartons and boxes are other examples of objects that require developments, though they use cardboard instead of sheet metal.

17–2 INTERSECTION BETWEEN A LINE AND A PLANE

The basic step is finding an intersection between geometric shapes is the determination of the intersection between a line and a plane. This is illustrated in Fig. 17–5, where the plane is inclined at a 45° angle and the intersecting line is *AB*.

Step 1. The point of intersection between a line and a plane can be found in the view in which the plane appears as an edge. The plane appears as an edge in the right side view in this example; consequently the piercing point (the point of intersection) is found in this view. The point of intersection is then projected to the front view.

Step 2. The visibility of the line must be determined to complete the problem. A line of sight from the front view to the right side view is used to determine the visibility in the front view.

If you can understand the simple principle involved in this problem, it will be easy for you to solve more complex problems, since all shapes are composed of lines. Review this problem as often as necessary during your progress through this chapter.

17–3 INTERSECTION BETWEEN PLANES

The intersection between two planes is a straight line. This line can be seen in the view in which one of the planes appears as an edge. From this view it can be projected to the other orthographic views. An example is shown in Fig. 17–6. In the front view of the plane *ABCD*, the points *A* and *B* are closer to the viewer than are the points *C* and *D*. The right side view of this plane is identical to the front view; however, in the right side view the points *C* and *D* are closer to the viewer. In the front view of the plane *EFGH*, the points *F* and *G* are closer to the viewer than are the points *E* and *H*.

Step 1. Plane *EFGH* appears as an edge in the right side view. Lines *AB* and *CD* intersect this plane at

FIGURE 17-5. INTERSECTION OF A LINE AND A PLANE

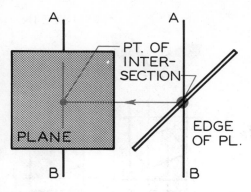

Step 1. The point of intersection can be found in the view where the plane appears as an edge.

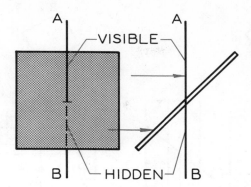

Step 2. Visibility in the front view is determined by looking from the front view to the right side view.

FIGURE 17-6. INTERSECTION BETWEEN PLANES

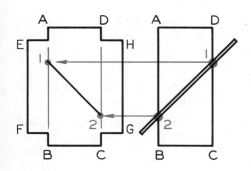

Step 1. The points where the plane *EFGH* intersects the lines *AB* and *DC* are found in the view where the plane appears as an edge. These points are projected to the front view.

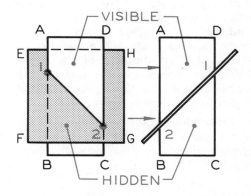

Step 2. Line 1-2 is the line of intersection. Visibility is determined by looking from the front view to the right side view.

points 1 and 2. These points are projected to the front view and are connected to give the line of intersection between the two planes.

Step 2. The visibility in the front view is determined by looking from the front view to the right side view as indicated by the arrows.

17-4 INTERSECTION BETWEEN A PLANE AND A PRISM

A *prism* is an object that is composed of planes that are parallel to the axis of the prism. The right section that is perpendicular to the axis may be triangular, rectangular, or be of any other shape that

FIGURE 17–7. INTERSECTION BETWEEN A PLANE AND A PRISM

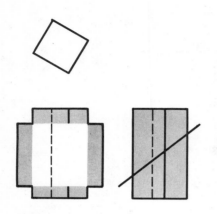

Given: A prism and a plane. Find the intersection between them.

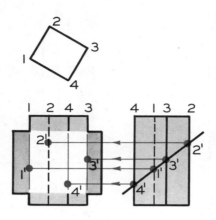

Step 1. The points of intersection of the corner edges of the vertical prism can be found in the view in which the inclined plane appears as an edge.

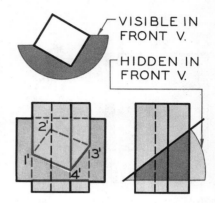

Step 2. The points of intersection are connected to form lines of intersection. Visibility is found by referring to the right side view.

---

is composed of straight lines. The ends of a prism may be slanted at an angle (truncated); in this case, these ends will not be right sections.

The intersection of a prism and a plane is an extension of the previous problem of the intersection between two planes. In the case of the prism, you must find the intersection between several planes. An example is shown in Fig. 17–7.

Step 1. The corner edges of the prism intersect the edge view of the plane at points 1′, 2′, 3′, and 4′. These points are projected to their respective lines in the front view.

Step 2. Points 1′, 2′, 3′, and 4′ are connected to form the lines of intersection in the front view. As in the previous problems, visibility in the front view is found by looking at the right side view from the front view. Note that the visible and hidden zones are marked in the top and right side views, since these views determine the visibility in the front view.

Another example of the intersection of two prisms is shown in Fig. 17–8. The sides of the two prisms appear as edges in the top and side views. The points of intersection can be found in these edge views.

Step 1. Points of intersection 1, 2, and 3 can be found in the top view and the right side view. These points are located in the front view by projection to this view. All of these points are visible in the front view; therefore, the lines of intersection will be visible.

Step 2. Point of intersection 4 is projected from the top and right side views to the front view.

Step 3. Point 4 will be hidden in the front view since it is on the back side of the vertical (triangular) prism. To complete the problem, point 4 is connected to points 1 and 2 with hidden lines of intersection in the front view.

17–5 INTERSECTION OF A VERTICAL AND AN INCLINED PRISM

A vertical prism is intersected by an inclined prism in Fig. 17–9. The line of intersection can be found by applying the previously discussed principles.

Step 1. An auxiliary view is constructed to show the end view of the inclined prism and the corner line *AB*. This is needed to locate the point where the line of intersection bends around the corner *AB*.

FIGURE 17–8. INTERSECTION BETWEEN PRISMS

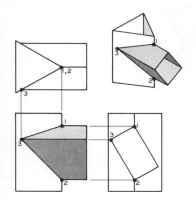

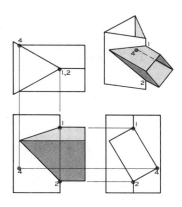

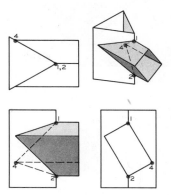

Step 1. Points of intersection 1, 2, and 3 are found in the top and right side views, where the planes appear as edges. These points are projected to the front view.

Step 2. Point 4 is found in the top and right side views and is projected to the front view, where it is a hidden point.

Step 3. Lines 1–4 and 4–2 are drawn as hidden lines since they are on the back side of the vertical prism.

Step 2. Since the sides of the vertical prism appear as edges in the top view, points of intersection 2′ and 3′ can be found in the front view. The line of intersection from 2′ to 3′ bends around the corner line *AB* at point *X* in the front view. Visibility is shown in this view.

Step 3. Point of intersection 1′ is found in the front view. Point *Y* is projected to the front view from the auxiliary view to locate the point where line of intersection 1′–2′ bends around the corner edge. Visibility is determined to complete the problem.

An alternative method of finding the line of intersection between two prisms is illustrated in Fig. 17–10. Vertical cutting plane *A* is passed through the corner line 3–4 in the top view, and points 1 and 2 are found on the inclined prism. Since the cutting plane is parallel to the corner edges of the upper surface of the inclined prism, line 1–2 will be drawn parallel to these sides in the front view. Line 1–2 intersects line 3–4 at point 2. This is where the line of intersection bends around corner line 3–4. The other points of intersection are found as in the previous examples.

The conduit connector shown in Fig. 17–11 is an application of the intersection of planes and prisms. This connector was designed to intersect an inclined wall.

17–6 INTERSECTION OF A CYLINDER AND A PLANE

The principle presented in Article 17–2 applies to the determination of the line of intersection between a cylinder and a plane. To do this construction you must visualize the cylinder as being composed of many parallel lines lying on the surface of the cylinder. The intersection of each of these lines with the plane can be found in the view in which the plane appears as an edge. The method of construction is shown in Fig. 17–12.

Step 1. The plane appears as an edge in the left side view. Two lines are found on the surface of the cylinder by passing cutting plane *A–A* through the center of the cylinder in the top view. These lines intersect the edge view of the inclined plane in the left side view. They are projected to the front view from the top and left side views.

FIGURE 17–9. INTERSECTION BETWEEN TWO PRISMS

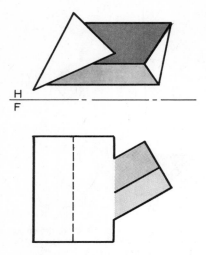

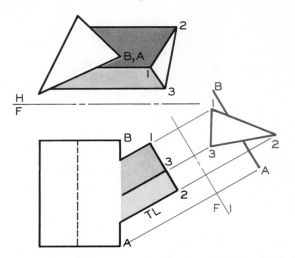

Given: The top and front views of two prisms.
Required: The line of intersection between the two prisms in both views with visibility indicated.

Step 1. Construct the end view of the inclined prism by projecting an auxiliary view from the front view. Show only line *AB*, the corner line of the vertical prism, in the auxiliary view, because this is the only important line. Letter the points.

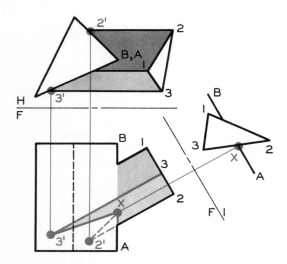

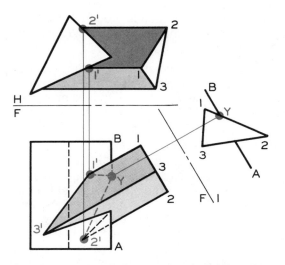

Step 2. Locate the piercing points of lines 2–2′ and 3–3′ in the top view and project them to the front view to the extension of the corner lines. It is rather obvious that a line connecting points 2′ and 3′ will not be a straight line, but will bend around the corner line *AB*. The point where this line intersects the corner is found to be point *X* in the primary auxiliary. Project it back to the front view.

Step 3. It can be seen in the primary auxiliary view that line 1′–2′ bends around corner line *AB* at point *Y*. Draw line 1′–*Y*–2′ in the front view. This line is found, by inspection of the primary auxiliary view, to be invisible in the front view. Draw line 1′–3′ as a visible line; it does not bend around a corner.

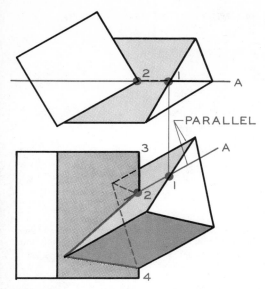

Fig. 17–10 The line of intersection is found here by using vertical cutting planes that pass through the corner edges of the inclined prism.

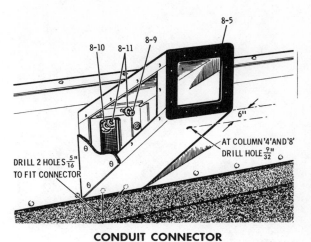

CONDUIT CONNECTOR

Fig. 17–11 This conduit connector is an example of the application of an intersection between a plane and a prism. (Courtesy of the Federal Aviation Agency.)

FIGURE 17–12. INTERSECTION BETWEEN A CYLINDER AND A PLANE

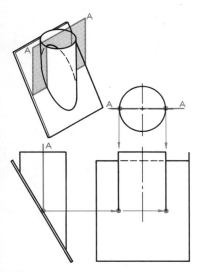

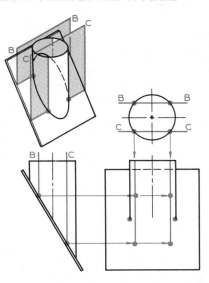

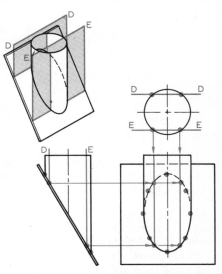

Step 1. A vertical cutting plane, *A–A*, is passed through the cylinder parallel to its axis to find two points of intersection.

Step 2. Two more cutting planes, *B–B* and *C–C*, are used to find four additional points in the top and the left side views; these points are projected to the front view.

Step 3. Additional cutting planes are used to find more points. The points are connected to give an elliptical line of intersection.

Fig. 17-13 A scientist is making an adjustment on a Van de Graaff accelerator. This machine is an example of an intersection between two cylinders. (Courtesy of Humble Oil & Refining Company.)

Step 2. Cutting planes *B–B* and *C–C*, which are parallel to cutting plane *A–A* and equidistant from it, locate two more lines on the cylinder in the top and left side views. The points of intersection between these lines and the inclined plane are found in the front view by projecting from the top and left side views.

Step 3. Cutting planes *D–D* and *E–E* locate two more lines on the cylinder in the top and left side views. The points where these lines intersect the inclined plane in the front view are found by projection and are connected with a smooth curve of intersection. This curve is an ellipse that can be drawn with the proper ellipse template or with an irregular curve.

FIGURE 17-14. INTERSECTION BETWEEN TWO CYLINDERS

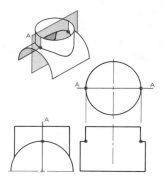

Step 1. A cutting plane, *A–A*, is passed through the cylinders parallel to the axes of both. Two points of intersection are found.

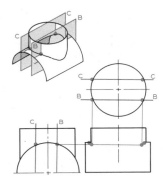

Step 2. Cutting planes *C–C* and *B–B* are used to find four additional points of intersection.

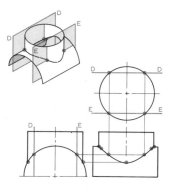

Step 3. Cutting planes *D–D* and *E–E* locate four more points. Points found in this manner are connected to give the line of intersection.

Fig. 17–15 This model of a processing system illustrates many applications of intersections between cylinders. (Courtesy of Monsanto Corporation.)

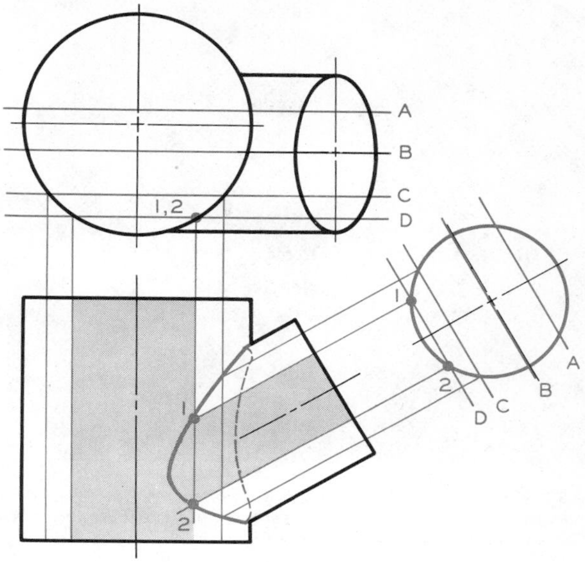

Fig. 17–16 Cutting planes and an auxiliary view are used to find the line of intersection between these two cylinders.

17–7 INTERSECTION BETWEEN CYLINDERS

The Van de Graaff accelerator shown in Fig. 17–13 illustrates the intersection of two cylinders. This intersection can be found by graphical construction as shown in Fig. 17–14.

Step 1. Cutting plane *A–A* is passed through the top and left side views of the two cylinders. The cutting plane appears as an edge in both of these views. This cutting plane locates two lines on the vertical cylinder in the front view. The points of intersection of these two lines with the other cylinder are projected to the front view.

Step 2. Cutting planes *B–B* and *C–C* are constructed in the same manner as in Step 1 to locate more points of intersection. These are projected to the front view.

Step 3. Cutting planes *D–D* and *E–E* are passed through the intersecting cylinders to locate other

points on the line of intersection. These points are connected in the front view to complete the problem. Additional cutting planes would yield more points on the line of intersection and thus a more accurate curve.

17–8 INTERSECTION BETWEEN A VERTICAL AND AN INCLINED CYLINDER

The working model of the processing system in Fig. 17–15 shows many examples of complex intersections between geometric shapes. Many of these are intersections between cylinders. Figure 17–16 illustrates the method of constructing the line of intersection between an inclined cylinder and a vertical cylinder.

The intersection between the cylinders is found by the use of cutting planes drawn in the top view. For example, points 1 and 2 were found in the front view by projecting from the auxiliary

Fig. 17–17 The Apollo Spacecraft Command Module was designed using principles of intersection on conical surfaces. (Courtesy of NASA.)

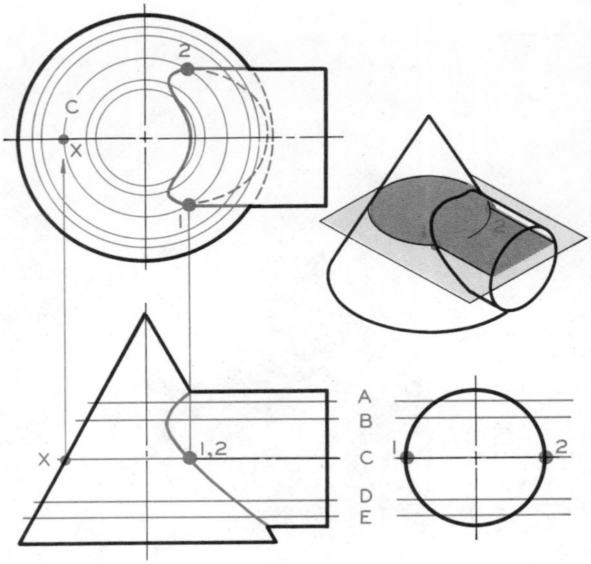

Fig. 17–18 Cutting planes perpendicular to the axis of a cone are used to find the intersection between this cone and a cylinder.

view and the top view, where plane *D* intersects these cylinders. The auxiliary view is needed to find the edge view of the inclined cylinder. Points 1 and 2 are on the line of intersection in the front view. The colored area in the front view shows the path of cutting plane *D*.

Additional points are found and connected to give the complete line of intersection. Visibility is shown in the front view.

17–9 INTERSECTION BETWEEN A CONE AND A CYLINDER

The Apollo Spacecraft Command Module shown in Fig. 17–17 is a conical shape. The portals and the equipment installed inside the conical shape were designed by using principles of intersection between various geometric shapes with a cone. The intersection between a cone and a cylinder is shown in Fig. 17–18.

Horizontal cutting planes are passed through the cone perpendicular to its axis to cut sections that appear as circles in the top view. These horizontal

cutting planes also locate lines on the horizontal cylinder that can be projected to intersect the circular sections in the top view. Points 1 and 2 are given as examples of points on the line of intersection between the cylinder and the cone which were found by this method.

This method is feasible only if the cylinder is horizontal and the cone's axis is vertical. The sections cut by a cutting plane that was not perpendicular to the cone's axis would not be easy-to-construct circles.

17–10 INTRODUCTION TO DEVELOPMENTS

A dramatic example of large-scale use of developments is the C–5 transport fuselage (Fig. 17–19). This huge body with its irregular forms is composed of flat pieces of sheet metal attached to the frame. These pieces are cut in accordance with layouts called developments, and their proper shapes are found to a great extent by graphical methods. The completed C–5 is shown in flight in Fig. 17–20.

Fig. 17–19 Principles of developments were used to find the patterns for the sheet metal covering for this C-5 fuselage. (Courtesy of Lockheed-Georgia Company.)

Fig. 17–20 The completed C-5 is shown taking off. Note that the main landing gear is rotating about each strut. (Courtesy of Lockheed-Georgia Company.)

Fig. 17–21 All ductwork, such as this example in a Montana carpet mill, must be designed using principles of developments. (Courtesy of Bureau of Reclamation, Department of the Interior).

A smaller-scale example of developments is the sheet-metal ductwork in the carpet mill in Fig. 17–21. These developments began at the drawing board where their specifications were laid out. The air conditioning and heating system in your school is composed of developments of this type.

17–11 DEVELOPMENT OF A PRISM

A development of any geometric shape can be laid out either as an inside or an outside pattern. Inside patterns are used more often so that the markings and etchings on the material will not show on the finished product. Besides, most bending machines make inward folds at the markings. You should always indicate whether your pattern is an outside or an inside pattern.

The simple prism shown in Fig. 17–22 is developed into a flat pattern. The corner edges of the prism are vertical lines and are true length in the front view. The right section is perpendicular to the axis of the prism; consequently the right section

appears as an edge in the front view. A stretch-out line is drawn parallel to the edge view of the right section, beginning at point 1. The prism is imagined to be rolled out along its right section.

If an inside pattern is desired, the next point selected will lie to the right of point 1, since the pattern will be laid out in this direction. If you assume that you are standing inside the prism as illustrated pictorially in Fig. 17–22 and that you are looking at point 1, then point 2 will be to your right. You should use the top view for this analysis. Distance 1–2 is transferred from the top view to the stretch-out line, with point 2 to the right of point 1. Line 1–2 is on the right section. All right section lines are true length in the top view.

Lines 2–3, 3–4, and 4–1 taken from the right section are laid out in sequence along the stretch-out line. The length of each of the fold lines is found by projecting its true length from the front view. The ends of the fold lines are connected to form the limits of the developed surface. Fold lines are drawn as thin lines on the development drawing.

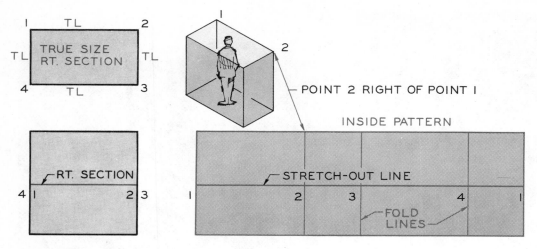

Fig. 17-22 The development of a prism with a rectangular section.

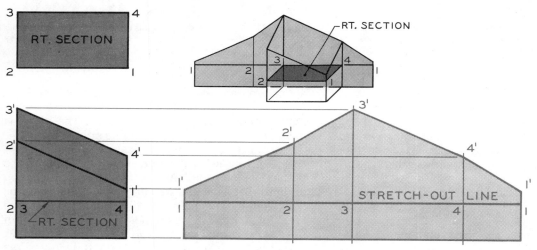

Fig. 17-23 The development of a prism with a beveled end to give an inside pattern.

17-12 DEVELOPMENT OF A TRUNCATED PRISM

A truncated prism is a prism that has been cut across its end in an oblique direction. The top and front views of a typical truncated prism are shown in Fig. 17-23.

The method of developing this prism is very similar to the development of the regular prism shown in Fig. 17-22. The only difference is the variation in the lengths of the vertical fold lines.

The stretch-out line is drawn to the right of the front view and parallel to the edge view of the right section shown in the front view. Since the right section is true size in the top view, the distances from fold line to fold line can be found in the top view. These distances are transferred to the stretch-

Intersections and developments   17-12

FIGURE 17-24. DEVELOPMENT OF AN INCLINED PRISM

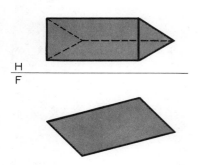

Given: The top and front views of an inclined prism.
Required: The inside pattern of the developed surface of the prism and the end sections.
Reference: Article 17–13.

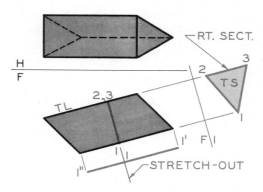

Step 1. The edge view of the right section will appear perpendicular to the true-length axis of the prism in the front view. Determine the true size of the right section by constructing an auxiliary view of the right section. Project bend line 1′–1″ as the first line of the development.

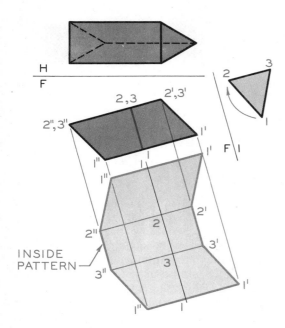

Step 2. Since the pattern is developed toward the right, beginning with line 1′–1″, the next point is found to be line 2′–2″ by referring to the auxiliary view. Transfer true-length lines 1–2, 2–3, and 3–1 from the right section to the stretch-out line to locate the elements. Determine the lengths of the bend lines by projection.

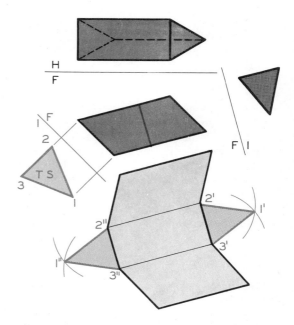

Step 3. Construct true-size views of the end pieces by projecting auxiliary views from the front view. Connect these surfaces to the development of the lateral sides to form the completed pattern. Fold lines are drawn with thin lines; outside lines are drawn as regular object lines.

out line where the fold lines are drawn and numbered. The length of each fold line is found in the development by projecting from the front view. The ends of the fold lines are connected with straight lines to complete the pattern.

Note that the starting line of the pattern was selected at corner 1 because this was the shortest line. This choice minimizes the cost and time required to join the sides of the pattern, since the joining seam is shortest at this point.

17–13 DEVELOPMENT OF AN INCLINED PRISM

The prism in Fig. 17–24 is inclined in the front view; consequently the right section does not appear true size in the top view. To find the development, an auxiliary view must be constructed to find the right section true size. This auxiliary view is projected from the front view, since the right section appears as an edge in the front view where it is perpendicular to the axis of the prism (Step 1).

The pattern is laid out in the same manner as shown in Fig. 17–23. The stretch-out line is drawn parallel to the edge view of the right section in the front view. The distances between the fold lines are taken from the true-size view of the right section and are laid off on the stretch-out line in the developed view (Step 2).

The developments of the end pieces can be found by a secondary auxiliary view, which is projected perpendicularly from the edge view of the end of the inclined prism. The patterns for the end pieces are drawn as part of the total development. You could cut out your completed pattern and fold it into a three-dimensional model. This would, in fact, be a good exercise to help you to visualize the principles of developments.

17–14 DEVELOPMENT OF CYLINDERS

An assembly involving intersections and developments with cylinders is shown in Fig. 17–25. The problems encountered in the design of such an assembly can be solved graphically.

Figure 17–26 illustrates how a cylinder can be developed. The axis of the cylinder is true length

Fig. 17–25 Intersections and developments of cylinders were necessary for the construction of this portion of the asphalt terminal. (Courtesy of Arco.)

in the front view. The right section, since it is perpendicular to the axis, appears as an edge in the front view. The stretch-out line is drawn parallel to the edge view of the right section, and point 1 is chosen as the beginning point since it is on the shortest line that could be used for the seam. The first step in the development is to divide the circular view of the cylinder into equal divisions. For accurate results the sectors should be no larger than 15°; they should certainly never be larger than 30°.

To find the inside pattern, assume that you are standing inside the cylinder in the top view as

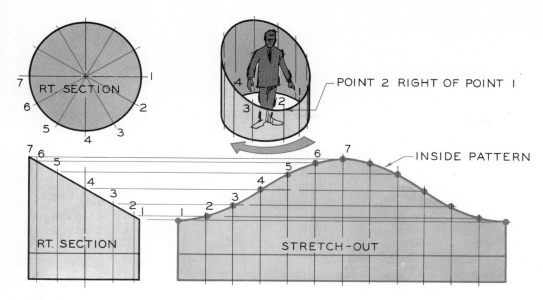

Fig. 17–26 The development of an inside pattern of a cylinder.

illustrated pictorially in Fig. 17–26. Since the pattern will be laid out to the right, point 2 will be to the right of point 1. Thus this sequence of points is followed in laying out the distances between the fold lines along the stretch-out line.

The distances between the elements of the cylinder are taken from the top (true-size) view of the right section as chordal distances to approximate the circumference around the cylinder. These distances are transferred to the stretch-out line. The closer the intervals between the lines on the circular section, the closer the graphical solution will be to the actual circumference. If accuracy is very important, the circumference can be determined mathematically and laid out true length along the stretch-out line. It can then be divided into the desired number of divisions.

The formula for the circumference of a circle is 3.14 × D, where D = the diameter. If a cylinder had a 10″ diameter, its circumference would be 31.4″.

The ends of the lines in the circular view are projected to the front view and then to the respective fold lines in the development. The points thus found are connected with a smooth curve.

17–15 DEVELOPMENT OF A PYRAMID

In order to construct the development of a pyramid, you must know how to find a line true length, since the fold lines of a pyramid do not appear true length in either the top or the front view. An example of finding a line true length is shown in Fig. 17–27.

Step 1. A vertical axis is passed through point *A* and the top view of line *AB* is used as a radius for drawing the cone of which *AB* is an element.

Step 2. Line *AB* is revolved to position *AB'* to be parallel to the frontal plane. In this position, *AB'* will show as an outside element of the cone in the front view, where it will be true length and can be measured.

The development of a pyramid is illustrated in Fig. 17–28. Since all fold lines have point 0 as a

FIGURE 17–27. TRUE LENGTH BY REVOLUTION

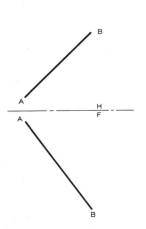

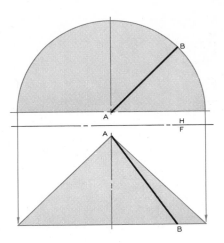

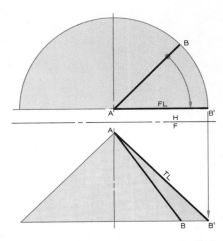

Given: The top and front views of line *AB*.

Step 1. The top view of line *AB* is used as a radius for drawing a half view of the base of a cone. The front view of the cone is drawn with its axis passing vertically through point *A*.

Step 2. The top view of *AB* is revolved into position *AB'*. where it is parallel to the frontal plane. In this position it is the outside element of a cone in the front view, where it can be measured true length.

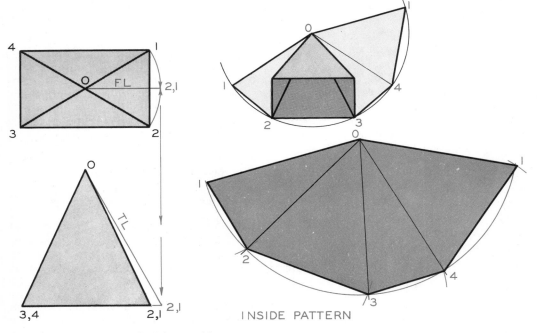

INSIDE PATTERN

Fig. 17–28 Development of a right pyramid.

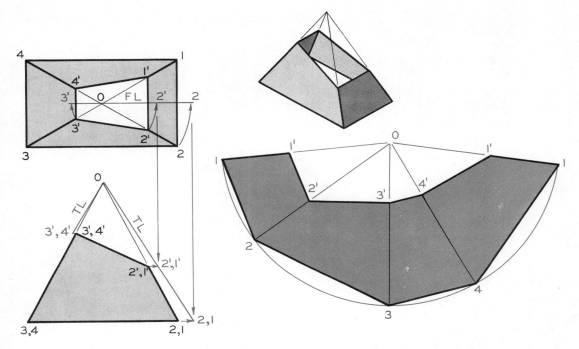

Fig. 17–29 Development of a truncated pyramid.

common point, a stretch-out line will not be used in this type of problem; instead, a series of adjoining triangles will be drawn in the development.

Recall that *all lines* in a development must be true length. Lines 1–0 and 2–0 are revolved into the frontal plane in the top view so that their true length will be seen in the front view, as shown. Since the pyramid is a right pyramid (its axis is perpendicular to the center of its base), all bend lines are equal in length. Consequently, in the development, line 1–0 is used as a radius for constructing an arc that will contain all the corner points lying on the base of the pyramid. Since the base is a horizontal plane, the lines of the base appear true length in the top view. Distance 1–2 is measured in the top view and transferred to the development, where it is a chord intersecting the arc at points 1 and 2. Lines 2–3, 3–4, and 4–1 are found in the same manner. The bend lines are drawn with thin lines from the base to the apex, point 0.

17–16 DEVELOPMENT OF A TRUNCATED PYRAMID

The truncated pyramid shown in Fig. 17–29 is developed in the same manner as the pyramid in Fig. 17–28. However, an additional step is required to find the upper lines of the development, the lines which form the plane of truncation.

The development is laid out as though the object were a complete pyramid with point 0 as the apex. The true-length lines from the apex to points 1', 2', 3', and 4' are found by revolution as shown in Fig. 17–29. The distances thus found are measured along the respective lines from point 0 to locate the corner points on the upper surface of the truncated pyramid. These points are then connected to complete the inside development.

The mounting pads in Fig. 17–30 are pyramids that intersect an engine body. This is an example of a design that involves both intersections and developments.

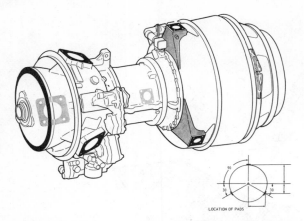

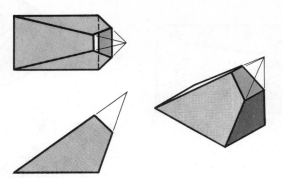

FIGURE 17–31. DEVELOPMENT OF AN OBLIQUE PYRAMID

Given: The top and front views of an oblique, truncated pyramid.
Required: Find the inside development of the pyramid's surface.
Reference: Article 17–17.

Fig. 17–30 Examples of pyramid shapes used in the design of the mounting pads of an engine. (Courtesy of Lycoming Division of the Avco Corporation.)

17–17 DEVELOPMENT OF AN OBLIQUE PYRAMID

The three steps in constructing the development of an oblique pyramid are shown in Fig. 17–31. The true lengths of all bend lines are found in Step 1 by revolving the lines into the frontal plane and projecting them to the front view. These lines are found to vary in length, since the pyramid is not a right pyramid.

The plane of each triangular surface of the pyramid is shown true size in the development. The method of constructing a triangle when three sides are known can be reviewed in Article 5–8. Since the base is horizontal, the base lines are true length in the top view.

The triangles are drawn adjoining each other, with point 0 common to them all (Step 2). The upper edges of the developed surface are located by finding the true-length distances from point 0 to points 1', 2', 3', and 4' by revolution. These distances are measured along each bend line from point 0. The points thus found are connected to form the upper line of the development.

17–18 DEVELOPMENT OF A CONE

A widely used application of intersections and developments is the construction of forms for concrete structures. The forms must be accurately built and braced to hold the concrete until it sets

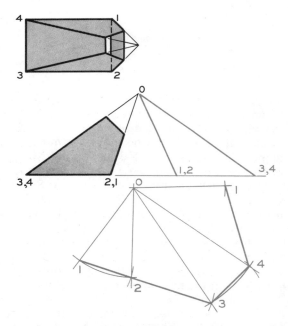

Step 2. The base lines appear true length in the top view. Using these true-length lines from the top view and the revolved lines in the front view, draw the development triangles. All triangles have one side and point 0 in common. This gives a development of the surface, excluding the truncated section.

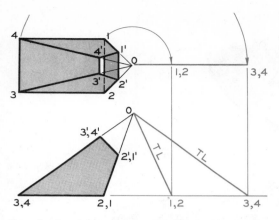

Step 1. Revolve each of the bend lines in the top view until it is parallel to the frontal plane. Project these lines to the front view to find their true length. Let point 0 remain stationary but project points 1, 2, 3, and 4 horizontally in the front view to the projectors from the top view.

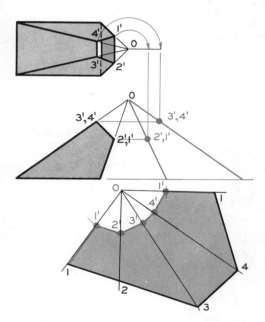

Step 3. The true lengths of the lines from point 0 to the points 1′, 2′, 3′, and 4′ are found by revolving these lines. These distances are laid off from point 0 along the respective lines to establish points along the upper edge of the developed pattern. The points are then sequentially connected by straight lines to complete the development.

Fig. 17–32 This spillway structure was constructed after forms were designed to receive the concrete. The design of the forms required the application of the development of conical shapes. (Courtesy of the Bureau of Reclamation, Department of the Interior.)

to form the permanent structure. A concrete spillway is shown in Fig. 17–32. This is a conical shape whose forms were designed in accordance with the principles of developments that will be discussed in the following paragraphs.

The cone in Fig. 17–33 is divided into a number of sectors in the top view and triangular sections in the front view. The smaller the sectors and triangles, the more accurate will be the development.

Element 0–10 is true length in the front view since it is a frontal line in the top view. All elements of a right cone are equal; therefore, line 0–10 will be used to construct the arc on which the developed base will lie. The inside pattern of the cone is drawn beginning with point 1 and proceeding to the right. The point to the right of point 1 is point 2, as is evident from inspection of the top view and the pictorial view of the cone.

The true-length chordal distance from point 1 to point 2 is transferred from the top view to locate point 2 in the development. Successive triangles are constructed in this manner until point 1 is reached again at the opposite edge of the development. The base of the development is then drawn as an arc rather than a series of chords.

A more accurate approximation of the distances between the base points on the arc can be found

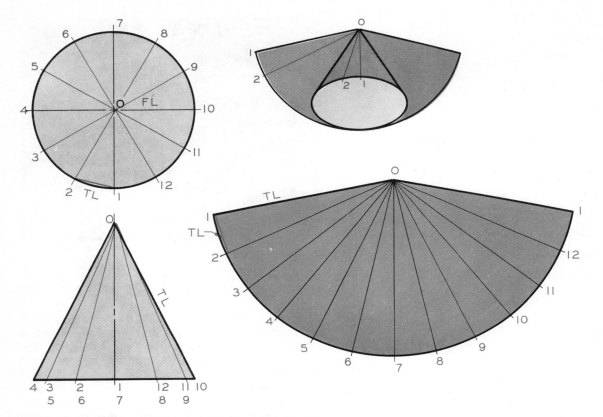

Fig. 17–33 The development of an inside pattern of a right cone.

Fig. 17–34 This fireplace made of sheet steel was designed using the principles of conical developments. (Courtesy of American Iron and Steel Institute.)

by determining the circumference mathematically (3.14 × *D*) and laying off this distance along the arc formed by the radius 0–1. However, the graphical approximation is sufficient in most cases.

17–19 DEVELOPMENT OF A TRUNCATED CONE

The sheet-metal fireplace in Fig. 17–34 was designed and constructed according to principles of conical developments and intersections. Note that the conical shape has been truncated so that it is not a complete cone.

To develop a truncated cone, it is best to begin by constructing the pattern as if it were a complete cone with an apex (Fig. 17–35). This construction is almost identical to the problem in Fig. 17–33.

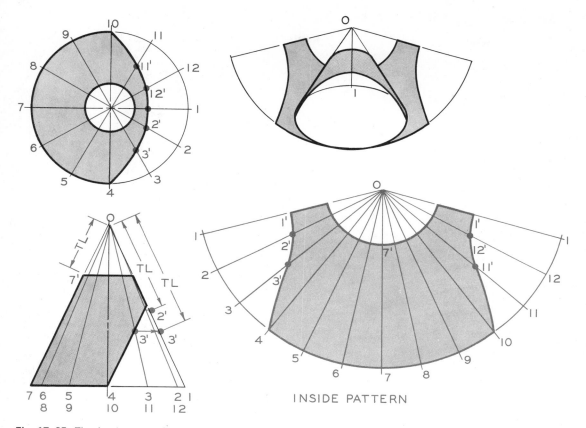

Fig. 17–35 The development of a truncated cone.

A conical section has been removed from the upper portion of the cone. This section can be removed from the development pattern by constructing an arc using the true-length line 0–7' in the front view as the radius.

Another section has also been removed from the cone. To remove the corresponding section from the developed pattern, true-length measurements from point 0 to the line of truncation are found by revolution. Lines 0–2' and 0–3' in the front view are projected horizontally to the extreme element, 0–1, where they appear true length. These true-length distances are measured along the respective lines in the development to find the points through which a smooth curve can be drawn to complete the development.

Fig. 17–36 Transition pieces are used to join a circular shape to a rectangular section. (Courtesy of Western Precipitation Group, Joy Manufacturing Company.)

FIGURE 17-37. DEVELOPMENT OF A TRANSITION PIECE

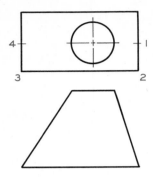

Given: The top and front views of a transition piece.
Required: An inside development of the surface from point 1 to point 4.
Reference: Article 17-20.

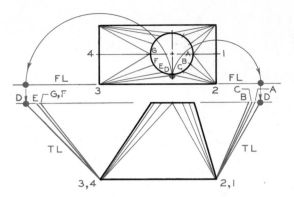

Step 1. Divide the circular edge of the surface into equal parts in the top view. Connect these points with bend lines to the corner points, 2 and 3. Find the true length of these lines by revolving them into a frontal plane and projecting them to the front view. These lines represent elements on the surface of an oblique cone.

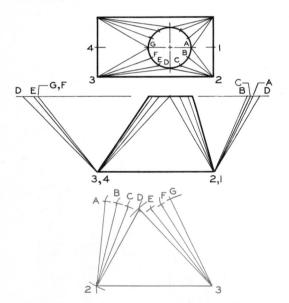

Step 2. Using the true-length lines found by revolution and the chordal distances between the points on the circular edge in the top view, draw a series of triangles joined together at common sides to form the development. *Example:* Find point *D* by drawing arcs with centers at points 2 and 3 and with radii equal to the true lengths of the lines 2–*D* and 3–*D* respectively. The intersection of these two arcs is point *D*. Now, using point 2 as center, draw an arc with radius equal to the true length of the line 2–*C*. Then, using *D* as center, draw an arc having the chordal distance *CD* as its radius. The intersections of these two arcs is point *C*.

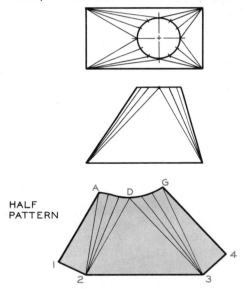

HALF
PATTERN

Step 3. Construct the remaining planes, *A*–1–2 and *G*–3–4, by triangulation to complete the inside half pattern of the transition piece. Draw the fold lines as thin lines at the places where the surface is to be bent slightly. The seam line of the pattern is *A*–1, the shortest possible line.

17-20 DEVELOPMENT OF A TRANSITION PIECE

A transition piece is used to create a smooth connection between two objects of different shapes. The transition has the shape of one object at one end and the shape of the other object at the other end. A duct with a rectangular cross section is connected to a cylinder with a transition piece in Fig. 17-36.

The development of a transition piece is illustrated in Fig. 17-37. The circle in the top view of the transition piece is divided into equal parts and radial lines are drawn to each corner of the base. The true lengths of these lines are found by revolu-

tion (Step 1). The chordal lines between the points on the circular section and the lines which form the rectangular base appear true length in the top view, since these lines are horizontal. The line of separation for the development is line 1–A, the shortest line of the pattern.

A portion of the development is laid out by triangulation in Step 2, utilizing the true lengths of the lines. The remaining planes of the surface are found in Step 3 to complete half of the symmetrical development. The upper points are connected with a smooth curve and the points on the base are connected with straight lines. Thin fold lines are given to indicate the curving surface at the corners.

PROBLEMS

These problems are to be solved in accordance with Article 3–15 and the specifications of your instructor. Problems are to be drawn on Size A ($8\frac{1}{2}'' \times 11''$) or Size B ($11'' \times 17''$) paper using ink or pencil.

General Problems

Problems 1 through 22 should be laid out as shown in Fig. 17-38 with two problems per sheet. The given problems are sketched on a grid where each square represents $\frac{1}{4}''$. These should be transferred to grid paper of the same type, or else drawn on blank paper with the aid of an architects' scale. Lay out the problems *with instruments*. Refer to specific articles in this chapter when necessary to review principles that must be used in solving the problems.

Problems 23 through 27 should be laid out on a Size A sheet with the horizontal format shown in Fig. 17-41 and the type of endorsement shown in Article 3–15.

Intersections

1 Lay out the two problems shown in Fig. 17-38 with instruments. Complete the lines of intersection and show visibility in all views.

2-10 Lay out the views given in Fig. 17-39 with instruments. Complete the intersections in all views and show visibility.

11-22 Lay out the given views of the problems in Fig. 17-40 using instruments. Complete the lines of intersection in all views and show visibility. Note that some views are half views to conserve space.

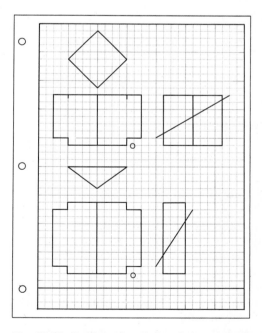

Fig. 17-38 Problems 1 and 2 and the layout for Problems 2 through 22.

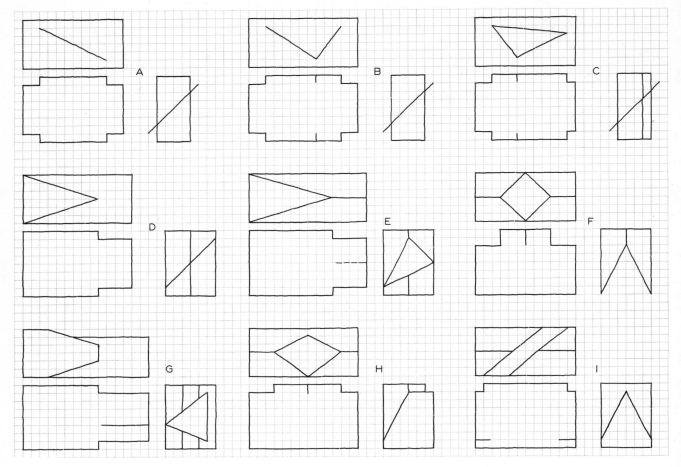

Fig. 17–39 Problems 2 through 10: Intersections.

You should draw these as full views in the problems that you solve.

23 Lay out the problem given in Fig. 17–41 on a Size A sheet with a horizontal format using instruments. Complete the lines of intersection and show visibility.

24–27 Lay out the given views of the intersection problems in Fig. 17–42 with instruments. Complete the lines of intersection in all views and show visibility. Use the same sheet layout as shown in Fig. 17–41.

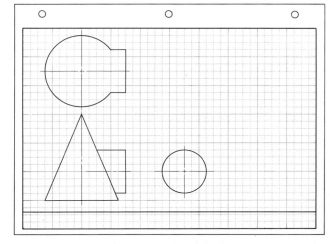

Fig. 17–41 Problems 23 and 61 and the layout for Problems 24 through 27.

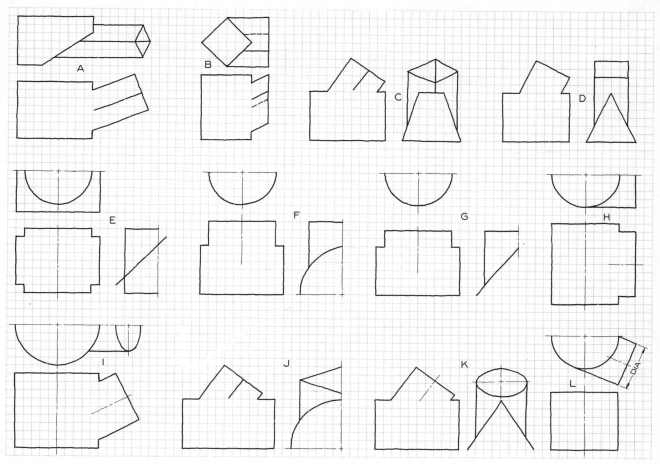

Fig. 17–40 Problems 11 through 22 and 49 through 60: Intersections and developments.

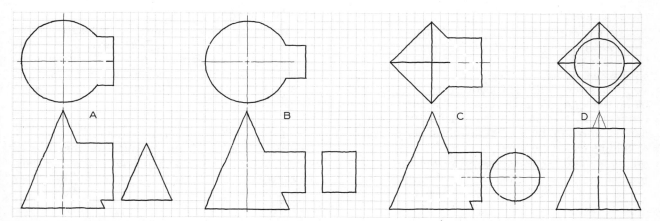

Fig. 17–42 Problems 24 through 27 and 62 through 65: Intersections and developments.

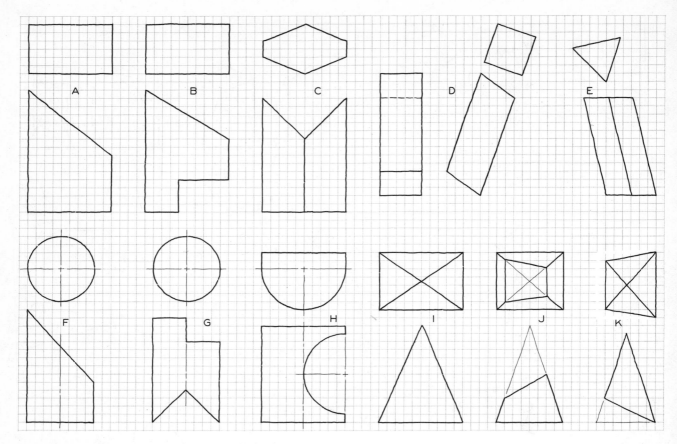

Fig. 17–43 Problems 28 through 38: Developments.

Developments

28–38 Lay out the development problems shown in Fig. 17–43 with instruments. Each problem should be drawn on a Size B sheet (11″ × 17″). Size A sheets can be used if the problems are drawn half size. Use the horizontal layout with the title strip along the long side of the sheet. Position the given views at the left of the sheet so that the developments can be drawn to the right of the given views. These should be *inside* patterns.

39–48 Follow the instructions for Problems 28–38 but use the views given in Fig. 17–44.

Combination Problems

49–65 After finding the lines of intersection of the problems in Figs. 17–40, 17–41, and 17–42, construct developments of the parts with instruments. These developments must either be drawn on Size B (11″ × 17″) sheets or drawn half size on Size A sheets.

Design Problems

Design problems are more typical of the type of work that is performed by draftsmen and technicians. They require that you use your judgment to supply

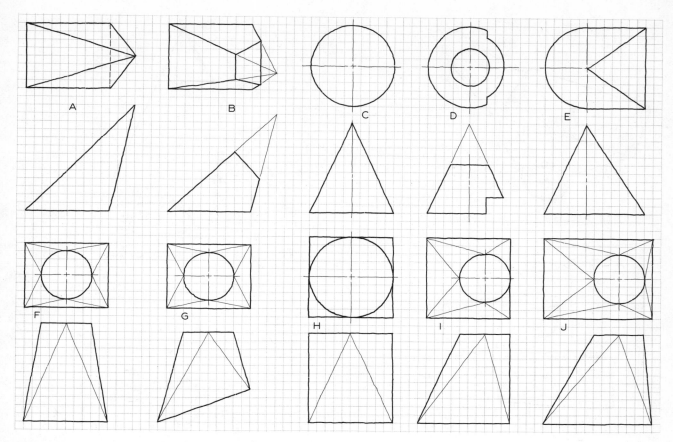

Fig. 17–44 Problems 39 through 48: Developments.

missing dimensions and details that are not clearly indicated. In some cases, only several important dimensions are given; the other details are left for you to design and to present in the form of orthographic views, developments, and intersections. Design problems can be presented on Size A or B paper using instruments or as assigned by your instructor. You should begin each problem by preparing a freehand sketch—pictorials and view drawings—to help you refine your ideas.

You will be responsible for selecting the proper scale and placing your drawings on the sheet to give the best arrangement.

66 *Garden wheelbarrow* (Fig. 17–45). This sketch of a designer's idea for a wheelbarrow must be laid out to determine the flat patterns of sheet metal necessary to make the body. Prepare the necessary drawings and developments with instruments. Redesign this wheelbarrow if you can think of a better, more functional shape.

67 *Mailboxes* (Fig. 17–46). Several examples of sheet-metal mailboxes are shown. Design a mailbox that could be manufactured and sold. You must first determine the best dimensions for a mailbox. Prepare the necessary drawings and developments

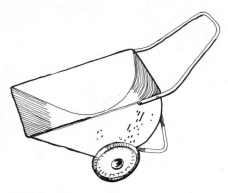

Fig. 17–45 Problem 66: Garden wheelbarrow.

Fig. 17–46 Problem 68: Mailbox design.

Fig. 17–47 Problem 67: Design for a trash can lid.

Fig. 17–48 Problem 69: Backyard tepee design.

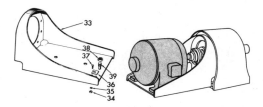

Fig. 17–49 Problem 70: Motor mount for an electric motor. (Courtesy of the Falk Corporation.)

to explain your design. Show the dimensions for each portion of your design.

68 *Trash can lid* (Fig. 17–47). An example of a lid with a push-door that fits on top of a 55-gallon can is shown. Design a better lid that would serve the same purpose but in a different way. Prepare the necessary drawings and developments to explain your design. The diameter of the drum is $22\frac{1}{2}''$.

69 *Tepee* (Fig. 17–48). Make a working drawing of the parts of this backyard tepee. It is to be made of $\frac{1}{4}''$ plywood. You must first make development drawings of its panels.

70 *Motor mount* (Fig. 17–49). The motor mount is designed to hold an electric motor as shown. Make

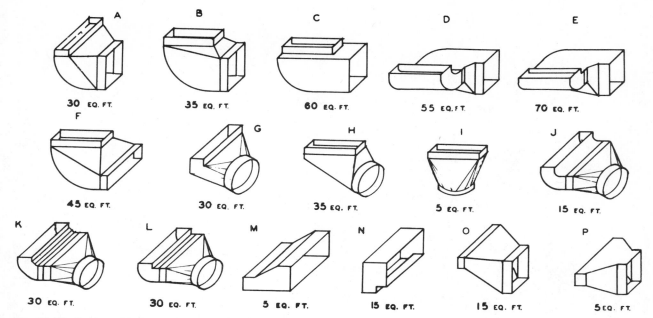

A
30 EQ. FT.

B
35 EQ. FT.

C
60 EQ. FT.

D
55 EQ. FT.

E
70 EQ. FT.

F
45 EQ. FT.

G
30 EQ. FT.

H
35 EQ. FT.

I
5 EQ. FT.

J
15 EQ. FT.

K
30 EQ. FT.

L
30 EQ. FT.

M
5 EQ. FT.

N
15 EQ. FT.

O
15 EQ. FT.

P
5 EQ. FT.

Fig. 17–50   Problems 71 through 86: Boot fittings for forced-air ductwork.   (Courtesy of National Warm Air Heating and Air Conditioning Association.)

the development drawings of the mount. Estimate the dimensions. Consider other designs that could be used to hold the motor.

71–86 The boot fittings used for forced-air heating and air conditioning are made of sheet metal (Fig. 17–50).   Prepare drawings of these fittings and make developments of each.

87 *Golf cart* (Fig. 17–51).   Make development drawings of the front cowling of the cart. This is the sheet-metal cover on which the Viking symbol is painted. Estimate the dimensions.

88 Make development drawings of a sheet-steel fireplace similar to the one shown in Fig. 17–34. It will be necessary for you to determine suitable dimensions for a fireplace of this type.

89 Design a container made of cardboard that could be used for carrying canned products or bottled drinks.   Examine existing packs, and attempt to design a better one. Make a full-size model of your completed design.

Fig. 17–51   Problem 87: Cowling design for a golf cart. (Courtesy of Versal Incorporated.)

18
TECHNICAL
ILLUSTRATION

Fig. 18–1 A technical illustrator's orthographic views of a P-47D Thunderbolt. (Courtesy of Paul K. Guillow, Inc.)

Fig. 18–2 A technical illustrator's pictorial of the Thunderbolt shown in Fig. 18–1. (Courtesy of Paul K. Guillow, Inc.)

18–1 INTRODUCTION TO TECHNICAL ILLUSTRATION

The draftsman and designer prepare working drawings from which various products can be built. Even the trained draftsman often finds working drawings hard to read; consequently, pictorials are often used to help the draftsman visualize the appearance of the finished product. The pictorial is one type of *technical illustration*.

Three views of the P-47D Thunderbolt are shown in Fig. 18–1. Even in orthographic projection, the technical illustrator has represented the plane with as much realism as possible. Most people can understand the plane's form by studying the orthographic views. However, the illustration in Fig. 18–2 combines the three orthographic views into a single pictorial that leaves little doubt about the plane's shape and proportions.

The illustration in Fig. 18–2 is an artistic form of technical illustration that is usually prepared for advertising purposes or for reproduction in special publications. There are many forms of technical illustration, most of which are prepared to serve a functional purpose with less artistic expression than this example.

18–2 THE TECHNICAL ILLUSTRATOR

The technical illustrator is responsible for preparing all types of illustrations of products, mechanisms, and devices. His job differs from the artist's in that his illustrations must be technically correct and must faithfully represent the object being illustrated. The artist has more freedom, and his primary objective is the creation of an impression, not necessarily a true likeness.

To be successful, the technical illustrator must have both a technical and an artistic background. Many of his illustrations are prepared by referring to working drawings; he must, therefore, be able to understand working drawings. At the same time he must understand the tools and methods used by the artist. Practically all technical illustrations are prepared for reproduction in manuals, bulletins

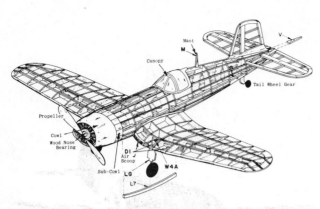

Fig. 18–3 A technical illustration showing how the parts of a model of the F4U-5 Corsair are assembled. (Courtesy of Sterling Models.)

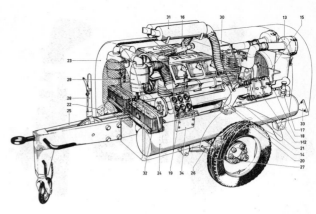

Fig. 18–5 Technical illustrations are used in catalogs and product literature. (Courtesy of Planaprint International Inc.)

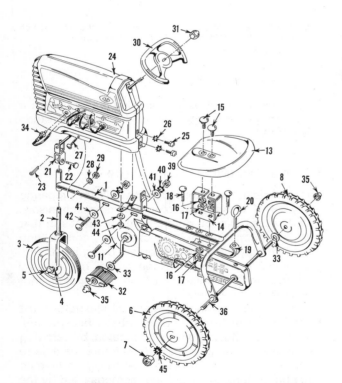

Fig. 18–4 A technical illustration of a toy tractor that describes the method of assembly of the various parts. (Courtesy of Murray Ohio Manufacturing Company.)

Fig. 18–6 The stylist is concerned with the outward appearance of a product. (Courtesy of Ford Motor Company.)

brochures, and other publications; the technical illustrator must understand the methods of reproduction so that he can prepare the illustrations properly for the printer.

Technical illustrators play an important role in industry by preparing illustrations to explain methods of construction and maintenance that must be shown pictorially. Many technical illustrators are employed in the manufacturing industries to illustrate and prepare product manuals that describe the assembly and repair of various products. The field of

Fig. 18–7   A stylist's drawing of a body style for an automobile. (Courtesy of Ford Motor Company.)

technical illustration is a promising area of work. It is expected that more technical illustrators will be needed in the future.

18–3 TYPES OF TECHNICAL ILLUSTRATION

The line drawing of the F4U-5 Corsair model (Fig. 18–3) is an example of a technical illustration that is less artistic than the previous examples. This illustration, however, serves the purpose of describing the construction of the model. Additional shading and artistic techniques would not have enhanced the usefulness of the drawing. This type of drawing is sometimes referred to as an assembly, since it shows how the parts are put together.

Many products are shipped unassembled to conserve shipping space. An example is the toy tractor shown in Fig. 18–4. After purchase, the parts must be assembled by referring to this drawing and a set of plans that includes written instructions. Imagine how difficult it would be to assemble this toy without the help of the technical illustrator who prepared this drawing.

Other technical illustrations are used to illustrate advertising booklets and catalogs. Figure 18–5 is an example of an illustration that explains a product, in this case a compressor, much more fully than would a photograph. This view was taken through the cover of the body, as if the cover were trans-

parent. You can obtain a very good understanding of the interior parts with the help of this drawing.

A specialist in technical illustration is the product stylist, who is concerned with the exterior appearance of the product. Stylists of automobiles must be excellent illustrators in order to develop and communicate their ideas for body styles to others (Fig. 18–6). They prepare many freehand sketches of automobiles (Fig. 18–7) and the details of the various parts of automobile bodies. These illustrations are used as the basis for preparing the detailed working drawings once the final design is decided upon.

Figures 18–3 through 18–6 are only a few types of illustration used in industry. Technical illustrations are used extensively in catalogs, parts manuals, maintenance publications, advertisements, and production pictorials.

18–4 TYPES OF PICTORIAL

The three basic types of pictorial construction used by the technical illustrator are (1) the isometric, (2) the oblique, and (3) the perspective (Fig. 18–8). You will remember that isometrics and obliques were discussed in Chapter 9. You should refer to that chapter whenever necessary to review the techniques described there.

The technical illustrator must become familiar with the advantages and disadvantages of each of

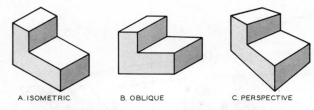

Fig. 18–8 The basic types of pictorials used by the technical illustrator: isometric, oblique, and perspective.

A. ISOMETRIC B. OBLIQUE C. PERSPECTIVE

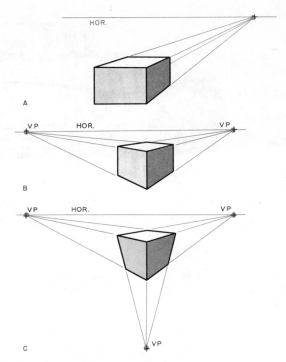

Fig. 18–9 Three types of perspectives: (A) one-point, (B) two-point, and (C) three-point.

these pictorial methods so that he can select the most appropriate type for a particular requirement. An understanding of the fundamentals of pictorials is necessary to the illustrator.

18–5 PERSPECTIVES

Perspectives are the most realistic pictorials that can be drawn, especially where large objects are involved. A perspective is a view that attempts to reproduce what is actually seen by the eye or by the lens of a camera. Three types of perspective are shown in Fig. 18–9. These are (A) one-point, (B) two-point, and (C) three-point perspectives.

Note that the sides of the objects shown in perspective tend to converge at a point called the *vanishing point* (VP) even though these lines are parallel on the actual object. This is true also of objects that you observe with your eye; parallel lines tend to converge as they get farther away from you.

One-point and two-point perspectives are the most commonly used types of perspective illustration. The three-point perspective is used less often because it is the most complicated type to construct.

18–6 CONSTRUCTION OF A ONE-POINT PERSPECTIVE

Figure 18–10 shows the steps involved in constructing a one-point perspective. The top and side views of a block are given, along with the horizon, station point, ground line, and picture plane. These terms are defined below; you should become familiar with them because they are used to describe the construction of all perspectives.

Picture plane is the plane on which the perspective is projected; it corresponds to the film in a camera on which the image is projected. It is drawn as a horizontal edge in the top view.

Horizon is a line in the front view that represents the infinite extension of the horizontal plane; it corresponds to the line along which the ocean appears to meet the sky when you are looking out to sea.

Vanishing points are points on the horizon where the horizontal lines of a perspective converge.

Station point is the location of the observer's eye in the plan view. In the front view the station point will always lie on the horizon.

An example of an architect's drawing of a one-point perspective is shown in Fig. 18–11. Note that this illustration shows the internal construction of

FIGURE 18–10. CONSTRUCTION OF A ONE-POINT PERSPECTIVE

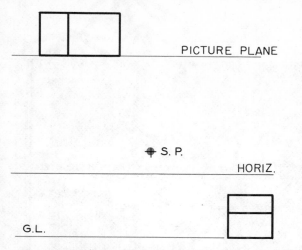

PICTURE PLANE

✛ S.P.

HORIZ.

G.L.

Given: The top and side views of an object, the station point (position of the observer's eye), horizon, and ground line.
Required: Construct a perspective of the object.

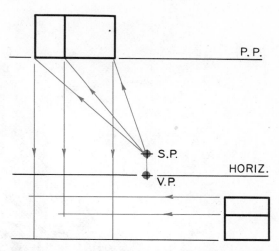

P.P.

✛ S.P.

HORIZ.

V.P.

Step 1. Since the object is parallel to the picture plane, there will be only one vanishing point, located on the horizon below the station point. Projections from the top view and side view establish the front plane of the object. This surface is true size, since it lies in the picture plane.

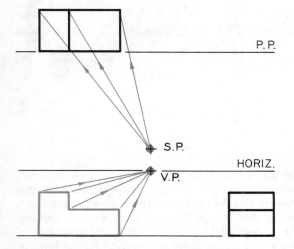

P.P.

✛ S.P.

HORIZ.

V.P.

Step 2. Draw projectors from the station point to the rear points of the object in the top view and from the front view to the vanishing point on the horizon. In a one-point perspective, the vanishing point is the front view of the station point.

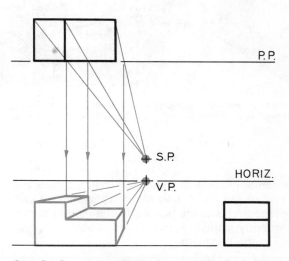

P.P.

✛ S.P.

HORIZ.

V.P.

Step 3. Construct vertical projectors to the front view from the points where the projectors from the station point cross the picture plane. These projectors intersect the lines leading to the vanishing point to establish the rear points of the object in the perspective view. This is called a one-point perspective because the lines converge at a single point.

Fig. 18–11 A one-point perspective prepared by an architect. (Courtesy of Kaiser Permanente Cement Co. and A. Quincy Jones, Architect.)

the concrete block wall. The wall that occupies the right half of the figure and the entry at the left end of the receding wall are parallel to the picture plane; consequently, parallel lines on these surfaces appear parallel in the perspective.

18–7 TYPES OF TWO-POINT PERSPECTIVE

In a two-point perspective, two planes of an object are inclined to the picture plane; thus two vanishing points are required on the horizon. Different perspective views can be obtained by varying the position of the horizon. Three extremes are shown in Fig. 18–12. An aerial view is obtained when the height of the object does not extend to the horizon (part A). A ground view is found when the bottom of the object lies on the horizon (part B). A general type of perspective is seen in part C; in this type, a portion of the object extends above and below the horizon.

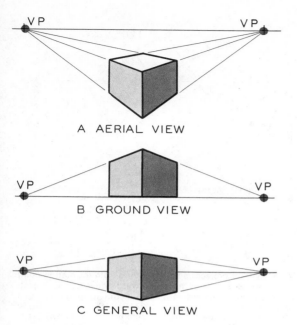

Fig. 18–12 Three views of a two-point perspective.

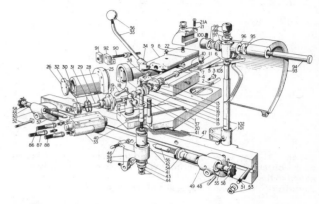

Fig. 18–13 A two-point perspective of a lathe assembly shaded with ink lines. (Courtesy of T. S. Harrison & Sons Limited.)

18–8 CONSTRUCTION OF A TWO-POINT PERSPECTIVE

Figure 18–13 is an example of a lathe assembly that was drawn pictorially as a perspective. Note that the parallel lines tend to converge in this two-point perspective.

The construction of a two-point perspective is shown in Fig. 18–14. The top and front views of the object and the station point are given.

Step 1. The ground line is drawn where the front view is positioned to find the heights that will be used. The horizon is located somewhat above the object to give a slight aerial view. The vanishing points are found by drawing lines parallel to the sides of the object in the top view through the station point. The points where these lines intersect the picture plane are projected to the horizon in the front view to locate two vanishing points.

Step 2. Line *AB* in the top view lies in the picture plane; hence it will be true length in the perspective view. Its height can be determined by projecting point *A* from the front view to intersect the projection of point *A* downward from the top view. Lines are drawn connecting each end of line *AB* in the perspective view with the vanishing points. These lines represent infinite extensions of the surfaces of the objects. Projectors are now drawn from the station point to the corners of the object in the top view. The points where these projectors intersect the picture plane are projected to the front view. Here the projectors from the picture plane intersect the lines connecting *A* and *B* with the vanishing points. These points of intersection locate the corners of the block.

Step 3. The notch is removed in the perspective view by locating point *C* on the true-length line *AB*

FIGURE 18–14. CONSTRUCTION OF A TWO-POINT PERSPECTIVE

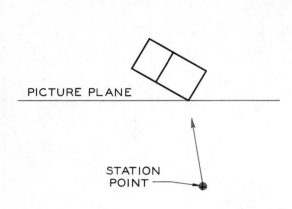

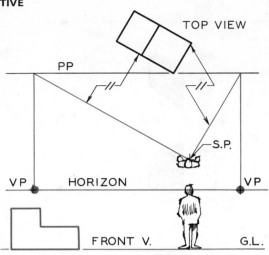

Given: The top view of an object and the station point (position of the observer's eye). The front view is also known and will be added to the drawing in Step 1.

Required: Draw the perspective of the object.

Step 1. Construct projectors which extend from the station point to the picture plane parallel to the forward edges of the object. Project these points vertically to a conveniently located horizontal line (horizon) in the front view to establish vanishing points. Draw the ground line below the horizon and construct the known front view on the ground line.

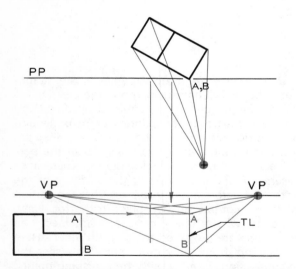

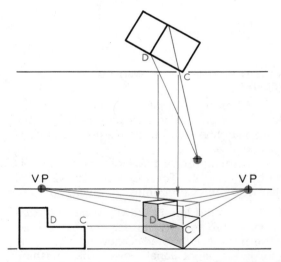

Step 2. Since all lines in the picture plane are true length, line *AB* is true length. Consequently, *AB* is projected from the front view to the perspective. Then each end of *AB* is projected to one of the vanishing points to determine two perspective planes. Projectors are drawn from the station point to the exterior edges of the top view. The points where these projectors intersect the picture plane are projected to the perspective view to determine the limits of the object.

Step 3. A notch must be removed from the box found in Step 2 to complete the perspective. Point *C* is determined in the perspective view by projecting from the front view to the true-length line *AB*, A projector is drawn from *C* to the left vanishing point. Point *D* will lie on this projector directly below the point where a projector from the station point to *D* in the top view crosses the picture plane. The notch is completed by projection to the respective vanishing points.

Fig. 18–15 The construction of a two-point perspective of an object that is not in contact with the picture plane.

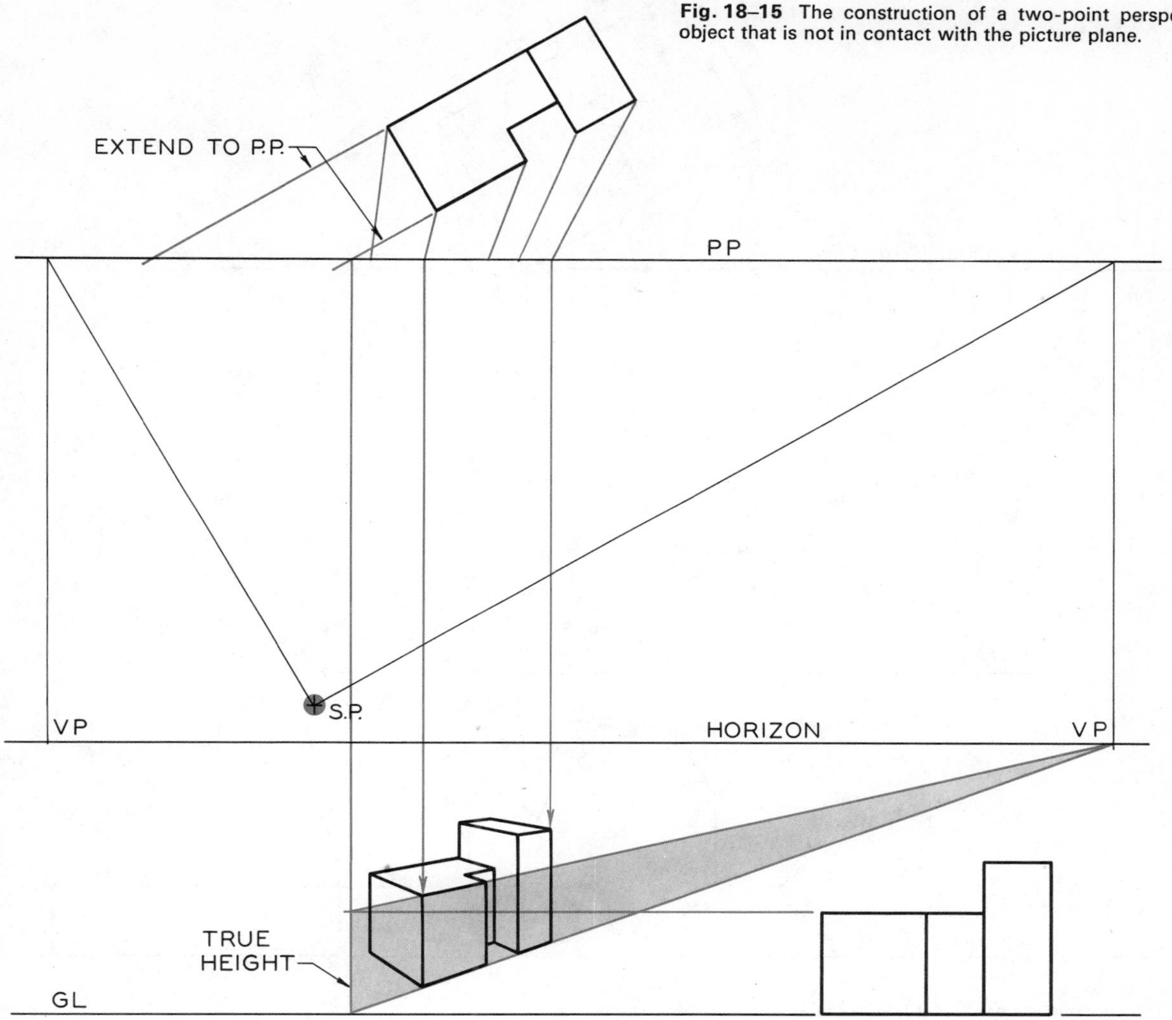

by projection from the front view. Lines are drawn from point *C* to the vanishing points. Point *D* in the perspective can be found by projecting from the top view as shown.

18–9 TWO-POINT PERSPECTIVE OF AN OBJECT NOT IN CONTACT WITH THE PICTURE PLANE

In the two-point perspective shown in Fig. 18–14, one corner of the block was in contact with the picture plane and was true length in the perspective. All vertical measurements had to be made along this line, since this was the only true-length line in the perspective.

A perspective view of an object can be drawn even though the object does not touch the picture plane. A perspective of this type is illustrated in Fig. 18–15. The sides of the object are extended to the picture plane as though the object were unlimited in size. True heights can be measured in

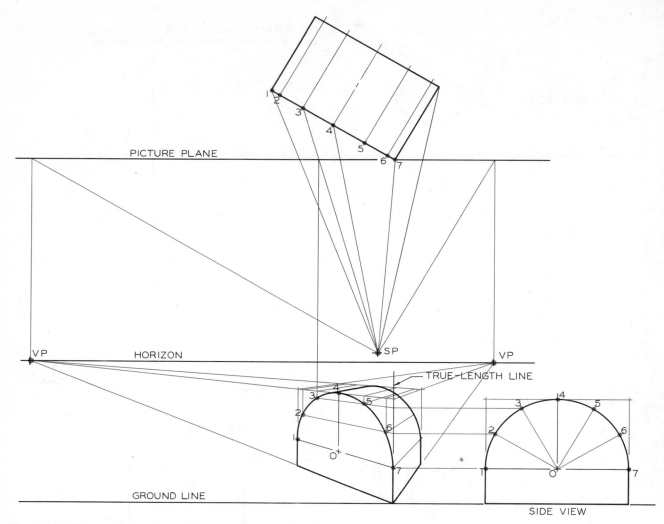

Fig. 18–16 The construction of circular features in a two-point perspective.

the perspective view where the extended sides intersect the projectors from the picture plane.

Once the true height of a surface is established, lines are drawn connecting this true height with one of the vanishing points. The tinted area in Fig. 18–15 thus represents an infinite extension of one of the surfaces of the object. To find what portion of this area is occupied by the actual surface of the object,

projections are drawn from the station point to the corners of this surface in the top view. The points where these projectors intersect the picture plane are projected to the perspective view to locate the vertical edges of the surface.

Note that the front corner of the block is less than true height since it is behind the picture plane. The heights of the other features must be measured

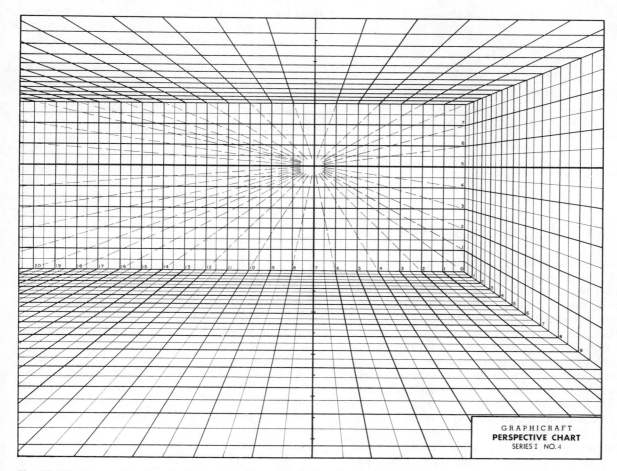

Fig. 18–17 A perspective chart for drawing a one-point perspective. (Courtesy of Graphicraft.)

along the true-height line and then projected to the object in the same manner.

18–10 TWO-POINT PERSPECTIVE OF A CURVED OBJECT

The technical illustrator must be able to construct perspectives of parts with curves and arcs, since these shapes are often used in products. Figure 18–16 shows an object with a semicircular end that is to be drawn as a two-point perspective.

The arc is divided into equal divisions in the right side view. The points thus created are located in the top view by a true projection. Each point is located its true distance from the center of the semicircle. A line is drawn from each point in the too

Fig. 18–18 The use of a perspective grid. The chart is overlaid with tracing paper. (Courtesy of Graphicraft.)

view to the back edge of the block parallel to the centerline.

The object is blocked in and drawn in perspective as if it did not have a semicircular end. Projectors are drawn from the station point to the points on the arc in the top view. The points where the projectors intersect the picture plane are projected to the perspective view, where they locate points on the front face of the object. For example, to locate point 3 in the perspective view, a projector is drawn from point 3 in the side view to the true-length corner of the object in the perspective view. The point where this projector intersects the true-length line is projected to the left vanishing point. Point 3 in the perspective is the point where the projector to the vanishing point intersects the projector from the picture plane. The remaining points on the front edge of the curved surface are found in the same manner.

Points on the rear arc are found by drawing projectors from the points on the front arc to the right vanishing point. Projectors are then drawn from the station point to the points on the rear arc in the top view. The points where these projectors intersect the picture plane are projected to the perspective view. The points where the projectors from the picture plane intersect the projectors to the right vanishing point are points on the rear arc.

18–11 PERSPECTIVE CHARTS

Perspective charts are available with perspective grids printed on them for different kinds of perspective views. A grid can be selected for an aerial view, a ground view, or a general view. Different angles of views are available for both one-point and two-point perspective charts.

An example of a chart for a one-point perspective is shown in Fig. 18–17. This grid is drawn to scale; consequently, the designer can simply assign a scale to the grid and then draw the perspective on a sheet of tracing paper placed over the grid.

A two-point perspective chart is shown in Fig. 18–18. This type of chart is excellent for preliminary sketches, since it gives a general idea of the appearance of the finished perspective. The finished perspective can be drawn with instruments in the same manner. To benefit fully from perspective charts you should understand the principles of perspective construction.

18–12 SHADES AND SHADOWS

Shades and shadows are used to give technical illustrations added depth and increased realism. Only the most basic types of objects will be discussed here to introduce the fundamentals of projecting shadows.

A surface is in *shade* when it is not exposed to light. For example, if you were facing the sun, your back would be in shade since it would be shielded from the direct rays of light. Likewise, your body would shield a portion of the ground from the light; this area is called *shadow*.

An isometric drawing of a block is given in Fig. 18–19 to illustrate the method of finding shades and shadows of an object. The principles presented here apply to more complicated objects also.

Step 1. A light source is constructed that is parallel to the surface of the paper. This source is the hypotenuse of a right triangle which represents a ray of light. Since the ray of light is parallel to the surface of the paper, the vertical and horizontal sides of the right triangle are true length and perpendicular.

Step 2. The shadow cast from the front vertical corner of the cube is found by drawing a line parallel

FIGURE 18–19. SHADES AND SHADOWS OF A CUBE

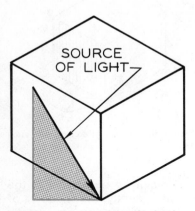

Step 1. The light-source triangle is constructed for a ray of light that is parallel to the drawing paper.

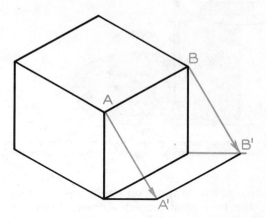

Step 2. The shadows cast from vertical corners passing through the points *A* and *B* are found. Note that the projectors from each end of the vertical corners are parallel to the sides of the light-source triangle.

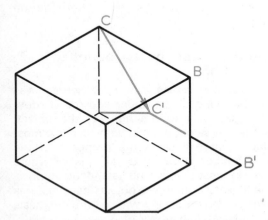

Step 3. The shadow of the vertical line through point *C* is found even though it is hidden. Line *C′B′* is drawn to complete the outline of the shadow.

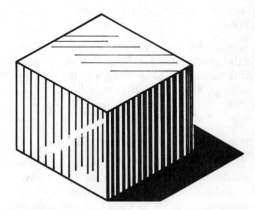

Step 4. The object is shaded to indicate the surface in shade and the shadow.

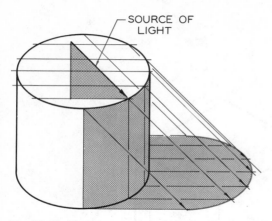

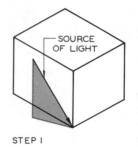

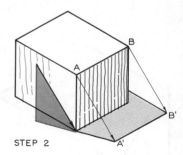

Fig. 18–20 The construction of the shade and shadow of a cylindrical shape. The light source is parallel to the surface of the paper.

Fig. 18–21 The construction of the shadow of an isometric cube with an oblique source of light.

to the source of the light through point *A*. This line intersects the horizontal projector drawn from the bottom of the vertical corner to locate point *A′*. The shadow cast from the back corner is found in the same manner. The line connecting *A′* and *B′* is the shadow of line *AB* and is parallel to line *AB*.

Step 3. The shadow cast from the vertical corner through point *C* is found using the method described in Step 2. This shadow will, of course, be hidden. Point *C′* is then connected to *B′* to represent the shadow of line *CB*.

Step 4. The shadow area is made solid black, and the surface of the object that is in shade is shaded with parallel lines.

The finished drawing of the cube is more realistic than the line drawing in Step 1. The addition of shades and shadows to a drawing makes the illustration appear more like the actual object as seen by the eye.

18–13 SHADES AND SHADOWS—CYLINDER

Finding the shadow cast by a cylinder requires the application of the same principles used to find the shadow of a cube. However, since the shadow cast by a cylinder involves a curve, a number of points must be plotted. An example of this technique is shown in Fig. 18–20.

The light source is drawn to be parallel to the surface of the paper; consequently, the shadows of vertical lines on the cylinder will be cast horizontally to the right.

A number of vertical lines are drawn on the shade side of the cylinder. Projectors are drawn parallel to the light source through the upper ends of these lines, and horizontal projectors are drawn from the lower ends of the lines. The intersections of these projectors locate points on the curve of the shadow cast by the cylinder. Note that the elliptical curve of the shadow is the same shape as the elliptical end of the cylinder, since both lie on horizontal planes.

18–14 SHADES AND SHADOWS—OBLIQUE SOURCE OF LIGHT

In the previous examples, the light source was parallel to the plane of the paper and the shadow was cast horizontally to the right of the object. However, the source of light can be placed in almost any position that will serve the purposes of the illustrator. The light source is usually placed where it will give the most readily understandable impression of the object. Sometimes objects have features that cannot be shown clearly without the emphasis given by shades and shadows.

An isometric drawing of a cube is shown in Fig. 18–21. In this figure the light source is oblique

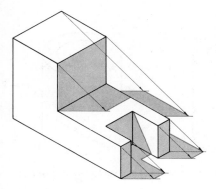

Fig. 18–22 Shades and shadows give realism to an illustrator's drawing.

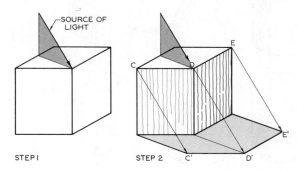

Fig. 18–23 The construction of the shadow of an oblique drawing of a cube with an oblique light source.

rather than parallel to the surface of the paper. Once the sides of the light-source triangle have been established, the shadows are located by means of the previously discussed methods.

Step 1. Begin by drawing a triangle with one side parallel to the vertical lines of the cube. The base of the triangle is established by connecting the bottom of the vertical side to the corner of the cube. If these two sides of the triangle meet at any angle other than 90°, then the light source is oblique to the plane of the paper. Always imagine the light-source triangle as a right triangle. If you do this, you will realize that if the angle between the vertical side and the base is 90°, you are looking at a true-size view of the triangle and the light source is parallel to the plane of the paper. If the angle is not 90°, then your view of the triangle is not a true-size view and the light source is oblique. You may select any angle that you think will give a descriptive shadow of the object. The third side of the triangle, the hypotenuse, represents a ray of the light source.

Step 2. Projectors are drawn parallel to the sides of the light-source triangle through the end points of the vertical lines of the cube. The projectors from the upper ends of lines A and B in Fig. 18–21 will intersect the projectors from the lower ends at points A' and B'. Note that the projectors from the upper ends are parallel to the hypotenuse of the

light-source triangle, and the projectors from the lower ends are parallel to the base. The points A' and B' are points on the shadow cast by the object. To complete the outline of the shadow, it is necessary to find the shadow cast from the hidden edge of the cube, as illustrated in Fig. 18–19.

A more complex isometric with shades and shadows is shown in Fig. 18–22. Note that the shadows give depth to the drawing and make it appear more realistic. While looking at the drawing, squint your eyes so that you see a fuzzy view of the object. Even though you can barely see the lines of the object, the areas of shade and shadow give you a good three-dimensional impression of its form. The principles used to construct this drawing are the same as those introduced in the previous examples.

18–15 SHADES AND SHADOWS—OBLIQUE DRAWINGS

Shades and shadows can be constructed on oblique drawings as well as on isometric drawings. The method is shown in Fig. 18–23.

Step 1. A triangle is constructed to locate the source of light. This light source is oblique to the surface of the paper.

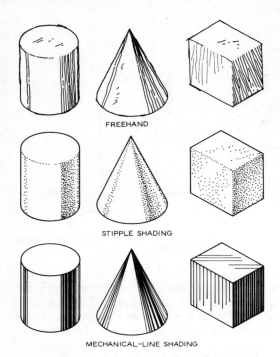

FREEHAND

STIPPLE SHADING

MECHANICAL–LINE SHADING

Fig. 18–24 Methods of applying ink shading to several basic geometric shapes.

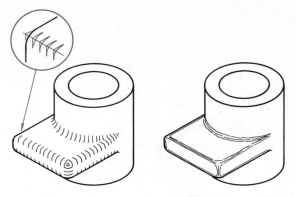

Fig. 18–25 Two methods of illustrating fillets and rounds with ink.

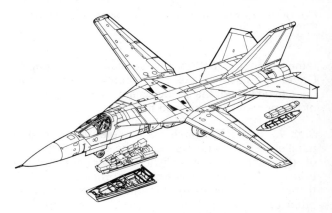

Fig. 18–26 An ink illustration of the RF-111 that does not use shading or shadows. (Courtesy of General Dynamics.)

Step 2. Projectors are drawn through each end of the vertical lines parallel to the sides of the light-source triangle. The intersections of these projectors locate points *C'*, *D'*, and *E'* on the shadow. These points are connected to form the outline of the shadow.

18–16 FAKING SHADES AND SHADOWS

It is important for you to understand the fundamentals of constructing shades and shadows. The principles that have been presented here are no more than a brief introduction to the subject. Once you understand these fundamentals, you will be able to approximate shadows on a drawing without spending a great deal of time on construction.

The technical illustrator refers to the technique of approximating shadows as *faking* shadows. Shades and shadows that are incorrectly faked will be noticed by even the untrained observer. There-

fore, when you are undecided as to how the shadows should appear on an illustration, you must always apply the rules of construction given in the previous articles.

Shades and shadows can also be constructed on perspective drawings, but the techniques for doing this are not presented here. A number of textbooks are available on the construction of shades and shadows for those interested in learning more about this subject.*

---

* See Lawton M. Patten and Milton L. Rogness, *Architectural Drawing*, 3rd ed. Dubuque, Iowa: William C. Brown, 1968. Also C. Leslie Martin *Design Graphics*, rev. ed. New York: Macmillan, 1968.

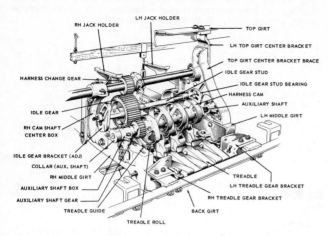

RH JACK HOLDER
LH JACK HOLDER
TOP GIRT
LH TOP GIRT CENTER BRACKET
TOP GIRT CENTER BRACKET BRACE
IDLE GEAR STUD
IDLE GEAR STUD BEARING
HARNESS CAM
AUXILIARY SHAFT
LH MIDDLE GIRT
HARNESS CHANGE GEAR
IDLE GEAR
RH CAM SHAFT CENTER BOX
IDLE GEAR BRACKET (ADJ)
COLLAR (AUX. SHAFT)
RH MIDDLE GIRT
AUXILIARY SHAFT BOX
AUXILIARY SHAFT GEAR
TREADLE GUIDE
TREADLE ROLL
TREADLE
LH TREADLE GEAR BRACKET
RH TREADLE GEAR BRACKET
BACK GIRT

Fig. 18–27 An ink illustration of a portion of a weaving loom. Line shading is used to emphasize the shapes of the parts. (Courtesy of the Draper Corporation.)

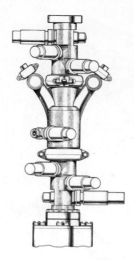

Fig. 18–28 An ink illustration using a stipple technique and parallel lines to add depth to an orthographic drawing. (Courtesy of L. G. Whitfield, Illustrator.)

18–17 RENDERING TECHNIQUES

Any technical illustration that attempts to give a three-dimensional effect is called a *rendering*. The techniques of rendering a drawing involve different materials and styles.

The basic means of rendering are (1) ink shading, (2) pencil shading, (3) overlay film, (4) scratchboard, and (5) airbrush. These methods of rendering will be discussed in the following articles.

18–18 INK SHADING

Ink is a popular medium for rendering technical illustrations. Most technical illustrations are intended for use in publications, and ink reproduces very well for this purpose. Several techniques of ink rendering are shown in Fig. 18–24.

The upper portion of the figure illustrates a freehand technique with line shading. Note that no attempt is made to make the freehand lines look like mechanically drawn lines.

A stipple technique is used in the middle section of the figure. The objects are outlined with mechanically drawn lines. A pen point is then used to form areas of shade with groups of dots.

Mechanically drawn lines are used to shade the geometric shapes in the lower portion of the figure. Note that the width of the lines is varied to distinguish the various surfaces of the objects.

Fillets and rounds must be rendered with a special technique when ink is used. Two of the most common methods are shown in Fig. 18–25. The first method uses a series of elliptical curves to represent the contours of the fillets and rounds. Intersecting straight lines are used as a guide for drawing each of the freehand ellipses. The right part of Fig. 18–25 shows an easier method of representing fillets and rounds. In place of straight-line corners, parallel freehand lines are drawn to indicate fillets and rounds.

Figure 18–26 is an example of an ink line drawing that has no shades or shadows drawn. However, the lines that outline the major features of the plane are darker than the lines used to show the panels of the plane's body. In addition, a three-dimensional effect is achieved in the small supplementary drawings by the use of heavy lines.

Mechanically drawn line shading is used in the assembly drawing of a portion of a weaving loom in Fig. 18–27. Each part is outlined mechanically; then parallel lines are used to shade the surfaces of

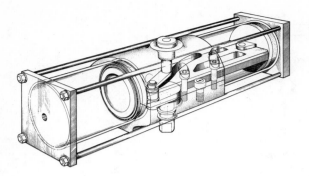

Fig. 18–29 An ink illustration using both stipple and line-shading techniques. Note that the drawing is transparent to show the inside parts. (Courtesy of L. G. Whitfield, Illustrator.)

Fig. 18–30 A pencil drawing of an automobile made by an automobile stylist. (Courtesy of Ford Motor Company.)

the parts. Care must be taken to use only the amount of shading necessary to describe the parts clearly.

A stipple technique is used in an orthographic view in Fig. 18–28 to give it a pictorial appearance. Note the use of shadows under each of the horizontal cylinders that intersect the vertical column. Mechanically drawn lines give the horizontal cylinders a rounded, shiny appearance. The use of different rendering techniques in this drawing also distinguishes the materials of the assembly.

A combination of stipple and parallel lines is used in Fig. 18–29. Portions of the assembly are drawn as if they were transparent in order to show internal features. The technical illustrator can use almost any technique or combination of techniques that will make his illustration easy to understand.

18–19 PENCIL SHADING

You are probably more familiar with pencil shading as a technique of rendering an illustration than any other, since most of your writing and drawing has been done with a pencil. This medium can be used effectively by the technical illustrator.

Figure 18–30 is a realistic and attractive pencil drawing of an automobile. This freehand sketch was drawn and shaded in a rather loose, casual style. Soft pencils in the HB–3B range are most appropriate for sketching and shading. Paper with a slight texture provides the best drawing surface for pencil illustrations.

Pencil shading can be applied by smudging or line shading. *Line shading* is done by varying the shape of the pencil point and its pressure against

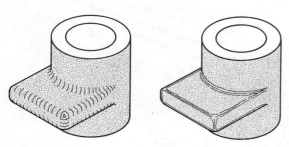

Fig. 18–31 Overlay film can be used to give a texture to the surfaces of a drawing. This pattern gives the appearance of cast iron.

the paper. For a *smudged* tone appearance, the graphite of the pencil is smoothed with the fingertips or with a piece of cotton.

18–20 OVERLAY FILM

Overlay film is an acetate film on which is printed a pattern that can be applied to a drawing to give a tone to an illustration. An example of an overlay texture applied to an ink line drawing is shown in Fig. 18–31. A stipple pattern is used to give the appearance of a rough casting. The ends of the cylinder are left white to look like machined surfaces.

Overlay films have adhesive backings that adhere permanently to a drawing when burnished to the surface by rubbing with a hard, blunt instrument. The film can be cut out around the outline of the drawing with a sharp knife and the excess removed before the final burnishing. This method of application is illustrated in Fig. 18–32. A number of available patterns are shown in Fig. 18–33.

Overlay films are available from several commercial sources under different brand names. Some films have adhesive backings that will withstand the heat of the diazo (blue-line) reproduction process without separating from the drawing. Some films have a glossy surface; others have a dull (mat) surface that is hardly noticeable on the finished drawing.

Fig. 18–32 The steps in applying overlay film to shade an area. (Courtesy of Artype® Incorporated.)

Fig. 18–33 Examples of patterns available in 9″ × 12″ sheets of overlay film. (Courtesy of Artype® Incorporated.)

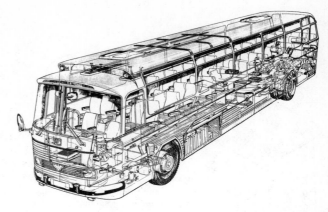

Fig. 18–34 Overlay film has been used to shade the surfaces of this drawing. (Courtesy of Planaprint International Incorporated.)

Fig. 18–35 An example of a scratchboard illustration. (Courtesy of Paslode Company.)

Overlay films are available that allow you to transfer a pattern from the film to the drawing by burnishing the area occupied by the pattern onto the drawing. The film can then be lifted to separate the pattern from the film. The bus illustration in Fig. 18–34 is an example of a drawing that has been shaded with overlay film to give gray areas on the various surfaces.

Symbols, numbers, and letters are also available on overlay film. The use of overlay film helps the technical illustrator to prepare attractive drawings both quickly and economically.

18–21 SCRATCHBOARD ILLUSTRATION

Scratchboard renderings are made on a specially prepared board with a chalky surface. Figure 18–35 is an example of a scratchboard drawing.

Ink is applied to a small area of the board. This area is then scratched with a sharp stylus point to

Fig. 18–36 An airbrush being used to shade a drawing.

Fig. 18–37 An airbrush illustration. (Courtesy of L. G. Whitfield, Illustrator.)

remove portions of the inked area. Another small area is then inked and scratched in the same manner to obtain the desired effect. This procedure continues until the drawing is completed.

Different types of lines are made by using different types of scratching points. Various types of scratching points that can be inserted in penholders are available from art suppliers.

18–22 AIRBRUSH SHADING

An airbrush is a small spray gun that sprays diluted ink or water colors onto the drawing surface to give gradual variations in shading (Fig. 18–36). A high degree of realism can be obtained with the airbrush.

When working with an airbrush, the illustrator uses a transparent paper or plastic sheet called a *frisket* to protect the portion of the paper that is not being sprayed. Frisket paper usually has a backing of several thin coats of rubber cement so that it will adhere to the drawing surface. Openings are cut in the frisket with a sharp knife to expose the area that is to be shaded. Compressed air for the airbrush can be supplied by a motor-driven compressor or by a carbon dioxide cylinder.

Airbrush shading is the most advanced rendering technique used by technical illustrators. An example of an airbrush illustration is shown in Fig. 18–37.

18–23 PICTORIAL ASSEMBLIES

Many orthographic working drawings are difficult to understand without a great deal of study. This is

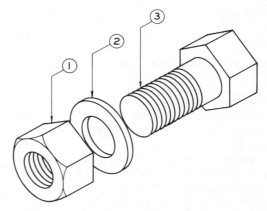

Fig. 18–38 An exploded isometric assembly of three parts.

particularly true when parts must be assembled to form a composite. In such a case, pictorial assemblies are very helpful in describing the relationship of the parts.

Figure 18–38 is a simple isometric pictorial assembly of three parts that clearly explains their relationship. The parts are "exploded" to show each part with more detail and also to explain their order of assembly. A number is given to each part; this number can be checked against the parts list (parts

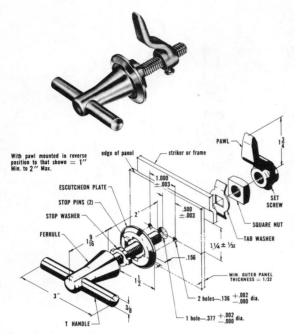

Fig. 18-39 An exploded assembly of a door latch. (Courtesy of Southco Inc.)

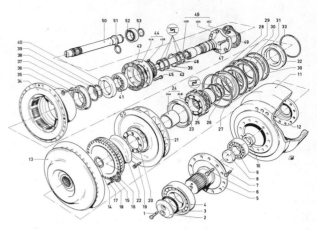

Fig. 18-40 An exploded perspective assembly. (Courtesy of Planaprint International Inc.)

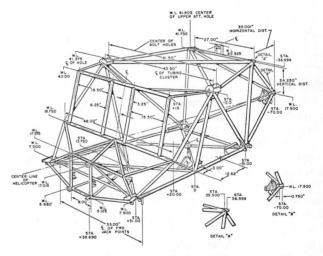

Fig. 18-41 A dimensioned pictorial of an assembly of a helicopter frame. (Courtesy of Bell Helicopter Corporation.)

lists were discussed in Chapter 14). Note that the threads in this assembly drawing are a series of ellipses drawn with an ellipse template at intervals along the centerline of the nut and bolt. This same assembly could have been drawn more easily as an oblique; in an oblique, the circular features could have been drawn as true circles instead of ellipses.

A somewhat more complex pictorial assembly is shown in Fig. 18-39. The parts of this door latch assembly are fully labeled rather than simply numbered, and dimensions are given. This is also an exploded assembly drawing.

An example of an exploded assembly of a large number of parts is given in Fig. 18-40. In this drawing, because of limitations of space, the parts are not placed in a single straight line. The centerline is continuous but it doubles back and forth across the paper to reduce the amount of space required for the drawing.

This assembly is drawn in perspective. Each part is given a number that is keyed to a parts list.

As was noted in Fig. 18-39, pictorial assembly drawings can also be dimensioned. Figure 18-41 is an example of a dimensioned pictorial assembly that is not exploded. A drawing of this type can be used by the shop personnel to assemble the helicopter frame.

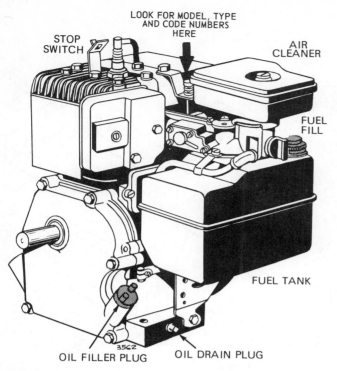

Fig. 18–42 An example of an ink drawing that was prepared by referring to the photograph of the engine at the right. (Courtesy of Briggs & Stratton Corporation.)

18–24 ILLUSTRATIONS FROM PHOTOGRAPHS

Many illustrators work from photographs if the product to be illustrated is available. Figure 18–42 shows an illustration of a gasoline engine that was drawn in ink by working from the photograph shown at the right of the figure. The line drawing is the same view of the engine shown in the photograph.

The illustrator can overlay the photograph with a transparent plastic drafting film and trace the outline of the object. He can then add shades and shadows to emphasize its shape. He can also have a slide made from the photograph so that he can project the slide onto the drawing surface and trace the outlines of the object, thus saving drawing time. Opaque projectors are also available for projecting photographs directly without the slide. The illustrator should use whatever techniques of illustration

Fig. 18–43 An ink drawing of a riding lawnmower made from a photograph. (Courtesy of the Huffy Corporation.)

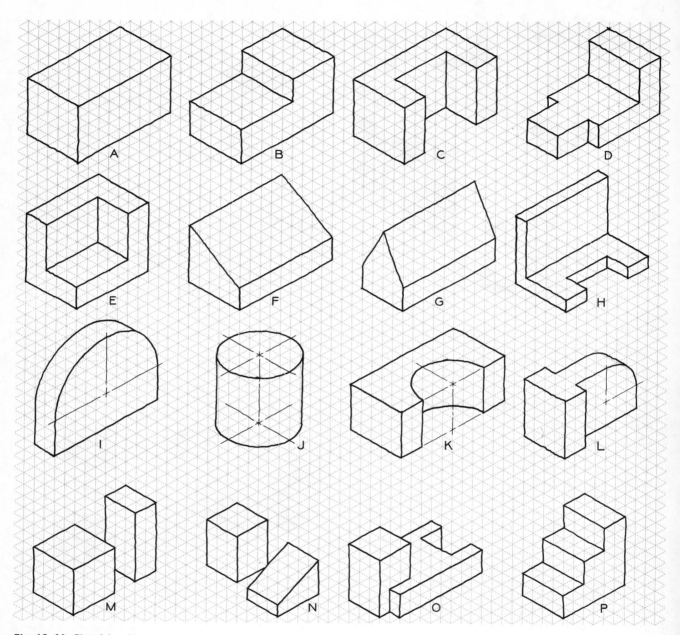

Fig. 18–44 Pictorial problems.

will give the desired result with the least expenditure of time and money.

The illustration of a riding lawnmower in Fig. 18–43 was made in ink from a photograph. You should practice this technique. Choose a photograph from a magazine and overlay it with transparent tracing paper. Then make a rendered ink drawing from the photograph.

PROBLEMS

Problems should be presented on the size of paper specified in each series of problems. Follow the formats introduced in Article 3–15 and the specifications of your instructor.

General Problems

One-Point Perspectives

1 Using the specifications given in Table 18–1 and Fig. 18–45, draw one-point perspectives of the

Table 18–1

Dimensions in inches, Fig. 18–45

Specification	X	Y	θ
A	4	3½	25°
B	4	4	30°
C	3½	4½	30°
D	3½	5½	40°
E	4	3½	45°
F	4	5½	45°

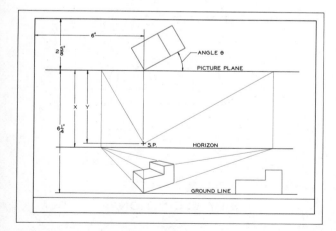

Fig. 18–45 The layout for perspective problems on Size B sheets.

objects assigned from Fig. 18–44. For example, you may be assigned to draw a perspective of object D using specifications C in Table 18–1. Specifications A through F may be assigned for any of these objects. Place the front surface of each object parallel to the picture plane in the top view. Use Size B paper. Each grid in Fig. 18–44 is equal to ¼″.

Two-Point Perspectives

2 Using the specifications given in Table 18–1 and Fig. 18–45, draw two-point perspectives of the objects assigned from Fig. 18–44. Specifications A through F may be assigned for any of these objects. Use Size B paper. Each grid in Fig. 18–45 is equal to ¼″.

Shades and Shadows

3 Make either isometric or oblique drawings of the assigned objects in Fig. 18–44 on Size A paper. Each isometric grid is equal to ¼″. Construct shades and shadows for a light source coming from the upper left at 45° and parallel to the surface of the paper.

4 Repeat Problem 3 but construct shadows for a light source that comes from the upper left and is oblique to the surface of the paper. Select whatever angle you desire for this source of light. Refer to Fig. 18–21.

Rendering Techniques

5 Prepare finished technical illustrations of the objects drawn in the previous problems. Transfer these drawings to a suitable grade of drawing paper and render them using one of the methods presented in this chapter—ink, pencil, overlay film, scratchboard, or airbrush.

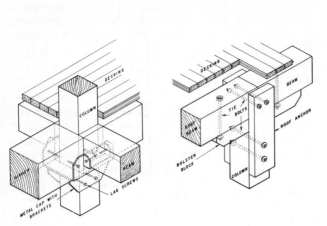

Fig. 18–46 Problem 6: Beam and column framing details. (Courtesy of the National Lumber Manufacturers Association.)

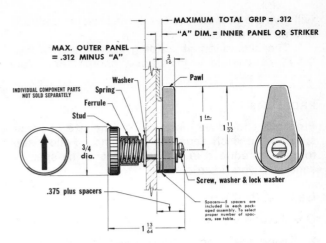

Fig. 18–48 Problems 9 and 10: Door latch. (Courtesy of Southco, Inc.)

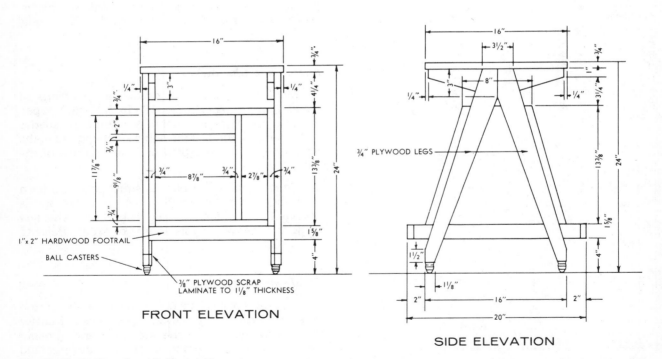

FRONT ELEVATION

SIDE ELEVATION

Fig. 18–47 Problems 7 and 8: Picnic table.

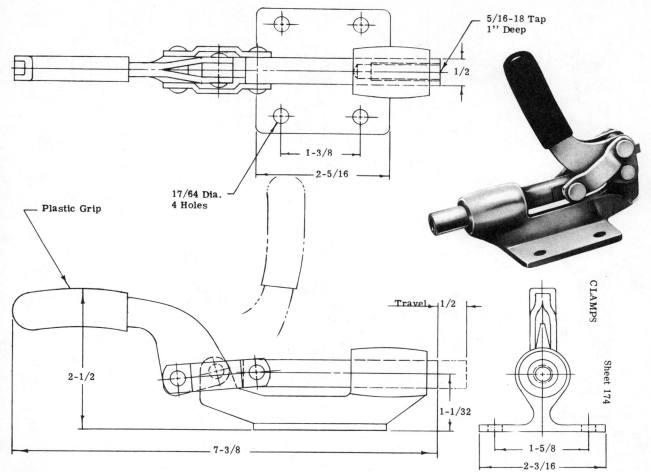

Fig. 18–49 Problems 11 and 12: Clamping device. (Courtesy of Universal Engineering Corporation.)

Advanced Problems

The following problems are somewhat more advanced than those above. The solutions will require more judgment on your part in selecting the appropriate type of pictorial, type and size of paper, and the shading techniques to be used.

6 Prepare an exploded illustration of the beam and column assemblies shown in Fig. 18–46. Your illustration should explain the details of these joints better than the given illustration does. Use oblique,

isometric, or perspective construction. Select the technique of illustration that you feel is best for this problem.

7 Draw an exploded pictorial assembly of the picnic table in Fig. 18–47 to explain its construction. Use oblique, isometric, or perspective construction. Two views of the table are given in Fig. 18–47.

8 Repeat Problem 7 but show the parts assembled.

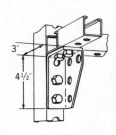

B-919

right hand gusset connector
1/8" and 1/4" steel   102#/C

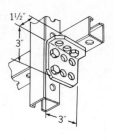

B-930

angle support
1/4" steel   70#/C

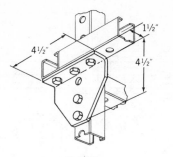

B-932

heavy angle connector
1/4" steel   136#/C

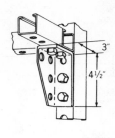

B-918

left hand gusset connector
1/8" and 1/4" steel   102#/C

B-934

outside corner connector
1/4'" steel   57#/C

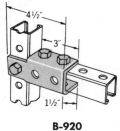

B-920

end connector
3/16" steel   80#/C

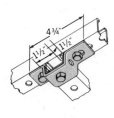

B-927

U-support
3/16" steel   57#/C

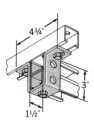

B-928

deep U-support
3/16" steel   77#/C

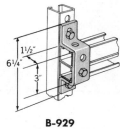

B-929

wide U-support
3/16" steel   63#/C

Fig. 18–50 Problem 13: Joint connectors. (Courtesy of Midland Ross Corporation.)

9 Draw an exploded pictorial assembly drawing of the door latch assembly in Fig. 18–48 to explain its construction. Use oblique, isometric, or perspective construction.

10 Repeat Problem 9 but show the parts assembled.

11 Draw an exploded pictorial assembly of the clamping device in Fig. 18–49 to explain its construction. Use oblique, isometric, or perspective construction.

12 Repeat Problem 11 but show the parts assembled.

13 Draw exploded pictorials of the assigned parts of the joints shown in Fig. 18–50.

14 Select problems from other chapters of the book to illustrate as obliques, isometrics, or perspectives with shades and shadows. Discuss these with your instructor to obtain approval before beginning. Many suitable problems may be found at the ends of Chapters 7 and 8.

Photo courtesy of Bureau of Reclamation, U. S. Department of the Interior

19
ARCHITECTURAL
DRAFTING

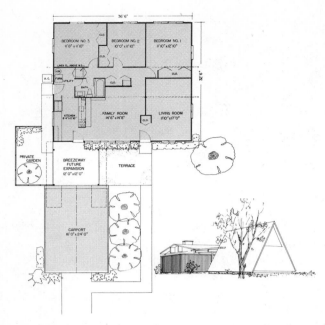

Fig. 19–1 A display drawing of the floor plan of a house. (Courtesy of the National Association of Home Builders.)

19–1 INTRODUCTION

The architect designs houses, buildings, neighborhoods, and sometimes entire cities. His main concern is to provide structures that will fit the needs of those who will use them; consequently, he is primarily a designer. He must also know how to communicate the details of his designs so that they can be implemented in accordance with his specifications. The architect is an expert draftsman, because it was through assignments involving drafting that he learned his profession after graduation. Still, he must rely on his office draftsmen to assist with the preparation of working drawings to free him for his primary function of designing.

The architect prepares rough freehand sketches of his preliminary designs; these are given to his draftsmen to be drawn to scale with instruments. The scale drawings are studied and refined, and eventually they become part of the final working drawings for the project. The architect must work as a member of a team composed of engineers, contractors, draftsmen, landscapers, and decorators.

19–2 PLANNING A HOUSE

This chapter will discuss the techniques used by the architectural planner in designing and detailing his plans for a small vacation house. The same house will be used as an example for each step of the planning process.

The usual sequence of designing a house begins with the development of the floor plan and the plot plan at the same time. One cannot be designed without consideration of the other, since the house must fit the lot and take advantage of its better features.

Next, the foundation and exterior walls must be designed. This is done with consideration for the types of windows and exterior materials that will be used. A wall section and foundation plan will be developed to explain these details.

The exterior walls of the house will be planned on the basis of the wall section. The exterior will be shown as a series of elevations that are orthographic views of the sides of the house. Other plans will show construction details for windows, doors, fireplaces, stairways, cabinets, and other framing features that need explanation.

19–3 THE FLOOR PLAN

The floor plan in Fig. 19–1 is not a working drawing from which a house will be built. This plan is drawn for display purposes, to present the floor plan so that it can be studied by the client or the designer. Note that the walls are drawn to scale as solid black lines of approximately the same width as the actual walls. Bathroom and kitchen fixtures and built-ins are shown to clarify room arrangements.

The garage and patios are shown with planting and trees located. This type of plan may be drawn by the architect for his client, in addition to the working drawing. The working drawing has many confusing lines, dimensions, and notes that make it more difficult to understand than the general plan shown in Fig. 19–1.

FIGURE 19-2. STEPS OF DEVELOPING A FLOOR PLAN

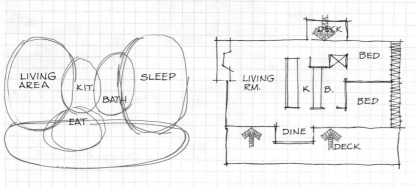

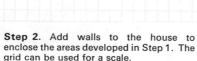

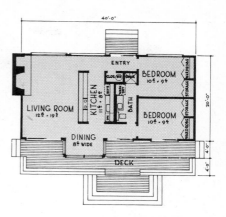

Step 1. Make a number of freehand sketches on grid paper to develop the relationship between the areas of the house. These will be used as a guide for arranging the rooms.

Step 2. Add walls to the house to enclose the areas developed in Step 1. The grid can be used for a scale.

Step 3. The final scale drawing is a refinement of the rough plan developed in Step 2. This procedure may have to be repeated several times to arrive at the best design.

The planning or designing of a floor plan is usually done on grid paper so that a scale can be approximated and the grid lines can be used as guidelines. The steps involved in developing a floor plan are shown in Fig. 19-2. Areas are drawn freehand to indicate the relationship of the various functions of the house (Step 1). Many sketches of this type will be made before the best arrangement is determined. The plan is then sketched on grid paper, with walls drawn to separate the rooms (Step 2). The final step is the preparation of the finished scale drawing of the plan using the sketches as a guide (Step 3).

The exterior of the house is drawn in Fig. 19-3 as a perspective. You should be able to relate the pictorial of the house to its floor plan in Fig. 19-2C.

A similar type of house is shown in Fig. 19-4 in perspective and plan. The same floor plan can be used with a number of different exteriors. The floor plan is the most important part of architectural planning, since it is used as the basis for all the other details that will be developed.

A floor plan must be functional; that is, it must serve its purpose with the least amount of wasted

Fig. 19-3 A perspective drawing of the house developed in Fig. 19-2. (Courtesy of the American Plywood Association.)

space and inconvenience. Closets must be large enough, but not too large; furniture must fit properly into each room with adequate circulation area.

It is wise to draw the finished plan of a house with the furniture in place to identify cramped areas that would not be functional. The plan in Fig. 19-5 is an example of a plan that shows the furniture in position. Since the dimensions of furniture vary greatly, a house must be designed to fit the client's furniture.

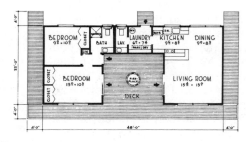

Fig. 19–4 A vacation house. (Courtesy of the American Plywood Association and the Home Building Plan Service, Portland, Oregon.)

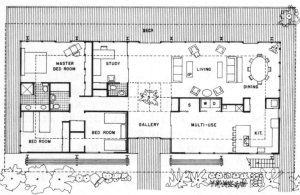

Fig. 19–5 A display drawing of a floor plan with furniture shown. (Courtesy of Bethlehem Steel Company.)

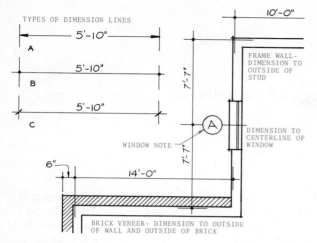

Fig. 19–6 Dimensioning symbols and techniques used on architectural plans.

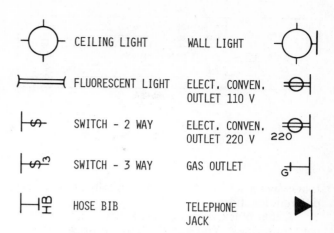

Fig. 19–8 Common symbols used on architectural plans.

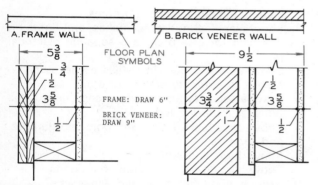

Fig. 19–7 Frame walls (left) and brick veneer walls (right) are shown in section and in plan.

19–4 FLOOR PLAN SYMBOLS

Standard symbols are used in working drawings of a floor plan. Three types of dimension lines (A, B, and C) are shown in Fig. 19–6. Note that dots or slashes can be used at the ends of dimension lines instead of arrowheads. Also, dimension numerals can be placed either above the dimension line or in an opening in the dimension line.

Examples of dimensions are shown in the plan view of the walls. Dimensions are drawn from the outside of the studs (2″ × 4″ vertical members) onto which the exterior siding is nailed. This dimension is easier for the carpenters to use than a measurement to the outside of the siding. Windows are located by dimensioning to their centerlines. The letter "A" in the circle is a window note referring to a window schedule that describes the type of window used (window schedules will be discussed in Article 19–26).

The width of a wall shown on a floor plan depends on the type of wall used. A frame wall and a brick veneer wall are illustrated in Fig. 19–7. The brick-covered wall is referred to as "brick veneer" because the brick does not support a load but serves simply as a wall covering. The overall width of the frame wall is $5\frac{3}{8}″$; of the brick veneer wall, $9\frac{1}{2}″$. These are drawn on the plan as 6″ and 9″ walls, respectively.

Some of the more often used floor plan symbols are given in Fig. 19–8. Architectural templates are available for drawing most of these symbols.

The S_3 symbol represents a three-way switch. When a three-way—that is, three-pole—switch is used, a light may be turned on and off from two different locations. The symbol S_4 represents a

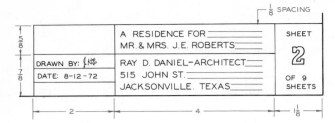

Fig. 19–9 A title block for class assignments.

four-way switch, which can be controlled from three different locations.

A title block must be placed on all sheets of a set of drawings. You may wish to design your own, but it should include the information given in the one shown in Fig. 19–9.

19–5 A WORKING DRAWING OF A FLOOR PLAN

The plan shown in Fig. 19–10 is a typical working drawing of a floor plan. The vacation house shown here will be used as an example for a complete set of plans.

The plan is provided with full dimensions and notes so that it can be used for building. Light fixtures and switches and other utility outlets are given on the plan. Dashed lines connect the fixtures with the switches that control them.

Doors and their arcs of swing are shown. Kitchen and bathroom fixtures are shown, even though some of them are not built into the house. Windows and doors are numbered and lettered to refer to window and door schedules on the same sheet. A legend of symbols explains the symbols used on this plan to prevent misinterpretation. Water faucets are not shown, since it is understood that they are required at kitchen and bathroom fixtures.

The dimensions for the floor plan are spaced outside the floor plan in order not to crowd the exterior walls. Along the lower edge of the plan there are circles with letters and numbers in them. These indicate the location of sections. The number represents the sheet number of the set of drawings where the section will be shown. The letter

identifies the detail on that sheet. For example, detail D/7 is shown on sheet 7 (Fig. 19–44) and is labeled "Section D/4" to show that it came from sheet 4.

Rules for Drawing Floor Plans

1. Draw plans at a scale of $\frac{1}{4}'' = 1'\text{-}0''$.
2. Include full dimensions and notes.
3. Show electrical outlets, switches, and lights on this plan, or else prepare a separate electrical plan.
4. Show as many built-in details as necessary—fireplaces, cabinets, stairways, etc.
5. Draw a separate floor plan for each floor if the house is multi-leveled.
6. Show all attached terraces, porches, garages, and carports.
7. Show doors and door swings.
8. Show heating and air conditioning units.
9. Number and letter doors and windows.

19–6 DEVELOPING THE PLOT PLAN

The plot plan can be developed using the same steps that were used for developing the floor plan (Fig. 19–11). The plot is sketched on a grid sheet with the dimensions of the lot indicated (Step 1). The property line outlines the portion of the lot that belongs to the owner.

Most cities and neighborhoods have restrictions that specify setbacks from each side of the property line. In this case they are 15' at the front and back and 5' at the sides. No permanent structure can be built outside the building restriction lines.

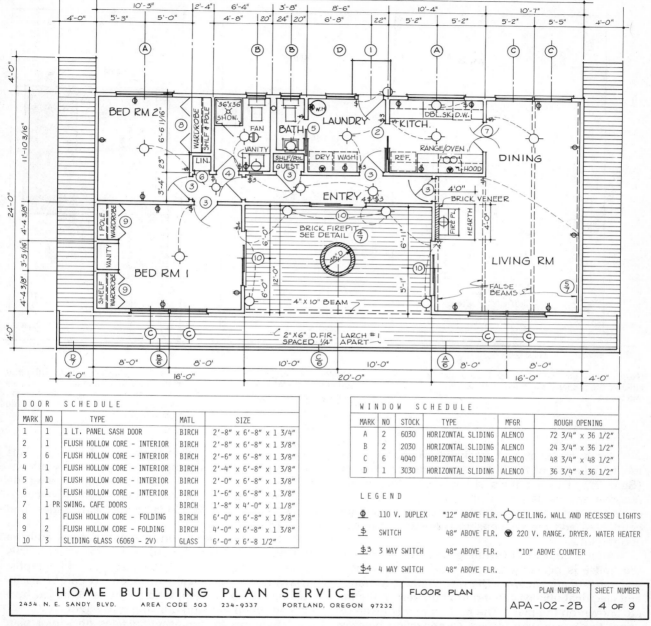

DOOR SCHEDULE				
MARK	NO	TYPE	MATL	SIZE
1	1	1 LT. PANEL SASH DOOR	BIRCH	2'-8" x 6'-8" x 1 3/4"
2	1	FLUSH HOLLOW CORE - INTERIOR	BIRCH	2'-8" x 6'-8" x 1 3/8"
3	6	FLUSH HOLLOW CORE - INTERIOR	BIRCH	2'-6" x 6'-8" x 1 3/8"
4	1	FLUSH HOLLOW CORE - INTERIOR	BIRCH	2'-4" x 6'-8" x 1 3/8"
5	1	FLUSH HOLLOW CORE - INTERIOR	BIRCH	2'-0" x 6'-8" x 1 3/8"
6	1	FLUSH HOLLOW CORE - INTERIOR	BIRCH	1'-6" x 6'-8" x 1 3/8"
7	1 PR	SWING, CAFE DOORS	BIRCH	1'-8" x 4'-0" x 1 1/8"
8	1	FLUSH HOLLOW CORE - FOLDING	BIRCH	6'-0" x 6'-8" x 1 3/8"
9	2	FLUSH HOLLOW CORE - FOLDING	BIRCH	4'-0" x 6'-8" x 1 3/8"
10	3	SLIDING GLASS (6069 - 2V)	GLASS	6'-0" x 6'-8 1/2"

WINDOW SCHEDULE					
MARK	NO	STOCK	TYPE	MFGR	ROUGH OPENING
A	2	6030	HORIZONTAL SLIDING	ALENCO	72 3/4" x 36 1/2"
B	2	2030	HORIZONTAL SLIDING	ALENCO	24 3/4" x 36 1/2"
C	6	4040	HORIZONTAL SLIDING	ALENCO	48 3/4" x 48 1/2"
D	1	3030	HORIZONTAL SLIDING	ALENCO	36 3/4" x 36 1/2"

LEGEND

⏚ 110 V. DUPLEX *12" ABOVE FLR. ○ CEILING, WALL AND RECESSED LIGHTS

$ SWITCH 48" ABOVE FLR. ◉ 220 V. RANGE, DRYER, WATER HEATER

$3 3 WAY SWITCH 48" ABOVE FLR. *10" ABOVE COUNTER

$4 4 WAY SWITCH 48" ABOVE FLR.

HOME BUILDING PLAN SERVICE		FLOOR PLAN	PLAN NUMBER	SHEET NUMBER
2454 N. E. SANDY BLVD. AREA CODE 503 234-9337 PORTLAND, OREGON 97232			APA-102-2B	4 OF 9

Fig. 19–10 A working drawing of the floor plan of the vacation house that will be used as an example throughout this chapter. (*Note:* This plan was developed for the American Plywood Association by the Home Building Plan Service, 2454 N.E. Sandy Boulevard, Portland, Oregon.)

FIGURE 19-11. STEPS OF DEVELOPING A PLOT PLAN

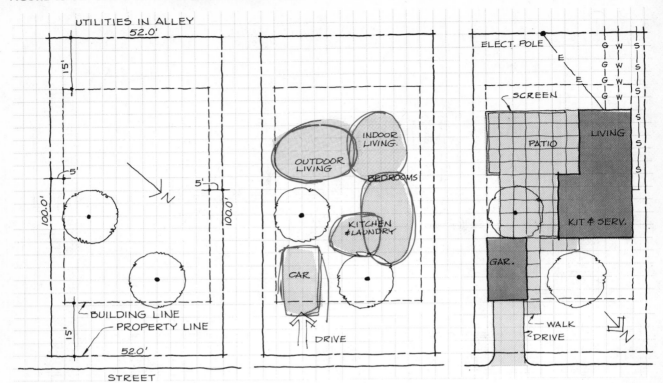

Step 1. Lay out the lot on grid paper and indicate the property and building lines, trees, and street.

Step 2. Develop the floor plan and lot design together with sketches showing the relationship of the activity areas.

Step 3. A finished sketch of the plot plan is prepared using the area analysis plan developed in Step 2. The working drawing of the plot plan can be made from this sketch.

Areas are sketched freehand to identify the functional areas of the house and garage on the lot (Step 2). Existing trees should be saved where possible and made part of the plan. The freehand ovals represent the areas where various activities are conducted and the relationship between the house and the lot.

After a number of planning sketches are made, the house is positioned on the lot; patios, fences, and screens are shown. The gas, water, sewerage, and electrical utilities coming from the rear of the lot are shown on the plan. The north arrow is given to orient the house with respect to prevailing breezes and sunlight.

Another plot plan is shown in Fig. 19-12. This is not a working drawing with the necessary dimensions and notes, but a scaled drawing showing the placement of the building and lot improvements. This building is a kindergarten with slides and seesaws at its rear.

Shadows are shown next to the trees and the building to give a three-dimensional effect. This type of plan is a combination of orthographic drawing and technical illustration. It can be easily understood by a client who might be confused by a dimensioned working drawing of the plot.

Symbols for representing trees on a plot plan can take a number of forms (Fig. 19-13). These

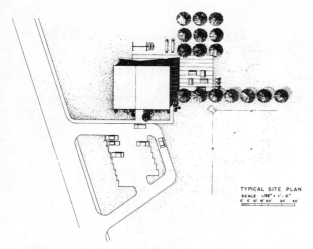

Fig. 19–12 A display drawing of a plot plan of a kindergarten. (Courtesy of Naval Facilities Engineering Command.)

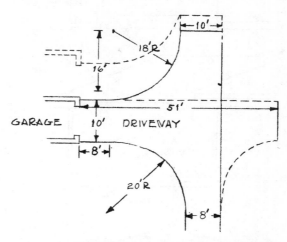

DIMENSIONS FOR A DRIVEWAY TURNING AREA DOTTED LINES SHOW THE ADDITIONAL SPACE NEEDED FOR A 2-CAR GARAGE AND AN ALTERNATE ARRANGEMENT FOR BACKING STRAIGHT OUT.

Fig. 19–14 Turning radii for driving into and backing out of a garage.

Fig. 19–13 Tree symbols that are available on transfer film for use on plot plans. (Courtesy of Para-Tone Incorporated.)

particular symbols are available on transparent overlay film that can be transferred to the drawing as discussed in Article 18–20. Additional symbols for representing trees are shown on the various plot plans given in this chapter.

An important consideration in plot planning is the provision of driveways and walkways. The diagram in Fig. 19–14 gives the turning radii necessary for a car to back out of a garage and turn around. Walkways are usually between 30″ and 36″ wide. The materials used for lot improvements should be indicated on the plot plan with explanatory notes and symbols.

The garage should have a minimum interior space of 10′ × 20′ (Fig. 19–15). These dimensions apply to carports as well as to garages.

19–7 A WORKING DRAWING OF A PLOT PLAN

A typical plot plan of a residential lot is shown in Fig. 19–16 with the usually required notes and dimensions. In this example, the outline of the house represents the walls instead of the roof. Either can be used at the option of the draftsman, but dimensions should locate the walls. The *swale* that is noted is a slight valley that will carry drainage in the direction of the arrows.

The plot plan of the vacation house introduced in Fig. 19–10 is given in Fig. 19–17. This is a working drawing that could be used by a contractor to provide the lot improvements shown.

Numbers are shown at each corner of the house to represent the elevations of the earth after it has

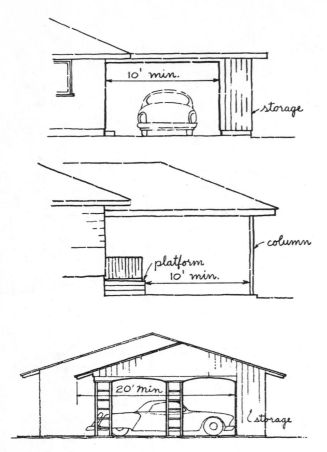

Fig. 19–15 Minimum dimensions for a garage or carport. (Courtesy of the Federal Housing Administration.)

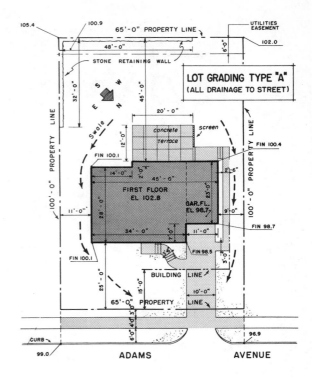

Lot 1 Block 7
CHESTNUT HILL – BRAINARD, COLUMBIA

Scale $\frac{1}{16}'' = 1'-0''$

Fig. 19–16 An example of a plot plan. (Courtesy of the Federal Housing Administration.)

been graded. An *elevation* is the height of the earth above some reference point on the lot. The elevation of a city is given from sea level. Elevations tell the contractor how the area around the house must be filled or earth removed.

Contour lines are lines that join points having the same elevation. Contour lines are usually drawn at regular elevation intervals (for example, at one-foot intervals, as in Fig. 19–17). The front left corner of the lot is used as the beginning elevation of 10′. By surveying the lot with a level (a special surveying instrument) the 9′ contour line can be

found, then the 8′ line, and so on. You can see that the lot slopes from the street to the back, where the elevation is 4′, which is 6′ lower than the front elevation of 10′.

Rules for Drawing a Plot Plan

1. Use a civil engineers' scale for best results. It is preferable to use a scale of 1″ = 10.0′. Architects' scales can be used, but decimal dimensions from a civil engineers' scale make arithmetic easier.

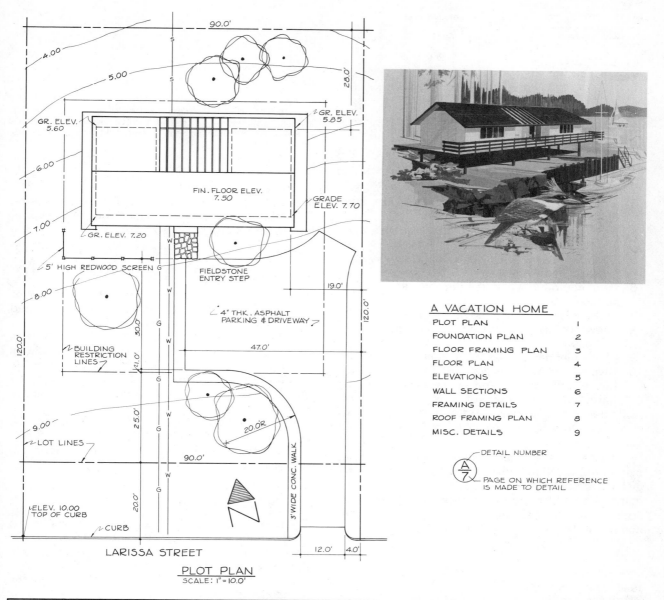

A VACATION HOME

DETAIL NUMBER

A / 7

PAGE ON WHICH REFERENCE IS MADE TO DETAIL

GR. ELEV. 5.60

GR. ELEV. 5.85

FIN. FLOOR ELEV. 7.50

GRADE ELEV. 7.70

GR. ELEV. 7.20

5' HIGH REDWOOD SCREEN

FIELDSTONE ENTRY STEP

BUILDING RESTRICTION LINES

4" THK. ASPHALT PARKING & DRIVEWAY

LOT LINES

ELEV. 10.00 TOP OF CURB

CURB

3' WIDE CONC. WALK

LARISSA STREET

PLOT PLAN
SCALE: 1" = 10.0'

HOME BUILDING PLAN SERVICE

2454 N. E. SANDY BLVD.   AREA CODE 503   234-9337   PORTLAND, OREGON 97232

PLOT PLAN	PLAN NUMBER	SHEET NUMBER
	APA-102-2B	1 OF 9

Fig. 19-17 A working drawing of a plot plan for the vacation house. (Courtesy of the American Plywood Association.)

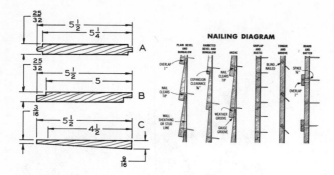

Fig. 19-18 Standard siding materials are shown on the left: (A) tongue and groove, (B) shiplap, and (C) bevel siding. Methods of nailing are shown at the right. (Courtesy of the California Redwood Association.)

2. Show compass north point.
3. Give dimensions of the lot, property lines, and building lines.
4. Give dimensions to locate houses, garages, and other buildings.
5. Dimension walls, driveways, walks, patios, and other lot improvements.
6. Give contours when the lot has an uneven surface.
7. Show trees, planting, and landscaping.
8. Show utilities—electricity, water, sewerage, and gas.
9. Give street names and lot numbers.
10. Give the following elevations: (a) first floor of house and garage and other buildings; (b) finish curb or crown of street at points of extension of lot lines; (c) finish grade elevation at each principal corner of the structure.

These rules are generally applied in the plot plan of the vacation house in Fig. 19-17. Notes are given to describe all important features. Remember that this plot plan was developed jointly with the floor plan so that the two plans would be compatible.

19-8 LUMBER SIZES

Construction details must be prepared to communicate the designer's ideas before they can be implemented. The designer must, therefore, be familiar with available materials and their sizes.

A 2 × 4 piece of lumber is actually $1\frac{5}{8}'' \times 3\frac{5}{8}''$. It is called a 2 × 4 because this is its *nominal size.* The table below gives the dimensions of lumber in their nominal and actual sizes:

Nominal size	1″	2″	4″	6″	8″	10″	12″
Actual size	$\frac{5}{8}''$	$1\frac{5}{8}''$	$3\frac{5}{8}''$	$5\frac{1}{2}''$	$7\frac{1}{2}''$	$9\frac{1}{2}''$	$11\frac{1}{2}''$

You can see that a 4 × 6 piece of lumber is actually $3\frac{5}{8}'' \times 5\frac{1}{2}''$. The actual dimensions listed above should be used in all detail drawings.

Types of exterior siding are shown in Fig. 19-18. Most of these patterns are available in nominal sizes of 1 × 4, 1 × 6, 1 × 8, and 1 × 10. The thicknesses remain approximately the same for all sizes. Exterior and interior plywood is available in 4′ × 8′ sheets with thicknesses of $\frac{3}{8}''$, $\frac{1}{2}''$, $\frac{5}{8}''$, $\frac{3}{4}''$, and $\frac{7}{8}''$. A number of surface patterns may be selected for exterior and interior effects. The plywood patterns currently available can be found in pamphlets obtained from your local lumberyard.

19-9 SILL DETAILS

The lowest member of any structure that sits on top of the foundation is called a *sill.* Likewise, the lowest member of a door or a window is called a sill. When we discuss sill details here, we shall also discuss the framing of the structure and the foundation support.

The most traditional sill is a structural beam supported by freestanding piers (Fig. 19-19A). The pier may be concrete, masonry, or concrete block supported on a concrete footing. Freestanding piers

FIGURE 19–19. SILL DETAILS—PIERS

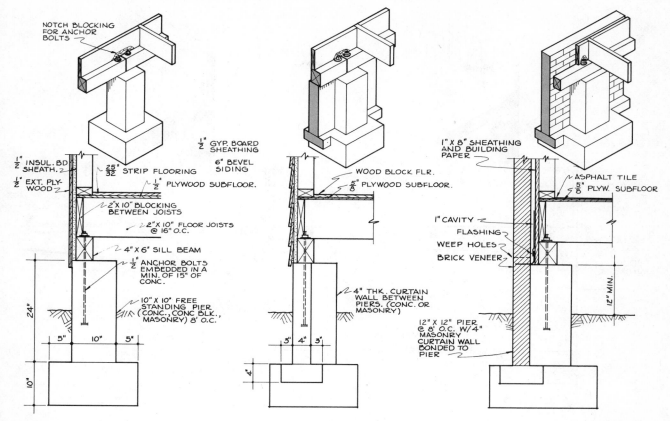

NOTCH BLOCKING FOR ANCHOR BOLTS

$\frac{1}{2}$" GYP. BOARD SHEATHING

6" BEVEL SIDING

$\frac{1}{2}$" INSUL. BD SHEATH.

$\frac{1}{2}$" EXT. PLY-WOOD

$\frac{25}{32}$" STRIP FLOORING

$\frac{1}{2}$" PLYWOOD SUBFLOOR.

2"X 10" BLOCKING BETWEEN JOISTS

2"X 10" FLOOR JOISTS @ 16" O.C.

4"X 6" SILL BEAM

$\frac{1}{2}$" ANCHOR BOLTS EMBEDDED IN A MIN. OF 15" OF CONC.

10"X 10" FREE STANDING PIER (CONC., CONC BLK., MASONRY) 8' O.C.

24"

5" 10" 5"

10"

WOOD BLOCK FLR.

$\frac{5}{8}$" PLYWOOD SUBFLOOR.

4" THK. CURTAIN WALL BETWEEN PIERS. (CONC. OR MASONRY)

5" 4" 3"

4"

1"X 8" SHEATHING AND BUILDING PAPER

ASPHALT TILE
$\frac{5}{8}$" PLYW. SUBFLOOR

1" CAVITY

FLASHING

WEEP HOLES

BRICK VENEER

12"X 12" PIER @ 8' O.C. W/4" MASONRY CURTAIN WALL BONDED TO PIER

12" MIN.

A. Freestanding pier supporting a frame wall with a 4 × 6 sill beam.

B. Masonry pier with a curtain wall between the piers supporting a frame wall.

C. Masonry pier with a curtain wall between the piers supporting a brick veneer wall.

are spaced about 8' to 12' apart depending on loading requirements.

In Fig. 19–19B the spaces between the piers are connected with curtain walls to enclose the crawl space under the house. The curtain wall in Fig. 19–19C also carries the brick veneer exterior wall.

Sill details for a concrete slab foundation are shown in Fig. 19–20. The sill plate is 2" × 4" rather than 4" × 6" because the concrete footing is

continuous around the perimeter of the building and will support the walls. The 2 × 4 is bolted to the slab with $\frac{1}{2}$" anchor bolts. Both frame and brick veneer construction are shown in Fig. 19–20.

Reinforcing steel rods or steel mesh must be used in concrete slabs to add extra strength. The numbers used in specifying the sizes of the rods represent eighths of an inch. A No. 3 rod is $\frac{3}{8}$" in diameter. Steel mesh comes in rolls of welded steel rods. The rods in steel mesh are much smaller than

FIGURE 19–20. CONCRETE SLAB SILLS

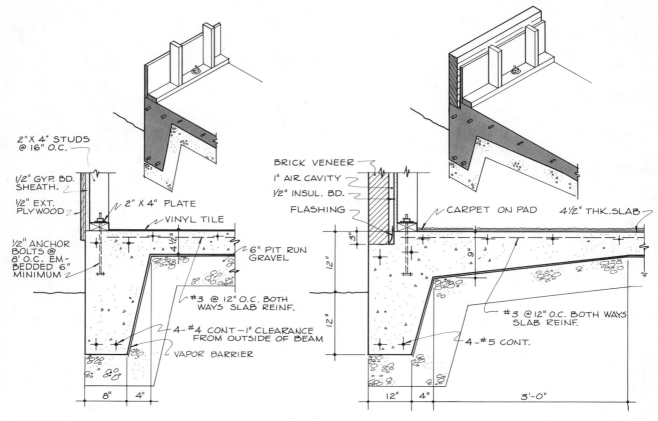

2" X 4" STUDS
@ 16" O.C.

1/2" GYP. BD.
SHEATH.

1/2" EXT.
PLYWOOD

2" X 4" PLATE

VINYL TILE

1/2" ANCHOR
BOLTS @
8' O.C. EM-
BEDDED 6"
MINIMUM

4½"

6" PIT RUN
GRAVEL

#3 @ 12" O.C. BOTH
WAYS SLAB REINF.

4-#4 CONT—1" CLEARANCE
FROM OUTSIDE OF BEAM

VAPOR BARRIER

8"   4"

BRICK VENEER

1" AIR CAVITY

1/2" INSUL. BD.

FLASHING

CARPET ON PAD   4½" THK.SLAB

3"

9"

12"

12"

#3 @ 12" O.C. BOTH WAYS
SLAB REINF.

4-#5 CONT.

12"   4"   3'-0"

A. A sill detail for a frame wall supported by a concrete slab.

B. A sill detail for a brick veneer wall supported by a concrete slab.

the reinforcing steel rods, but they are placed closer together to give the same amount of steel as when steel rods are used.

The concrete wall sill is often used in residential construction. This detail will be discussed in Fig. 19–24.

19–10 FOUNDATION PLANS

A foundation plan is a working drawing that describes the details of the foundation of a house. Three common types of foundations are (A) slabs,

(B) concrete wall foundations, and (C) pier foundations. These will be shown in the following examples.

Slab foundations are poured into forms to give a one-piece foundation supported by *grade beams* that are poured as part of the total slab. The earth is used as a form; trenches are dug to the proper size and the concrete is poured into them.

The plan of the foundation is drawn to the same scale as the floor plan; this makes it possible for the draftsman to overlay the floor plan with tracing paper

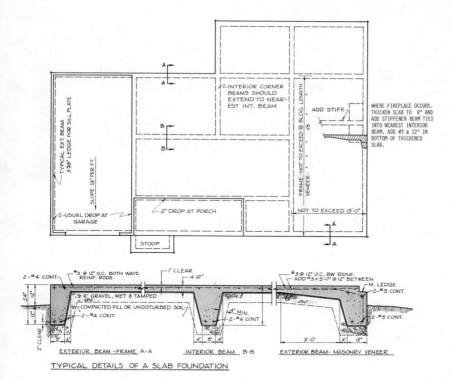

WHERE FIREPLACE OCCURS, THICKEN SLAB TO 8" AND ADD STIFFENER BEAM TIED INTO NEAREST INTERIOR BEAM. ADD #3 @ 12" IN BOTTOM OF THICKENED SLAB.

TYPICAL DETAILS OF A SLAB FOUNDATION

Fig. 19–21 A general working drawing of a slab foundation plan and detail sections.

and trace the foundation plan outline. An example of a slab foundation is shown in Fig. 19–21. The plan is not dimensioned in this case, but dimensions are necessary in the finished working drawing. The hidden lines in the plan view represent the width of the grade beams at their lowest point, 8" in section A–A in Fig. 19–21.

Sections through the grade beams are drawn at a scale of $\frac{3}{4}'' = 1'\text{-}0''$. These give dimensions and specify the fill and the placement of steel reinforcing.

An alternative slab detail is shown in Fig. 19–22. The grade beams are rectangular in section rather than tapered, but the plan view would be the same as shown in Fig. 19–21.

Carpet pads may be placed over concrete slabs and carpet applied over the pad to finish the floor.

Vinyl and asphalt floor tiles can also be applied on concrete floors.

Concrete wall foundations support a house by means of a concrete wall around the exterior of the house. Interior support beams may be girders of wood or steel, or they also may be concrete walls. The girders in Fig. 19–23 are supported on concrete piers spaced approximately 10' apart. When a concrete wall foundation is used, a crawl space 18" in height is usually provided under the house.

The sill details of a concrete block foundation can be seen in section A–A of Fig. 19–23. The concrete wall should extend at least 12" above the finished grade. The depth of the concrete wall must be determined by local engineering standards; how-

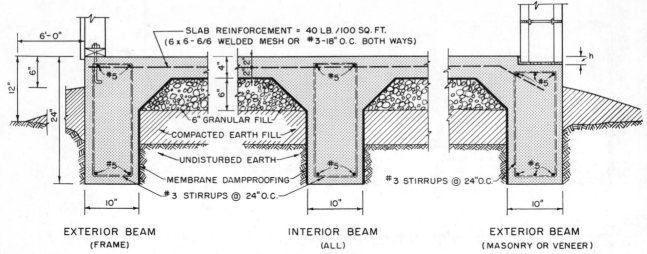

SLAB REINFORCEMENT = 40 LB./100 SQ. FT.
(6 x 6 - 6/6 WELDED MESH OR #3-18" O.C. BOTH WAYS)

6'-0"

6"

12"

24"

#5

4"

6"

#5

6" GRANULAR FILL
COMPACTED EARTH FILL
UNDISTURBED EARTH
MEMBRANE DAMPPROOFING
#3 STIRRUPS @ 24" O.C.

#5

#5

#3 STIRRUPS @ 24" O.C.

h

#5

#5

10"

10"

10"

EXTERIOR BEAM
(FRAME)

INTERIOR BEAM
(ALL)

EXTERIOR BEAM
(MASONRY OR VENEER)

Note:
All dimensions are minimum recommended.
h—offset in edge of slab for masonry may be adjusted to work out coursing pattern with top of door openings.
Interior beams required near load-bearing partitions; others to complete waffle pattern.
The above details are suggested as a guide for average conditions in areas not controlled by local building codes or regulations.

Fig. 19–22 An alternative detail for grade beams under a concrete slab. (Courtesy of the Portland Cement Association.)

ever, concrete walls usually extend below the freezing line to prevent damage from variation in soil pressure due to freezing and thawing.

Pier foundations are composed of a series of piers made of concrete or timber that support girders on which the floor is built. An exterior freestanding pier is shown in Fig. 19–19.

In Fig. 19–23, three interior concrete piers are used to support a girder consisting of three 2 × 10 timbers. The girders fit into pockets in the concrete walls for additional support. This foundation uses both concrete walls and piers to support the house.

Typical details for the attachment of a porch or stoop to a concrete wall or to a slab are given in Fig. 19–24. The porch or stoop may be poured at the

same time or at a later stage of construction. Note that where the concrete foundation wall is used, steel rods extend from the concrete wall into the porch slab to tie the two together. The sections in Fig. 19–24 are taken through door sills to illustrate how the door is framed into the floor.

19–11 A WORKING DRAWING OF A FOUNDATION PLAN

Figure 19–23 is a working drawing of a foundation plan, but its purpose is to give the standard details of a concrete wall foundation rather than the details for a particular house. Many of the notes are of a general nature.

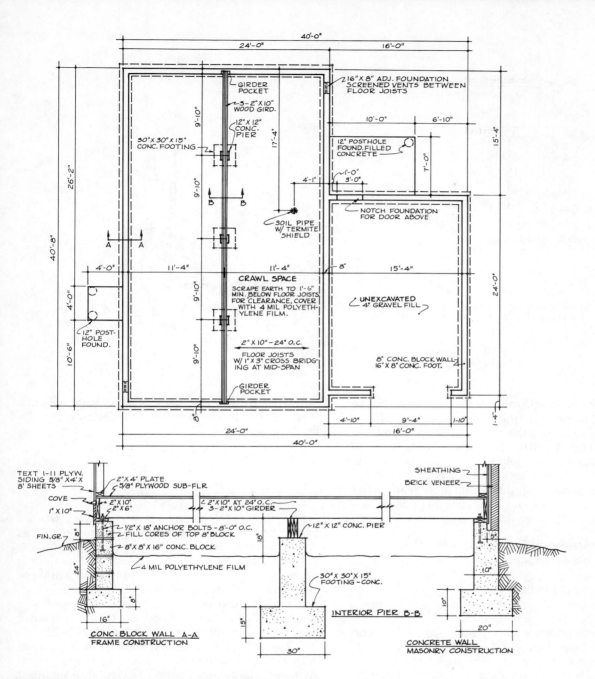

Fig. 19–23 A working drawing of a foundation plan with concrete walls and freestanding piers. (Courtesy of National Plan Service, Inc.)

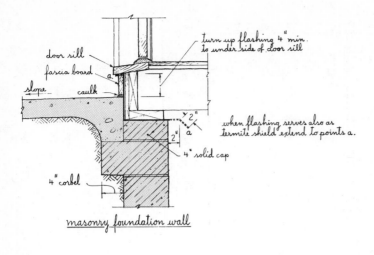

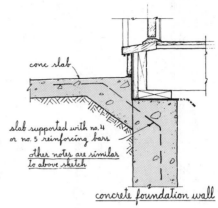

Fig. 19–24 Typical details for attaching a porch or patio to a concrete wall foundation. (Courtesy of the Federal Housing Administration.)

The foundation plan of the vacation house introduced in Fig. 19–10 is shown in Fig. 19–25. It was drawn by tracing the major dimensions from the floor plan (Fig. 19–10). This house has a concrete wall foundation with interior piers to support the floor joists. Dimensions and notes are given to specify the details of the foundation plan. The hidden lines at the walls in the plan view are outlines of the footings that support the walls.

Rules for Drawing Foundation Plans

1. Draw the foundation plan at the same scale as the floor plan, $\frac{1}{4}'' = 1'\text{-}0''$, so that it can be traced from the floor plan.
2. Show the outlines of the grade beams, piers, and other structural features.
3. Draw sections through grade beams, piers, and support members. Show sill details.
4. Dimension the plan completely so that the foundation can be built without referring to other sheets.
5. Show directions of floor joists.

Refer to the floor plan of the vacation house (Fig. 19–10) to compare the foundation plan with the floor plan.

19–12 FLOOR FRAMING PLAN

A floor framing plan shows how the floor joists are placed on the foundation and how the flooring is applied to the joists. A floor framing plan for the vacation house is given in Fig. 19–26. The floor is designed for 4' × 8' sheets of plywood with the minimum of waste and cutting.

Bridging is used to give floor joists support and to prevent them from twisting when heavily loaded. Two types of bridging are shown in Fig. 19–27.

The floor of the vacation house is to be covered with asphalt tile applied over the plywood underlayment. Hardwood flooring (called strip flooring) can also be applied to a plywood underlayment of this type (Fig. 19–28).

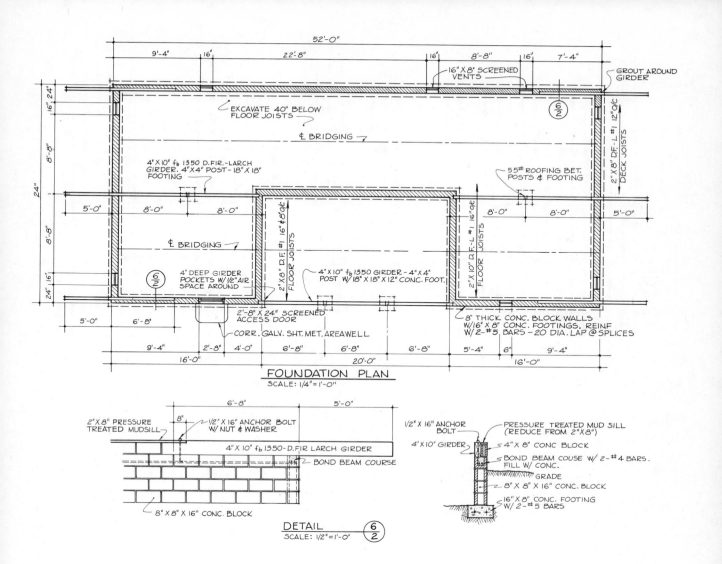

FOUNDATION PLAN
SCALE: 1/4"=1'-0"

52'-0"

9'-4" · 16" · 22'-8" · 16" · 8'-8" · 16" · 7'-4"

16"X8" SCREENED VENTS

GROUT AROUND GIRDER

16" 24"

16"

8'-8"

24"

8'-8"

24" 16"

EXCAVATE 40" BELOW FLOOR JOISTS

℄ BRIDGING

4"X 10" fb 1350 D.FIR.-LARCH GIRDER. 4"X 4" POST-18" X 18" FOOTING

55# ROOFING BET. POSTS & FOOTING

2"X 8" D.F-L # 12"O.C DECK JOISTS

5'-0" · 8'-0" · 8'-0"

8'-0" · 8'-0" · 5'-0"

℄ BRIDGING

4" DEEP GIRDER POCKETS W/ 1/2" AIR SPACE AROUND

2"X 8" D.F. #1 16"O.C FLOOR JOISTS

4"X 10" fb 1350 GIRDER - 4"X 4" POST W/18" X 18" X 12" CONC. FOOT.

2"X 10" D.F.-L #1 16"O.C FLOOR JOISTS

5'-0" · 6'-8"

2'-8"X 24" SCREENED ACCESS DOOR

CORR. GALV. SHT. MET. AREAWELL

8" THICK CONC. BLOCK WALLS W/16" X 8" CONC. FOOTINGS. REINF W/2-#5 BARS - 20 DIA. LAP @ SPLICES

9'-4" · 2'-8" · 4'-0" · 6'-8" · 6'-8" · 6'-8" · 5'-4" · 6" · 9'-4"

16'-0" · 20'-0" · 16'-0"

DETAIL
SCALE: 1/2"=1'-0" (6/2)

6'-8" · 5'-0"

8"

2"X 8" PRESSURE TREATED MUDSILL

1/2" X 16" ANCHOR BOLT W/ NUT & WASHER

4"X 10" fb 1350-D.FIR LARCH GIRDER

BOND BEAM COURSE

8" X 8" X 16" CONC. BLOCK

1/2" X 16" ANCHOR BOLT

4"X 10" GIRDER

PRESSURE TREATED MUD SILL (REDUCE FROM 2"X8")

4" X 8" CONC BLOCK

BOND BEAM COUSE W/ 2-#4 BARS. FILL W/ CONC.

GRADE

8" X 8" X 16" CONC. BLOCK

16"X 8" CONC. FOOTING W/ 2-#5 BARS

HOME BUILDING PLAN SERVICE 2454 N. E. SANDY BLVD. AREA CODE 503 234-9337 PORTLAND, OREGON 97232	FOUNDATION PLAN	PLAN NUMBER APA-102-2B	SHEET NUMBER 2 OF 9

Fig. 19–25 Foundation plan of the vacation house, with a concrete block foundation wall and freestanding piers. (Courtesy of the American Plywood Association.)

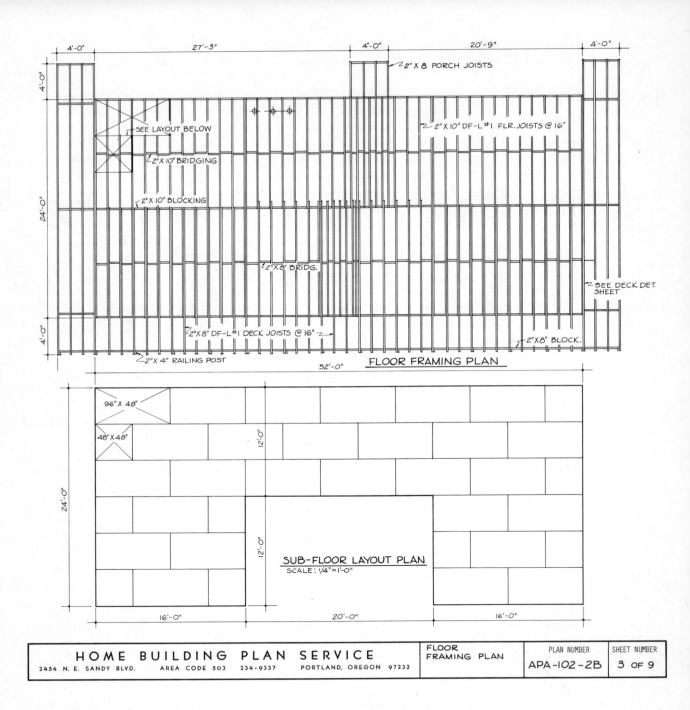

Fig. 19–26 Floor framing plan for the vacation house. (Courtesy of the American Plywood Association.)

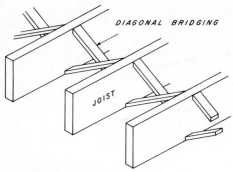

DIAGONAL BRIDGING

JOIST

Diagonal bridging of floor joists.

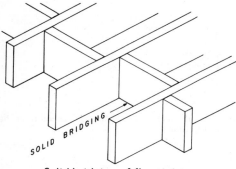

SOLID BRIDGING

Solid bridging of floor joists.

Fig. 19–27 Two types of bridging used to add strength to joists. (Courtesy of the American Plywood Association.)

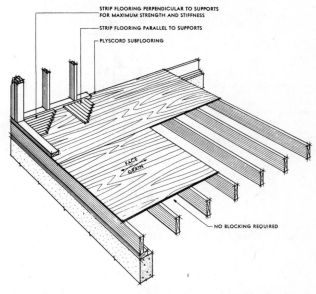

STRIP FLOORING PERPENDICULAR TO SUPPORTS FOR MAXIMUM STRENGTH AND STIFFNESS

STRIP FLOORING PARALLEL TO SUPPORTS

PLYSCORD SUBFLOORING

FACE GRAIN

NO BLOCKING REQUIRED

Fig. 19–28 The application of a plywood underlayment over floor joists. (Courtesy of the American Plywood Association.)

FIGURE 19–29. CORNICE DETAILS

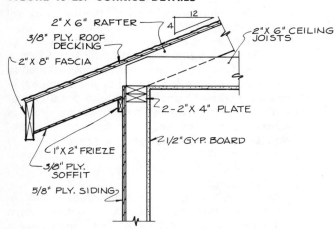

2" X 6" RAFTER
3/8" PLY. ROOF DECKING
2" X 8" FASCIA
12
4
2" X 6" CEILING JOISTS
2-2" X 4" PLATE
1/2" GYP. BOARD
1" X 2" FRIEZE
3/8" PLY. SOFFIT
5/8" PLY. SIDING

A. A rake cornice with a soffit.

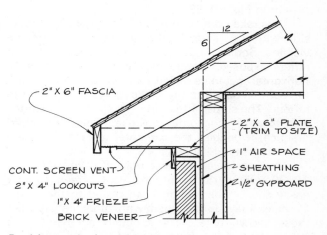

2" X 6" FASCIA
12
6
2" X 6" PLATE (TRIM TO SIZE)
1" AIR SPACE
SHEATHING
1/2" GYPBOARD
CONT. SCREEN VENT
2" X 4" LOOKOUTS
1" X 4" FRIEZE
BRICK VENEER

B. A box cornice for a brick veneer wall.

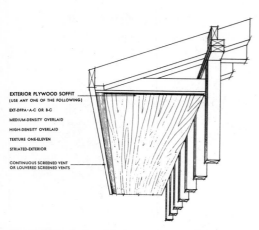

EXTERIOR PLYWOOD SOFFIT
(USE ANY ONE OF THE FOLLOWING)

EXT-DFPA - A-C OR B-C

MEDIUM-DENSITY OVERLAID

HIGH-DENSITY OVERLAID

TEXTURE ONE-ELEVEN

STRIATED-EXTERIOR

CONTINUOUS SCREENED VENT
OR LOUVERED SCREENED VENTS

Fig. 19–30 A pictorial of a plywood soffit applied to a box cornice. (Courtesy of the American Plywood Association.)

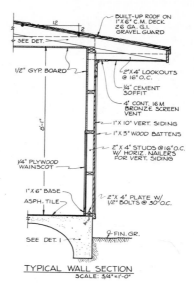

BUILT-UP ROOF ON
1"X 6" C. M. DECK
26 GA . G.I.
GRAVEL GUARD

SEE DET.

1/2" GYP. BOARD

2"X 4' LOOKOUTS @ 16" O.C.

1/4" CEMENT SOFFIT

4' CONT. 16 M BRONZE SCREEN VENT

1"X 10" VERT. SIDING

1"X 3" WOOD BATTENS

2"X 4" STUDS @16"O.C. W/ HORIZ. NAILERS FOR VERT. SIDING

1/4" PLYWOOD WAINSCOT

1"X 6" BASE

ASPH. TILE

2"X 4" PLATE W/ 1/2" BOLTS @ 30"O.C.

FIN. GR.

SEE DET. I

6'-1"

TYPICAL WALL SECTION
SCALE: 3/4"=1'-0"

Fig. 19–31 A typical wall section shows the full section from the foundation through the cornice.

19–13 CORNICE DETAILS

The cornice is the portion of a house where the exterior walls meet the roof. Two types of cornices are (A) rake cornices and (B) box cornices; these are shown in Fig. 19–29.

The rake cornice in A is enclosed on the underside with a $\frac{3}{8}$" *soffit* so that the rafters will not be visible. Some cornice designs are open, with the rafters exposed. In the box cornice shown in B, horizontal members called *lookouts* are added, and the soffit is nailed to the lookouts rather than to the rafters. The slope of the rafters is shown in relationship to a 12" horizontal distance. This is standard practice; it enables the carpenter to read the slope from his framing square.

A pictorial of a box cornice is shown in Fig. 19–30, where the soffit and vent screen can be easily seen. The lookouts are nailed to the studs. Cornices may be designed with other details than those shown here. These details are left to the imagination of the designer.

19–14 THE WALL SECTION

The wall section is a complete section through a wall or through an entire building from the foundation to the cornice. This detail is important to show how the roof will be attached and how the walls will fit onto the foundation.

An example of a wall section is given in Fig. 19–31. This is a frame wall with board-and-batten exterior walls and a gypsum board interior applied to 2 × 4 studs. A note is supplied at the cornice that directs the builder to another detail to get a clearer idea of this construction. The foundation detail is explained elsewhere on the foundation plan; consequently the outline of the grade beam is sufficient here. The inside walls are 8'-1" in height so that 4' × 8' sheets of gypsum board will fit without trimming.

Brick cavity walls are sometimes used in residential construction. This type of wall is shown in a section view in Fig. 19–32. The inner cavity is filled with insulation material to prevent temperature

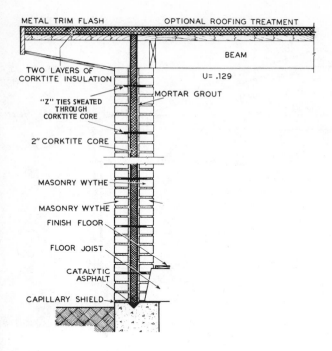

METAL TRIM FLASH   OPTIONAL ROOFING TREATMENT

BEAM

TWO LAYERS OF
CORKTITE INSULATION

U= .129

MORTAR GROUT

"Z" TIES SWEATED
THROUGH
CORKTITE CORE

2" CORKTITE CORE

MASONRY WYTHE

MASONRY WYTHE

FINISH FLOOR

FLOOR JOIST

CATALYTIC
ASPHALT

CAPILLARY SHIELD

Fig. 19–32 A brick cavity wall section. (Courtesy of W. R. Meadows, Inc.)

loss. The two courses of brick are tied together with metal ties called Z-ties. This type of wall supports the roof of the house at the exterior.

19–15 A WORKING DRAWING OF A WALL SECTION

The vacation house is used in Fig. 19–33 as an example of a wall section that explains framing construction. The sizes and grades of lumber and structural members are noted on the drawing. The abbreviation D.F.–L #1 means Douglas Fir–Larch, grade No. 1.

Wall sections are shown as portions of sections through the entire house. Extensive notes are given to explain how each part of the house is constructed. Each section is detailed and labeled with a number such as A/4. This means that detail A on sheet 4 of the set of drawings can be used to identify the relationship between the section and the floor plan from which it was taken.

Various components of the house are labeled. Refer to these details to identify such items as rafters, joists, blocking, gutter, posts, girders, underlayment, decking, collar tie, ridge, beams, and other elements used in architectural construction.

19–16 ELEVATIONS

The exterior appearance of each side of a house as shown in an orthographic view is called an *elevation.* The style of a house is determined more by its elevations than by its plan. For example, the appearance of the house in Fig. 19–34 can be changed in several different ways by varying its exterior. These variations are left to the option of the designer and the client.

Two exterior elevations and an interior elevation are shown in Fig. 19–35. These are left undimensioned to emphasize the general appearance of the house. Planting and shadows are shown to add depth to the illustrations. Symbols are used to

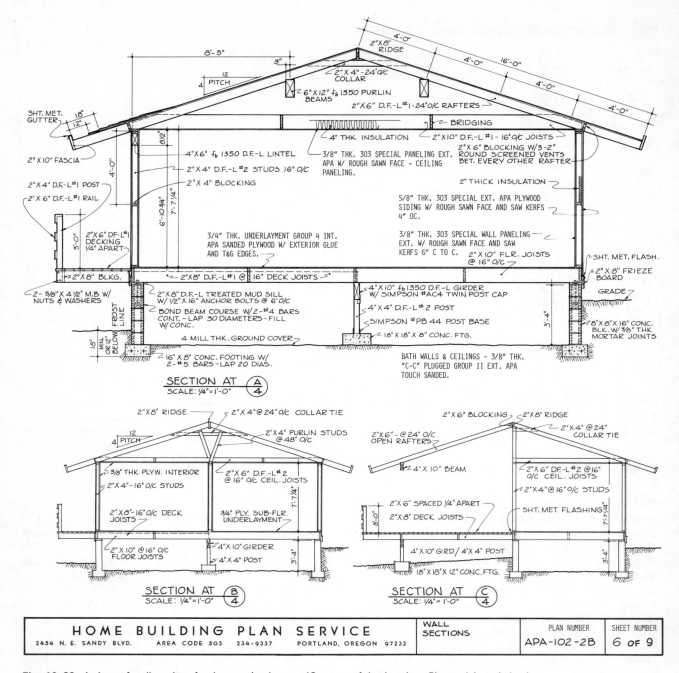

SECTION AT (A/4)
SCALE: 1/4"=1'-0"

SECTION AT (B/4)
SCALE: 1/4"=1'-0"

SECTION AT (C/4)
SCALE: 1/4"=1'-0"

Section at A labels:

8'-5"

3"

4'-0"

2"X8" RIDGE

4'-0"

16'-0"

12 / 4 PITCH

2"X4"-24"O/c COLLAR

4'-0"

4'-0"

SHT. MET. GUTTER

18"
12"

6"X12" fb 1350 PURLIN BEAMS

2"X6" D.F.-L #1-24"O/c RAFTERS

2"X10" FASCIA

8½"

4" THK. INSULATION

2"X10" D.F.-L #1 - 16"O/c JOISTS

BRIDGING

2"X6" BLOCKING W/3-2" ROUND SCREENED VENTS BET. EVERY OTHER RAFTER

4"X6" fb 1350 D.F.-L LINTEL

3/8" THK. 303 SPECIAL PANELING EXT. APA W/ ROUGH SAWN FACE - CEILING PANELING.

2" THICK INSULATION

2"X4" D.F.-L #1 POST

4'-0"

2"X4" D.F.-L #2 STUDS 16" O/c

5/8" THK. 303 SPECIAL EXT. APA PLYWOOD SIDING W/ ROUGH SAWN FACE AND SAW KERFS 4" OC.

2"X6" D.F.-L #1 RAIL

2"X4" BLOCKING

6'-10¾"

7'-7¼"

3/4" THK. UNDERLAYMENT GROUP 4 INT. APA SANDED PLYWOOD W/ EXTERIOR GLUE AND T&G EDGES.

3/8" THK. 303 SPECIAL WALL PANELING EXT. W/ ROUGH SAWN FACE AND SAW KERFS 6" C TO C.

2"X6" DF-L #1 DECKING ¼" APART

5'-0"

2"X10" FLR. JOISTS @ 16" O/c

SHT. MET. FLASH.

2"X8" BLKG.

2"X8" D.F.-L #1 @ 16" DECK JOISTS

2"X8" FRIEZE BOARD

2- 5/8" X 4½" M.B W/ NUTS & WASHERS

FROST LINE

2"X8" D.F.-L TREATED MUD SILL W/ ½" X 16" ANCHOR BOLTS @ 6'O/c

4"X10" fb1350 D.F.-L GIRDER W/ SIMPSON #AC4 TWIN POST CAP

GRADE

BOND BEAM COURSE W/2-#4 BARS CONT. - LAP 30 DIAMETERS - FILL W/ CONC.

4"X4" D.F.-L #2 POST

3'-4"

8"X8"X16" CONC. BLK. W/3/8" THK. MORTAR JOINTS

18" MIN. OR 12" BELOW

SIMPSON #PB 44 POST BASE

4 MILL THK. GROUND COVER

18"X18"X8" CONC. FTG.

16"X8" CONC. FOOTING W/ 2-#5 BARS - LAP 20 DIAS.

BATH WALLS & CEILINGS - 3/8" THK. "C-C" PLUGGED GROUP II EXT. APA TOUCH SANDED.

Section at B labels:

2"X8" RIDGE

2"X4" @ 24" O/c COLLAR TIE

12 / 4 PITCH

2"X4" PURLIN STUDS @ 48" O/c

3/8" THK PLYW. INTERIOR

2"X6" D.F.-L #2 @ 16" O/c CEIL. JOISTS

2"X4"-16" O/c STUDS

7'-7¼"

2"X8"-16" O/c DECK JOISTS

3/4" PLY. SUB-FLR. UNDERLAYMENT

2"X10" @16" O/c FLOOR JOISTS

4"X10" GIRDER

3'-4"

4"X4" POST

Section at C labels:

2"X6" BLOCKING

2"X8" RIDGE

2"X4" @ 24" COLLAR TIE

2"X6"- @ 24" O/c. OPEN RAFTERS

2"X6" DF-L #2 @16" O/c CEIL. JOISTS

4"X 10" BEAM

2"X4"@16"O/c STUDS

2"X6" SPACED ¼" APART

3'-0"

SHT. MET. FLASHING

2"X8" DECK JOISTS

7'-7¼"

4"X10" GIRD./ 4"X 4" POST

3'-4"

18"X18"X12" CONC.FTG.

HOME BUILDING PLAN SERVICE	WALL SECTIONS	PLAN NUMBER	SHEET NUMBER
2454 N. E. SANDY BLVD. AREA CODE 503 234-9337 PORTLAND, OREGON 97232		APA-102-2B	6 OF 9

Fig. 19–33 A sheet of wall sections for the vacation house. (Courtesy of the American Plywood Association.)

Fig. 19–34 The outward appearance of a house can be changed by changing the elevation designs. (Courtesy of National Plan Service, Inc.)

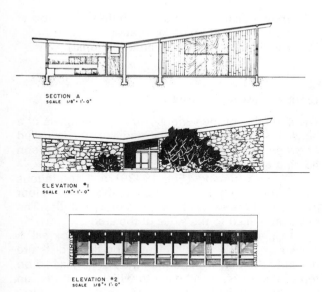

SECTION A
SCALE 1/8" = 1'-0"

ELEVATION #1
SCALE 1/8" = 1'-0"

ELEVATION #2
SCALE 1/8" = 1'-0"

Fig. 19–35 Display elevations of a kindergarten building. (Courtesy of Naval Facilities Engineering Command.)

Fig. 19–36 These tree symbols are available on transfer film that can be applied to elevation drawings. (Courtesy of Para-Tone Incorporated.)

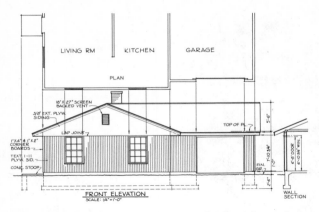

LIVING RM   KITCHEN   GARAGE

PLAN

18" X 27" SCREEN
BACKED VENT

3/8" EXT. PLYW.
SIDING

TOP OF PL.

5'-6"

LAP JOINT

1"X4" & 1"X2"
CORNER
BOARDS

TEXT. 1-11
PLYW. SID.

CONC. STOOP

7'-10 3/4"

1'-0"

6'-6" DOOR

6'-10 3/4" WIN.

FIN.
GR.

2'-6"

FRONT ELEVATION
SCALE: 1/4"=1'-0"

WALL
SECTION

Fig. 19–37 The elevation of a house can be drawn by overlaying the floor plan and wall section with tracing paper and projecting to the elevation as shown.

represent materials in much the same way as a technical illustrator would render a drawing.

Plants can be drawn on the elevations or transferred from transfer film. Examples of transfer-film trees are shown in Fig. 19–36. These can be transferred from the film to the drawing by burnishing the acetate film on which they are printed.

An elevation is drawn at the same scale as the floor plan, $\frac{1}{4}'' = 1'\text{-}0''$, so that the views can be projected from the floor plan with the minimum of measurement. Once the floor plan is completed and the wall section designed, the elevations can be projected from these (Fig. 19–37). A sheet of tracing paper is placed over the plan, and dimensions for the elevations are projected from the plan and wall section as shown.

Symbols are drawn to represent siding materials and other features. The hidden lines below grade level are the outlines of the foundation. Dimensions are shown from the bottom of the foundation to the finished grade, to the finished floor, to the top of the plate, and to the top of the ridge.

The designer must select windows before he can complete the elevations, since they will affect the elevations. These are selected from window brochures and are drawn in the elevation to look as much like the actual window as possible.

19–17 WORKING DRAWINGS OF ELEVATIONS

The elevations of the vacation house are shown in Fig. 19–38. The elevations are positioned on the same sheet so that all views can be studied together. Larger houses may require that elevations be drawn on more than one sheet.

These elevations can be related to the wall sections shown in Fig. 19–33. A number of exterior details are noted. The left side view refers to three section views that will be shown on sheet 7 of this set of plans.

The dimensions from the foundation to the finished grade and to the top of the ridge are not shown, since these were given on sheet 6 (Fig. 19–33) of this set of plans.

Rules for Drawing Elevations

1. Draw elevations at the same scale as the floor plans, $\frac{1}{4}'' = 1'\text{-}0''$.
2. Draw elevations of all sides of the house and label each.
3. Show placement of windows and doors.
4. Indicate exterior wall finishes with symbols and notes.
5. Show finish grade lines, finish floor lines, top of plate, and bottom of foundation.
6. Show trees and other plants (optional).

19–18 FRAMING DETAILS

The assembly of the various structural members of a house—studs, joists, rafters, and so on—is called *framing.* Two major framing methods are (A) balloon framing and (B) platform framing.

Balloon framing (Fig. 19–39) has continuous studs from the sill to the top of the plate. Floor joists sit on the same sill plate as do the studs. The joists are nailed to the sides of the studs.

In platform framing (Fig. 19–40) a box sill is placed on top of the sill plate. The floor joists are nailed to the box sill, and then the flooring is laid on top of the joists. A sill plate to which the studs can be nailed is nailed to the top of the floor, or "platform." This framing technique is used for upper floors also.

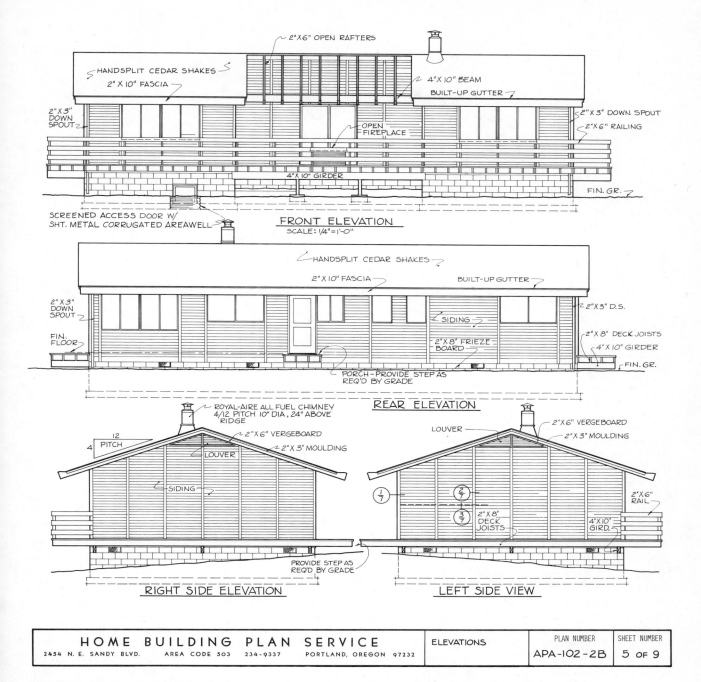

FRONT ELEVATION
SCALE: 1/4"=1'-0"

2"X6" OPEN RAFTERS

HANDSPLIT CEDAR SHAKES

2" X 10" FASCIA

4"X 10" BEAM

BUILT-UP GUTTER

2"X 3" DOWN SPOUT

OPEN FIREPLACE

2"X 3" DOWN SPOUT

2"X 6" RAILING

4"X 10" GIRDER

FIN. GR.

SCREENED ACCESS DOOR w/
SHT. METAL CORRUGATED AREAWELL

HANDSPLIT CEDAR SHAKES

2" X 10" FASCIA

BUILT-UP GUTTER

2" X 3" DOWN SPOUT

2"X 3" D.S.

SIDING

2"X 8" DECK JOISTS

4"X 10" GIRDER

FIN. GR.

FIN. FLOOR

2"X 8" FRIEZE BOARD

PORCH - PROVIDE STEP AS REQ'D BY GRADE

REAR ELEVATION

ROYAL-AIRE ALL FUEL CHIMNEY
4/12 PITCH 10" DIA, 24" ABOVE RIDGE

2"X 6" VERGEBOARD

2" X 3" MOULDING

LOUVER

12 PITCH
4

SIDING

LOUVER

2"X 6" VERGEBOARD

2"X 3" MOULDING

2"X 6" RAIL

1/7

2/7

3/7

2"X 8" DECK JOISTS

4"X 10" GIRD.

PROVIDE STEP AS REQ'D BY GRADE

RIGHT SIDE ELEVATION

LEFT SIDE VIEW

HOME BUILDING PLAN SERVICE
2454 N. E. SANDY BLVD.   AREA CODE 503   234-9337   PORTLAND, OREGON 97232

ELEVATIONS

PLAN NUMBER
APA-102-2B

SHEET NUMBER
5 OF 9

Fig. 19–38 Working drawing of the elevations for the vacation house. (Courtesy of the American Plywood Association.)

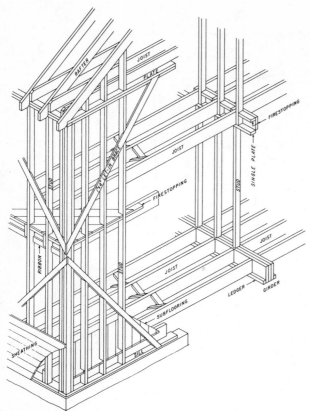

Fig. 19–39 Balloon frame construction. (Courtesy of the American Plywood Association.)

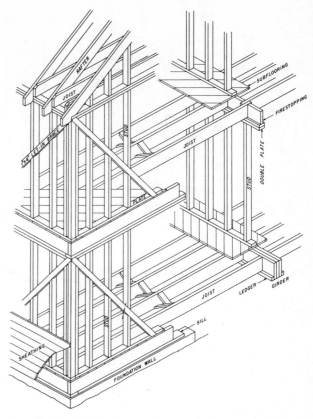

Fig. 19–40 Platform frame construction. (Courtesy of the American Plywood Association.)

19–19 BRICK VENEER FRAMING

A brick veneer wall is used to give a covering of brick to the exterior of a house (Fig. 19–41). A 1″ cavity is left between the sheathing and the brick wall for insulation. Flashing is used at the bottom of the wall to direct moisture to the outside of the brick veneer through *weep holes* left between the bricks by the brick mason.

Brick hangers are used to hold the brick course to the wall of the house. These are placed about 2′ apart between masonry joints. Sheathing paper or pretreated sheathing must be used to moisture-proof the interior wall.

19–20 STAIRWAY DETAILS

A pictorial of a stairway with a landing is shown in Fig. 19–42. This is shown as a framing detail in the architectural plans.

The stringers are usually 2 × 10′s or 2 × 12′s into which notches are cut for the *treads* that will be used as steps. The vertical cuts are called *risers*; they may be left open in a basement, but they are usually enclosed in an interior stairway.

The general dimensions for risers and treads are shown in Fig. 19–43. This figure shows the minimum standards for designing the proper step sizes for stairways.

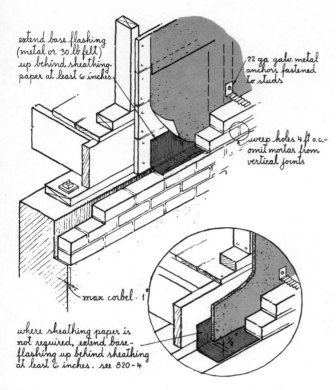

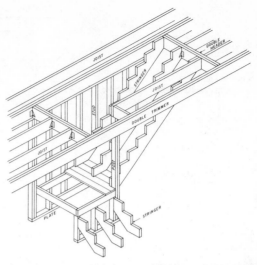

Fig. 19–41 Details of brick veneer construction. (Courtesy of the Federal Housing Administration.)

Fig. 19–42 A pictorial of the framing construction for a stairway with a landing. (Courtesy of the American Plywood Association.)

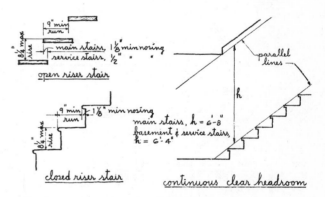

Fig. 19–43 Minimum standards for designing stairways. (Courtesy of the Federal Housing Administration.)

19–21 WORKING DRAWINGS OF FRAMING DETAILS

The framing details for the vacation house are partially shown in Fig. 19–44. This figure shows sections taken from sheets 4 and 5 (Figs. 19–10 and 19–38) of the set of plans. These details describe how the house is to be framed at various sections indicated on the floor plan and foundation plan. Refer to the sheets of the set of plans as directed by the detail numbers and interpret the meaning of the details.

These details are drawn at different scales so that the details will be easy to read. A rear wall framing detail shows the placement of lintels (headers) and studs and the blocking. The plywood siding will be placed over this wall.

19–22 ROOF FRAMING PLAN

A roof framing plan is similar to a floor framing plan. It shows the position of the rafters and the application of plywood decking. The plan shown in Fig. 19–45 represents the roof of the vacation house used as an example throughout this chapter.

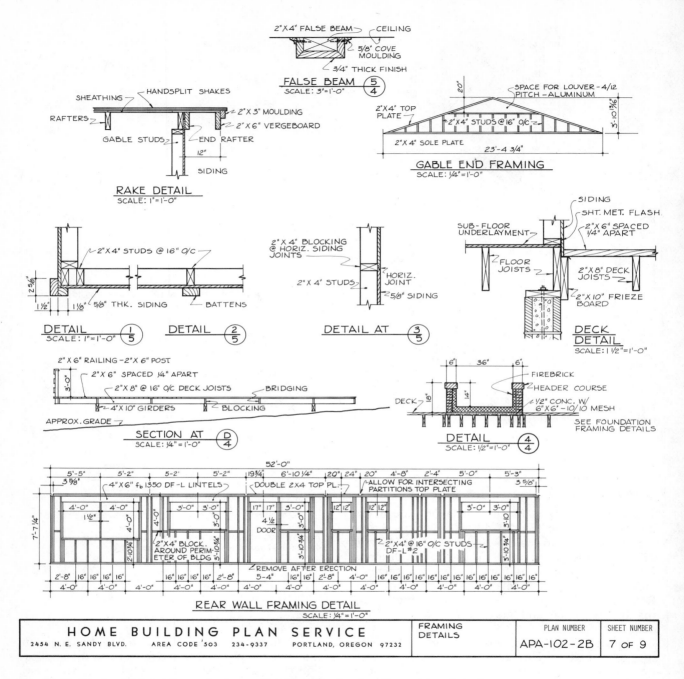

2"X4" FALSE BEAM — CEILING
5/8" COVE MOULDING
3/4" THICK FINISH

FALSE BEAM $\frac{5}{4}$
SCALE: 3"=1'-0"

20"
SPACE FOR LOUVER - 4/12 PITCH - ALUMINUM
2"X4" TOP PLATE
2"X4" STUDS @ 16" O/C
2"X4" SOLE PLATE
23'-4 3/4"
3'-10 13/16"

GABLE END FRAMING
SCALE: 1/4"=1'-0"

SHEATHING — HANDSPLIT SHAKES
RAFTERS
2"X3" MOULDING
2"X6" VERGEBOARD
GABLE STUDS
END RAFTER
12"
SIDING

RAKE DETAIL
SCALE: 1"=1'-0"

2"X4" STUDS @ 16" O/C
2 5/8"
1 1/2"   1 1/8"   5/8" THK. SIDING
BATTENS

DETAIL $\frac{1}{5}$
SCALE: 1"=1'-0"

DETAIL $\frac{2}{5}$

2"X4" BLOCKING @ HORIZ. SIDING JOINTS
2"X4" STUDS
HORIZ. JOINT
5/8" SIDING

DETAIL AT $\frac{3}{5}$

SIDING
SHT. MET. FLASH.
2"X6" SPACED 1/4" APART
SUB-FLOOR UNDERLAYMENT
FLOOR JOISTS
2"X8" DECK JOISTS
2"X10" FRIEZE BOARD

DECK DETAIL
SCALE: 1 1/2"=1'-0"

2"X6" RAILING - 2"X6" POST
3'-0"
2"X6" SPACED 1/4" APART
2"X8" @ 16" O/C DECK JOISTS
BRIDGING
4"X10" GIRDERS
BLOCKING
APPROX. GRADE

SECTION AT $\frac{D}{4}$
SCALE: 1/4"=1'-0"

6"   36"   6"
FIREBRICK
HEADER COURSE
DECK
18"   14"
1/2" CONC. W/ 6"X6" - 10/10 MESH
SEE FOUNDATION FRAMING DETAILS

DETAIL $\frac{4}{4}$
SCALE: 1/2"=1'-0"

52'-0"
5'-5"   5'-2"   5'-2"   5'-2"   19 3/4"   6'-10 1/4"   20"   24"   20"   4'-8"   2'-4"   5'-0"   5'-3"
3 5/8"   5 5/8"
4"X6" f_b 1350 DF-L LINTELS
DOUBLE 2X4 TOP PL.
ALLOW FOR INTERSECTING PARTITIONS TOP PLATE
7'-7 1/4"
4'-0"   4'-0"   3'-0"   3'-0"   17"   17"   3'-0"   12"12"   12"12"   3'-0"   3'-10"
1 1/2"
4'-0"   4'-0"   4 1/2" DOOR   3'-0"   3'-0"
2"X4" BLOCK. AROUND PERIMETER OF BLDG
2"X4" @ 16" O/C STUDS DF-L #2
REMOVE AFTER ERECTION
2'-8"   16"   16"   16"   16"   16"   16"   16"   2'-8"   16"   16"   16"   16"   16"   16"   16"   16"   16"   16"   16"
4'-0"   4'-0"   4'-0"   4'-0"   5-4"   4'-0"   4'-0"   4'-0"   4'-0"   4'-0"   4'-0"   4'-0"

REAR WALL FRAMING DETAIL
SCALE: 1/4"=1'-0"

HOME BUILDING PLAN SERVICE	FRAMING DETAILS	PLAN NUMBER	SHEET NUMBER
2454 N. E. SANDY BLVD. AREA CODE 503 234-9337 PORTLAND, OREGON 97232		APA-102-2B	7 OF 9

Fig. 19–44 Framing details for the vacation house. (Courtesy of the American Plywood Association.)

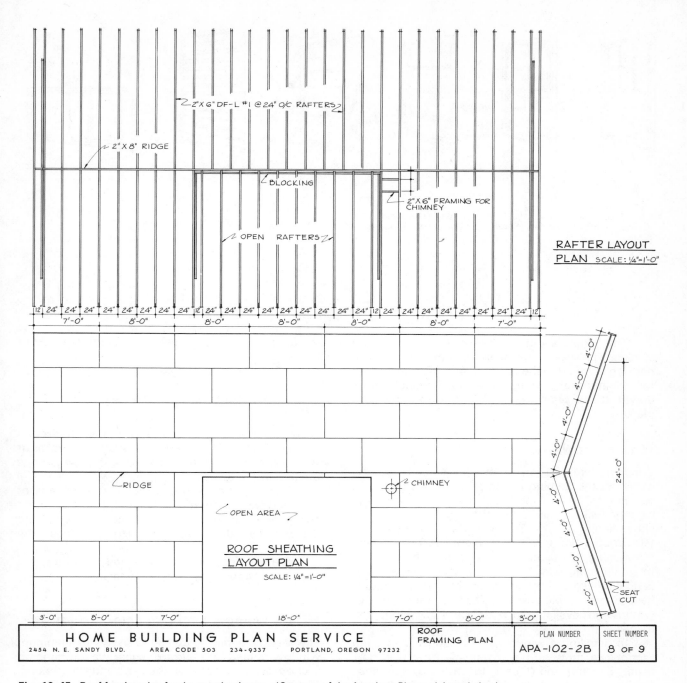

2"X 6" DF-L #I @ 24" O/C RAFTERS

2" X 8" RIDGE

BLOCKING

2"X 6" FRAMING FOR CHIMNEY

OPEN RAFTERS

RAFTER LAYOUT
PLAN SCALE: ¼"=1'-0"

| 12" | 24" | 24" | 24" | 24" | 24" | 24" | 24" | 24" | 12" | 24" | 24" | 24" | 24" | 24" | 24" | 24" | 24" | 24" | 12" | 24" | 24" | 24" | 24" | 24" | 24" | 24" | 24" | 24" | 12" |

| 7'-0" | 8'-0" | 8'-0" | 8'-0" | 8'-0" | 8'-0" | 7'-0" |

RIDGE

CHIMNEY

OPEN AREA

ROOF SHEATHING
LAYOUT PLAN
SCALE: ¼"=1'-0"

4'-0"
4'-0"
4'-0"
4'-0"
24'-0"
4'-0"
4'-0"
4'-0"
4'-0"

SEAT CUT

| 3'-0" | 8'-0" | 7'-0" | 18'-0" | 7'-0" | 8'-0" | 3'-0" |

HOME BUILDING PLAN SERVICE
2454 N. E. SANDY BLVD.   AREA CODE 503   234-9337   PORTLAND, OREGON 97232

ROOF FRAMING PLAN

| PLAN NUMBER | SHEET NUMBER |
| APA-102-2B | 8 OF 9 |

Fig. 19–45 Roof framing plan for the vacation house. (Courtesy of the American Plywood Association.)

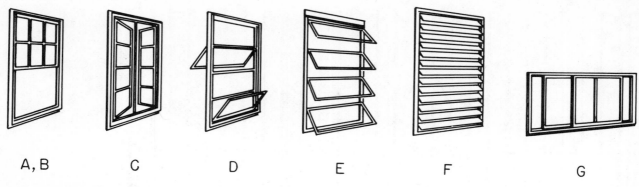

Fig. 19–46 Types of windows: (A) single-hung, (B) double-hung, (C) casement, (D) projected, (E) awning, (F) jalousie, (G) horizontal sliding.

The rafter layout shows how the rafters are spaced. The sheathing plan shows how the plywood decking is nailed to the rafters in 4' × 8' sheets with the minimum of cutting. The roof framing plan is drawn at the same scale, $\frac{1}{4}'' = 1'\text{-}0''$, as the floor plan.

19–23 WINDOWS

Windows are not made by the carpenters who construct the framing of the house, but are bought as units to fit into the rough openings left in the exterior walls. The standard types of window are shown in Fig. 19–46. They include (A) single-hung, (B) double-hung, (C) casement, (D) projected, (E) awning, (F) jalousie, and (H) horizontal sliding. In single-hung windows there is only one sash that can be moved up and down; double-hung windows have two movable sashes. These various types of window are available in both wood and aluminum frames.

In detailing a window, the designer uses three sections to show how it is framed into a wall: (A) head, (B) jamb, and (C) sill. Pictorial views of these three sections are shown in Fig. 19–47. The head is at the top of the window, the sill at the bottom, and

the jamb is a horizontal section through the side of the window.

19–24 A WINDOW SECTION THROUGH A FRAME WALL

A window section through a wood, horizontal sliding window is shown as a pictorial and as it would appear in section (Fig. 19–48). The jamb is omitted in the detail.

The parts tinted in color are standard parts of the window that are ready-made for insertion in the rough opening in the wall. Other trim parts are standard mouldings that are used to enclose the frame.

The exterior siding is frame and the inside is a plaster wall applied to a metal plaster lath.

19–25 A WINDOW SECTION—BRICK VENEER

The window detail in Fig. 19–49 shows an aluminum window framed into a brick veneer wall. The jamb section is placed between the head and sill sections. The rough opening dimensions and actual window openings are given.

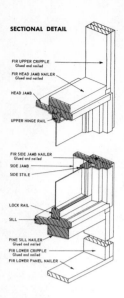

SECTIONAL DETAIL

FIR UPPER CRIPPLE
Glued and nailed

FIR HEAD JAMB NAILER
Glued and nailed

HEAD JAMB

UPPER HINGE RAIL

FIR SIDE JAMB NAILER
Glued and nailed

SIDE JAMB

SIDE STILE

LOCK RAIL

SILL

PINE SILL NAILER
Glued and nailed

FIR LOWER CRIPPLE
Glued and nailed

FIR LOWER PANEL NAILER

Fig. 19–47 Windows are detailed by showing sections through the head, jamb, and sill. (Courtesy of Andersen Corporation.)

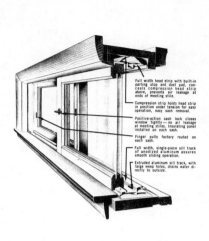

Full width head strip with built-in parting stop and dust pad, conceals compression head strip above, prevents air leakage at ends of meeting stile.

Compression strip holds head strip in position under tension for easy operation, easy sash removal.

Positive-action sash lock closes window tightly—no air leakage at meeting stiles. Insulating panel installed on each sash.

Finger pulls factory routed on each sash.

Full width, single-piece sill track of anodized aluminum assures smooth sliding operation.

Extruded aluminum sill track, with large weep holes, drains water directly to outside.

Fig. 19–48 A detail of a window through its head and sill. (Courtesy of Rock Island Millwork.)

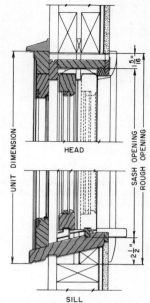

HEAD

UNIT DIMENSION

SASH OPENING

ROUGH OPENING

$1\frac{5}{16}''$

$2\frac{1}{2}''$

SILL

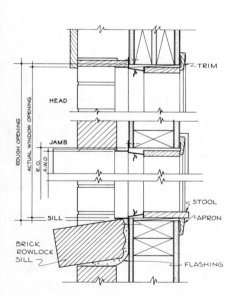

TRIM

HEAD

JAMB

ROUGH OPENING

ACTUAL WINDOW OPENING

R.O.

A.W.O.

STOOL

APRON

SILL

BRICK ROWLOCK SILL

FLASHING

Fig. 19–49 A window detail of a horizontal sliding window in a brick veneer wall.

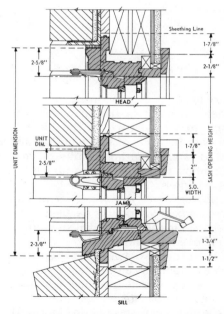

Sheathing Line

2-5/8''

1-7/8''

2-1/8''

HEAD

UNIT DIMENSION

UNIT DIM.

2-5/8''

1-7/8''

2''

S.O. WIDTH

SASH OPENING HEIGHT

JAMB

2-3/8''

1-3/4''

1-1/2''

SILL

Fig. 19–50 A window detail of a wood casement window in a brick veneer wall. Brick is supported over the opening with a steel angle lintel. (Courtesy of Andersen Corporation.)

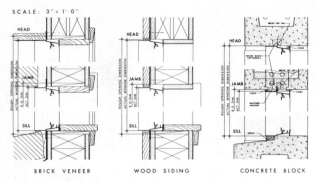

SCALE: 3" = 1'-0"

BRICK VENEER   WOOD SIDING   CONCRETE BLOCK

Fig. 19–51 Examples of installation details supplied by window manufacturers that can be traced by designers. (Courtesy of Alenco Corporation.)

WINDOW SCHEDULE					
MARK	NO	STOCK	TYPE	MFGR	ROUGH OPENING
A	2	6030	HORIZONTAL SLIDING	ALENCO	72 3/4" x 36 1/2"
B	2	2030	HORIZONTAL SLIDING	ALENCO	24 3/4" x 36 1/2"
C	6	4040	HORIZONTAL SLIDING	ALENCO	48 3/4" x 48 1/2"
D	1	3030	HORIZONTAL SLIDING	ALENCO	36 3/4" x 36 1/2"

Fig. 19–52 A window schedule.

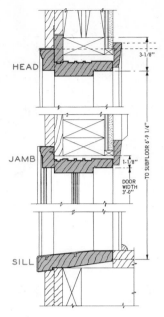

Fig. 19–53 A door detail in an exterior frame wall. (Courtesy of Andersen Corporation.)

In this detail no brick is supported above the windows. Instead a soffit is placed across the window openings to fill the cavity. The frieze is positioned even with the tops of the windows and doors, usually 6'-8" above the floor. This reduces the cost of supporting the brick course above the windows with steel lintels.

Brick is supported over the windows in Fig. 19–50, where a casement window is detailed. You can see the steel lintel in the head detail supporting the brick course above the windows.

Windows are usually drawn at a scale of 3" = 1'-0" so that all details can be clearly shown. Most manufacturers supply details of their windows at this scale that can be traced by draftsmen. Examples of details of this type are given in Fig. 19–51 for windows that are to be framed into brick veneer, into frame walls, and into concrete block.

19–26 WINDOW SCHEDULES

Window schedules are tables of dimensions and notes that specify the types of windows that will be used in a house. The window schedule used on the floor plan of the vacation house (Fig. 19–10) is shown in Fig. 19–52. This schedule specifies the number of each type of window needed, identifying numbers, stock numbers, manufacturers, and rough opening sizes required.

The window schedule supplies the necessary information in one table for easy reference by the builder. Sizes of windows are available at 6" intervals. For example, most manufacturers make windows that are 24", 30", 36", and 42" wide. Always select windows from manufacturers' specifications given in their brochures, which are available at lumberyards.

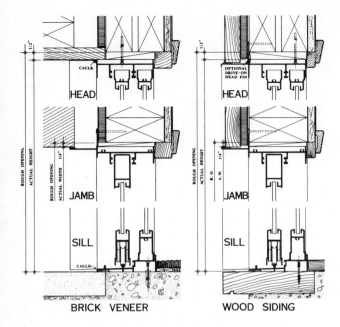

HEAD

JAMB

SILL

BRICK VENEER

HEAD

JAMB

SILL

WOOD SIDING

Fig. 19–54 Installation details for sliding glass patio doors. (Courtesy of Alenco Corporation.)

DOOR	SCHEDULE				
MARK	NO	TYPE	MATL	SIZE
1	1	1 LT. PANEL SASH DOOR	BIRCH	2'-8" x 6'-8" x 1 3/4"
2	1	FLUSH HOLLOW CORE – INTERIOR	BIRCH	2'-8" x 6'-8" x 1 3/8"
3	6	FLUSH HOLLOW CORE – INTERIOR	BIRCH	2'-6" x 6'-8" x 1 3/8"
4	1	FLUSH HOLLOW CORE – INTERIOR	BIRCH	2'-4" x 6'-8" x 1 3/8"
5	1	FLUSH HOLLOW CORE – INTERIOR	BIRCH	2'-0" x 6'-8" x 1 3/8"
6	1	FLUSH HOLLOW CORE – INTERIOR	BIRCH	1'-6" x 6'-8" x 1 3/8"
7	1 PR	SWING. CAFE DOORS	BIRCH	1'-8" x 4'-0" x 1 1/8"
8	1	FLUSH HOLLOW CORE – FOLDING	BIRCH	6'-0" x 6'-8" x 1 3/8"
9	2	FLUSH HOLLOW CORE – FOLDING	BIRCH	4'-0" x 6'-8" x 1 3/8"
10	3	SLIDING GLASS (6069 – 2V)	GLASS	6'-0" x 6'-8 1/2"

Fig. 19–55 A door schedule.

19–27 DOOR DETAILS

Door details have the same sections as window details—head, jamb, and sill. A detail of a door framed into a frame wall is shown in Fig. 19–53.

The standard height of a door is 6'-8". Standard widths are 2'-0", 2'-6", and 3'-0". The 2'-0" doors are used for closets and pantries. Interior doors are usually 2'-6" and exterior doors 3'-0".

The door shown in Fig. 19–53 can be installed in a brick veneer wall using details similar to those used for the window in Fig. 19–50. Can you draw these details?

Details are shown in Fig. 19–54 for installing a sliding glass door in both brick veneer and frame walls. Sliding glass doors usually open onto patios or overlook a pleasing view. The standard height of a patio sliding glass door is 6'-8". The standard

widths of two-panel units are 5', 6', 8', and 12'. Other sizes are available, but these are standard for most manufacturers.

19–28 DOOR SCHEDULES

Door schedules are similar to window schedules (discussed in Article 19–26). The door schedule used on the floor plan of the vacation house (Fig. 19–10) is shown in Fig. 19–55. The various types of doors are assigned numbers on the door schedule. If the doors are given numbers, the windows are given letters, and vice versa.

The information given in the door schedule can be used for ordering the required door units and can be referred to for construction dimensions.

19–29 KITCHEN CABINETS

Kitchen cabinets may be either custom built or they may be prebuilt units that are bought and installed by the builder. Examples of cabinet details are shown in Fig. 19–56 as sections and elevations. Sections A, B, C, and D give the dimensions that are ordinarily required.

Kitchen cabinets must be built to accommodate the appliances that will be installed in the kitchen. The basic dimensions of standard kitchen and laundry appliances are shown in Fig. 19–57. Sizes vary with each manufacturer, but none will vary greatly from those given here.

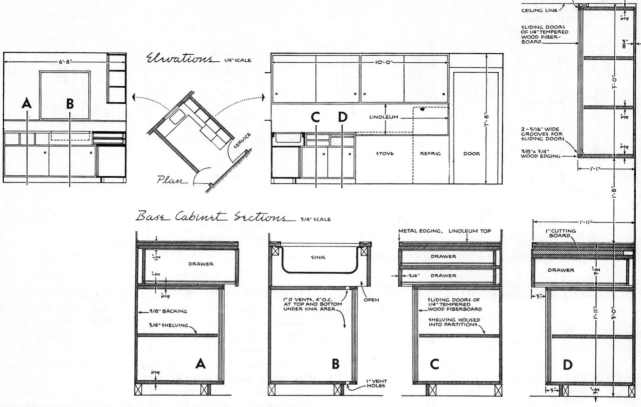

Fig. 19–56 Kitchen elevations and cabinet details. (Courtesy of Architectural Woodwork Institute.)

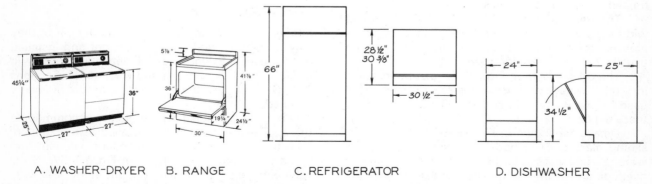

A. WASHER-DRYER   B. RANGE   C. REFRIGERATOR   D. DISHWASHER

Fig. 19–57 Dimensions of kitchen and laundry appliances. (Courtesy of General Electric.)

Fig. 19–58 Examples of floor plan layouts for kitchens.

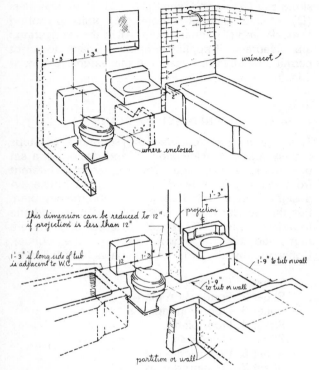

Fig. 19–59 Minimum spacing dimensions for bathroom appliances. (Courtesy of the Federal Housing Administration.)

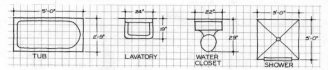

Fig. 19–60 Typical sizes of bathroom fixtures for floor plan development.

Several kitchen floor plans are shown in Fig. 19–58. The same planning principles are used in developing a kitchen plan as were used in developing the floor plan and the plot plan. The available space must be put to good use, and the layout should be arranged so that the minimum number of steps are required of the housewife as she goes about her work.

19–30 BATHROOM DETAILS

The bathroom must be planned in the same way as the kitchen, since it has to be equipped with standard fixtures that are available in predetermined sizes. Again, it is important for the bathroom to be functional, with the minimum of unused space.

The recommended spacing of fixtures is shown in Fig. 19–59. Typical sizes of the fixtures used in bathrooms are given in Fig. 19–60; however, there is great variation in the dimensions of bathroom fixtures. Templates are available for drawing these fixtures on working drawings.

Several bathroom layouts are given in Fig. 19–61. These are examples of arrangements that can be used in rooms of different shapes and proportions.

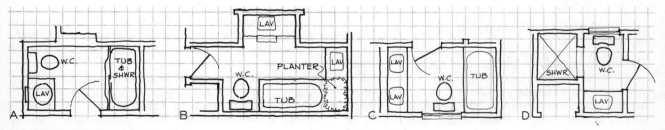

Fig. 19–61 Examples of bathroom layouts.

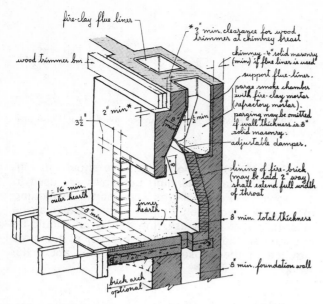

Labels on figure:
fire-clay flue liners

*2" min. clearance for wood trimmer at chimney breast

wood trimmer bm

chimney-4" solid masonry (min.) if flue liner is used

support flue-liner.

parge smoke chamber with fire-clay mortar (refractory mortar).

parging may be omitted if wall thickness is 8" solid masonry.

adjustable damper.

2" min*

3½"

½" min.

lining of fire-brick (may be laid 2" way) shall extend full width of throat

16" min. outer hearth

inner hearth

8" min. total thickness

8" min. foundation wall

brick arch optional

Fig. 19–62 A pictorial of the construction of a standard fireplace. (Courtesy of the Federal Housing Administration.)

19–31 FIREPLACE DETAILS

The details for fireplaces are quite standard, since it is risky to design a fireplace that departs from previously tested designs. A newly designed fireplace may not burn properly because of a faulty draft.

The fireplace pictorial in Fig. 19–62 is an example of masonry construction. The actual details on the working drawing are shown in dimensioned orthographic views and sections. The fireplace detail is usually drawn at a scale of $\frac{1}{2}$″ = 1′-0″.

19–32 WORKING DRAWINGS OF INTERIOR DETAILS

The interior details of the vacation house used as an example throughout this chapter are shown in Fig. 19–63. These details include a fireplace, window details, door details, kitchen and bathroom cabinets, and a spindle wall. These details are drawn at different scales to give the best representation of

each item. These details should be checked with the floor plan of the vacation house (Fig. 19–10). The previously discussed principles of detailing and framing have been used on this sheet.

19–33 ROOF COVERINGS

The basic types of roof covering are (A) asphalt shingles, (B) wood shingles, (C) slate shingles, (D) asbestos-cement shingles, (E) built-up roofing (gravel), and (F) concrete tile. All of these coverings are acceptable if applied properly. Space does not permit a detailed discussion of this extensive area of construction.

19–34 THE FINISHED SET OF PLANS

This chapter has followed the sequence of steps usually required in developing and designing a set of plans for a residence. This sequence is different from the sequence used in building the house. A designer begins with the floor plan and the plot plan, but the builder begins with the plot plan and the foundation plan. The sheets in a set of plans are numbered for the convenience of the builder. Consequently, the order of the sheets is as follows:

Sheet 1: Plot plan
Sheet 2: Foundation plan
Sheet 3: Floor framing plan
Sheet 4: Floor plan
Sheet 5: Elevations
Sheet 6: Wall sections
Sheet 7: Framing details
Sheet 8: Roof framing plan
Sheet 9: Built-ins, kitchen, bath, door and window details

You can see that the order of the sheets is closely related to the order of the actual construction. Construction of the built-ins is the last step in building a house.

The finished set of plans is stapled together at the left side. If you have drawn adequate plans, the builder will be able to construct the house from these plans, with only small decisions left to his judgment.

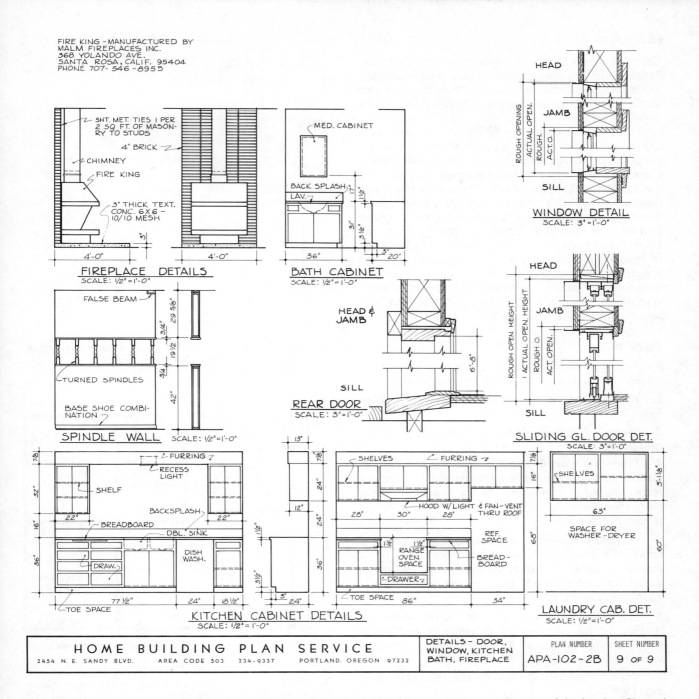

Fig. 19–63 A working drawing sheet showing the framing and interior details of the vacation house. (Courtesy of the American Plywood Association.)

PROBLEMS

These problems are to be solved in accordance with Article 3–15 and the specifications of your instructor. Some can be solved on Size A or Size B paper, but the larger working drawings should be presented on Size C sheets.

Most architectural drafting problems include a certain amount of design, since many variations are possible in the representation of plans and details. Consequently the following problems will exercise the student's ability to utilize the general principles introduced in this chapter in preparing these drawings. A number of drafting problems are given that require only that details be copied from the book; these problems will familiarize the student with techniques and terminology. The general rules for preparing each type of drawing must be followed; therefore, the proper scale must be selected for each type of drawing. Select the best sheet size or use the size assigned by your instructor.

Floor Plans

1 Prepare a display drawing of the floor plan of the house shown in Fig. 19–2 (omit dimensions).

2 Repeat Problem 1, but use the plan shown in Fig. 19–4.

3 Make a freehand sketch of your classroom on grid paper.

4 Prepare a scale drawing of your classroom with instruments and show overall dimensions. Can you recognize ways to improve this layout to make it more functional? Show these changes on a separate sheet.

5 Prepare a freehand sketch of a floor plan for a small efficiency apartment to be occupied by a married couple. The plan should be rectangular in shape so that it could be used as a unit in an apartment complex.

6 Prepare a scaled floor plan of the house shown in Fig. 19–64. Show the dimensions and notes necessary for your plan to be used as a finished working drawing.

7 Repeat Problem 6, but use the plan shown in Fig. 19–65.

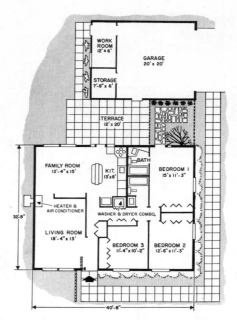

Fig. 19–64 Problem 6: A display drawing of a floor plan. (Courtesy of the National Association of Home Builders.)

Fig. 19–65 Problem 7: A display drawing of a floor plan. (Courtesy of National Plan Service, Inc.)

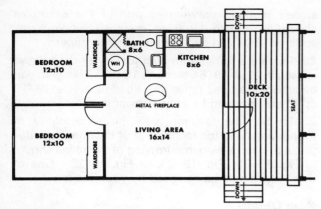

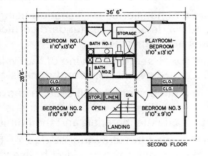

Fig. 19–66 Problem 8: A vacation cabin. (Courtesy of the American Plywood Association.)

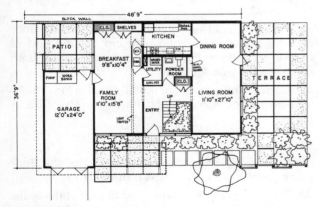

Fig. 19–67 Problem 9: A two-story residence. (Courtesy of the National Association of Home Builders.)

8 Repeat Problem 6, but use the plan shown in Fig. 19–66.

9 Repeat Problem 6, but use the plan shown in Fig. 19–67.

10 Design a floor plan for a study room to be built in a back yard of a residential house for your own use. It should be designed so that it can be used for study, recreation, and hobbies. Measure a yard or assume the dimensions for one and design the floor plan to fit properly to take advantage of the yard's features. Present your plan as a display drawing with only overall dimensions given.

11 Prepare a finished working drawing of the study room designed in Problem 10.

12 Make a list of things that should be considered in designing a floor plan for maximum efficiency.

Plot Plans

13 Make a freehand sketch of a different layout for the house and plot from one of the following figures: Fig. 19–11, Fig. 19–16, or Fig. 19–17.

14 Make a freehand sketch of one of the following plot plans: an outdoor patio, a child's outdoor play area, a parking area for a residence, a campsite at a resort.

15 Make scale drawings with instruments of the layouts developed in Problem 14.

16 Make scale drawings of the trees shown in Fig. 19–13 that can be placed under tracing paper and traced. These can be used many times on different drawings.

17 Select a lot in your neighborhood or from a magazine and prepare a plot plan of the lot showing actual measurements. Develop a floor plan for a residence that will fit on the lot and take advantage of its features. Develop the plan and plot together and make a display drawing of each with only overall dimensions given.

18 Measure your house and its lot. Make a working drawing of the floor plan and the plot of your house as it is now built.

19 Prepare a plot plan of the lot used in Problem 17.

20 The plot plan in Fig. 19–68 is a plan for the house shown in Fig. 19–67. Make a completely

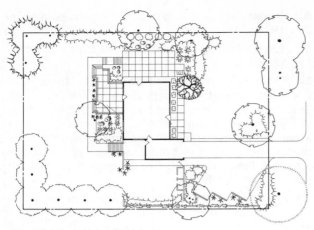

Fig. 19-68 Problem 20: A display drawing of a plot plan.

dimensioned working drawing of this plot plan, following the rules given in Article 19–7.

21 Prepare a dimensioned working drawing of the plot plan of the study room developed in Problem 10. Show the location of the existing house on this same plot.

22 As a drafting exercise, make a drawing of the plot plan shown in Fig. 19–17.

23 Prepare a dimensioned working drawing of the plot plan of the kindergarten shown in Fig. 19–12. Estimate dimensions that are not given.

24 Prepare a display drawing of the lot on which a house (perhaps your own home) is located. Show your ideas for improving this plan. Show landscaping and other modifications that you would make.

Foundation Details

25 Make a pictorial sketch of the interior foundation piers that support the girder in Fig. 19–23. The purpose of this sketch is to illustrate the construction of a typical pier and the attachment of the girder.

26 Make a pictorial sketch of one of the detail sections in Fig. 19–24 to give a better understanding of this construction method.

27 To become familiar with the terminology and techniques of drawing sill details, make a dimen-

sioned working drawing of one of the examples shown in Article 19–9 as assigned by your instructor. This can be drawn on Size A paper.

28 Prepare a foundation plan for any of the houses shown in Figs. 19–64 through 19–67. This plan can be any of the three types described in Article 19–10 or a type assigned by your instructor.

29 To become familiar with the terminology of foundations and the techniques of detailing foundations, prepare a working drawing of the plans shown in Fig. 19–21, Fig. 19–23, or Fig. 19–25. One of these plans may be assigned by your instructor.

Wall Details

30 Prepare a drawing of one of the cornice details shown in Fig. 19–29. This can be drawn on Size A paper.

31 Referring to Fig. 19–29 as an example, design a different cornice detail using standard materials.

32 Prepare a dimensioned wall section using one of the standard sill details and a standard cornice detail. Show notes and dimensions.

33 Prepare a wall section drawing of the wall shown in Fig. 19–31. Show all notes and dimensions.

34 Prepare a dimensioned wall section showing the brick cavity wall (Fig. 19–32). Add dimensions and notes that specify the materials and their dimensions.

35 Prepare a working drawing of one of the wall sections taken through the vacation house shown in Fig. 19–33.

36 Prepare a wall section detail through a first-floor sill of a house built using platform framing and of one using balloon framing techniques. Draw both on the same Size A sheet.

37 Convert the pictorial of the sill detail in Fig. 19–41 into an orthographic detail drawing. Use Size A paper.

Elevations

38 Prepare elevation drawings for any of the floor plans developed in Problems 6 through 11.

39 Prepare an elevation drawing of one of the walls of your classroom after the measurements have been determined.

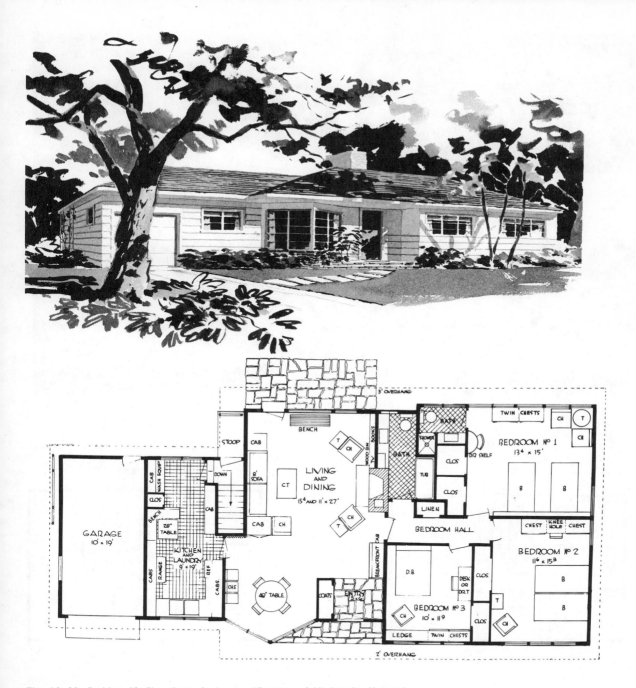

Fig. 19–69 Problem 40: Elevations of a house. (Courtesy of All-America Homes.)

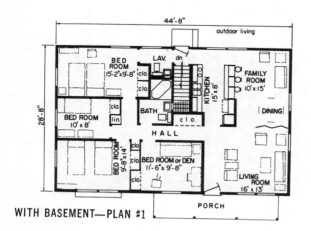

WITH BASEMENT—PLAN #1

44'-8"

28'-8"

outdoor living

BED ROOM 15'-2"x9'-8"   clo.   LAV.   dn.

clo.   clo.   BATH   KITCHEN 15'x8'

FAMILY ROOM 10'x15'

BED ROOM 10' x 8'   clo.   lin.   c l o.

DINING

HALL

BED ROOM 9'-8'x14   clo.   BED ROOM or DEN 11'-6"x 9'-8"   clo.

LIVING ROOM 16' x 13'

PORCH

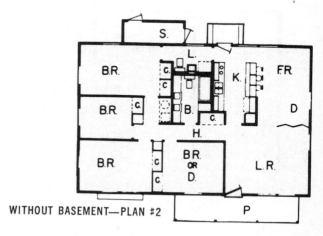

WITHOUT BASEMENT—PLAN #2

S.

B.R.   c   L.   c   K.   FR.

B.R.   c   B.   c   D

H.

B.R.   c   B.R. OR D.   L.R.

P

Fig. 19-70   Problem 41: Elevations of a house.   (Courtesy of National Plan Service, Inc.)

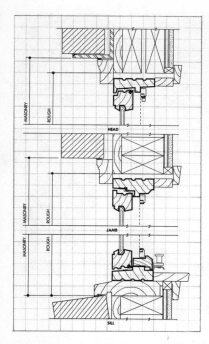

Fig. 19–71 Problem 46: Window details. (Courtesy of Rolscreen Company.)

40 Prepare elevation drawings for the house shown in Fig. 19–69.

41 Several elevations for the same floor plan are shown in Fig. 19–70. Prepare elevation drawings for this floor plan using one of the examples as a guide.

42 Design and draw a completely different elevation to go with the floor plan shown in Fig. 19–70.

Details

43 Prepare a window schedule similar to the one in Fig. 19–52 using a manufacturer's brochure as a source of information. This is to familiarize you with the use of commercial literature and with the window schedule.

44 Repeat Problem 43, but prepare a door schedule similar to the one in Fig. 19–55.

45 Prepare a detail drawing of the stairway shown in Fig. 19–42. This should consist of orthographic views and sections with dimensions.

46 Prepare working drawings of the head, jamb, and sill details of the window shown in Fig. 19–71. Each grid square represents 1".

47 Prepare detail drawings of the windows shown in Figs. 19–48, 19–49, and 19–50.

48 Obtain a window brochure from a window manufacturer or from your local lumberyard. Prepare window details using these specifications.

49 Prepare detail drawings of the head, sill, and jamb of the doors shown in Figs. 19–53 and 19–54.

50 Prepare a detail drawing of the head, sill, and jamb of the door shown in Fig. 19–53, but show the door framed into a brick veneer wall instead of a frame wall.

Room Plans and Built-ins

51 Prepare a kitchen layout on grid paper to show several functional arrangements. Show cabinets and appliances.

52 Repeat Problem 51, but make layouts of a bathroom plan.

53 Prepare interior elevations of the kitchen plan developed in Problem 51.

54 Prepare interior elevations of the bathroom plan developed in Problem 52.

55 Prepare a detailed working drawing of the fireplace shown in Fig. 19–62.

56 Prepare working drawings of the cabinets designed in Problem 51.

57 Prepare working drawings of the interior built-ins for the bathroom designed in Problem 52.

Complete Architectural Plans

58 Prepare a complete set of working drawings for the construction of the houses shown in Figs. 19–72 and 19–73. These plans should utilize all the principles covered in this chapter. Each set of plans should have at least six sheets to show adequately the details of construction.

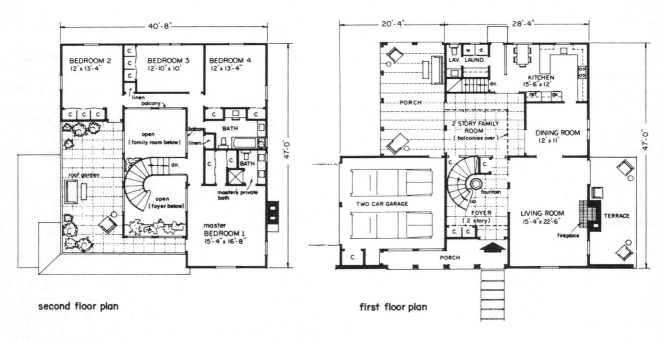

second floor plan

first floor plan

Fig. 19–72 Problem 58: Architectural plans. (Courtesy of Master Plan Service, Inc.)

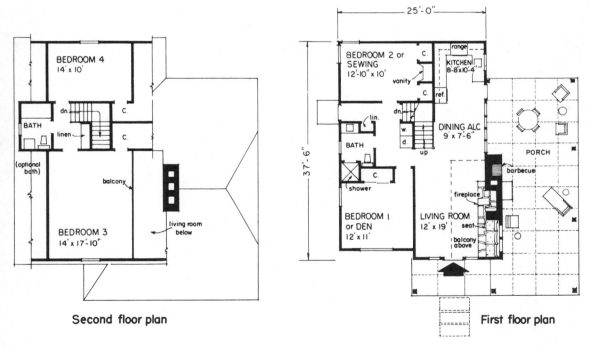

Second floor plan

BEDROOM 4
14' x 10'

dn.

C.

BATH

linen

C.

(optional bath)

balcony

BEDROOM 3
14' x 17'-10"

living room below

25'-0"

37'-6"

BEDROOM 2 or SEWING
12'-10" x 10'

vanity

C.

range

KITCHEN
8-8'x10-4'

C.

ref.

dn.

lin.

w.

DINING ALC
9' x 7'-6"

d.

up

BATH

PORCH

barbecue

shower

C.

fireplace

BEDROOM 1 or DEN
12' x 11'

LIVING ROOM
12' x 19'

seat

balcony above

First floor plan

Fig. 19–73 Problem 58: Architectural plans. (Courtesy of Master Plan Service, Inc.)

59 Repeat Problem 58, but use the houses shown in Figs. 19–64 through 19–69 or any of the previous plans that you have developed for other problems. Obtain the approval of your instructor before beginning.

SUGGESTED READING

The following books are available to provide a more thorough study of the field of architectural drafting than is possible in one chapter of this textbook.

Bellis, H. F., and W. A. Schmidt, *Architectural Drafting*. New York: McGraw-Hill Book Co.

Buss, Truman C., *Simplified Architectural Drawing*. Chicago: American Technical Society.

Goodban, W. T., and J. J. Hayslett, *Architectural Drawing and Planning*. New York: McGraw-Hill Book Co.

Hepler, Donald E., and Paul I. Wallach, *Architecture—Drafting and Design*. New York: McGraw-Hill Book Co.

Hornung, William J., *Architectural Drafting*. Englewood Cliffs, N.J.: Prentice-Hall, Inc.

Patten, L. M., and M. L. Rogness, *Architectural Drafting*. Dubuque, Ia.: William C. Brown Co.

Ramsey, C. G., and H. R. Sleeper, *Architectural Graphic Standards*. New York: John Wiley and Sons, Inc.

Stegman, G. K., and H. J. Stegman, *Architectural Drafting*. Chicago: American Technical Society.

Weidhaas, Ernest R., *Architectural Drafting and Design*. Boston: Allyn and Bacon, Inc.

Fig. 5.

Gaspard Monge 1746-1818

20
INTRODUCTION TO
DESCRIPTIVE
GEOMETRY

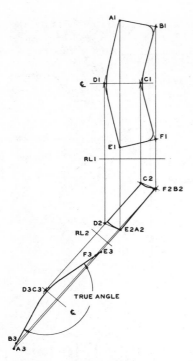

20–1 INTRODUCTION

Descriptive geometry is the study of points, lines, and surfaces that form three-dimensional shapes. It is often useful in developing designs for products or engineering projects.

An example of the application of descriptive geometry is the determination of the angle between the planes of an automobile windshield (Fig. 20–1). The designer has made a preliminary scale drawing of the top and side views of the windshield to give the effect that he desires. Since these views are drawn using orthographic projection, an auxiliary view can be used to find the edge view of both planes in one view, and thus the angle between the planes. It would be considerably more difficult to find this angle by using any other method than descriptive geometry.

Descriptive geometry has little application when the points, lines, and surfaces lie in the same plane (that is, in two-dimensional drawing). However, three-dimensional objects require a higher degree of analysis, which can be performed by descriptive geometry. This analysis is performed on a flat, two-dimensional drawing surface to describe the geometry of a three-dimensional shape; hence the name, *descriptive geometry.*

Descriptive geometry was developed by Gaspard Monge (1746–1818), a French mathematician. The newly discovered discipline was used to develop designs for fortifications and battlements used in military defense. It proved so superior to the inefficient mathematical methods that it was kept a military secret for 15 years. Monge later became a scientific aide to Napoleon.

This chapter will merely introduce the basic principles of descriptive geometry. Little attention will be given to the application of this subject, since that would require an entire college-level course. You will note that much of descriptive geometry is a disciplined approach to orthographic projection. To solve problems by descriptive geometry, the designer must apply logic and the principles of geometry.

20–2 PROJECTIONS OF POINTS AND LINES

Descriptive geometry is based on a thorough understanding of orthographic projection. You know how to find the top, front, and side views of a solid

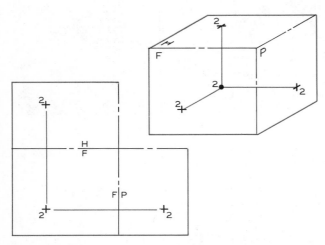

Fig. 20–2 The three views of a point projected onto the three principal planes: horizontal, frontal, and profile.

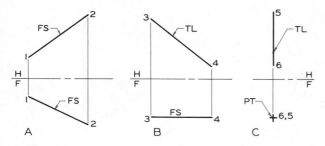

Fig. 20–3 A line in orthographic projection can appear as a point (PT), foreshortened (FS), or true length (TL).

object in orthographic projection, but can you find these views of a single point?

Three views of a point are shown orthographically and pictorially in Fig. 20–2. Note that point 2 is projected onto the three planes of projection—horizontal (H), frontal (F), and Profile (P)—in the pictorial. The orthographic projections are found when this projection box is opened into a single plane.

Each of the imaginary fold lines between the planes is labeled F, H, or P on each side to represent the principal planes. If you refer to the pictorial, you will understand why the fold lines are labeled as shown. For example, the H–F line is the intersection between the horizontal and frontal planes.

Finding the views of a line in orthographic projection is no more than finding the views of two

points, since two points establish a line. A line may be projected to appear true length, foreshortened, or as a point. These three projections are shown in Fig. 20–3. Both views of line 1–2 in part A are foreshortened (FS). The top views of lines 3–4 and 5–6 in B and C are true length (TL). The front view of line 3–4 in B is foreshortened; but since it is parallel to the horizontal plane, you know that the top view is true length. Line 5–6 is a point in the front view, parallel to the horizontal plane, and therefore true length in the top view.

20–3 PRINCIPAL LINES

The three principal planes of orthographic projection are the horizontal, frontal, and profile planes. Any line that is parallel to one of these principal planes is called a *principal line*. Your line of sight is assumed to be perpendicular to the principal planes of projection; consequently, your line of sight will be perpendicular to any line that is parallel to a principal plane.

The three principal lines are shown in Fig. 20–4 pictorially and orthographically. Line 1–2 in part A is a *horizontal line*; it is parallel to the horizontal projection plane. This can be seen in the pictorial and in the orthographic layout. Note that the line is parallel to the horizontal edge in the front and side views. Any line, regardless of its direction, will be true length in the top view if it is parallel to the

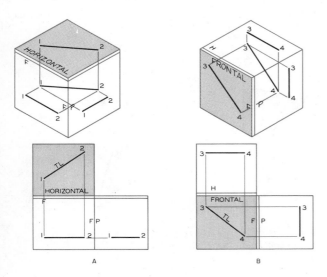

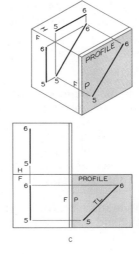

Fig. 20–4 Projections of the three principal lines: horizontal, frontal, and profile. Each of these is parallel to at least one of the projection planes.

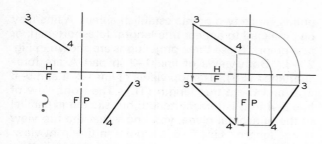

Fig. 20–5 The third view of a line can be found by orthographic projection if two views are given.

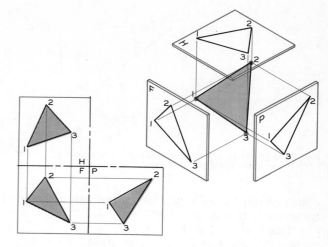

Fig. 20–6 The three projections of an oblique plane.

horizontal plane in the front and side views. Lines that appear as points in these views are parallel to the horizontal plane, also. You must inspect the front view to determine whether a line is true length in the top view; observation of the top view alone will not reveal whether or not the line is true length in the top view.

A *frontal line* is parallel to the frontal projection plane (Fig. 20–4B) and is true length in the front view. Note that this line is parallel to the edge of the frontal plane in the top and side views. A line that appears as a point in the top and side views is also parallel to the frontal plane and is true length in the front view.

A *profile line* is parallel to the profile projection plane and is true length in the profile view (Fig. 20–4C). Therefore, a profile line must be parallel to the edge of the profile plane in both the top and front views or appear as a point in one of these views.

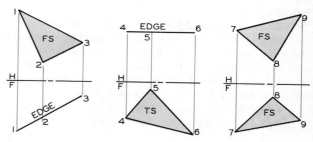

Fig. 20–7 A plane in orthographic projection can appear as an edge, true size (TS), or foreshortened (FS).

20–4 THREE VIEWS OF A LINE

The third view of a line can be found by orthographic projection if two views are given. Line 3–4 in Fig. 20–5 is an *oblique line* that is neither parallel nor perpendicular to one of the principal planes. The top and side views are given and we are required to find the front view. The rules of orthographic projection introduced in Chapter 7 apply to this construction.

Projectors from the top view are drawn downward to the front view and the end points of the line

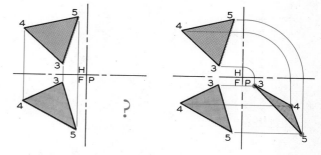

Fig. 20–8 The third view of an oblique plane can be found by orthographic projection if two views are given.

are projected horizontally to the left from the right side view. The intersections of these projectors locate the end points of the line in the front view. It is very helpful if you number or letter the ends of the line to ensure that you use the correct intersections of the projectors.

If the top and front views had been given, you could have found the right side view by applying the principles of orthographic projection.

20–5 PROJECTIONS OF PLANES

A plane that is not parallel or perpendicular to a principal plane is called an *oblique plane.* This type of plane will project onto the principal projection planes as shown in Fig. 20–6.

Plane 1–2–3 can be completely identified in three-dimensional space with two views. However, three views are given here to define the plane and to give its relationship to the three projection planes.

A plane can appear in three ways in orthographic projection: as an edge, foreshortened (FS), or as a true-size (TS) surface. These projections are illustrated in Fig. 20–7. Plane 1–2–3 appears as an edge in the front view and foreshortened in the top view. The top view of plane 4–5–6 is an edge and parallel to the frontal projection plane; therefore, the front view is true size. Plane 7–8–9 is foreshortened in both views.

In Fig. 20–8 two views of plane 3–4–5 are given and you are required to find the third view, the right side view in this case, by orthographic projection. Projectors from the points 3, 4, and 5 in the front view are drawn horizontally to the right side view. Note that it is necessary to use dividers to transfer these points from the top view to the side view. Review Article 7–10 if the method of transferring dimensions from the top view to the side view is not clear to you.

20–6 PRINCIPAL PLANES

Principal planes are planes that are parallel to one of the principal projection planes—horizontal, frontal, or profile. Examples of these three principal planes are shown in Fig. 20–9.

A *frontal plane* is parallel to the frontal projection plane and appears true size in the front view,

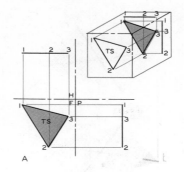

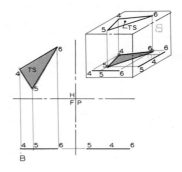

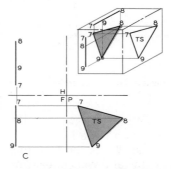

Fig. 20–9 Projections of the three principal planes: (A) frontal, (B) horizontal, and (C) profile. Each of these planes is parallel to one of the principal projection planes.

as shown in Fig. 20–9A. Note that plane 1–2–3 appears as an edge in the top and side views and is parallel to the edge view of the frontal plane in these views.

A *horizontal plane* is parallel to the horizontal projection plane and appears true size in the horizontal view (the top view), as shown in Fig.

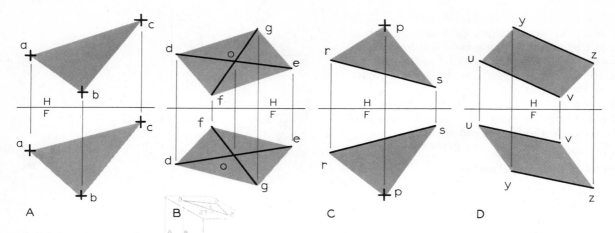

Fig. 20–10 Methods of representing a plane.

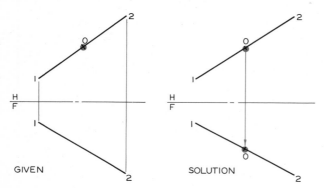

Fig. 20–11 A point on a line in the top view can be projected to the front view of the line.

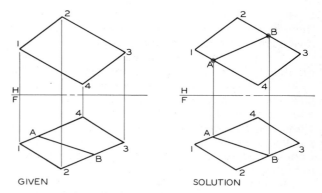

Fig. 20–12 To find the top view of the line *AB* on the plane, points *A* and *B* are projected to lines 1–4 and 2–3 respectively.

20–9B. If a plane appears as an edge in both the front and side views and is parallel to the H–F fold line, then it is a horizontal plane and will appear true size in the top view.

A *profile plane* is parallel to the profile projection plane and appears true size in the side view (Fig. 20–9C). Note that plane 7–8–9 appears as an edge in the top and front views and that these edges are parallel to the edge view of the profile plane.

20–7 REPRESENTATION OF PLANES

Whereas lines have only one dimension, length, planes have two dimensions that establish an area. Planes may be considered as infinite in some problems; however, in most solutions segments of planes are used for convenience.

Four methods of representing planes are shown in Fig. 20–10. These are (a) three points not in a straight line, (b) two intersecting lines, (c) a point and a line, and (d) two parallel lines. The areas of the planes established by these representations need not be limited by the bounds of the points or lines used. The points and lines merely establish the location of the plane in three-dimensional space.

20–8 LOCATION OF A POINT ON A LINE

A line is composed of an infinite number of points. Figure 20–11 illustrates how a point can be pro-

FIGURE 20–13. PROJECTION OF A POINT ON A PLANE

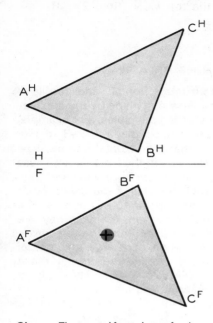

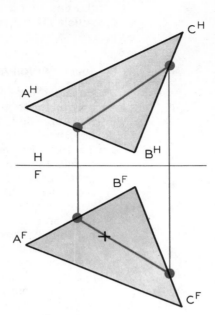

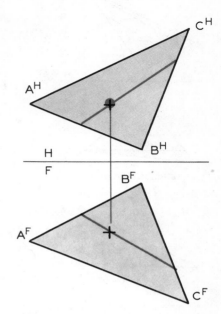

Given: The top and front views of a plane and a point on the front view.
Required: Find the top view of the point on the plane.

Step 1. Draw a line through the point in the front view and project the line to the top view.

Step 2. To locate the point, project the point from the front view to the line in the top view.

jected from one view to another by orthographic projection. The end points of the line 1–2 in both views are found by constructing projectors perpendicular to the fold lines, and any point on the line can be projected from one view to the other by applying the projection principles shown in this figure.

Point O is located in the top view and is found in the front view by projecting perpendicularly to the H–F line. Any point on the line can be projected in this manner.

20–9 LOCATION OF A LINE ON A PLANE

Plane 1–2–3–4 is given as a top and a front view in Fig. 20–12. Line AB is drawn on the surface of the plane in the front view. We are required to find the top view of this line lying on the plane.

Note that each corner of the plane is numbered to help with the identification of the lines. Point B

lies on line 2–3 in the front view. This point is projected to the top view of line 2–3 using the same principles as in Article 20–8. Point A lies on line 1–4 in the front view and is projected to the top view of this line. Points A and B can now be connected to give the line AB, which lies on the surface of the plane in this view.

20–10 LOCATION OF A POINT ON A PLANE

Plane ABC in Fig. 20–13 has a point on its surface in the front view. We are required to locate the top view of this point on the surface of the plane.

A line is drawn in any direction other than vertical through the point in the front view (Step 1). The points where this line intersects the edges of the plane in the front view are projected to these same edges in the top view and the projected points are joined to give the top view of the line. The required

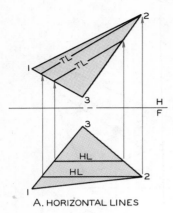

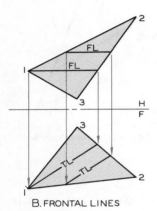

B. FRONTAL LINES

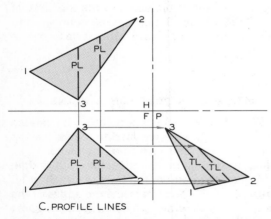

C. PROFILE LINES

Fig. 20–14 Construction of the principal lines on the given planes.

point is located by projecting from the front view to the line found in the top view (Step 2). Review Article 20–8 if necessary.

20–11 PRINCIPAL LINES ON A PLANE

Principal lines—horizontal, frontal, and profile—may be found in any view of a plane by the application of previously discussed principles. For example, horizontal lines are given on plane 1–2–3 in Fig. 20–14A. Remember that a horizontal line must be parallel to the H–F fold line in the front view. These lines must be drawn first in the front view and then projected to the top view. This is the only way of determining their location in the top view when the front and top views are given. Since they are horizontal, they will be true length in the top view.

Frontal lines are drawn parallel to the frontal plane in the top view, where the frontal plane appears as an edge (Fig. 20–14B). The ends of these lines are projected to the respective edges of the plane in the front view, where the lines will be true length.

Profile lines appear true length in the side view. Consequently, they must be drawn parallel to the edge view of the profile plane in the top and front views (Fig. 20–14C).

You should observe that principal lines in any view of an oblique plane are parallel. Thus, many profile lines could have been drawn in Fig. 20–14C, but all would have been parallel in all views and would have appeared true length in the side view.

20–12 PARALLELISM OF LINES

Two parallel lines will remain parallel when projected to any other view except the view where both lines appear as points. However, when only one view of the lines is available, the lines cannot be assumed to be parallel even though they project parallel in the given view. More than one orthographic view is required to determine parallelism.

In Figure 20–15, we are required to construct a line equal in length and parallel to line 3–4 with its midpoint at *O*. Since the midpoint of a line will also be the midpoint of any projection of that line, the

FIGURE 20–15. CONSTRUCTION OF A LINE PARALLEL TO A GIVEN LINE

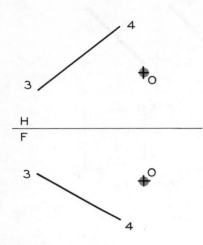

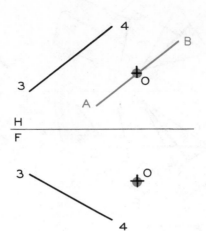

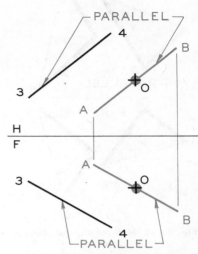

Given: The top and front views of a line 3–4 and a point O.
Required: Construct a line with its midpoint at O that is parallel to line 3–4.

Step 1. Draw line *AB* parallel to the top view of line 3–4.

Step 2. Draw the front view of line *AB* parallel to the front view of line 3–4.

top view of the line is drawn through point O as its midpoint, as shown in Step 1. The projection of this line is the same length as the projection of line 3–4.

The front view of the line is drawn parallel to the frontal projection of line 3–4 in Step 2. The ends of the lines are found by projecting from the top view. The frontal projections of the two lines are also equal in length, and the resulting line is parallel to the given line 3–4.

20–13 PARALLELISM OF A LINE AND A PLANE

A line is parallel to a plane if it is parallel to any line in that plane. We are required to construct a line parallel to the plane 1–2–3 with its midpoint at O (Fig. 20–16).

Line *AB* is drawn through point O in the top view with a convenient length and parallel to line 1–3 of plane 1–2–3. Line *AB* must also be parallel to line 1–3 in the front view, since two parallel lines

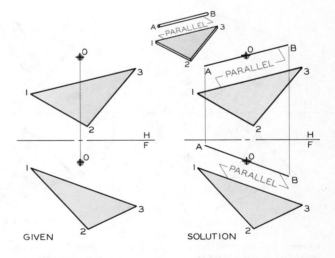

Fig. 20–16 Construction of a line through point O parallel to plane 1–2–3. Line *AB* is drawn parallel to line 1–3 in the front and top views.

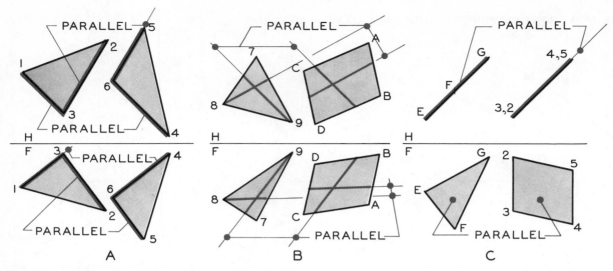

Fig. 20–17 Methods of constructing views of parallel planes.

FIGURE 20–18. CONSTRUCTION OF A PLANE THROUGH A POINT PARALLEL TO A GIVEN PLANE

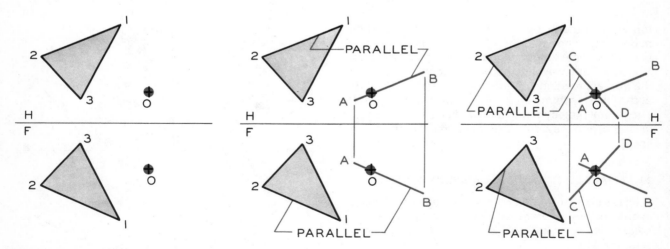

Given: The top and front views of a plane 1–2–3 and a point O.
Required: Construct a plane through point O parallel to plane 1–2–3.

Step 1. Draw line AB parallel to line 1–2 in both views.

Step 2. Draw line CD parallel to line 2–3 in both views. Plane ABCD is parallel to plane 1–2–3.

appear parallel in all views. The ends of the line in the front view are found by projection from the top view.

Line *AB* could have been constructed parallel to line 1–2 or line 2–3 or any other line lying on the plane and would still have been parallel to the plane. Note that when you hold a pencil parallel to your desk top, there is an infinite number of directions in which the pencil can be pointing.

20–14 PARALLELISM OF PLANES

If two planes are parallel, intersecting lines in one plane are parallel to intersecting lines in the other. Three examples of parallel planes are shown in Fig. 20–17. Note that either exterior lines or interior lines within the plane may be used to establish parallelism. When two planes appear as parallel edges in one view, as in part C, they are parallel in space.

In Fig. 20–18 we are required to construct a plane through point *O* that is parallel to plane 1–2–3. Line *AB* is drawn parallel to line 1–2 of the plane in the top and front views in Step 1. Line *CD* is then drawn through point *O* parallel to line 2–3 in both views in Step 2. Since these lines intersect at point *O*, they form a plane. This plane is parallel to plane 1–2–3, since two intersecting lines of one plane are parallel to two intersecting lines of the other.

20–15 PERPENDICULARITY OF LINES

Figure 20–19 illustrates pictorially and orthographically the basic rules of perpendicularity. Two perpendicular lines will project as perpendiculars in any view where one or both are true length. As shown in the pictorial, a line may be revolved around another line as a spoke revolves around an axle while remaining perpendicular to the axis.

In the orthographic views, lines *OA* and *OB* can be projected as perpendicular to the axis in the view where the axis is true length. Line *OA* is true length in this view but *OB* is not true length. However, both are perpendicular to the axis, since the axis is true length. Thus the rule of perpendicularity is satisfied.

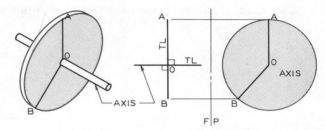

Fig. 20–19 Perpendicular lines will be projected as perpendicular in a view where one or both of the lines appear true length.

When two lines are perpendicular but neither is true length, they will not project with a true 90° angle. The plane of the 90° angle will appear foreshortened and distorted.

20–16 A LINE PERPENDICULAR TO A PRINCIPAL LINE

Frontal line 1–2 and point *O* are given in Fig. 20–20. We are to construct the top and front views of a line through point *O* that intersects 1–2 and is perpendicular to it.

Line 1–2 is a principal line, a frontal line, and is consequently true length in the front view. By applying the rules of perpendicularity from Article 20–15, it is possible to construct line *OP* in the front view perpendicular to the true-length line (Step 1). Since point *P* lies on the line, it may be found in the top view by projecting above its front view to line 1–2, as shown in Step 2. These lines do not appear perpendicular in the top view, since neither is true length in this view.

20–17 A LINE PERPENDICULAR TO AN OBLIQUE LINE

The top and front views of an oblique line, line 3–4, are given in Fig. 20–21. We are required to construct a line through the midpoint of line 3–4 that is perpendicular to it. Before a perpendicular can be found, a

FIGURE 20–20. CONSTRUCTION OF A LINE PERPENDICULAR TO A PRINCIPAL LINE

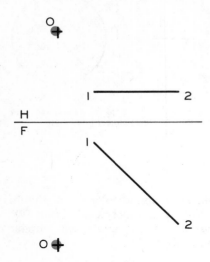

Given: The top and front views of a principal line 1–2 and a point O.
Required: Construct a line from point O perpendicular to line 1–2.

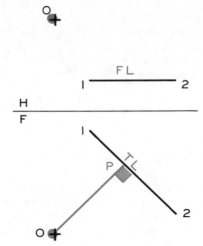

Step 1. Draw a line perpendicular to the true-length line 1–2 in the front view.

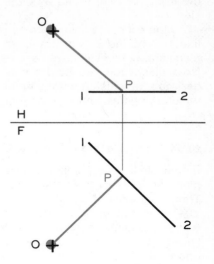

Step 2. Locate point P on line 1–2 in the top view and connect this point with point O.

true-length line must be constructed. Thus in Step 1 a horizontal line *OP* is drawn through the midpoint of the front view of line 3–4 to some convenient length.

Since it is horizontal, line *OP* will be projected true length in the top view. It may be drawn in any direction and still be true length; therefore, it is constructed perpendicular to line 3–4 through point O (Step 2). The top view of point *P* is found by projecting from the front view. These two lines are perpendicular, because they are perpendicular in the view where one of them is true length.

20–18 PERPENDICULARITY INVOLVING PLANES

A plane or a line can be constructed perpendicular to another plane by applying the principles of the previous articles. A line is perpendicular to a plane if it is perpendicular to two intersecting lines on that plane, as illustrated in Fig. 20–22A.

Also, a plane is perpendicular to another plane if a line in one plane is perpendicular to the other plane. This is illustrated in Fig. 20–22B.

20–19 A LINE PERPENDICULAR TO A PLANE

Plane *ABC* and point O on the plane are given in Fig. 20–23. We are required to construct a line perpendicular to the plane through point O. We can find a true-length line on any view of a plane by constructing a principal line as discussed in Article 20–11.

A true-length line is found in the front view by constructing a frontal line through point O in the top view and projecting it to the front view (Step 1). This line is true length and is a line on the plane; consequently, line *OP* can be drawn through point O perpendicular to the frontal line.

If line *OP* is perpendicular to another line as well, we can draw a horizontal line on the plane in

FIGURE 20–21. CONSTRUCTION OF A LINE PERPENDICULAR TO AN OBLIQUE LINE

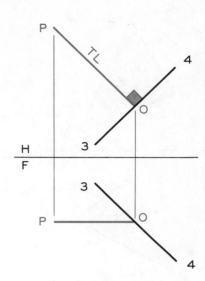

Given: The top and front views of an oblique line 3–4.
Required: Construct a line from the midpoint of the oblique line 3–4 that is perpendicular to it.

Step 1. Construct a horizontal line from the midpoint of the front view of line 3–4.

Step 2. Project point O to the top view of the line and draw line OP (which is true length in the top view) perpendicular to line 3–4.

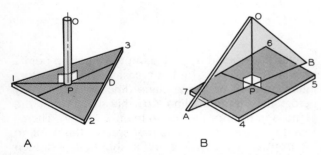

Fig. 20–22 (A) A line is perpendicular to a plane if it is perpendicular to two intersecting lines on the plane. (B) A plane is perpendicular to another plane if the plane contains a line that is perpendicular to the other plane.

the front view (Step 2) and project it to the top view, where it appears true length. The top view of OP is constructed perpendicular to this line to establish the top view of line OP.

This line is perpendicular to the plane, because it is perpendicular to two intersecting lines on the plane. This relationship is apparent where the lines on the plane are shown true length.

20–20 A PLANE PERPENDICULAR TO AN OBLIQUE LINE

Line 1–2 and point O are given in Fig. 20–24. We are required to construct a plane through point O that is perpendicular to line 1–2.

A plane may be constructed through point O by drawing two intersecting lines that intersect at point O. These lines will be true length if they are principal lines; this will permit perpendicularity to be established.

Frontal line AB is drawn through point O in the top view and projected to the front view, where it is true length (Step 1). It is drawn perpendicular to

FIGURE 20–23. CONSTRUCTION OF A LINE PERPENDICULAR TO A PLANE

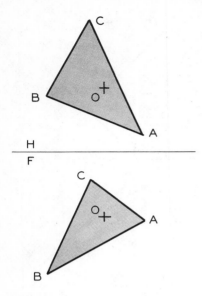

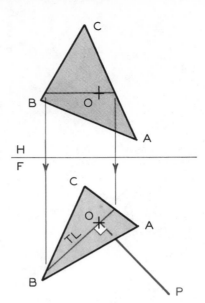

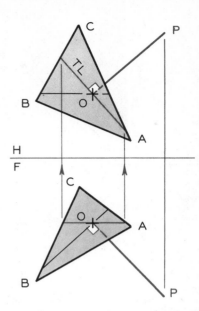

Given: The top and front views of a plane *ABC* and a point *O* on the plane. **Required:** Construct a line from point *O* that is perpendicular to the plane *ABC*.

Step 1. Construct a frontal line through point *O* in the top view to find a true-length view of the line in the front view. Construct a perpendicular to this line.

Step 2. A true-length horizontal line is found in the top view and a perpendicular is drawn to this line.

line 1–2, which gives one line on the plane that is perpendicular to line 1–2.

A second line, *CD*, is drawn as a horizontal line (Step 2) in the front view and is projected to the top view, where it will be true length and perpendicular to line 1–2. Line 1–2 is perpendicular to two intersecting lines in the plane. We have now constructed a plane perpendicular to the given line.

20–21 VISIBILITY OF A LINE AND A PLANE

Figure 20–25 illustrates the method of determining the visibility of a line and a plane in the top and front views. In this example, the line does not intersect the plane.

Line *AB* crosses lines 1–3 and 2–3 in the front view of the plane in Step 1. The visibility in the front

view is determined by projecting the crossing points to the top view. In both cases, the projectors intersect the lines of the plane (lines 1–3 and 2–3) before they intersect line *AB*; this means that the plane is in front of the line in the front view. Therefore, the portion of the line that crosses the plane in the front view is invisible and is shown as a hidden line.

The visibility in the top view is found similarly by projecting the crossing points in the top view to the front view (Step 2). These projectors intersect line *AB* before they intersect lines 1–3 and 2–3. Consequently, line *AB* is higher than the plane in the top view and is visible.

The same method can be used to determine visibility in essentially all orthographic problems, including auxiliary views.

FIGURE 20–24. CONSTRUCTION OF A PLANE THROUGH A POINT PERPENDICULAR TO AN OBLIQUE LINE

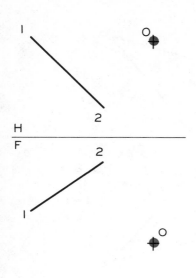

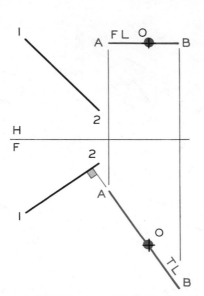

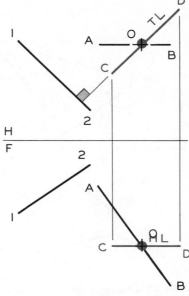

Given: The top and front views of an oblique line 1–2 and a point O.
Required: Construct a plane through point O that is perpendicular to oblique line 1–2.

Step 1. Draw frontal line AB in the top view and perpendicular to the front view of line 1–2. Line AB is true length in the front view.

Step 2. Draw horizontal line CD in the front view and perpendicular to the top view of line 1–2. Line CD is true length in the top view. Plane ABCD is perpendicular to line 1–2.

FIGURE 20–25. VISIBILITY OF A LINE AND A PLANE

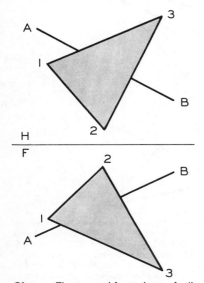

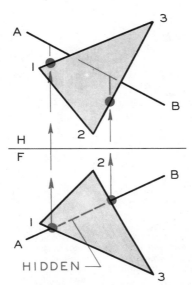

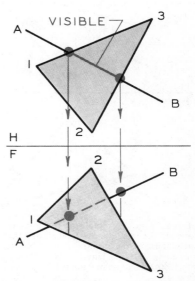

Given: The top and front views of a line AB and a plane 1–2–3.
Required: Find the visibility of the line and the plane.

Step 1. Line AB crosses lines 1–3 and 2–3 in the front view. Project these intersections to the top view. You will find that the lines of the plane are closer to the viewer than the line AB. Thus the line is hidden in the front view.

Step 2. Project the points where line AB crosses lines 1–3 and 2–3 in the top view to the front view. You will find that the line AB is higher than the lines of the plane. Thus the line AB is visible in the top view.

FIGURE 20-26. PIERCING POINT OF A LINE ON A PLANE

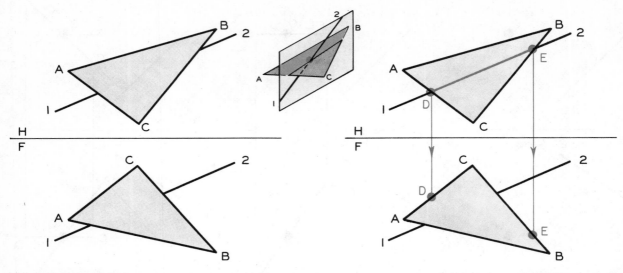

Given: The top and front views of a plane *ABC* and a line 1–2.
Required: Determine the piercing point of line 1–2 on the plane and visibility of both views by projection.

Step 1. Assume that a vertical cutting plane is passed through the top view of line 1–2. The plane intersects *AC* and *BC* at points *D* and *E*. Project points *D* and *E* to the front view.

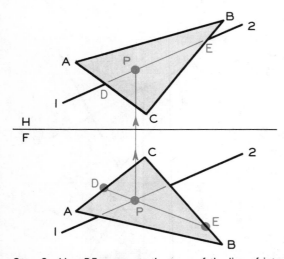

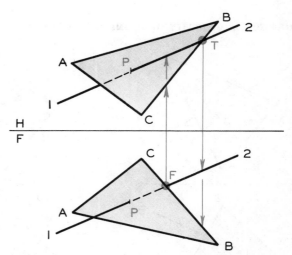

Step 2. Line *DE* represents the trace of the line of intersection between the imaginary vertical cutting plane and plane *ABC*. Any line that lies in the cutting plane and intersects plane *ABC* will intersect along line *DE*. Line 1–2 lies in the cutting plane; therefore, it intersects *ABC* at point *P* in the front view. Project point *P* to the top view.

Step 3. The visibility of line 1–2 in the front view is found by analyzing point *F*, where lines *P*–2 and *BC* cross. By projecting this point to the top view, we see that *BC* is in front of *P*–2; therefore, *BC* is visible in the front view. The visibility in the top view is found by analyzing point *T* in the same manner; we find that *P*–2 is higher than *BC* in the front view and is therefore visible in the top view.

FIGURE 20–27. INTERSECTION OF PLANES BY PROJECTION

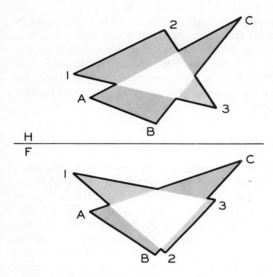

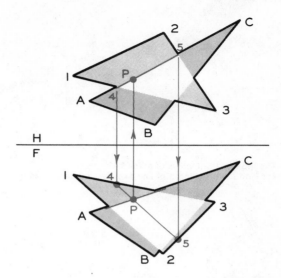

Given: The top and front views of planes 1–2–3 and *ABC*.
Required: Find the line of intersection between the planes and determine visibility in both views.

Step 1. Pass a vertical cutting plane through line *AC* in the top view to establish points 4 and 5. Project points 4 and 5 to lines 1–3 and 2–3 in the front view. Line *AC* pierces plane 1–2–3 where it crosses line 4–5. Project point *P* to line *AC* in the top view.

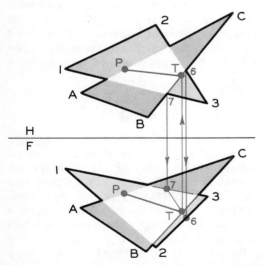

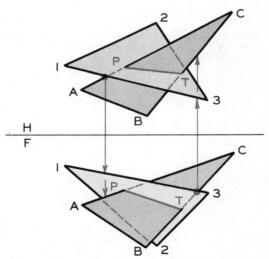

Step 2. Pass a vertical cutting plane through line *BC* in the top view to find points 6 and 7. Project line 6–7 to the front view. Point *T* is the piercing point of line *BC* in plane 1–2–3. Line *PT* is the line of intersection between the planes. The piercing points of lines *AC* and *BC* have been found as though they were independent lines rather than lines of a plane.

Step 3. Analyze the intersection of *AP* and 1–3 in the top view for visibility by projecting to the front view, where 1–3 is found to be higher and, consequently, visible in the top view. Line *PC* is also visible in the top view; therefore, *PCT* is visible. Frontal visibility is found by analysis of the intersection of lines *CT* and 1–3; line 1–3 is found to be in front and visible.

FIGURE 20–28. TRUE LENGTH OF A LINE BY A PRIMARY AUXILIARY VIEW

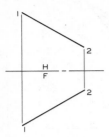

Given: The top and front views of a line 1–2.
Required: Find the true length of line 1–2 by a primary auxiliary view.

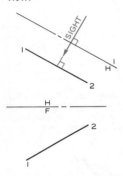

Step 1. The line of sight is drawn perpendicular to the top view of the line. Reference line *H–1* is constructed parallel to the line and perpendicular to the line of sight.

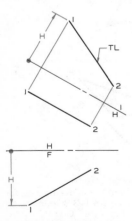

Step 2. Distances are transferred from the edge view of the horizontal plane in the front view with dividers to the primary auxiliary view, where the line is true length.

20–22 INTERSECTION BETWEEN A LINE AND A PLANE

The sequence of steps necessary to find the point of intersection (piercing point) of a line and a plane is given in Fig. 20–26. Note that the visibility of the line is determined by the principles presented in Article 20–21. If a line intersects a plane, it will be visible on one side of the piercing point and hidden on the other side.

20–23 INTERSECTION BETWEEN PLANES

The line of intersection between two intersecting planes can be found by locating the points of intersection of two lines of one plane on the surface of the second. The procedure is shown in Fig. 20–27.

Observe that lines 1–2, 2–3, and *AB* do not pierce either of the planes, since they fall outside the planes in the given views. Therefore, lines *AC* and *BC* are selected as the lines most likely to intersect plane 1–2–3. Line *AC* is analyzed as though it were a single line rather than a line on a plane. The piercing point *P* is found and projected to both views. The line *BC* is then analyzed in the same manner, and piercing point *T* is found. Note that it is necessary to work with one plane, instead of finding the piercing point of one line of a plane and then skipping to a line on the other plane. The solution should be approached in a systematic fashion.

20–24 TRUE LENGTH OF A LINE

A line can be found true length by a primary auxiliary view (primary auxiliary views were introduced in Article 10–2). Line 1–2 is given in the top and front views in Fig. 20–28. It can be seen true length if your line of sight is perpendicular to the line as shown in the top view of Step 1. A reference line is drawn parallel to the top view of the line and perpendicular to the line of sight. The H–1 line represents the fold line between the horizontal plane and the primary projection plane.

A primary auxiliary view is projected parallel to the line of sight and perpendicularly from the top view of the line in Step 2. The end points of line 1–2 are found by measuring perpendicularly from the edge of the horizontal plane in the front view and transferring the dimensions with your dividers to the auxiliary view. Dimension H is used as an example in Step 2 of Fig. 20–28.

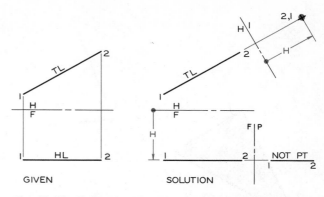

Fig. 20–29 Finding the point view of a line. Since line 1–2 is true length in the top view, a primary auxiliary view is projected from this view to find a point view of the line. Dimension H is transferred from the front view to the auxiliary view with dividers.

20–25 POINT VIEW OF A LINE

The point view of a line can be found in a primary auxiliary view when the line is true length in a principal view. Line 1–2 in Fig. 20–29 is a horizontal line in the front view; thus it is true length in the top view. When an auxiliary plane, H–1, is drawn perpendicular to the top view of line 1–2, the resulting auxiliary view will project as a point view of line 1–2.

To obtain the point view, a line must appear true length in the view from which the auxiliary view is projected. Note that the auxiliary view projected from the front view of line 1–2 does not result in a point view of the line, but instead gives a foreshortened view. This particular projection is actually a right side view.

20–26 EDGE VIEW OF A PLANE

A plane will appear as an edge in any view where a line on the plane appears as a point. The con-

struction of the edge view of a plane is illustrated in Fig. 20–30. In Step 1, a horizontal line passing through one of the corners of the plane is drawn on the plane in the front view and is projected to the top view, where it is true length. Since this line is true length in the top view, its point view may be found by using a line of sight parallel to the line. Reference line H–1 is drawn perpendicular to the true-length line and the line of sight (Step 1).

FIGURE 20–30. FINDING THE EDGE VIEW OF A PLANE

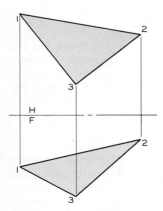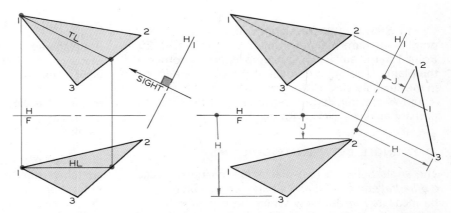

Given: The top and front views of a plane 1–2–3.
Required: Find the edge view of plane 1–2–3.

Step 1. Find a horizontal line on the plane. Establish the line of sight parallel to the true-length view of the horizontal line.

Step 2. Project a primary auxiliary view from the top view parallel to the true-length line. Transfer measurements from the front view to locate the edge view of the plane.

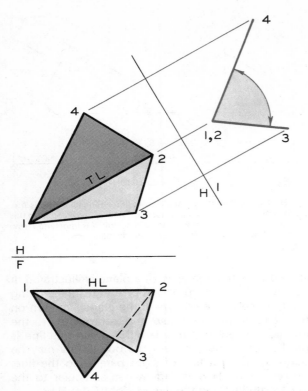

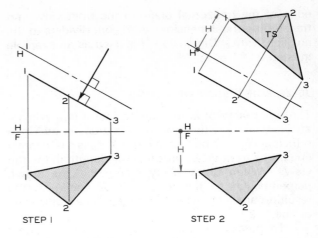

Fig. 20–32 Finding the true size of a plane.

Fig. 20–31 The angle between two planes can be found by a primary auxiliary view if the line of intersection is true length in one of the principal views.

In Step 2, the true-length line is found as a point in the same manner as line 1–2 in Article 20–25. Point 1 in the auxiliary view represents one corner of the plane. The other corners of the plane are found in the auxiliary view in the same manner. Dimensions *J* and *H* are transferred from the front view to the primary auxiliary view with dividers.

20–27 ANGLE BETWEEN TWO PLANES

The angle between two planes is sometimes called a *dihedral* angle. The angle between two planes can be measured in the view where both planes appear as an edge. This is the view where the line of intersection between them appears as a point.

The angle between planes 1–2–3 and 1–2–4 in Fig. 20–31 can be found in a primary auxiliary view, since the line of intersection, 1–2, is true length in the top view. Auxiliary plane H–1 is drawn so that it is perpendicular to the top view of line 1–2. The point view of line 1–2 is found by projection to the auxiliary plane. The edge views of both planes can be found in this view, since line 1–2 is a line common to both planes. The dihedral angle is measured in this view.

20–28 TRUE SIZE OF A PLANE

If a plane appears as an edge in a principal view, the plane can be found true size by a primary auxiliary view. The procedure is illustrated in Fig. 20–32.

In Step 1, a line of sight is drawn perpendicular to the edge view of the plane. Reference line H–1 is drawn perpendicular to the line of sight and parallel to the edge view of the plane.

In Step 2, the primary auxiliary view is found by projecting parallel to the line of sight. Measurements are taken from the edge view of the horizontal plane in the front view and are transferred with dividers to the primary auxiliary view. Dimension *H* is used as an example. The resulting auxiliary view is a true-size view of the plane 1–2–3.

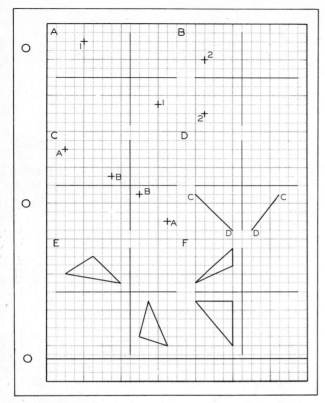

Fig. 20–33 Problem 1: Projections of points, lines, and planes.

PROBLEMS

These problems are to be solved in accordance with Article 3–15 and the specifications of your instructor. Most problems are to be drawn on standard Size A ($8\frac{1}{2}'' \times 11''$) paper using ink or pencil.

The problems can be drawn on printed grid paper or on blank sheets. Use the standard endorsement, title strip, and border as described in Article 3–15. The squares on the printed grid of the problems represent $\frac{1}{4}''$. Refer to the text of this chapter to assist you in the solution of the problems.

1 Construct the missing views of the points, lines, and planes in Fig. 20–33A through F.

2 Construct the missing views of lines and planes in Fig. 20–34A through F.

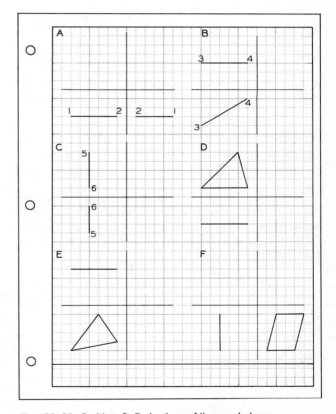

Fig. 20–34 Problem 2: Projections of lines and planes.

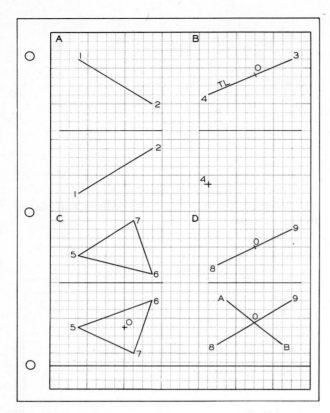

Fig. 20–35 Problem 3: Locations of points on lines and planes.

3 Refer to Fig. 20–35. (A) Find point *O* at the midpoint of line 1–2 in both views. (B) Find the front view of point *O* on horizontal line 3–4. (C) Find point *O* on plane 5–6–7 in the top view. (D) Find the top view of frontal line *AOB*.

4 Refer to Fig. 20–36. Construct three principal lines on each plane as follows: on the plane in (A) three horizontal lines, on the plane in (B) three frontal lines, on the plane in (C) three profile lines, and on the plane in (D) three horizontal lines. Letter each plane in all views.

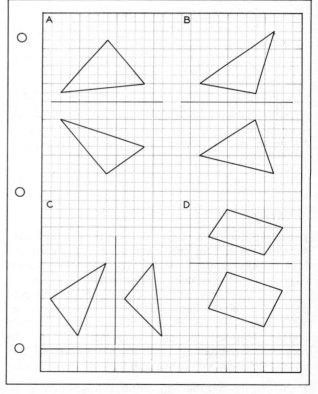

Fig. 20–36 Problem 4: Construction of principal lines of planes.

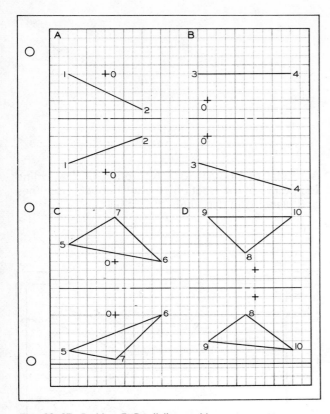

Fig. 20–37 Problem 5: Parallelism problems.

5 Refer to Fig. 20–37. (A and B) Construct lines with their midpoints at *O* parallel to the given lines. (C and D) Construct lines through point *O* parallel to the given planes. The lines can be drawn any convenient length.

6 Refer to Fig. 20–38. (A) Construct a line through point *O* perpendicular to line 1–2. (B) Construct a line from the midpoint of line 3–4 that is perpendicular to it. (C) Construct a line from the intersection of the two lines that is perpendicular to plane 5–6–7–8. (D) Construct a line from the point on the plane 9–10–11 that is perpendicular to the plane.

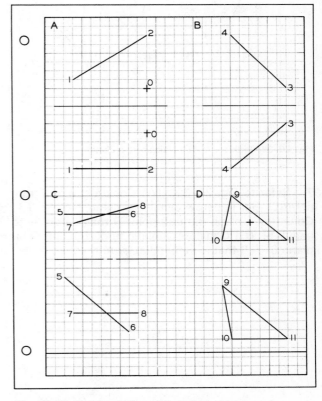

Fig. 20–38 Problem 6: Perpendicularity problems.

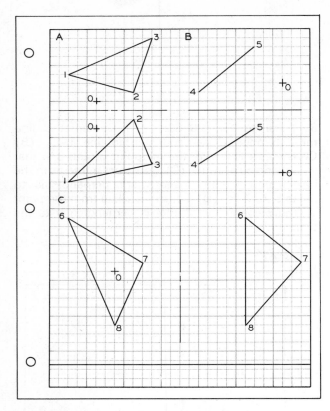

Fig. 20–39   Problem 7: Perpendicularity problems.

7   Refer to Fig. 20–39. (A) Construct a line from point *O* that is perpendicular to plane 1–2–3. (B) Construct a plane through point *O* that is parallel to line 4–5. (C) Construct a plane through point *O* on plane 6–7–8 that is perpendicular to the plane.

8   Refer to Fig. 20–40. (A through D) Determine the points of intersection (if any) between the lines and planes and determine the visibility.

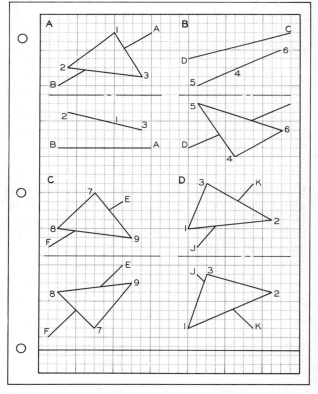

Fig. 20–40   Problem 8: Intersection problems.

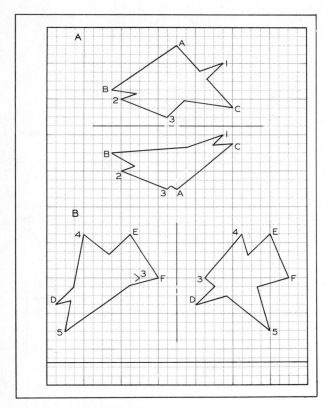

Fig. 20–41 Problem 9: Intersection problems.

9 Refer to Fig. 20–41. (A and B) Find the line of intersection between the two planes and the visibility of each.

10 Refer to Fig. 20–42. (A and B) Find the true-length views of the lines. (C and D) Find the point views of the lines.

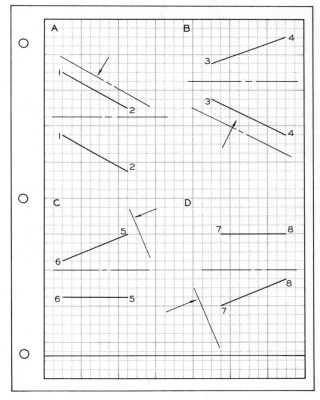

Fig. 20–42 Problem 10: Auxiliary views of lines.

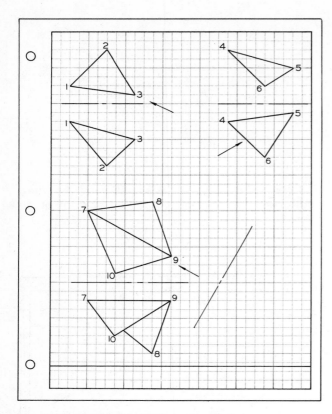

Fig. 20–43 Problem 11: Auxiliary views of planes.

11 Refer to Fig. 20–43. (A and B) Find the edge views of the planes. (C) Find the angle between the planes.

12 Refer to Fig. 20–44. (A) Find the angle between the planes. (B and C) Find the true-size views of the planes.

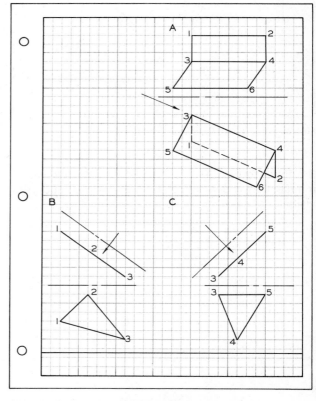

Fig. 20–44 Problem 12: Auxiliary views of planes.

APPENDIXES

DECIMAL EQUIVALENTS—INCH-MILLIMETER CONVERSION TABLE

1/2	1/4	1/8	1/16	1/32	1/64	Decimals	Millimeters
					1	.015625	.396875
				1		.031250	.793750
					3	.046875	1.190625
			1			.062500	1.587500
					5	.078125	1.984375
				3		.093750	2.381250
					7	.109375	2.778125
		1				.125000	3.175000
					9	.140625	3.571875
				5		.156250	3.968750
					11	.171875	4.365625
			3			.187500	4.762500
					13	.203125	5.159375
				7		.218750	5.556250
					15	.234375	5.953125
	1					.250000	6.350000
					17	.265625	6.746875
				9		.281250	7.143750
					19	.296875	7.540625
			5			.312500	7.937500
					21	.328125	8.334375
				11		.343750	8.731250
					23	.359375	9.128125
		3				.375000	9.525000
					25	.390625	9.921875
				13		.406250	10.318750
					27	.421875	10.715625
			7			.437500	11.112500
					29	.453125	11.509375
				15		.468750	11.906250
					31	.484375	12.303125
1						.500000	12.700000

1/2	1/4	1/8	1/16	1/32	1/64	Decimals	Millimeters
					33	.515625	13.096875
				17		.531250	13.493750
					35	.546875	13.890625
			9			.562500	14.287500
					37	.578125	14.684375
				19		.593750	15.081250
					39	.609375	15.478125
		5				.625000	15.875000
					41	.640625	16.271875
				21		.656250	16.668750
					43	.671875	17.065625
			11			.687500	17.462500
					45	.703125	17.859375
				23		.718750	18.256250
					47	.734375	18.653125
	3					.750000	19.050000
					49	.765625	19.446875
				25		.781250	19.843750
					51	.796875	20.240625
			13			.812500	20.637500
					53	.828125	21.034375
				27		.843750	21.431250
					55	.859375	21.828125
		7				.875000	22.225000
					57	.890625	22.621875
				29		.906250	23.018750
					59	.921875	23.415625
			15			.937500	23.812500
					61	.953125	24.209375
				31		.968750	24.606250
					63	.984375	25.003125
	4	8	16	32	64	1.000000	25.400000

APPENDIX 2. AMERICAN STANDARD GRAPHICAL SYMBOLS FOR ELECTRONIC DIAGRAMS

1. Amplifier

2. Antenna, general

3. Antenna, dipole

4. Antenna, loop

5. Antenna, counterpoise

6. Battery, long line positive

7. Multicell battery

8. Capacitor, general

9. Capacitor, variable

10. Capacitor, polarized

11. Circuit breaker

12. Ground

13. Chassis ground

14. Connectors, jack and plug

15. Engaged connectors

16. Triode with directly heated cathode and envelope connection to base terminal

17. Pentode using elongated envelope

18. Twin triode using elongated envelope

19. Voltage regulator, also, glow lamp

20. Phototube

21. Inductor, winding, reactor, general

22. Magnetic core inductor

23. Adjustable inductor

24. Adjustable inductor

25. Ballast lamp

26. Fluorescent, 2-terminal lamp

27. Incandescent lamp

28. Microphone

29. Receiver, earphone

30. Rectifier

31. Resistor, general

32. Resistor, adjustable

33. Resistor, variable

34. Transformer, general

35. Transformer, magnetic core

36. Shielded transformer, magnetic core

37. Auto-transformer, adjustable

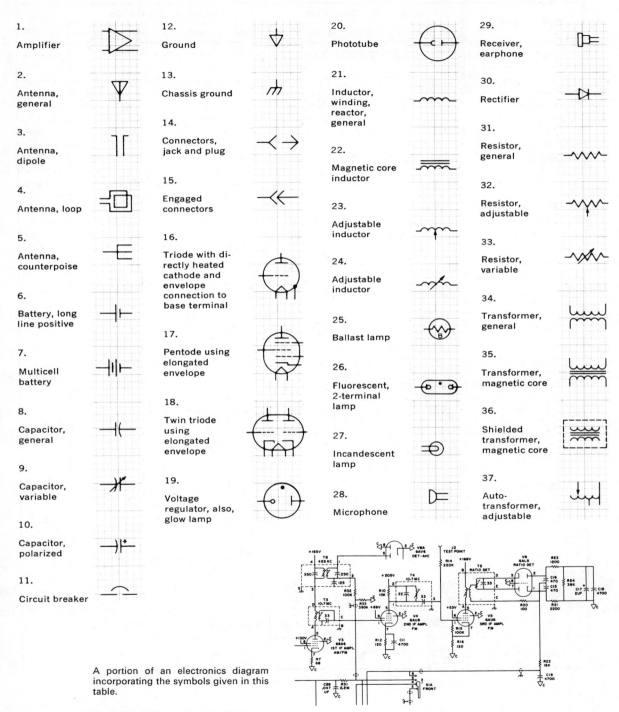

A portion of an electronics diagram incorporating the symbols given in this table.

Courtesy of ANSI; Y32.2-1962 and Y14.15-1966.

TYPE OF FITTING		DOUBLE LINE CONVENTION					SINGLE LINE CONVENTION					FLOW DIAGRAM
		FLANGED	SCREWED	B & S	WELDED	SOLDERED	FLANGED	SCREWED	B & S	WELDED	SOLDERED	
1	Joint											
2	Joint - Expansion											
3	Union											
4	Sleeve											
5	Reducer											
6	Reducer - Eccentric											
7	Reducing Flange											
8	Bushing											
9	Elbow - 45°											
10	Elbow - 90°											
11	Elbow - Long radius											
12	Elbow - (turned up)											
13	Elbow - (turned down)											
14	Elbow - Side outlet (outlet up)											
15	Elbow - Side outlet (outlet down)											
16	Elbow - Base											
17	Elbow - Double branch											
18	Elbow - Reducing											
19	Lateral											
20	Tee											
21	Tee - Single sweep											

TYPE OF FITTING		DOUBLE LINE CONVENTION					SINGLE LINE CONVENTION					FLOW DIAGRAM
		FLANGED	SCREWED	B & S	WELDED	SOLDERED	FLANGED	SCREWED	B & S	WELDED	SOLDERED	
22	Tee-Double sweep											
23	Tee-(outlet up)											
24	Tee-(outlet down)											
25	Tee-Side outlet (outlet up)											
26	Tee-Side outlet (outlet down)											
27	Cross											
28	Valve-Globe											
29	Valve-Angle											
30	Valve-Motor operated globe											Motor operated
31	Valve-Gate											
32	Valve-Angle gate											
33	Valve-Motor operated gate											Motor operated
34	Valve-Check											
35	Valve-Angle check											
36	Valve-Safety											
37	Valve-Angle safety											
38	Valve-Quick opening											
39	Valve-Float operating											
40	Stop Cock											

APPENDIX 4. SQUARE AND ACME THREADS

Size	Threads per inch	Size	Threads per inch	Size	Threads per inch	Size	Threads per inch
$\frac{3}{8}$	12	$\frac{7}{8}$	5	2	$2\frac{1}{2}$	$3\frac{1}{2}$	$1\frac{1}{3}$
$\frac{7}{16}$	10	1	5	$2\frac{1}{4}$	2	$3\frac{3}{4}$	$1\frac{1}{3}$
$\frac{1}{2}$	10	$1\frac{1}{8}$	4	$2\frac{1}{2}$	2	4	$1\frac{1}{3}$
$\frac{9}{16}$	8	$1\frac{1}{4}$	4	$2\frac{3}{4}$	2	$4\frac{1}{4}$	$1\frac{1}{3}$
$\frac{5}{8}$	8	$1\frac{1}{2}$	3	3	$1\frac{1}{2}$	$4\frac{1}{2}$	1
$\frac{3}{4}$	6	$1\frac{3}{4}$	$2\frac{1}{2}$	$3\frac{1}{4}$	$1\frac{1}{2}$	over $4\frac{1}{2}$	1

APPENDIX 5. AMERICAN STANDARD UNIFIED AND AMERICAN NATIONAL THREADS

SCREW THREAD SERIES

Size	Basic Major Dia	Coarse (UNC or NC)*	Fine (UNF or NF)*	Extra Fine (UNEF or NEF)*	8 Thread Series (UN, N or NS)*	12 Thread Series (UN or N)*	16 Thread Series (UN or N)*	Size
0	0.0600	–	80	–	–	–	–	0
1	0.0730	64	72	–	–	–	–	1
2	0.0860	56	64	–	–	–	–	2
3	0.0990	48	56	–	–	–	–	3
4	0.1120	40	48	–	–	–	–	4
5	0.1250	40	44	–	–	–	–	5
6	0.1380	32	40	–	–	–	–	6
8	0.1640	32	36	–	–	–	–	8
10	0.1900	24	32	–	–	–	–	10
12	0.2160	24	28	32	–	–	–	12
1/4	0.2500	20	28	32	–	–	–	1/4
5/16	0.3125	18	24	32	–	–	–	5/16
3/8	0.3750	16	24	32	–	–	–	3/8
7/16	0.4375	14	20	28	–	–	–	7/16
1/2	0.5000	13	20	28	–	12	–	1/2
9/16	0.5625	12	18	24	–	12	–	9/16
5/8	0.6250	11	18	24	–	12	–	5/8
11/16	0.6875	–	–	24	–	12	–	11/16
3/4	0.7500	10	16	20	–	12	16	3/4
13/16	0.8125	–	–	20	–	12	16	13/16
7/8	0.8750	9	14	20	–	12	16	7/8
15/16	0.9375	–	–	20	–	12	16	15/16
1	1.0000	–	14 **	–	–	–	–	1
1	1.0000	8	12	20	8	12	16	1
1 1/16	1.0625	–	–	18	–	12	16	1 1/16
1 1/8	1.1250	7	12	18	8	12	16	1 1/8
1 3/16	1.1875	–	–	18	–	12	16	1 3/16
1 1/4	1.2500	7	12	18	8	12	16	1 1/4
1 5/16	1.3125	–	–	18	–	12	16	1 5/16
1 3/8	1.3750	6	12	18	8	12	16	1 3/8
1 7/16	1.4375	–	–	18	–	12	16	1 7/16
1 1/2	1.5000	6	12	18	8	12	16	1 1/2
1 9/16	1.5625	–	–	18	–	–	16	1 9/16
1 5/8	1.6250	–	–	18	8	12	16	1 5/8
1 11/16	1.6875	–	–	18	–	–	16	1 11/16
1 3/4	1.7500	5	–	16	8	12	16	1 3/4
1 13/16	1.8125	–	–	–	–	–	16	1 13/16
1 7/8	1.8750	–	–	–	8	12	16	1 7/8
1 15/16	1.9375	–	–	–	–	–	16	1 15/16
2	2.0000	4 ½	–	16	8	12	16	2
2 1/16	2.0625	–	–	–	–	–	16	2 1/16
2 1/8	2.1250	–	–	–	8	12	16	2 1/8
2 3/16	2.1875	–	–	–	–	–	16	2 3/16
2 1/4	2.2500	4 ½	–	–	8	12	16	2 1/4
2 5/16	2.3125	–			–	–	16	2 5/16
2 3/8	2.3750	–			–	12	16	2 3/8
2 7/16	2.4375	–			–	–	16	2 7/16
2 1/2	2.5000	4			8	12	16	2 1/2
2 5/8	2.6250	–			–	12	16	2 5/8
2 3/4	2.7500	4			8	12	16	2 3/4
2 7/8	2.8750	–			–	12	16	2 7/8
3	3.0000	4			8	12	16	3
3 1/8	3.1250	–			–	12	16	3 1/8
3 1/4	3.2500	4			8	12	16	3 1/4
3 3/8	3.3750	–			–	12	16	3 3/8
3 1/2	3.5000	4			8	12	16	3 1/2
3 5/8	3.6250	–			–	12	16	3 5/8
3 3/4	3.7500	4			8	12	16	3 3/4
3 7/8	3.8750	–			–	12	16	3 7/8
4	4.0000	4			8	12	16	4
4 1/4	4.2500	–			8	12	16	4 1/4
4 1/2	4.5000	–			8	12	16	4 1/2
4 3/4	4.7500	–			8	12	16	4 3/4
5	5.0000	–	–	–	8	12	16	5
5 1/4	5.2500	–	–	–	8	12	16	5 1/4
5 1/2	5.5000	–	–	–	8	12	16	5 1/2
5 3/4	5.7500	–	–	–	8	12	16	5 3/4
6	6.0000	–	–	–	8	12	16	6

* For Series Symbols applying to a particular thread, see dimensional tables ASA B1.1
** NS

Courtesy of ANSI; Y14.6-1957.

APPENDIX 6. AMERICAN STANDARD SQUARE BOLTS AND NUTS

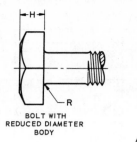

BOLT WITH
REDUCED DIAMETER
BODY

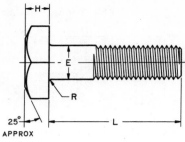

25°
APPROX

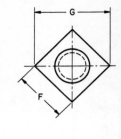

Dimensions of Square Bolts

Nominal Size or Basic Product Dia		Body Dia E	Width Across Flats F			Width Across Corners G		Height H			Radius of Fillet R
		Max	Basic	Max	Min	Max	Min	Basic	Max	Min	Max
1/4	0.2500	0.260	3/8	0.3750	0.362	0.530	0.498	11/64	0.188	0.156	0.031
5/16	0.3125	0.324	1/2	0.5000	0.484	0.707	0.665	13/64	0.220	0.186	0.031
3/8	0.3750	0.388	9/16	0.5625	0.544	0.795	0.747	1/4	0.268	0.232	0.031
7/16	0.4375	0.452	5/8	0.6250	0.603	0.884	0.828	19/64	0.316	0.278	0.031
1/2	0.5000	0.515	3/4	0.7500	0.725	1.061	0.995	21/64	0.348	0.308	0.031
5/8	0.6250	0.642	15/16	0.9375	0.906	1.326	1.244	27/64	0.444	0.400	0.062
3/4	0.7500	0.768	1 1/8	1.1250	1.088	1.591	1.494	1/2	0.524	0.476	0.062
7/8	0.8750	0.895	1 5/16	1.3125	1.269	1.856	1.742	19/32	0.620	0.568	0.062
1	1.0000	1.022	1 1/2	1.5000	1.450	2.121	1.991	21/32	0.684	0.628	0.093
1 1/8	1.1250	1.149	1 11/16	1.6875	1.631	2.386	2.239	3/4	0.780	0.720	0.093
1 1/4	1.2500	1.277	1 7/8	1.8750	1.812	2.652	2.489	27/32	0.876	0.812	0.093
1 3/8	1.3750	1.404	2 1/16	2.0625	1.994	2.917	2.738	29/32	0.940	0.872	0.093
1 1/2	1.5000	1.531	2 1/4	2.2500	2.175	3.182	2.986	1	1.036	0.964	0.093

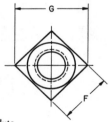

25°

Dimensions of Square Nuts

Nominal Size or Basic Major Dia of Thread		Width Across Flats F			Width Across Corners G		Thickness H		
		Basic	Max	Min	Max	Min	Basic	Max	Min
1/4	0.2500	7/16	0.4375	0.425	0.619	0.584	7/32	0.235	0.203
5/16	0.3125	9/16	0.5625	0.547	0.795	0.751	17/64	0.283	0.249
3/8	0.3750	5/8	0.6250	0.606	0.884	0.832	21/64	0.346	0.310
7/16	0.4375	3/4	0.7500	0.728	1.061	1.000	3/8	0.394	0.356
1/2	0.5000	13/16	0.8125	0.788	1.149	1.082	7/16	0.458	0.418
5/8	0.6250	1	1.0000	0.969	1.414	1.330	35/64	0.569	0.525
3/4	0.7500	1 1/8	1.1250	1.088	1.591	1.494	21/32	0.680	0.632
7/8	0.8750	1 5/16	1.3125	1.269	1.856	1.742	49/64	0.792	0.740
1	1.0000	1 1/2	1.5000	1.450	2.121	1.991	7/8	0.903	0.847
1 1/8	1.1250	1 11/16	1.6875	1.631	2.386	2.239	1	1.030	0.970
1 1/4	1.2500	1 7/8	1.8750	1.812	2.652	2.489	1 3/32	1.126	1.062
1 3/8	1.3750	2 1/16	2.0625	1.994	2.917	2.738	1 13/64	1.237	1.169
1 1/2	1.5000	2 1/4	2.2500	2.175	3.182	2.986	1 5/16	1.348	1.276

Courtesy of ANSI; B18.2.1-1965 and B18.2.2-1965.

APPENDIX 7. AMERICAN STANDARD HEXAGON HEAD BOLTS AND NUTS

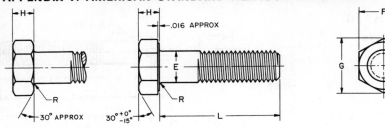

Dimensions of Hex Cap Screws (Finished Hex Bolts)

Nominal Size or Basic Product Dia		Body Dia E		Width Across Flats F			Width Across Corners G		Height H			Radius of Fillet R	
		Max	Min	Basic	Max	Min	Max	Min	Basic	Max	Min	Max	Min
1/4	0.2500	0.2500	0.2450	7/16	0.4375	0.428	0.505	0.488	5/32	0.163	0.150	0.025	0.015
5/16	0.3125	0.3125	0.3065	1/2	0.5000	0.489	0.577	0.557	13/64	0.211	0.195	0.025	0.015
3/8	0.3750	0.3750	0.3690	9/16	0.5625	0.551	0.650	0.628	15/64	0.243	0.226	0.025	0.015
7/16	0.4375	0.4375	0.4305	5/8	0.6250	0.612	0.722	0.698	9/32	0.291	0.272	0.025	0.015
1/2	0.5000	0.5000	0.4930	3/4	0.7500	0.736	0.866	0.840	5/16	0.323	0.302	0.025	0.015
9/16	0.5625	0.5625	0.5545	13/16	0.8125	0.798	0.938	0.910	23/64	0.371	0.348	0.045	0.020
5/8	0.6250	0.6250	0.6170	15/16	0.9375	0.922	1.083	1.051	25/64	0.403	0.378	0.045	0.020
3/4	0.7500	0.7500	0.7410	1 1/8	1.1250	1.100	1.299	1.254	15/32	0.483	0.455	0.045	0.020
7/8	0.8750	0.8750	0.8660	1 5/16	1.3125	1.285	1.516	1.465	35/64	0.563	0.531	0.065	0.040
1	1.0000	1.0000	0.9900	1 1/2	1.5000	1.469	1.732	1.675	39/64	0.627	0.591	0.095	0.060
1 1/8	1.1250	1.1250	1.1140	1 11/16	1.6875	1.631	1.949	1.859	11/16	0.718	0.658	0.095	0.060
1 1/4	1.2500	1.2500	1.2390	1 7/8	1.8750	1.812	2.165	2.066	25/32	0.813	0.749	0.095	0.060
1 3/8	1.3750	1.3750	1.3630	2 1/16	2.0625	1.994	2.382	2.273	27/32	0.878	0.810	0.095	0.060
1 1/2	1.5000	1.5000	1.4880	2 1/4	2.2500	2.175	2.598	2.480	15/16	0.974	0.902	0.095	0.060
1 3/4	1.7500	1.7500	1.7380	2 5/8	2.6250	2.538	3.031	2.893	1 3/32	1.134	1.054	0.095	0.060
2	2.0000	2.0000	1.9880	3	3.0000	2.900	3.464	3.306	1 7/32	1.263	1.175	0.095	0.060
2 1/4	2.2500	2.2500	2.2380	3 3/8	3.3750	3.262	3.897	3.719	1 3/8	1.423	1.327	0.095	0.060
2 1/2	2.5000	2.5000	2.4880	3 3/4	3.7500	3.625	4.330	4.133	1 17/32	1.583	1.479	0.095	0.060
2 3/4	2.7500	2.7500	2.7380	4 1/8	4.1250	3.988	4.763	4.546	1 11/16	1.744	1.632	0.095	0.060
3	3.0000	3.0000	2.9880	4 1/2	4.5000	4.350	5.196	4.959	1 7/8	1.935	1.815	0.095	0.060

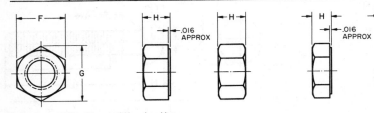

Dimensions of Hex Nuts and Hex Jam Nuts

Nominal Size or Basic Major Dia of Thread		Width Across Flats F			Width Across Corners G		Thickness Hex Nuts H			Thickness Hex Jam Nuts H		
		Basic	Max	Min	Max	Min	Basic	Max	Min	Basic	Max	Min
1/4	0.2500	7/16	0.4375	0.428	0.505	0.488	7/32	0.226	0.212	5/32	0.163	0.150
5/16	0.3125	1/2	0.5000	0.489	0.577	0.557	17/64	0.273	0.258	3/16	0.195	0.180
3/8	0.3750	9/16	0.5625	0.551	0.650	0.628	21/64	0.337	0.320	7/32	0.227	0.210
7/16	0.4375	11/16	0.6875	0.675	0.794	0.768	3/8	0.385	0.365	1/4	0.260	0.240
1/2	0.5000	3/4	0.7500	0.736	0.866	0.840	7/16	0.448	0.427	5/16	0.323	0.302
9/16	0.5625	7/8	0.8750	0.861	1.010	0.982	31/64	0.496	0.473	3/8	0.324	0.301
5/8	0.6250	15/16	0.9375	0.922	1.083	1.051	35/64	0.559	0.535	3/8	0.387	0.363
3/4	0.7500	1 1/8	1.1250	1.088	1.299	1.240	41/64	0.665	0.617	27/64	0.446	0.398
7/8	0.8750	1 5/16	1.3125	1.269	1.516	1.447	3/4	0.776	0.724	31/64	0.510	0.458
1	1.0000	1 1/2	1.5000	1.450	1.732	1.653	55/64	0.887	0.831	35/64	0.575	0.519
1 1/8	1.1250	1 11/16	1.6875	1.631	1.949	1.859	31/32	0.999	0.939	39/64	0.639	0.579
1 1/4	1.2500	1 7/8	1.8750	1.812	2.165	2.066	1 1/16	1.094	1.030	23/32	0.751	0.687
1 3/8	1.3750	2 1/16	2.0625	1.994	2.382	2.273	1 11/64	1.206	1.138	25/32	0.815	0.747
1 1/2	1.5000	2 1/4	2.2500	2.175	2.598	2.480	1 9/32	1.317	1.245	27/32	0.880	0.808

Courtesy of ANSI; B18.2.1-1965 and B18.2.2-1965.

Fillister Head
Cap Screws

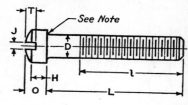

See Note

Nom- inal Size	D Body Diameter		A Head Diameter		H Height of Head		O Total Height of Head		J Width of Slot		T Depth of Slot	
	Max	Min	Max	Min	Max	Min	Max	Min	Max	Min	Max	Min
1/4	0.250	0.245	0.375	0.363	0.172	0.157	0.216	0.194	0.075	0.064	0.097	0.077
5/16	0.3125	0.307	0.437	0.424	0.203	0.186	0.253	0.230	0.084	0.072	0.115	0.090
3/8	0.375	0.369	0.562	0.547	0.250	0.229	0.314	0.284	0.094	0.081	0.142	0.112
7/16	0.4375	0.431	0.625	0.608	0.297	0.274	0.368	0.336	0.094	0.081	0.168	0.133
1/2	0.500	0.493	0.750	0.731	0.328	0.301	0.413	0.376	0.106	0.091	0.193	0.153
9/16	0.5625	0.555	0.812	0.792	0.375	0.346	0.467	0.427	0.118	0.102	0.213	0.168
5/8	0.625	0.617	0.875	0.853	0.422	0.391	0.521	0.478	0.133	0.116	0.239	0.189
3/4	0.750	0.742	1.000	0.976	0.500	0.466	0.612	0.566	0.149	0.131	0.283	0.223
7/8	0.875	0.866	1.125	1.098	0.594	0.556	0.720	0.668	0.167	0.147	0.334	0.264
1	1.000	0.990	1.312	1.282	0.656	0.612	0.803	0.743	0.188	0.166	0.371	0.291

All dimensions are given in inches.

The radius of the fillet at the base of the head:
For sizes 1/4 to 3/8 in. incl. is 0.016 min and 0.031 max,
7/16 to 9/16 in. incl. is 0.016 min and 0.047 max,
5/8 to 1 in. incl. is 0.031 min and 0.062 max.

Round Head
Cap Screws

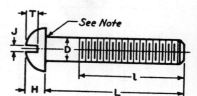

See Note

Nom- inal Size	D Body Diameter		A Head Diameter		H Height of Head		J Width of Slot		T Depth of Slot	
	Max	Min	Max	Min	Max	Min	Max	Min	Max	Min
1/4	0.250	0.245	0.437	0.418	0.191	0.175	0.075	0.064	0.117	0.097
5/16	0.3125	0.307	0.562	0.540	0.245	0.226	0.084	0.072	0.151	0.126
3/8	0.375	0.369	0.625	0.603	0.273	0.252	0.094	0.081	0.168	0.138
7/16	0.4375	0.431	0.750	0.725	0.328	0.302	0.094	0.081	0.202	0.167
1/2	0.500	0.493	0.812	0.786	0.354	0.327	0.106	0.091	0.218	0.178
9/16	0.5625	0.555	0.937	0.909	0.409	0.378	0.118	0.102	0.252	0.207
5/8	0.625	0.617	1.000	0.970	0.437	0.405	0.133	0.116	0.270	0.220
3/4	0.750	0.742	1.250	1.215	0.546	0.507	0.149	0.131	0.338	0.278

All dimensions are given in inches.

Radius of the fillet at the base of the head:
For sizes 1/4 to 3/8 in. incl. is 0.016 min and 0.031 max,
7/16 to 9/16 in. incl..is 0.016 min and 0.047 max,
5/8 to 1 in..incl. is 0.031 min and 0.062 max.

Courtesy of ANSI; B18.6.2-1956.

APPENDIX 9. FLAT HEAD CAP SCREWS

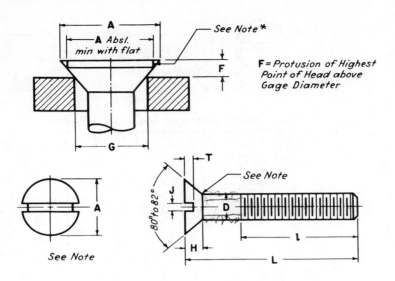

F = Protusion of Highest
Point of Head above
Gage Diameter

See Note

See Note

	D		A			G	H	J		T		F	
	Body Diameter		Head Diameter			Gaging Diam-eter	Height of Head	Width of Slot		Depth of Slot		Protrusion Above Gaging Diameter	
Nom-inal Size	Max	Min	Max	Min	Absolute Min with Flat		Aver-age	Max	Min	Max	Min	Max	Min
1/4	0.250	0.245	0.500	0.477	0.452	0.4245	0.140	0.075	0.064	0.068	0.045	0.0452	0.0307
5/16	0.3125	0.307	0.625	0.598	0.567	0.5376	0.177	0.084	0.072	0.086	0.057	0.0523	0.0354
3/8	0.375	0.369	0.750	0.720	0.682	0.6507	0.210	0.094	0.081	0.103	0.068	0.0594	0.0401
7/16	0.4375	0.431	0.8125	0.780	0.736	0.7229	0.210	0.094	0.081	0.103	0.068	0.0649	0.0448
1/2	0.500	0.493	0.875	0.841	0.791	0.7560	0.210	0.106	0.091	0.103	0.068	0.0705	0.0495
9/16	0.5625	0.555	1.000	0.962	0.906	0.8691	0.244	0.118	0.102	0.120	0.080	0.0775	0.0542
5/8	0.625	0.617	1.125	1.083	1.020	0.9822	0.281	0.133	0.116	0.137	0.091	0.0846	0.0588
3/4	0.750	0.742	1.375	1.326	1.251	1.2085	0.352	0.149	0.131	0.171	0.115	0.0987	0.0682
7/8	0.875	0.866	1.625	1.568	1.480	1.4347	0.423	0.167	0.147	0.206	0.138	0.1128	0.0776
1	1.000	0.990	1.875	1.811	1.711	1.6610	0.494	0.188	0.166	0.240	0.162	0.1270	0.0870
1 1/8	1.125	1.114	2.062	1.992	1.880	1.8262	0.529	0.196	0.178	0.257	0.173	0.1401	0.0964
1 1/4	1.250	1.239	2.312	2.235	2.110	2.0525	0.600	0.211	0.193	0.291	0.197	0.1542	0.1056
1 3/8	1.375	1.363	2.562	2.477	2.340	2.2787	0.665	0.226	0.208	0.326	0.220	0.1684	0.1151
1 1/2	1.500	1.488	2.812	2.720	2.570	2.5050	0.742	0.258	0.240	0.360	0.244	0.1825	0.1245

All dimensions are given in inches.

The maximum and minimum head diameters, A, are extended to the theoretical sharp corners.

The radius of the fillet at the base of the head shall not exceed 0.4 Max. D.

*Edge of head may be flat as shown or slightly rounded.

Courtesy of ANSI; B18.6.2-1956.

APPENDIX 10. MACHINE SCREWS

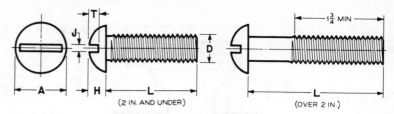

Dimensions of Slotted Round Head Machine Screws

Nom-inal Size	D Diameter of Screw	A Head Diameter		H Head Height		J Width of Slot		T Depth of Slot	
	Basic	Max	Min	Max	Min	Max	Min	Max	Min
0	0.0600	0.113	0.099	0.053	0.043	0.023	0.016	0.039	0.029
1	0.0730	0.138	0.122	0.061	0.051	0.026	0.019	0.044	0.033
2	0.0860	0.162	0.146	0.069	0.059	0.031	0.023	0.048	0.037
3	0.0990	0.187	0.169	0.078	0.067	0.035	0.027	0.053	0.040
4	0.1120	0.211	0.193	0.086	0.075	0.039	0.031	0.058	0.044
5	0.1250	0.236	0.217	0.095	0.083	0.043	0.035	0.063	0.047
6	0.1380	0.260	0.240	0.103	0.091	0.048	0.039	0.068	0.051
8	0.1640	0.309	0.287	0.120	0.107	0.054	0.045	0.077	0.058
10	0.1900	0.359	0.334	0.137	0.123	0.060	0.050	0.087	0.065
12	0.2160	0.408	0.382	0.153	0.139	0.067	0.056	0.096	0.073
1/4	0.2500	0.472	0.443	0.175	0.160	0.075	0.064	0.109	0.082
5/16	0.3125	0.590	0.557	0.216	0.198	0.084	0.072	0.132	0.099
3/8	0.3750	0.708	0.670	0.256	0.237	0.094	0.081	0.155	0.117
7/16	0.4375	0.750	0.707	0.328	0.307	0.094	0.081	0.196	0.148
1/2	0.5000	0.813	0.766	0.355	0.332	0.106	0.091	0.211	0.159
9/16	0.5625	0.938	0.887	0.410	0.385	0.118	0.102	0.242	0.183
5/8	0.6250	1.000	0.944	0.438	0.411	0.133	0.116	0.258	0.195
3/4	0.7500	1.250	1.185	0.547	0.516	0.149	0.131	0.320	0.242

All dimensions are given in inches.

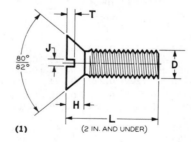

(1)

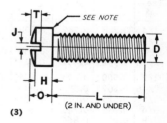

(3)

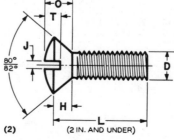

(2)

Courtesy of ANSI; B18.6.3-1962.

Three other common forms of machine screws are shown at the left and above: (1) flat head, (2) oval head, and (3) fillister head. Although dimension tables are not given for these three types of machine screws in this text, their general dimensions are closely related to those in the table above. Additional information on these screws can be obtained from the ANSI standard B18.6.3-1962.

APPENDIX 11. WIRE AND SHEET METAL GAGES

WIRE AND SHEET METAL GAGES
IN DECIMALS OF AN INCH

Name of Gage	United States Standard Gage*		The United States Steel Wire Gage	American or Brown & Sharpe Wire Gage	New Birmingham Standard Sheet & Hoop Gage	British Imperial or English Legal Standard Wire Gage	Birmingham or Stubs Iron Wire Gage	Name of Gage
Principal Use	Uncoated Steel Sheets and Light Plates		Steel Wire except Music Wire	Non-Ferrous Sheets and Wire	Iron and Steel Sheets and Hoops	Wire	Strips, Bands, Hoops and Wire	Principal Use
Gage No.	Weight Oz. per Sq. Ft.	Approx. Thickness Inches	Thickness, Inches					Gage No.
7/0's			.4900		.6666	.500		7/0's
6/0's			.4615	.5800	.625	.464		6/0's
5/0's			.4305	.5165	.5883	.432	.500	5/0's
4/0's			.3938	.4600	.5416	.400	.454	4/0's
3/0's			.3625	.4096	.500	.372	.425	3/0's
2/0's			.3310	.3648	.4452	.348	.380	2/0's
0			.3065	.3249	.3964	.324	.340	0
1			.2830	.2893	.3532	.300	.300	1
2			.2625	.2576	.3147	.276	.284	2
3	160	.2391	.2437	.2294	.2804	.252	.259	3
4	150	.2242	.2253	.2043	.250	.232	.238	4
5	140	.2092	.2070	.1819	.2225	.212	.220	5
6	130	.1943	.1920	.1620	.1981	.192	.203	6
7	120	.1793	.1770	.1443	.1764	.176	.180	7
8	110	.1644	.1620	.1285	.1570	.160	.165	8
9	100	.1495	.1483	.1144	.1398	.144	.148	9
10	90	.1345	.1350	.1019	.1250	.128	.134	10
11	80	.1196	.1205	.0907	.1113	.116	.120	11
12	70	.1046	.1055	.0808	.0991	.104	.109	12
13	60	.0897	.0915	.0720	.0882	.092	.095	13
14	50	0747	.0800	.0641	.0785	.080	.083	14
15	45	.0673	.0720	.0571	.0699	.072	.072	15
16	40	.0598	.0625	.0508	.0625	.064	.065	16
17	36	.0538	.0540	.0453	.0556	.056	.058	17
18	32	.0478	.0475	.0403	.0495	.048	.049	18
19	28	.0418	.0410	.0359	.0440	.040	.042	19
20	24	.0359	.0348	.0320	.0392	.036	.035	20
21	22	.0329	.0318	.0285	.0349	.032	.032	21
22	20	.0299	.0286	.0253	.0313	.028	.028	22
23	18	.0269	.0258	.0226	.0278	.024	.025	23
24	16	.0239	.0230	.0201	.0248	.022	.022	24
25	14	.0209	.0204	.0179	.0220	.020	.020	25
26	12	.0179	.0181	.0159	.0196	.018	.018	26
27	11	.0164	.0173	.0142	.0175	.0164	.016	27
28	10	.0149	.0162	.0126	.0156	.0148	.014	28
29	9	.0135	.0150	.0113	.0139	.0136	.013	29
30	8	.0120	.0140	.0100	.0123	.0124	.012	30
31	7	.0105	.0132	.0089	.0110	.0116	.010	31
32	6.5	.0097	.0128	.0080	.0098	.0108	.009	32
33	6	.0090	.0118	.0071	.0087	.0100	.008	33
34	5.5	.0082	.0104	.0063	.0077	.0092	.007	34
35	5	.0075	.0095	.0056	.0069	.0084	.005	35
36	4.5	.0067	.0090	.0050	.0061	.0076	.004	36
37	4.25	.0064	.0085	.0045	.0054	.0068		37
38	4	.0060	.0080	.0040	.0048	.0060		38
39			.0075	.0035	.0043	.0052		39
40			.0070	.0031	.0039	.0048		40

* U. S. Standard Gage is officially a weight gage, in oz. per sq. ft. as tabulated. The Approx. Thickness shown is the "Manufacturers' Standard" of the American Iron and Steel Institute, based on steel as weighing 501.81 lbs. per cu. ft. (489.6 true weight plus 2.5 percent for average over-run in area and thickness). The A.I.S.I. standard nomenclature for flat rolled carbon steel is as follows:

Widths, Inches	Thicknesses, Inch							
	0.2500 and thicker	0.2499 to 0.2031	0.2030 to 0.1875	0.1874 to 0.0568	0.0567 to 0.0344	0.0343 to 0.0255	0.0254 to 0.0142	0.0141 and thinner
To 3½ incl.	Bar	Bar	Strip	Strip	Strip	Strip	Sheet	Sheet
Over 3½ to 6 incl.	Bar	Bar	Strip	Strip	Strip	Sheet	Sheet	Sheet
" 6 to 12 "	Plate	Strip	Strip	Strip	Sheet	Sheet	Sheet	Sheet
" 12 to 32 "	Plate	Sheet	Sheet	Sheet	Sheet	Sheet	Sheet	Black Plate
" 32 to 48 "	Plate	Sheet	Sheet	Sheet	Sheet	Sheet	Sheet	Sheet
" 48	Plate	Plate	Plate	Sheet	Sheet	Sheet	Sheet	——

Courtesy of the American Institute of Steel Construction.

INDEX

INDEX

Harnessing the world's surging rivers for irrigation and power—a challenge met by engineers and construction men with many notable achievements. The first great masonry dam—the first Aswan—was constructed on the Nile, and completed in 1902. The Hoover Dam (726.4 feet high, 1200 feet long) was started in 1928, dedicated in 1935 and became one of the largest hydroelectric suppliers in the world.

Probing and observing, engineers begin to chart the course of a fabulous voyage—the penetration of outer space. To accomplish it, engineering on a massive scale, to unprecedented degrees of accuracy and reliability, produced the first manned satellites (1961), Telstar (1962), the first photographs of the moon and Mars. Giant radio telescopes now "see" to the outer edges of the universe.